Tree Roots in the Built Environment

Tree Roots in the Built Environment

John Roberts
Nick Jackson
Mark Smith

London: TSO

Published by TSO (The Stationery Office) and available from:

Online
www.tsoshop.co.uk

Mail,Telephone, Fax & E-mail
TSO
PO Box 29, Norwich, NR3 1GN
Telephone orders/General enquiries: 0870 600 5522
Fax orders: 0870 600 5533
E-mail:customer.services@tso.co.uk
Textphone 0870 240 3701

TSO Accredited Agents
(see Yellow Pages)
and through good booksellers

ISBN 13   978 0 11 753620 3
ISBN 10   0 11 753620 2

N134953 C20 06/06

Contents

Figure Acknowledgements

Where space allows we have included an acknowledgement alongside the figure.

Chapter 1

Figure 1.1   Photograph courtesy of Midsummer Place Shopping
Precinct, Milton Keynes.

Figure 1.2   Photograph provided by John Roberts.

Chapter 2

Figure 2.1   Modified after Craul, 1992.

Figure 2.2   Reproduced with permission from Elsevier.

Figure 2.3   (a) After Ashman and Puri, 2002; Blackwell Science
(permission applied for).
(b) Reproduced with permission of the International Society
of Arboriculture.

Figures 2.4,   Reproduced with permission from Elsevier.
2.5 and 2.6

Figure 2.7   After Craul, 1992.

Figure 2.8   Blackwell Science (permission applied for).

Figure 2.9   After Craul, 1992.

Figure 2.10   Reproduced with permission of the authors.

Figure 2.11   Reproduced with permission of Booker Tate Limited.

Box 2.1   Reproduced with permission of the International Society
of Arboriculture.

Chapter 3

Figure 3.1   Reproduced with permission of the authors.

Figure 3.2   Reproduced with permission of the McGraw-Hill
Companies.

Figure 3.4   After Köstler *et al.*, 1968; Paul Parey Verlag (permission
applied for).

Figure 3.5   (a) Reproduced with permission of Kluwer Academic
Publishers.
(b) After Mackie-Dawson and Atkinson, 1991; Reproduced
with permission of Blackwell Scientific Publications.

Figure 3.6   Reproduced with permission of AB Academic Publishers.

Figure 3.7   After Cutler and Richardson, 1989.

Figure 3.8   Reproduced with permission of AB Academic Publishers.

Figure 3.9   After Taylor and Gardner, 1963. Reproduced with
permission of Lippincott Williams & Wilkins.

Figure 3.10	After Taylor and Gardner, 1963. Reproduced with permission of Lippincott Williams & Wilkins.
Figure 3.11	Rendig and Taylor, 1989; McGraw-Hill (permission applied for).
Figure 3.12	After Gaumann, 1935. Reproduced with permission of the Swiss Botanical Society.
Figure 3.13	Reproduced with permission of the National Research Press.
Figure 3.14	After Marschner, 1995.
Figures 3.15 and 3.16	Reproduced with permission of the authors.
Figure 3.17, 3.18 and 3.19	Reproduced with permission of Her Majesty's Stationery Office.

Chapter 4

Figure 4.1 and 4.2	After Craul, 1992.
Figure 4.3	After Smith, 1987.
Figure 4.4	Reproduced with permission of The American Nursery & Landscape Association.
Figure 4.5	Reproduced with permission of the Soil Science Society of America.
Figure 4.6	Reproduced with permission from Elsevier.
Figure 4.7	American Society for Horticultural Science (permission applied for).
Figure 4.8	Reproduced with permission of Professor Nina Bassuk.
Figure 4.9, 4.10 and 4.11	Reproduced with permission of the International Society of Arboriculture.
Figure 4.12	Reproduced with permission of Dr Jason Grabosky.
Figure 4.13	Reproduced with permission of Professor Nina Bassuk.
Figure 4.14 and 4.15	Reproduced with permission of The American Nursery & Landscape Association.
Figure 4.16 and 4.17	Reproduced with permission of AB Academic Publishers.
Figure 4.18, 4.19 and 4.20	Reproduced with permission of the International Society of Arboriculture.
Figure 4.21	Reproduced with permission of Her Majesty's Stationery Office.
Figure 4.22	Reproduced with permission of The American Nursery & Landscape Association.
Figure 4.23	Reproduced with permission of the International Society of Arboriculture.
Figure 4.24	Reproduced with permission of the Golf Course Superintendents' Association of America.
Figure 4.25	Reproduced with permission of the International Society of Arboriculture.

Figure 4.26   Photograph supplied by DISAB Vacuum Technology AB, Eslöv, Sweden.

Figure 4.27   Photograph supplied by U-Mole, Eaton Socon, UK.

Figure 4.28   Photograph provided by Rob Gross.
and 4.29

Figure 4.30   Reproduced with permission of the International Society of Arboriculture.

Figure 4.31   Photograph provided by John Roberts.

Figures 4.32   Reproduced with permission of the International Society
(a and b),   of Arboriculture.
4.33 and
4.34

Chapter 5

Figure 5.1   Reproduced with the permission of British Standards Institution.

Figure 5.2   Reproduced with permission of NRC Research Press.

Figure 5.3   Reproduced with permission of E&FN Spon.

Figure 5.4   Reproduced with permission of Oxford University Press.

Figure 5.5   Photograph provided by John Roberts.

Figure 5.6,   Reproduced with permission of Her Majesty's Stationery
5.7, 5.8   Office.
and 5.9

Figure 5.10   Reproduced with permission of the International Society of Arboriculture.

Figure 5.11   Reproduced with permission of Kluwer Academic Publishers.

Figure 5.12,   Reproduced with permission of Her Majesty's Stationery
5.13 and   Office.
5.14

Figure 5.15   Reproduced with permission of Kluwer Academic Publishers.

Figure 5.16   Photograph provided by John Roberts.

Figure 5.17,   Reproduced with permission from Elsevier.
5.18 and
5.19

Figure 5.20   Reproduced with permission of E&FN Spon.
and 5.21

Figure 5.22   Photograph provided by John Roberts.

Chapter 6

Figure 6.1   After Salisbury and Ross, 1992; Wadsworth Publishing Company (permission applied for).

Figure 6.2   Reproduced with permission of the authors.

Figure 6.3   Photograph provided by John Roberts.

Figure 6.4   Reproduced with permission of the Food and Agriculture Organization of the United Nations.

Figure 6.5   (a) and (b). Images kindly supplied by Dr Jeff Luvall, NASA, USA.

Figure 6.6   Photograph provided by John Roberts.
Figure 6.7   Photograph provided by Dr Steve Green, Landcare,
               New Zealand.
Figure 6.8   Reproduced with permission of Kluwer Academic Publishers.
Figure 6.9   After Craul, 1992.
Figure 6.10   Photograph provided by John Roberts.
and 6.11

Chapter 7

Figure 7.1   Photograph provided by John Roberts.
Figure 7.2   Photograph provided by Derek Patch.
Figure 7.3   Photograph provided by John Roberts.
Figure 7.4   Photograph provided by Derek Patch.
Figure 7.5   Reproduced with permission of the publishers of the
               Journal of Environmental Quality.
Figure 7.6   Reproduced with permission of The Stationery Office.
Figure 7.7   Photograph provided by John Roberts.
Figure 7.8   Reproduced with permission of the Soil Science Society
and 7.9   of America.

Chapter 8

Figure 8.1   Photograph provided by John Roberts. Diagram with
               permission of *The Surveyor*.
Figure 8.2   Reproduced with permission of the National Joint Utilities
               Group.
Figure 8.3   Reproduced with permission of Pearson Education, Inc.
Figure 8.4   Photograph provided by Rebecca Ramage, Melbourne,
               Australia.
Figure 8.5   After Randolph and Wiest, 1981; American Society of
and 8.6   Horticultural Science (permission applied for).
Figure 8.7   Reproduced with permission from Elsevier.
and 8.8
Figure 8.9   After Schupp and Ferree, 1988; American Society of
               Horticultural Science (permission applied for).
Figure 8.10   Reproduced with permission of the International Society
               of Arboriculture.
Figure 8.11   Reproduced with permission of Bioscience.
Figure 8.12   Reproduced with permission of Forest Science.
Figure 8.13   Reproduced with permission of Bioscience.
Figure 8.14   Reproduced with permission of Oecologia.
Figure 8.15   Reproduced with permission of the International Society
               of Arboriculture.
Figure 8.16   Reproduced with permission of the British Standards
               Institution.
Figure 8.17   Reproduced with permission of National Joint Utilities
               Group, London.

Figure 8.18   Reproduced with permission of the British Standards
Institution; the National Joint Utilities Group, London;
the International Society of Arboriculture; and Pearson
Education, Inc.
Figure 8.19   Reproduced with permission of the National Urban Forestry
Unit.
Figure 8.20   Photograph courtesy of The Directional Drilling Company,
Bedford, UK.
Figure 8.21   Reproduced with permission of Tracto-Technik GMBh,
Germany.

Chapter 9

Figure 9.1   Photograph supplied by Peter Annett.
and 9.2
Figure 9.3   Photograph supplied by John Roberts.
Figure 9.4   Reproduced with permission of the International Society
and 9.5   of Arboriculture.
Figure 9.6   Photograph provided by John Roberts.
Figure 9.7   Photograph courtesy of Julian Forbes-Laird.
Figure 9.8   Leaflet provided courtesy of Mr Jim Harrisson, Reigate and
Banstead Council (formerly Lambeth Borough Council)
and Lambeth Borough Council.
Figure 9.9   Reproduced with permission of the International Society
of Arboriculture.
Figure 9.10   Reproduced with permission of Pearson Education, Inc.
Figure 9.11   (a) and (b). Photographs supplied by Jitze Kopinga, Alterra,
The Netherlands.
Figure 9.12   Reproduced with permission of the Arboricultural Advisory
and Information Service/Tree Advice Trust.
Figure 9.13   Reproduced with permission of the Arboricultural Advisory
and Information Service/Tree Advice Trust.
Figure 9.14   Courtesy of Cooper Clarke Group.
Figure 9.15   Courtesy of Peter Scott Ltd.
Figure 9.16   Photograph provided by John Roberts.
Figure 9.17   Photograph provided by Peter Annett.
Figure 9.18   Courtesy of Peter Scott Ltd.
Figure 9.19   Photograph provided by John Roberts.

Chapter 10

Figure 10.1, Data provided courtesy of ABI and CEH.
Figure 10.2, Reproduced with permission of the Buildings Research
10.3 and   Establishment.
10.4
Figure 10.5   Reproduced with permission of Willowmead Publishing
Limited.
Figure 10.6   Reproduced with permission of the New Jersey Federation
of Shade Tree Commissions.

Figure 10.7   After Boden and Driscoll, 1987. Reproduced with permission of the Institution of Civil Engineers.
Figure 10.8   Reproduced with permission of Willowmead Publishing Limited.
Figure 10.9   Reproduced with permission of CEH.
Figure 10.10 Reproduced with permission of the National House Building and 10.11   Council.
Figure 10.12 Photograph provided by John Roberts.
Figure 10.13 Reproduced with permission of the International Society and 10.14   of Arboriculture.

Chapter 11

Figure 11.1   Photograph provided by John Roberts.
and 11.2
Figure 11.3   Crown copyright.
Figure 11.4   Photograph provided by Peter Annett.
Figure 11.5   Photograph provided by Nick Jackson.
Figure 11.6   Reproduced with permission of the International Society and 11.7   of Arboriculture.
Figure 11.8   Photograph provided by Mr Gordon Mann, Redwood City, and 11.9   USA.
Figure 11.10 Reproduced with permission of Kluwer Academic Publishers.
Figure 11.11 Reproduced with permission of the International Society of Arboriculture.
Figure 11.12 Photograph provided by Mr Gordon Mann, Redwood City, USA.
Figure 11.13 Reproduced with permission of the Center for Urban Forest Research, Davis, California.

Chapter 12

Figure 12.1   After WRc, 1993.
Figure 12.2   Photograph used courtesy of *Reading Evening Post*.
Figure 12.3   Reproduced with permission of Her Majesty's Stationery and 12.4   Office.
Figure 12.5   Reproduced with permission of Insituform Technologies Ltd., and 12.6   UK.
Figure 12.7   [SOURCE – UNKNOWN WEBSITE]
Figure 12.8   Telespec Ltd, Surrey, England (permission applied for).

Chapter 13

Figure 13.1, Photograph provided by John Roberts.
13.2 and
13.3
Figure 13.4   Photograph courtesy of MBW (UK) Ltd, Bolton, UK.
Figure 13.5   Photograph courtesy of Dando Drilling, Littlehampton, UK.
Figure 13.7   Reproduced with permission of Cambridge University Press.
Figure 13.8   Blackwell Science (permission applied for).

Acknowledgements

We are privileged that Professor Tony Bradshaw has written a Foreword for this publication. We took inspiration from his book with Hunt and Walmsley and here we hope to carry forward several of the important messages from their text. We endorse the view of Bradshaw, Hunt and Walmsley that some of the messages about growing trees successfully in the built environment are not new ones but need re-emphasising to sustain their effectiveness.

This book was the product of a project 'Tree Roots: Form and Function' funded by the Government, latterly by the Office of the Deputy Prime Minister. The project officer was Mr Peter Annett. We are indebted to Peter for his unstinting support throughout the development of the book. Peter has read all of the text a number of times and there has been considerable interaction with the many contacts that Peter has facilitated.

The project benefited from a Steering Group drawn from a wide range of interested Stakeholders. The Steering Group comprised Dr Giles Biddle, OBE, Mr Ian Hopcraft, representing the Arboricultural Association, Ms Irene Elsom and Mr David Brooks of The National Joint Utilities Group; Mr Robert Checksfield and Mr John Glasgow represented the Construction Industry Training Board and Mr Donald Meyer represented the Royal Institution of British Architects. We are very grateful to these individuals and their organisations for their commitment to and support of the project.

Throughout the development of the work we have benefited greatly from the inspiration and the wise and friendly counsel of Mr Derek Patch, Director of the Tree Advice Trust, Farnham, who has given most freely of his time.

In addition to directing the project in its early stages the Steering Group also offered editorial advice on chapters at a number of stages. A number of UK professionals also kindly read individual chapters and we are very grateful for their input. These were Lesley Adams, Rupert Baker, John Flannigan, Jerry Ross and Richard Nicholson. Dr Gary Watson of the Morton Arboretum, Lisle, Illinois and Dr Larry Costello of the University of California also commented on certain chapters. The final text has also been made available to the BS 5837 review committee.

Dr John Thornes, School of Geography and Environmental Sciences, University of Birmingham, kindly commented on the section about ice prediction in relation to road salting in Chapter 7. Nick Eden, Director of the Arboricultural Association, formerly Tree Officer with Cheltenham Borough Council, provided further information relating to experience during cable TV installation in Cheltenham.

Mr John Castle, Executive Secretary, International Society for Trenchless Technology, is thanked for his interest, guidance and facilitating contracts in the Trenchless Technology industry.

A large number of individuals and organisations kindly contributed photographs. We are very grateful for these contributions which are recorded with the appropriate image in the text.

We are especially grateful to library staff at CEH-Wallingford: Sue Wharton, Dee Galliford and Pamela Moorhouse (now at CEH-Monks Wood), who responded promptly and cheerfully to our many and frequent requests for literature.

John Roberts is indebted to relatives, friends and colleagues for their support during his illness. Very special thanks go to Peter and Betty Atkins, MBE.

Foreword

Trees are beautiful objects. More than that, trees offer us important practical benefits: they provide protection, they remove pollutants from the air, they reduce noise, and they provide shelter for wildlife Their contribution to our cities is immense, especially to our own health and well-being. As a result, there is great public concern for trees. The values of houses where there are trees are higher than where there are not. And after the Great Storms of 1987 and 1988, £25 million was set aside by Government to ensure that what was lost was replaced.

Yet many people just take trees for granted, like they take lampposts – beneficial objects which have always been there. And they treat them as they would lampposts – stuck in the ground, requiring little or no attention. But trees are certainly not lampposts. They are living organisms. In the right conditions we can plant small trees and have them grow into objects of great size without any input from us. No lamppost can do this.

But this quality brings with it problems. Firstly, trees require an environment without adverse factors that could affect them. Secondly, they require continuing supplies of the materials, especially water and nutrients, necessary for growth. Thirdly, the growth itself requires that trees are given adequate room for expansion without upsetting their surroundings.

All this, you will say, is evident from looking at any tree. But is it so evident? We can see the above-ground parts of trees and appreciate their need for space and light. But it is all too easy to forget the very significant part of the tree that is below ground – the root system – which (as this book discusses) extends twice as far as the branches above ground. This means that trees occupy four times as much space below ground as they do above ground, and all this is within the top metre of the soil or less.

This occupation is by roots that are both tough and delicate, which are constantly growing and exploring new ground, which are absorbing essential resources of water and nutrients, and which are providing anchorage. Tough though they can be, their growth is strongly influenced by ground conditions and by the general health of the tree.

So what is below ground, and what we offer trees to root into, are very important, particularly in urban areas where little of the soil is natural, but made of subsoil, brick rubble and concrete. Equally, the structures that tree roots may affect, such as foundations and drains, are important. We are constantly asking trees in towns to grow in inhospitable situations, and in places where they can cause damage, trusting more to hope than to knowledge as to whether they will get into trouble, or cause trouble, without considering how these can be avoided.

Because these matters are important, in recent years a great deal of work has been carried out, both to define problems and to find sensible solutions. The only trouble is that, although much of this work has been written up, it has appeared in many different publications, not always easily accessible. This book is therefore admirable. It covers comprehensively the situations that trees meet underground, what are their effects on tree root growth, and how these can be avoided or minimised.

To some people this book may not be an 'easy' read. Nor should it be, because there is a wide range of information to be assimilated if sense is to be made of what is to be done. There is a deal of soil science throughout the book, perhaps unfamiliar to some readers. But it is wise to know your 'enemy', who may often turn to be your friend and save you a lot of money. The trouble is that soil is a complex material with many different properties. It is also a material that we can alter, or even synthesise. In towns and cities this is very important, and achievable. But we must not let this run away with our enthusiasm, in the imagination that we can easily achieve what the tree needs. We can get it right, but we can get it disastrously wrong.

Anyone involved in planting trees in cities will find this book a treasure house of information, from soil shrinkage to **Amsterdam Tree Soils**, and from root barriers to trenching damage. As a support for the successful greening of cities that concerns so many people at the present day, it will be invaluable.

A D Bradshaw, *University of Liverpool*

CHAPTER 1

Introduction

The substantial benefits provided by trees in built environments are not in question. Trees enhance the landscape and soften hard areas among buildings or other hard surfaces. Highway/street trees enhance visual amenity and form an extension to the planting in the front of private properties. Trees help to moderate climate, temperature, sunshine and wind conditions by providing shade and shelter. Along roadsides, trees offer shelter and shade, and also provide clues and cues to changing road configurations. Planting in streets ranges from formal ecologically limited mono-species avenues to mixed planting, which probably has a greater opportunity to enhance biodiversity potential.

There is considerable uncertainty and debate about the economic value of the tree population in urban areas. An economic value may be estimated for the separate benefits of trees, but there are several aspects of the tree population for which a precise economic value is difficult to make, so a realistic overall value is hard to achieve. The major uncertainties are in the number of trees and their age. Should the values of trees be based only on replacement costs? How should hedonic values be included and how should they be costed? Do trees increase the value of property? Nevertheless, although a precise value cannot be put on the tree population of built areas, there is no question that their monetary value is very considerable.

The benefits and values of trees in urban areas mostly relate to that which is visible above the soil surface. Arguably, however, it is the capacity of the root system to function in built environments and enable the trees to grow in these distinctly inhospitable situations that is the overriding and crucial factor. It is the root system that experiences the most abuse by human activities eg during excavation or construction, from **compaction** of soils or because of application of de-icing salts. Likewise, it is the root system, rather than the aerial part of the tree, that plays the biggest part in direct and indirect damage to infrastructure, such as damage to pavements and possibly contributing to **subsidence** on shrinkable soils.

To be able to predict the influence of such impacts as damage to roots by excavation or deterioration in soil quality on trees in hard landscapes, a benchmark is required. This yardstick can be provided from a comprehensive description of the form and functioning of vigorous root systems in built environments. Equally, information about the distribution of root systems and their behaviour will enable the prediction of direct and indirect threats to infrastructure.

Unfortunately, too little attention has been paid to the study and therefore understanding of the basic characteristics of healthy and vigorous root systems of trees that ensure their survival and successful growth in the built environment. This lack of understanding is largely due to an inability to observe the root systems of trees even in the most routine way. Some of the phrases used about root systems which imply that not only are they hidden but they are also an unknown, 'The dark side' and 'The hidden half', are wholly justified. Even in the best circumstances, for example beneath forests or farm woodlands, the difficulties of investigating the root systems of trees are large enough, but these difficulties become particularly severe and restrictive where trees are surrounded by buildings and hard surfaces, and the prospects of satisfying the needs of statistically robust sampling are daunting.

Very often it is inconvenient and impractical, if not impossible, to conduct experiments on adult trees rooted beneath avenues and streets. In place of such studies, experiments have been made on young trees at research sites. Unfortunately, we are not in a strong position to gauge how representative such studies are of real-world conditions. Because the root systems of trees are so effectively obscured it is not easy to gauge the degree of damage that has been inflicted as a fraction of the total root system, for example, by streetworks or salt spreading. It is therefore difficult to relate the likelihood of the impacts of change to responses observed in experimental situations, in which a known and fairly precise level of treatment has been administered, to real life situations with mature trees.

Nevertheless, it is relevant to consider what information is available about tree roots and their form and function, irrespective of whether the information has come directly from built environment situations with adult trees. Important issues then are: What information do we have about the form and function of tree roots in built environments? Particularly, what new understanding is available in the scientific literature about roots and root systems and is it relevant to problems related to tree roots in built environments? What are the gaps in our knowledge?

In general terms these were the types of questions asked about tree root systems in workshop discussions at the conference 'Arboricultural practice: Present and Future' held at the University of Warwick in 1995 (Claridge, 1997). The priorities for research were discussed at this meeting; the deliberations of the workshop sessions are summarised by Last (1997). At the Warwick conference there were a number of specific questions and issues raised about roots and their form and function:

1. What is the role of roots in sustaining water relations?

2. In what ways is water, lost from foliage by **transpiration**, replenished by water entering roots?

3. Can the relation between root impairment (for example that inflicted by trenching), stability and dieback be quantified? How will roots and root systems respond to damage?

4. Remembering that the balance of fine and **structural roots** in mature trees differs from that in saplings, can the responses of one be used to predict those of the other?

5. Much more needs to be known about the likely responses of roots to impenetrable barriers.

6. What are the responses of roots affected indirectly as well as directly by environmental and habitat variables including soil type and atmospheric pollutants?

7. What are the mechanisms that roots invoke on sites of dereliction that are compacted and/or contaminated with toxic concentrations of noxious chemicals?

8. Bearing in mind the notoriety that instances of damage attract it is not inappropriate to be reminded that these instances implicate a very small minority of trees. But exactly how is this damage brought about? What are the relative contributions of direct and indirect damage?

The conclusion from the workshop sessions was that the top priority for future research was an up-to-date, comprehensive and authoritative review of the many aspects of root biology with, additionally, the assessments of the effects of roots on man-made structures and vice versa. This recommendation led to the commissioning of such a review by the Department of Environment, Transport and the Regions (now the Office of the Deputy Prime Minister (ODPM)). This call for a review on tree roots and their form and function made the statement:

> 'Widespread concern about the effects of trenching by the utility services, and especially the installation of cable communications, have revealed that knowledge of root form and function and their responses to adversity lags behind our understanding of foliage and above ground woody structures. The project will prepare a practical handbook drawing together existing knowledge on tree roots and their interactions with soil, man-made structures and objects. Although primarily aimed at arboriculturists, the manual will also be relevant to other professionals. The project will also identify specific problems relating to tree roots where further research is required to develop sound and practical solutions.'

This book is the output of that research project. It reviews activities, including current engineering and cultural practices which may impact on tree roots. The book emphasises those practices that are sound and identifies where improvements in guidance are needed. The relevance of current research is considered and, more importantly, future research requirements on which better practice might be based are identified.

The source material used in the review process has been very wide-ranging but the core material has come from the arboricultural literature. Much of the published work on trees in built environments comes from research carried out in the USA and involves tree species commonly used there. There will always be some uncertainty about the direct applicability of results obtained in different conditions and with different species, but knowledge of the trends observed will still be valuable and the underlying principles can be established.

In the past decade or so, there has been a marked increase in research into roots and root systems and how a wide variety of environmental, soil and other factors influence root growth and survival. Although little research has been carried out on the species commonly planted in built environments there has been much useful information obtained elsewhere which may have application for urban species. It is therefore a good time to take stock and evaluate the relevance of this body of research in the light of the practical problems of growing and sustaining trees in built environments.

The stimuli for this recent research interest are various and in some cases only loosely connected with each other. A substantial area of research is related to the impacts of global climate change on vegetation dynamics. Concerns about the effects of **global change** have led to increased study of below-ground processes. The focus of this interest has tended to be on root dynamics and the sequestration of carbon below ground. The research is showing that up to a third of the annual **biomass** production goes into fine roots that are relatively short-lived. A significant part of the nutrient cycle of the tree will be linked to the turnover of fine roots. It is important to note that virtually nothing is known about these processes for trees growing in urban situations.

Of the several predictions of global change most will have important consequences for tree growth and survival. If proven correct some of the most important consequences of climate change, in northern Europe at least, are likely to be increases in the frequency of summer **droughts** and the prospect of wetter, windier winter climates. All of these changes have important consequences for trees, whether they are growing in forests or as individuals in artificial surroundings. In the case of trees growing in the built environment the effects of global climate change may be particularly critical if the current provision for the tree is already less than optimal. For example, the volume of soil available to supply water and other requirements may be limited to a modest tree pit. Alternatively the vigour of the tree may have been compromised by root damage during excavation or the root system may have been rendered less effective by soil compaction associated with construction work. In cases such as these the tree is much less likely to cope with additional stresses imposed by a changing climate.

In the course of discussing establishment of trees in this book the important, competitive, role of weeds is highlighted. There are other tree-growing enterprises in which below-ground competition between plants is regarded as important and has been researched substantially. **Agro-forestry** is a land-use system in which trees are combined with a variety of agricultural production systems. Of relevance here are combinations that involve trees growing with arable crops or pastures. The success or failure of an agro-forestry system is largely determined by competition above and below ground, and it is the studies into below-ground competition that have most direct relevance to **arboriculture** and especially to the successful establishment of young trees within a green landscape.

A substantial body of research has been pursued on the functions of the symbiotic relationship between the fungi and the tree roots with which they form **mycorrhizal** associations. There is strong evidence that such associations will benefit trees by enhancing drought tolerance, increasing the uptake of immobile nutrients and offering some tolerance to the presence of heavy metals or other contaminants in the soil. Hitherto, establishing a population of mycorrhizal fungi in soils where amenity trees are growing or augmenting an existing population has been a fairly haphazard process. It would be valuable if some of the large body of scientific research about the dynamics of populations of soil fungi and their requirements was exploited to improve tree survival and growth.

Some of the new insights into roots and their functioning have been obtained because of new methodologies and technical developments. Stable isotopes have been used successfully to identify sources of water that may be available to tree roots (eg Smith *et al*, 1997). The use of ground-penetrating radar shows promise as a means to detect large structural roots (Čermák *et al*, 2000). Examples are available of the successful use of fractal methods to predict fine root distribution from large roots at the tree base (van Noordwijk *et al*, 1994) and **sap flow** heat tracer approaches have been used to measure water transport through tree roots (eg Lightbody *et al*, 1994). These are a few examples and there is strong optimism for future innovations. Nevertheless, we are still a long way from the routine observation of root systems and we have no simple parallels to the visual assessments currently used to evaluate the condition of above-ground parts of trees.

Each chapter is summarised and has its own reference list. To start the review of root information we look at the two core ingredients – soils and roots. The fundamental properties of soils pertinent to the growth and functioning and the biology of roots are reported in Chapters 2 and 3 respectively. The main purpose of these chapters is to establish a background of the physical, chemical and biological properties and processes in soils and roots outside of the built environment.

In many cases new tree plantings are made in derelict and **contaminated land** or land with some particular constraint because of physical or chemical properties of the soil. In Chapter 4 we examine properties of soils likely to offer limitations to the successful growth of trees. The success rate of planting young trees is poor – in some cases as few as half of trees survive beyond the first two years after planting. In some cases the level of failure has been even higher. In Chapter 5, practices in the nursery, which help to provide the young tree with a healthy and vigorous root system, are examined. There is a very substantial risk that a young tree will not survive planting out in the landscape – the influence of weeds and an adequate water supply are key topics that are also discussed. In Chapter 6 this theme is extended to older trees. The enhanced demands for water that are associated with **evaporation** in built environments are discussed as well as the requirements and management of water supply for trees. Even though trees may be planted in good soil that is free from harmful contaminants, there is always the prospect of impacts from chemicals from human activity. In Chapter 7 we examine the influences of chemicals that particularly affect the root systems of trees. Emphasis is placed on those applied to control weeds or remove ice and snow from roads and pavements.

Chapters 8 and 9 deal with the influences of activities in the built environment on tree roots. These activities are separated into damage to tree roots by excavation (Chapter 8) and the deleterious impacts of compaction and changes in soil level during construction (Chapter 9). The separation of the material into these two chapters is for convenience and certainly does not suggest that the damage to roots by excavation or other building activities are mutually exclusive. In recent years, many of the concerns about the injuries to tree roots have focused on the effects of trenching during the installation of cables for communication. Although the peak of cable installation has passed there is still the prospect of further disruption to root systems as other ageing services are replaced. It is important, however, to understand that any excavations, no matter how trivial, can damage tree roots. Therefore, Chapter 8 takes a broader view of the impacts of any degree of disturbance by excavation near to the roots of trees. A wide range of activities that impoverish the conditions for the root systems of trees is associated with construction, whether small or large scale. One of the major effects of construction activities is through the compaction of the soil surface. This has important influences on **infiltration** of water, **soil aeration** and the mechanical properties of soils with respect to root growth. Equally important will be the changes in soil level that occur frequently during building and landscaping.

Of course trees are not always the injured party. In the built environment there may be problems caused, either directly or indirectly, by tree roots and these are dealt with in Chapters 10 to 12. In Chapter 10 the direct or indirect effects of tree roots on buildings are covered. This chapter further highlights the need for more information about the water requirements of trees, already identified in earlier chapters, in relation to establishment and survival of young trees and their continued growth in built environments. In Chapter 11 we discuss the impact of tree roots on low-rise structures and importantly, pavements. Chapter 12 examines the relationship of tree roots in damaging and entering pipes and sewers. In Chapter 13 we draw together the key conclusions and recommendations from earlier chapters and offer a list of priorities for future research on the root systems of trees in the built environment.

The impetus for this book arises from several underlying needs. There is a need to bring together information that is otherwise dispersed over a wide variety of scientific sources and published in a formal or less formal way. It would be unreasonable to expect the busy practitioners, either in arboriculture or any of the fields related to growing trees in the built environment, to be able to cover the full range of literature. In many aspects of tree roots in the built environment, but certainly not all, the amount of literature available is large and exists in a wide variety of forms. Information exists in formal research papers, book chapters, trade journal articles, extension notes, standards and guides. Much is now available on the internet. Clearly for a busy professional involved with any aspect of tree roots in the built environment there will be a need to be aware of research findings and associated guidance. All of the steps towards reaching an awareness about tree roots, identifying, acquiring and reading the sources of information, take time. It is hoped that this book will streamline some or all the processes of acquiring information about tree roots for professionals.

There is substantial guidance already set in place which seeks to enhance the establishment and protection of trees. It is not the intention of this book to provide new instructions but to review and suggest where current guidance might be revised in the light of new understanding. It would be particularly beneficial for all the industries and professions working with, or adjacent to, trees to promote and use best practice from the same knowledge base.

Many of the messages this book seeks to communicate are not new. We support the sentiments of Bradshaw *et al* (1995) who stressed the need to repeat and reiterate information related to good practice. A case in hand is that of the effect of soil compaction upon roots. It is well known that the compaction of soil increases the mechanical impedance to root penetration, and reduces the infiltration of water and the ease with which oxygen moves through the soil to be consumed by roots. In general terms there may be little new insight that recent scientific investigations can bring to this understanding. In contradiction to this wealth of scientific fact we still find that the legacy of soil compaction left by construction activities is still one of the major problems faced by trees in the built environment. Thus it seems the time is overdue to translate our wealth of knowledge into practices that can make a real and positive difference to our most valuable trees.

The indication that trees and infrastructure can coexist successfully both above and especially below ground will be a thriving population of trees in our towns and cities, streets and parks, along the highways and the heart of

Figure 1.1 Field oak tree incorporated into the Midsummer Place shopping precinct, Milton Keynes, UK.

Figure 1.2 Some of Cheltenham's thriving young and mature street trees.

pedestrian precincts. These situations might be those around which infrastructure has been developed while allowing the trees to flourish (Fig 1.1) or where trees have been incorporated in an existing built landscape (Fig 1.2).

REFERENCES

Bradshaw, A., Hunt, B. & Walmsley, T. 1995. *Trees in the urban landscape: Principles and practice*. E & FN Spon, London, UK. 272 pp.

Čermák, J., Hruška, J., Martinková, M. & Prax, A. 2000. Urban tree root systems and their survival near houses analysed using ground penetrating radar and sap flow techniques. *Plant and Soil*, 219, 103–116.

Claridge, J. 1997. (Ed.) *Arboricultural Practice: Present and Future. Research for Amenity Trees No. 6*, Department of the Environment, Transport and Regions, HMSO, London, UK. 152 pp.

Last, F.T. 1997. Research requirements in arboriculture: Synthesis of the views of conference participants. In: *Arboricultural Practice: Present and Future*, (Ed. by J. Claridge), pp. 139–147. Research for Amenity Trees No. 6, Department of the Environment, Transport and Regions, HMSO, London, UK.

Lightbody, K.E., Savage, M.J. & Graham, A.N.D. 1994. In situ measurement of the sap flow rate in lateral roots and stems of Eucalyptus grandis under conditions of marginality, using a steady state heat balance technique. *Journal of the South African Society for Horticultural Science*, 4, 1–7.

Smith, D.M., Jarvis, P.G. & Odongo, J.C.W. 1997. Sources of water used by trees and millet in Sahelian windbreak systems. *Journal of Hydrology*, 198, 140–153.

Van Noordwijk, M., Spek, L.Y. & de Willigen, P. 1994. Proximal root diameter as predictor of total root size for fractal branching models. I. Theory. *Plant and Soil*, 164, 107–117.

CHAPTER 2

Soil Conditions and Roots

2.1 Introduction

Soil is important for tree growth acting as a source of water and minerals, as the anchorage for the plants, and as a medium in which root systems develop and perform the essential functions of absorption and anchorage. The soil is a complex system, consisting of varying proportions of rock particles and organic matter constituting the solid matrix with soil solution and air occupying the **pore space**. Normally, soil also contains populations of bacteria, fungi, algae, a wide variety of invertebrates and occasionally a few vertebrates. This flora and fauna influences soil characteristics and root growth directly or indirectly (Kramer and Boyer, 1995).

Soil conditions are often central to many of the difficulties encountered where trees are planted in the built environment. Soil problems can be a serious limitation to the successful establishment and growth of trees. But, in some cases, the presence of trees can also influence soil conditions eg the differential drying of some clay soils and the threats to buildings founded on these soils. The difficulties associated with growing trees in urban soils can only be identified and remedies sought and applied if the basic properties of soils, how soil problems affect tree growth and what types of soil occur at different sites are recognised and understood. Using this knowledge would enable the most suitable site treatments to be implemented (Bradshaw *et al*, 1995).

2.2 Important characteristics of soils

Overall, soil consists of four components, the mineral fraction, organic material, water and the soil atmosphere (Fig 2.1). For a particular soil, the relative amounts of water and air in the soil will interchange with each other dynamically. When the soil is wetted by rain, irrigation or **water table** rise, air is driven out. When the soil dries out air returns to the emptying pore spaces. Soil characteristics such as composition, texture, structure and pore space have important influences on the suitability of a soil as a medium for tree root growth. The size, shape and chemical composition of the mineral particles together with the relative proportions of the four soil components give the soil its basic chemical and biological properties which influence how the soil responds to management and the growth of trees.

2.2.1 Composition and texture

Those characteristics of soil most important for tree growth, such as water and mineral storage capacity and suitability for root growth that is related to aeration and resistance to root penetration, depend largely on texture and structure. Soils are usually termed sands, loams, or clays, depending on the proportion of large – sand (2.0 – 0.02 mm), intermediate – silt (0.02 – 0.002 mm) and fine – clay particles (<0.002 mm) present in the mineral fraction. A comparison of scales of typically-sized particles of sand, silt and clay is shown in Fig 2.2 and Table 2.1. By definition, sands contain less than 15% of silt and clay, clay contains over 40% of fine particles, and loam soils contain intermediate amounts of sand and clay. The textural triangle diagram (Fig 2.3a) shows the nomenclature for soils with different proportions of sand, silt or clay.

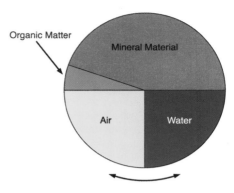

Figure 2.1 Volumetric composition of a medium-textured soil in a condition likely to be optimum for root growth. Solid matter constitutes 50% and pore space 50% of the soil volume. In this schematic, pore volume is divided equally between air and water but as the double-ended arrow suggests they interchange with each other. An increase in one is associated with a decrease in the other. (Modified after Craul, 1992.)

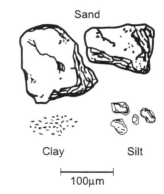

Figure 2.2 The comparative sizes of sand, silt and clay particles. (After Hillel, 1998.)

The different soil textural classes will have differing characteristics that will strongly influence their suitability for tree root growth (Fig 2.3b). Fig 2.4 shows the frequency distribution of size ranges of particles of different soil materials. Information such as that presented in Fig 2.4 would be acquired in a laboratory with fairly sophisticated equipment to conduct soil particle size analysis. Nevertheless, it is possible to make a broad assessment of soil texture without such facilities. Box 2.1 gives a simple key that enables **soil texture** classes to be identified in the field.

Clay soils are compact and cohesive, often poorly drained and aerated, but because they are composed mainly of fine particles they have a large surface area available that can store large amounts of water and nutrients. Sandy soils are loose, non-cohesive, drain well and are well aerated but with a limited storage capacity for water. Loamy soils are intermediate between clays and sands in the features mentioned here. Generally, a high clay content increases the storage capacity of soils for water and minerals (see cation exchange capacity in Section 2.6.2) but reduces the aeration that is so important for good root growth and functioning. Therefore, the fraction of clay is very important in determining the suitability of a soil for tree growth.

Table 2.1 Approximate dimensions (μm*) of soil constituents and of water-filled pore and water films at varying water potentials

Soil particles	stones	>2000
	coarse sand	200–2000
	fine sand	50–200
	silt	2–50
	coarse clay	0.2–2
	fine clay	<0.2
Plant material	root hairs	7–15
	fine roots	50–1000
	roots	>1000
Microbes	viruses	0.05–0.2
	bacteria	0.5–1.0
	actinomycetes	1.0–1.5
	fungi	0.3–10
Some soil animals	protozoa	10–80
	nematodes	500–2000
	mites	500–2000
	earthworms	2–5000
Water-filled pores	–10KPa	<30
	–100KPa	<3
	–1000KPa	<0.3
Water films	–100KPa	<0.003
	–1000KPa	few molecules thick

* μm = 0.001 mm

(a)

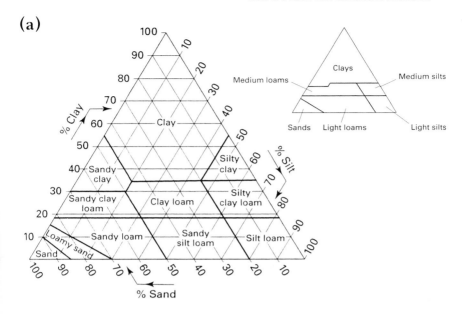

(b)

	Clay	Silt	Sand	Coarse Loam	Fine Loam
Air space	Low	Low	High	Moderate	Moderate
Drainage	Very	Slow	Rapid	Moderate	Moderately slow
Infiltration	Very slow	Moderately slow	Rapid	Moderately rapid	Moderately slow
Compactability	High	Very high	Low	Moderate	Moderately high
Nutrient capacity	Very high	High	Low	Moderate	Moderate
Tilth	Poor	Poor	Good	Very good	Good

Figure 2.3 (a) Textural triangle, showing the percentages of clay (below 0.002 mm), silt (0.002–0.02 mm), and sand (0.02–2.0 mm) in soil textural classes and to the right a simplified form. Diagrams based on the soil texture classes used by the Soil Survey of England and Wales (after Ashman and Puri, 2002). **(b)** Table showing the characteristics in use of soils dominated by the main textural classes. (After Watson and Himelick, 1997).

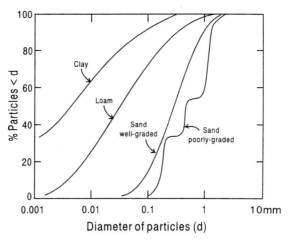

Figure 2.4 Particle size distribution curves for various types of soil material. (After Hillel, 1998.)

2.2.2 Structure and pore space

Soil structure and amount of pore space depends on soil particle size and the degree to which the basic particles are assembled into stable 'crumbs' or aggregates. Aggregation of clay particles to form stable crumbs is assisted by exudates from roots and organic compounds produced by soil organisms. The formation and maintenance of stable aggregates is important in clay soils particularly because it increases pore space that improves the infiltration of water and the maintenance of good aeration.

The relative amounts of capillary and non-capillary pore space strongly affect soil drainage and aeration and hence its suitability for tree root growth. Capillary pore space consists of small pores usually 0.03 to 0.06 mm in diameter or less that are able to retain water against gravity. This determines the **field capacity** or the water retained in a soil after rain or irrigation. Non-capillary pore space (>0.06 mm in diameter) is the fraction of soil volume from which the water drains by gravity, providing the air space so important for good aeration for the roots. Approximately half the volume of most soils consists of pore space, but the proportions of capillary and non-capillary pore space vary widely in different soils. Cultivation often damages soil structure and decreases non-capillary pore space. A comparison of a forest soil and an adjacent cultivated field (Fig 2.5) shows a significant reduction in the non-capillary pore space in the field soil.

2.2.3 Soil bulk density

The non-capillary pore space is especially relevant to root growth and distribution. Roots will only grow into pores of sufficient size. With increasing depth in the soil below both forest and grass there is a reduction in the non-capillary pore space (Fig 2.5) but in the forest soil, this type of pore space

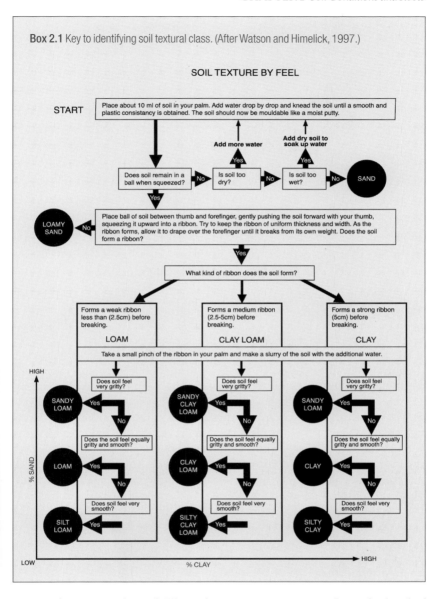

Box 2.1 Key to identifying soil textural class. (After Watson and Himelick, 1997.)

persists deeper into the soil. The reduction in pore space reduces the level of aeration in the soil and there is an increase in the **bulk density** (weight of soil per unit volume) of the soil. With increasing bulk density there is an increase in soil mechanical strength and an associated reduction in the ability of roots to penetrate the soil. Soils which have a bulk density of 1.4 g cm^{-3} or lower might be found in the surface layers of forest and agricultural soils and would be readily exploited by plant roots. At bulk densities above around 1.6 g cm^{-3} soils are regarded as limiting to root penetration (Brady and Weil, 1999). The increase in soil bulk density with soil depth in natural circumstances is due to **consolidation** of soil material mainly because of the weight of soil material

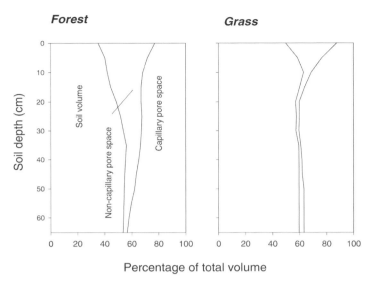

Figure 2.5 Soil volume, capillary pore and non-capillary pore volume in a forest and a field soil. (Modified after Kramer and Boyer, 1995.)

above but also due to the wash down of finer particles into empty soil spaces. We use the term consolidation to describe the creation of soil of high bulk density by natural processes. This makes a distinction from compaction which is the creation, in the course of human activities, of one or more layers in the soil profile with a high bulk density. Compaction occurs intentionally to provide soils with a greater capacity to bear loads, or unintentionally, eg during construction, as vehicles and plant are moving around and operating on sites. Compaction can also occur when humans and animals trample soils. With respect to urban soils and construction activities we deal with compacted soils and their influence on root growth more fully in Chapters 4 and 9 respectively. However, although the means by which soils develop high bulk densities may be different in natural, semi-natural or in the built environment, the consequences will be similar: soils will have a low frequency of pores of sufficient size in which roots can develop and oxygen diffusion rates will be low. These conditions will mean that tree root development will be poor or non-existent and root function will be inhibited.

A major challenge for growing trees in urban areas is the need to resolve the conflicting engineering and biological demands made of soil. Soils must be able to support pavements and other hard surfaces but at the same time possess the capacity to support tree root growth. In Chapter 9 we discuss attempts that have been made to resolve this conflict by creating **structural soils**. One approach in a structural soil is to include a stone component which can be compacted to give adequate support for pavements while retaining sufficient space between the stones for uncompacted soil which would accommodate root growth.

2.2.4 Soil organic matter

The second solid component of the soil, soil organic matter (SOM), is usually concentrated in the upper layer of the soil. It is essential for the maintenance of soil micro-organisms and it renders the soil porous and friable (breakable). These properties increase the water-holding capacity of the soil and improve its aeration. When it decays, SOM yields mineral nutrients and, especially, nitrogen for uptake and use by trees growing in the soil. In addition SOM has a high ion exchange capacity acting much like the mineral exchange sites found on clay particles (see Section 2.6.2).

SOM is formed as the result of biological activity, the combination of plant (and animal) growth and decay, most obviously in the form of litter. In some soils, perhaps because of low temperatures or **anaerobic** conditions, plant litter will remain only partially decomposed on the soil surface as a distinct horizon. In good soils, litter, if not removed is broken down to small particles to form what is known as **humus**, intimately mixed with the mineral fraction of the soil.

Humus is usually black or brown in colour, and is a collection of complex organic compounds that accumulate in soil because they are relatively resistant to decay. Just as the clay fraction is the colloidal fraction of the soil mineral matter, the humus is the colloidal fraction of the SOM. Because of their charged surfaces, both humus and clay act as contacts between soil particles; thus both humus and clay play an important role in the formation of soil structure. The surface charges of humus, like those of clay, attract and hold both nutrient **ions** and water molecules. However, on a weight basis, humus has a greater capacity than clay to hold nutrients and water. Humus also contains substances that have similar properties to growth regulators which occur naturally in plants such as the auxin, indole acetic acid (IAA) (see also Section 3.2.7). These substances might influence root development (eg Pizzeghello *et al*, 2001, 2002).

SOM is crucial both in the development of a good soil structure, and as a source of plant nutrients. Soils with textures that make them difficult to cultivate can be improved by the addition of organic matter and the water retention of free-draining soils can be increased with supplementary organic matter. At the same time organic matter can be a source of essential plant nutrients that are not released in sufficient quantities from the weathering of the mineral part of the soil. Most significantly, it is only in the organic fraction where nitrogen is stored in the soil. The SOM content of typical lowland soils in Britain ranges from 2 to 15% by weight (Bradshaw *et al*, 1995). In undisturbed woodland soils the values are often at the higher end of the range; in arable soils which have a long history of cultivation the values are close to the bottom end of the range.

The SOM is a major store of carbon in terrestrial ecosystems and cropping systems. In fact, more carbon is stored in the world's soils than there is in the biomass. The amount and fate of this carbon will have important implications to future atmospheric carbon dioxide (CO_2) concentrations. There is considerable release of carbon dioxide from soil. The sources of the CO_2 are **respiration** of roots and soil micro-organisms and from the breakdown of SOM. The rates of respiration and decomposition processes increase with temperature, so there is considerable interest in the fate and dynamics of SOM as global temperatures rise with climate change. Global temperature rises are regarded as a consequence of the increased concentration of 'greenhouse' gases eg CO_2 in the atmosphere. Therefore these temperature rises might in fact be enhancing the production of CO_2 as a positive feedback to global temperature increase.

A large amount of organic matter also increases the capacity of a soil to hold water and its **cation exchange capacity**. However, because of the adsorptive capacity of organic materials the effectiveness of soil-applied pesticides is reduced, but so also is the likelihood of injury by toxic substances. The more organic matter a soil contains the more herbicide, insecticide or nematocide needs to be applied to be effective (Wild, 1988).

2.3 Soil water

2.3.1 Rainfall amount

Typically, soil water is supplied directly from rainfall. Less typically, shallow groundwater can rise in winter and recharge soil with water up to the soil surface from below. The type of vegetation influences the amount and distribution of rainfall reaching the soil surface. Because of the spatial separation and roughness of their canopies tall woody vegetation has a greater impact on the quantity of rainfall reaching the ground than short vegetation. Although the **leaf area index** (leaf area per unit ground area, $m^2\ m^{-2}$) of a forest or individual tree may only be marginally more than for a pasture or cereal field, the foliage in trees is far more separated vertically and the canopy better ventilated by the wind. This parameter of vegetation canopies, their aerodynamic roughness, is high for trees and low for short, smooth vegetation such as pastures and cereal crops. The high aerodynamic conductance of a tree canopy compared to that of shorter plants means that the tree canopy is far better ventilated by air flow through it.

Raindrops impacting on foliage are intercepted and the canopy becomes partially or fully wetted. Evaporation can take place from canopies even during the rainstorm (if the air is not actually saturated and energy is available) and of course after the storm. The fraction of rainfall evaporated back to the atmosphere in this way is called the rainfall **interception loss**, the remaining fraction of rainfall which ultimately reaches the ground is called the net rainfall. The greater aerodynamic roughness of tree canopies means evaporation from wetted canopies occurs more rapidly than happens in a smooth, short canopy. This difference is analogous to the more rapid drying expected by hanging washing on a line as opposed to laying it on the ground. The high aerodynamic roughness of tree crowns and forest canopies also increases their ability to trap (scavenge) **particulates** (eg PM_{10}s, dust, dry deposited nutrients) and fog droplets from the atmosphere more efficiently than short vegetation.

In the United Kingdom (UK) rain occurs mostly as light showers in rain events that are of long duration. Thunderstorms, in which the rain falls at a high intensity for a short duration, are far less frequent. The fact that forest canopies remain wet for quite a large proportion of the time, particularly in the high-rainfall west of the UK, means that interception losses can be very high. Because of its relevance to the hydrological effects of afforestation by **conifers** in the uplands of the UK a large amount of information and understanding about rainfall interception loss by forest canopies has developed. Studies have shown that on an annual basis, up to 40% of gross rainfall is lost from the canopies of **evergreen** conifers and around 20% from **deciduous broadleaf** woodlands (Roberts, 1999). In winter, interception losses from leafless, broadleaf woodlands are below 10% of gross rainfall. Comprehensive measurements are not available for isolated trees in UK conditions but interception losses on a crown projected area basis are not likely to be less than from forests in the same rainfall conditions and could easily be more.

Because there is a tendency for raindrops to coalesce with each other on tree foliage, drips of rain from canopies will be larger than ordinary raindrops and will possess larger amounts of kinetic energy. In a study of a number of tropical tree species the change in raindrop size was shown to vary with tree species. Trees with large, entire leaves, eg teak, gave raindrops with the highest kinetic energy (Hall and Calder, 1993). The larger raindrops falling from tree canopies possess a greater potential to dislodge soil particles from unprotected soil surfaces and cause erosion. In natural forest ecosystems there are usually many layers within the vertical profile of the forest and there is normally a well-developed litter layer on the ground. Much of the kinetic energy of raindrops will be dissipated by the time raindrops reach the soil surface. In the case of some plantations and individual trees, raindrops will have a more direct path from the canopy to the soil. For this reason, therefore, it is important to consider some form of soil protection beneath tree canopies.

2.3.2 Distribution of rainfall

The distribution of rainfall to the soil surface is also influenced by vegetation type and in trees rainfall can be distributed differently depending on the species and the age of the tree. Raindrops falling above a tree canopy can reach the soil either directly (free throughfall) or less directly after dripping from the leaves and branches (throughfall). A further fraction of the net rainfall reaches the ground by running down the tree trunk, and is termed stemflow. In trees such as beech, the water coming down the trunk may continue running down the outside of the major roots, which might facilitate entry of water into the soil. This process might be enhanced when soil dryness causes the major roots to separate from the soil at the root collar. A number of factors determine the fraction of net rainfall which is stemflow. The shape of the tree crown, particularly the angle of the branches, and the smoothness of the bark are thought to be most important criteria determining the amount of net rainfall occurring as stemflow. Whether the tree is in leaf or not, or has been severely pruned will also influence stemflow. Trees with upwardly directed branches form a funnel, directing water along branches, inwards and downwards towards the tree trunk at its centre. Tree species with smooth bark (beech is a good example), may have as much as 20% of the net rainfall reaching the ground as stemflow. In rough-barked species, eg Scots pine, stemflow can be as little as 2% of net rainfall. It is likely that water held on the branches and trunks of rough-barked trees is re-evaporated. A number of studies have shown that the fraction of net rainfall that occurs as stemflow declines as trees age. As trees become older a larger fraction of the branches become longer, heavier and assume a more horizontal posture or even a downward curvature. This means that less of the water collected by the canopy is directed downwards and inwards towards the trunk. A study within the crown of a 9 m Douglas fir tree by Hutchinson and Roberts (1981) showed that 70% of the stemflow came from the upper half of the canopy.

2.3.3 Entry of water into soil

The rate of infiltration is important in the recharge of soil water by rain and irrigation. If infiltration is slow, surface runoff occurs with likely wastage of water and possibly soil erosion. Infiltration into some clays is hindered because they swell when wetted, reducing the non-capillary pore spaces. Infiltration into some sands is retarded because the particles are covered with **hydrophobic** substances. Infiltration is usually more rapid into forest soils than cultivated soils of the same type because forest soils usually contain more non-capillary pore space. In forest soils, large pores (Fig 2.5) left by decay of large roots offer efficient entry points for water to infiltrate. Infiltration rates exceeding 100 mm hr^{-1} have been measured in undisturbed forest soils. Infiltration rates of this order will exceed all but the very extreme rainfall events even under tropical conditions.

A number of additional factors can influence the amounts of water that can infiltrate into soils. If a site is sloping, water may run off downslope at the surface rather than enter the soil. Such a consideration may be relevant where trees are planted on inclined sites in built environments. One of the important factors that reduce rainfall infiltration in built environments will be compaction at the soil surface (See Section 4.2.3). The compaction might be as a result of vehicle movements or trampling by humans or animals. Another factor that will of course reduce infiltration will be the presence of hard surfaces such as concrete, asphalt and sealed paving (See Section 6.2.3). These will cause a major reduction of infiltration of water into the **root zones** of trees but will also promote the rapid discharge of water into gullies and drains which will also increase flood peaks in local water courses. More effective infiltration of rainfall in urban areas will help the soil moisture supply of trees. An increase in infiltration in urban areas will also mean that there will be less direct runoff to streams and rivers. This will mean that sharp flood peaks of streams and rivers draining urban areas will be lessened and that better control of water quality at source is possible.

2.3.4 Soil evaporation

Like rainfall lost by interception from vegetation canopies, soil evaporation might be regarded as a waste as this water does not enter the soil and therefore cannot contribute to production of plants. Soil evaporation can only occur from relatively wet soils and like all evaporation processes will require energy. This ultimately comes from solar radiation. In natural ecosystems with a well-developed canopy the amount of energy reaching the soil surface will be small so soil evaporation is usually trivial. In many agricultural systems, for example, cereal crops, the soil is bare for extended periods during the year. Immediately after a rainstorm, and for two to three days following, evaporation losses from bare soil can be significant, equivalent to losses from an open water surface. As the soil surface dries soil evaporation can only be supported by vapour movement from wet soil deeper in the profile. The rates of evaporation in these circumstances are usually very small.

So, physical studies of the controls of soil evaporation have shown that the predominant controls are a source of energy and a ready supply of water at the upper levels of the soil profile. This information can guide approaches to reducing soil evaporation and making the maximum amount of water available where young trees are planted and perhaps also irrigated. The aims should be to deliver water to below the soil surface and reduce radiation reaching the soil surface. **Mulches** can prevent evaporation losses from soil but they will be less valuable if the irrigation only serves to wet the mulch. An ideal situation might be a reasonable depth of a water-repellent mulch. This would provide a cover to limit energy receipt at the soil surface but would allow the applied water to pass to deeper soil layers.

2.3.5 Soil water content

The water content of a soil is usually expressed as a percentage of oven dry weight, or of volume. The percentage of soil volume is more informative with respect to the amount of water available for plants but is difficult to determine without disturbing the soil. Unfortunately water content on a percentage basis says little about the amount of water available to plants because, for example, a sand may be saturated at a water content which is close to the **wilting point** for a loam soil (See Fig 2.6).

The water content and rate of water movement in soils depend to a large extent on soil type. Sandy soils have relatively low surface area per gram of soil and have large spaces or channels between particles. At the other extreme is clay, in which particles are smaller than 0.002 mm in diameter. Clay soils have much greater surface area and smaller channels between particles. The spaces between soil particles may be filled with air or with water.

When a soil is fully watered by rain or irrigation, the water percolates downward by gravity through the spaces between soil particles, partially displacing, and in some cases trapping, air in these channels. Water in the soil may exist as a film adhering to the surface of soil particles or may fill the entire

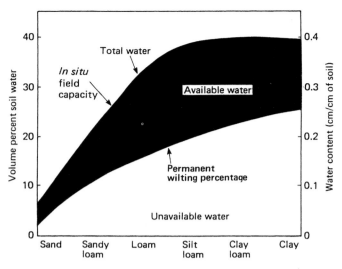

Figure 2.6 The relative amounts of available and unavailable water in soils ranging in texture from sands to clay. Amounts are expressed in percentages of soil volume and centimetres per centimetre of soil. (After Kramer and Boyer, 1995.)

channel between particles. In sandy soils, the spaces between particles are so large that water tends to drain from them and remain only on the particle surfaces and at interstices between particles. In clay soils, the channels are small enough that water does not freely drain from them but is held more rigorously. This phenomenon is reflected in the moisture holding capacity, or field capacity, of soils, which is large for clay soils and soils with a high humus content and much lower for sandy soils. Field capacity refers to the water content of a soil after it has been saturated with water and excess water has been allowed to drain away. Fig 2.6 shows the relative differences in soil water storage for a range of soil types. The plant-available water capacity of a soil is determined by its texture, organic matter content and structure. Fine-textured soils with poor crumb structures and containing very little organic matter, such as some clays, will hold large amounts of water but relatively little is available to plants. In contrast, coarse, sandy soils drain rapidly, retaining relatively small quantities of water. However, most of the water is available to plants. Between clays and sands are soils that are intermediate in textures and structures, with a better balance of properties. Organic matter can absorb large amounts of water.

2.3.6 Soil water potential

Information about the water content of soils is important. For example, it tells us how much water is available to plants given some information about the type of soil, and we are able to plan the amount of soil volume required by a tree (see for example Section 5.5.1). However, knowledge of soil water content does not tell us directly how tightly water is held within a soil and how difficult it is for trees to obtain that water. Nor does it tell us about the gradients which influence water movement through soil.

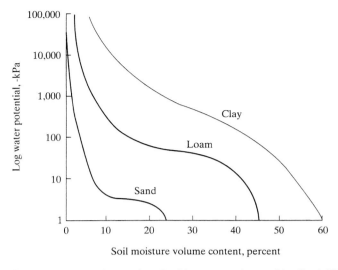

Figure 2.7 Soil moisture potential curves for soils of three texture classes. (After Craul, 1992.)

The concept of **water potential** was developed to describe the physical and chemical forces which retain water in soils. Water held in the soil has the potential to do work. Unless the soil is saturated, this potential is negative, because work must be done – energy must be used – to remove water from the soil. The drier the soil the greater the amount of work that must be expended to remove water from it. Soil water potential (ψ) has units of pressure and has a number of components (see Box 2.2). The most important component of water potential to tree water uptake in non-saline soils is the matric potential (ψ_m) which is controlled by the degree to which water is held by the soil matrix. Soil water potential becomes increasingly more negative as the soil water content is decreased. In fully wetted soils the water potential is 0 but in dry soils can reach around –2.0 MPa. The soil water content which coincides with the same water potential differs substantially in different soils (Fig 2.7). These differences show, for example, that clay soils contain substantial amounts of unavailable water because roots cannot attain a low enough water potential to acquire it. After substantial rainfall, water drains from the large pores in the soil, which become at least partially filled with air. Roots tend to have a more negative water potential value than that with which the soil holds water so water is taken up by the roots. However, as the soil dries, it will retain some of the water because as the soil dries the water is held at increasingly lower water potentials. At approximately –1.5 MPa (–15 bars) any water still held by the soil is unavailable to the plant roots. This value of water potential is often termed the wilting point. The water available to plants, the available water capacity of the soil, is, therefore, the quantity of water held by the soil between field capacity and wilting point.

Box 2.2 The terminology of soil water potential

Total soil water potential (ψ_{soil}) expresses the potential energy status of soil water relative to conditions associated with pure, free water. The value for free water is arbitrarily set as zero, so the energy available in soil water to do work will always be less than zero. The water potential of soil depends on four components that vary in importance:

$$\psi_{soil} = \psi_m + \psi_s + \psi_g + \psi_p$$

In this equation ψ_m represents the matric potential which is the force that attracts and binds the water as films onto soil particles and as capillary water in small pores and crevices. The restrictive nature of this force reduces the potential energy of pure free water. Matric potential is equivalent to forces described as soil water tension, suction or capillarity. Very largely the water potential developing in a typical soil is dominated by the matric potential.

ψ_s represents the osmotic potential due to solutes that decreases the potential energy of soil water. When a substance dissolves in water, dipolar water molecules in close proximity to the cation or anion orientate by either electrostatic attraction or repulsion. These forces reduce the potential energy of the water.

ψ_g, gravitational potential is the work needed to maintain soil water at the same suspended location in relation to the attraction of gravity.

ψ_p relates to external pressure and can generally be ignored because, in the soil zone where roots generally are, the pressure is close to atmospheric pressure.

Units

It is current practice to use the pascal (Pa) as the unit of soil water potential. To reduce the size of the numbers the kilopascal (kPa) or megapascal (MPa) are usually employed. 1000 kPa = 1 MPa. In practical terms modern units can be readily converted to units found in older reports, so 1 atmosphere (14.7 lbs/sq in) = 1 bar = 100 kPa = 0.1 MPa.

2.3.7 Water movement through soil

When there is a difference of water potential between two points, the water is not in equilibrium and there will be a tendency for water to move to equalise the potential, the rate of movement being proportional to the gradient of

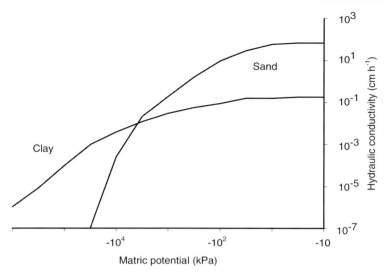

Figure 2.8 Soil hydraulic conductivity as a function of soil water potential for clay and sandy soils. (After White, 1997.)

potential and the **hydraulic conductivity** of the soil. Soil hydraulic conductivity is a measure of the ease with which water moves through the soil, and it varies with soil type. Sandy soils, with large spaces between their particles, have large hydraulic conductivities. Besides soil type the water content of the soil influences hydraulic conductivity of the soil. Fig 2.8 shows that as the water content (and hence water potential) of the soil falls, the hydraulic conductivity decreases drastically. There is a clear difference in responses of different soils. When they are both fully wetted, sandy soils have a higher conductivity than clay soils. However, at soil water potentials of –100 kPa (0.1 MPa or 1 bar) the hydraulic conductivity of sand begins to fall very sharply compared to clay. The decrease in soil hydraulic conductivity is mainly due to the replacement of water in soil channels with air which limits water movement to the periphery of pores and causes some pores to empty completely. This will mean that as the soil dries the pathways in the soil, from pores or voids that contain water or from the films of water on soil particles, to the roots, become longer and more tortuous. Therefore, as the soil hydraulic conductivity falls, there is an increase in the difficulty for roots to continue to acquire water from the soil to sustain losses by transpiration from the canopy.

Roots rarely occupy more than 5% of the soil volume even in the upper 1.0–1.5 m of soil where they are most abundant. For many cases of plant cover the volume of soil occupied by roots decreases rapidly with depth, and at a depth such as 0.5 m is often only a fraction of 1%. This means that only a fraction of the soil within the root zone is in direct contact with the roots. Thus the functioning of roots in soil is determined not only by the physiological properties of the root system but also by soil factors which determine the rate at which water, nutrients and oxygen can move to the soil/root interface.

Attempts have been made to increase water storage capacity of soil by adding water-absorbing, hydrophilic polymers (**hydrogels**) to soils. However, this is often not very effective. The subject is discussed more fully in Section 5.4.2.4.

2.3.8 Volume changes in drying soils

In most cases when soil dries the space vacated by water is replaced by air. In some clay soils, however, when the finest pores are emptied air may not be able to enter and the soil contracts to close up the pores. To accommodate these volume changes the soil fractures into larger blocks and vertical and horizontal cracks appear in the soil. Compared to the range of pore sizes present in soils, cracks formed in clay soils during drying are relatively massive. Typically, cracking of clay soils can be seen at the soil surface in cereal fields following periods of protracted dry weather.

The deep cracks in clay soils will be a preferred point of entry of water when rainfall returns and will probably mean that water will enter the bulk of the soil deeper in the soil profile than occurs in non-shrinking soils. In sandy soils, for example, water enters the soil at the surface passing downwards as a zone of wetting.

There are important implications for the shrinkage of clay soils by water removal by tree roots during dry periods. A possible consequence is uneven shrinkage and swelling of soils that will have serious implications for buildings founded on such soils. The detailed implications of shrinking and swelling of clay soils and the integrity of buildings located on them are dealt with more fully in Section 10.3.1.

2.4 Soil aeration

Soil air near the surface is composed of about 79% nitrogen, 20% oxygen, and 0.25% carbon dioxide, with the remainder consisting of other gases such as methane, ethane, hydrogen sulphide, and nitrous oxide (Brady and Weil, 1999). The gases move into and out of the soil by diffusion. The rate of this process depends on the tortuosity of the diffusion pathway and the temperature gradient (Hillel, 1998). As soil depth increases, the tortuosity and length of the diffusion pathway increase, decreasing the rate of diffusion, and, in turn, reducing the oxygen concentration at the given depth. Carbon dioxide is formed in the soil by organism and root respiration. It is removed from the soil by outward diffusion to the atmosphere. The inhibition or decrease of diffusion causes the carbon dioxide concentration to be higher in the soil than the atmosphere. It increases with soil depth, reaching a concentration as great as 4.5% in some soils. Restated in another way, oxygen has difficulty reaching the lower horizons of the soil profile, and the carbon dioxide produced in the soil has difficulty in being removed from the lower horizons. Fig 2.9 shows the changes of oxygen and carbon dioxide concentration with depth in the soil. The concentrations of oxygen and carbon dioxide are inversely related. The highest O_2 levels, particularly at depth, occur in February when root activity is

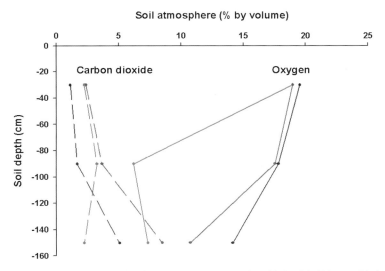

Soil atmosphere (% by volume)

Figure 2.9 Variation of carbon dioxide and oxygen concentration with depth in February (blue), May (green), and September (red). (After Craul, 1992.)

least. With increased root and microbial activity and their respiration in May and September, the oxygen levels are lower and CO_2 is consequently higher.

Diffusion is partially temperature driven. It occurs from a region of higher temperature to one of lower temperature. Temperatures tend to be higher at the soil surface during daytime, so the normal diffusion is of oxygen into the soil, which counteracts the outward diffusion of carbon dioxide. Carbon dioxide may diffuse outward more readily at night. The effect of temperature is more thoroughly discussed in Section 2.5 – Soil temperature.

Gaseous diffusion can occur only in air-filled pore space. Little diffusion occurs in saturated soils. Moist soil with more tortuous diffusion pathways from the presence of both water-filled and air-filled pore space has a diffusion rate less than that of a dry soil. Diffusion is not greatly restricted in surface horizons with a well-developed granular structure having a large proportion of **macropores**. Diffusion is reduced in the lower horizons as the pore size decreases and a greater proportion are water-filled. Coarse-textured soils are well-drained and moderate to small proportions of the pore space are water-filled. These soils will have a relatively high oxygen concentration deep in the profile enhancing root development to great depth, if there is no mechanical impedance. A fine-textured soil has a smaller proportion of air-filled pore space overall. Oxygen concentration decreases and carbon dioxide concentration increases sharply with depth in these soils. Well-developed structure in medium to fine-textured soils tends to offset this effect. Compacted soils have a greatly decreased air-filled pore space and a very low rate of gaseous diffusion in any direction.

Roots require oxygen, so aeration status is the primary factor determining the total rooting depth in most soils. Many plants growing on upland soils require at least 10 to 12% air-filled pore space volume for satisfactory growth. Sugar maple (*Acer saccharum*), white ash (*Fraxinus americana*), and basswood (*Tilia americana*) require more than 15% air-filled pore space. Norway spruce (*Picea abies*) grows well with only about 5% air-filled pore space. Carbon dioxide may be toxic to roots if present in a large concentration and may also inhibit water absorption. The required oxygen level for subsistence of roots is 3% by volume, 5 to 10% for root growth, and at least 12% or more for new roots to form.

Aeration status has other effects on the soil. Chemical processes and biological activity are influenced by oxygen concentration. Oxygen concentration above a minimum level of around 10% by volume favours oxidation processes and the soil is considered well aerated. The aerobic processes lead to the formation of carbohydrates, carbon dioxide, and water along with the release of large amounts of energy. Iron and manganese, abundantly present in many soils, are oxidised, lending characteristic colours to the soil. Many organism processes are oxidative in nature and good aeration favours activities of the beneficial soil-inhabiting bacteria, algae, fungi, and invertebrates. A soil atmosphere low in oxygen and high in carbon dioxide is anaerobic and harmful to some extent to some organisms. Reduction processes predominate, creating substances such as methane, fatty acids, alcohols, and the putrefying gases along with the release of limited amounts of energy. It is apparent that soil drainage has direct influence on soil aeration status. The soil air component has a composition different from atmospheric air. The atmosphere is composed of 79% nitrogen, 21% oxygen, and 0.03% carbon dioxide. Soil air near the surface is composed of about 79% nitrogen, 20% oxygen and 0.25% carbon dioxide. Plant roots and most other soil organisms require sufficient oxygen (O_2) for their **aerobic respiration** and acquire it directly from the soil. Gas-filled pores in well-drained, well-structured soil allow the diffusion of gaseous O_2 but because of the depths involved and the more tortuous nature of the diffusion pathways the concentrations of O_2 deep in the soil may be several per cent less than it is in the atmosphere (21%). In the case of carbon dioxide (CO_2) the opposite situation holds. The respiration of roots and the many soil organisms produces CO_2 that, because of diffusion rates and pathways, generates a concentration in the soil quite different from that in the atmosphere outside. There will however be some interaction with soil temperature in the case of both O_2 and CO_2. Although diffusion will increase with temperature in the case of O_2 and CO_2, the use of oxygen in respiratory metabolism by roots and soil organisms and the production of CO_2 will also increase. The diffusion of both gases will be reduced considerably in soils that have become flooded or **waterlogged** if they are poorly drained or if rain or irrigation is excessive. Water then fills all the soil pores and prevents the diffusion of O_2 and CO_2 in the gaseous phase. Dissolved oxygen diffuses very slowly in water so only the few centimetres close to the soil surface will be oxygenated in flooded, i.e. anaerobic, conditions.

2.5 Soil temperature

Soil temperature is determined by input of long- and short-wave radiation from the atmosphere. At the soil surface, the receipt of radiation is influenced by artificial surfaces, such as concrete or asphalt, vegetation cover and mulches, such as leaf litter. In the upper few centimetres of soil, diurnal fluctuations of soil temperature follow the variations that are observed in air temperature. Particularly in dry soils, however, the temperature can reach levels much higher than those in the atmosphere and may be harmful to organisms and roots in the soil. Deeper in the soil the maximum daily temperature becomes lower and occurs much later than in the soil surface. Similar relationships are observed for seasonal temperature trends with soil depth. At a significant depth in the soil eg 1 m, the amplitude of the annual temperature change can be as little as 2 or 3°C and the yearly temperature maximum will occur much later in the year than the maximum air and surface soil temperatures. At depths of around 2 m there will be no diurnal or seasonal variation in temperature.

2.6 Soil chemical properties

2.6.1 Plant nutrients in soil

Apart from carbon, hydrogen and oxygen that are provided from the air or water the essential elements required for plant growth are acquired from the soil. Table 2.2 lists these nutrients and separates them into those used in large quantities – macronutrients – and those used in relatively small amounts – the micronutrients.

Table 2.2 The essential elements available from soil solids.

Used in relatively large amounts (the macronutrients)	Used in relatively small amounts (the micronutrients)
Nitrogen	Iron
Phosphorus	Manganese
Potassium	Boron
Calcium	Molybdenum
Magnesium	Copper
Sulphur	Zinc
	Chlorine
	Cobalt

The elements are contained in the minerals released from the parent rocks of soils by weathering. The amounts of the elements present in the soil are strongly dependent on the mineral composition of the soil-forming rock and the predominant reactions of the weathering process. In moist, temperate soils

Table 2.3 Quantities of six essential elements found in soils of temperate regions.

Essential element	In solid framework	Exchangeable	In soil solution
		(kg ha^{-1})	
Calcium (Ca)	8,000	2,250	60–120
Magnesium (Mg)	6,000	450	10–20
Potassium (K)	38,000	190	10–30
Phosphorus (P)	900	–	0.05–0.15
Sulphur (S)	700	–	2–10
Nitrogen (N)	3,500	–	7–25

a major by-product of weathering is the formation of aluminosilicate mineral clay. The chemical behaviour of clay, along with that of organic matter, is responsible for the adsorption and retention of nutrients in the soil. The chemical composition of soils varies but a typical range for each of the macronutrients is shown in Table 2.3. Clearly, the purpose of supplying fertilisers to the soil in which trees are growing is to augment the supply of macro- and micronutrients in the soil. In some cases added fertilisers supply nutrients which are absent or severely deficient in the soil.

2.6.2 Nutrient availability to plants

Not all the nutrients are in a form available to plants. Some are compounds of rock minerals or organic compounds that must be simplified before they can be exploited by plants. The simple forms are water-soluble or easily available because they are located on the surfaces of clays or organic matter. Although the total amounts may be quite large, the available forms are generally in much smaller quantities.

Organic matter can be present in large quantities and is critically important to the plant's chemistry and soil fertility because it is the source of much of the nitrogen in some soils, most of the phosphorus and much of the sulphur. These nutrients will be in short supply if the content of organic matter in the soil is low.

Phosphorus is an important element and its availability may be limited for three main reasons. Firstly, it occurs at rather low levels in many soils. Secondly, most of the phosphorus compounds are relatively insoluble in water. It is rather insoluble when soils are acid ie having a low **pH**. Thirdly, phosphorus may be bound to soil and therefore rendered unavailable to plant roots. Nitrogen, sulphur and potassium compounds are usually quite soluble and are readily available and sufficient for plant growth, except perhaps in intensive agriculture. The amounts of calcium and magnesium in soils are strong functions of the parent material from which the soil was derived. Soils rich in calcium and magnesium have a neutral or alkaline pH and are derived from limestone or marine deposits, for example. Calcium and magnesium compounds are highly soluble and are readily leached from soils. There will be a limited availability of calcium and magnesium in acidic soils (Marschner, 1995).

Soil particles, both inorganic and organic, have negative charges on their surfaces. Inorganic clay particles contain crystal lattices consisting of arrangements of the cationic form of aluminium and silicon (Al^{3+} and Si^{4+}). These clay particles can become negatively charged by replacement of the Al^{3+} and Si^{4+} in the lattice by cations of lesser charge. The organic particles found in humus originate from the decomposition products of dead tissue from plants and animals formed by the action of soil microbes. The negative surface charges on organic particles result from the dissociation of hydrogen ions from carboxylic acid and **phenolic** groups present in the organic component of the soil.

Negative surface charges of soil particles are important in the adsorption of mineral cations to the surface of the particles. The high surface area to volume ratio of both inorganic and organic particles plays an important part in the amount of adsorption and the level of soil fertility. Mineral cations adsorbed to the surface of soil particles are not easily lost when soil is leached by water and, therefore, they provide a reserve of nutrients available to plant roots. Mineral nutrients adsorbed onto the surface of soil particles can be replaced by other cations in cation exchange (Fig 2.10) and the term cation exchange capacity (CEC) represents the degree to which a soil can absorb and exchange ions. Soils with a high CEC provide more mineral nutrients to plant roots than soils with a low CEC.

In contrast to mineral cations, which are adsorbed on the surface of soil particles, mineral **anions** are usually repelled by the negative charge of the soil particles and may remain dissolved in the soil solution. The anion exchange capacity of most soils is small in comparison with that of cations. Among the most commonly required anions, nitrate and chloride are not generally adsorbed onto soil particles and remain in soil solution, where they are susceptible to **leaching** by water movement through the soil. Phosphate ions may bind to soil particles containing aluminium or iron. These have hydroxyl (OH^-) groups that can be exchanged with sulphate, phosphate or other anions. Sulphate is usually fairly soluble in the absence of Ca^{2+} but in the presence of calcium precipitates as calcium sulphate ($CaSO_4$).

2.6.3 Soil pH

The soil pH or soil reaction is a measure of the hydrogen ion concentration in the soil solution. Soils can be extremely acid with a pH at 4 or below, or at the upper end of the range for soils, they can be very alkaline with pH exceeding 8 or 9. A major effect of soil pH is on the availability of nutrients (Fig 2.11). Consideration of this diagram shows that the major nutrients important to tree growth are most readily available at pH between 6 to 7.5. As soil becomes more acid the amounts of exchangeable calcium and magnesium decrease. The

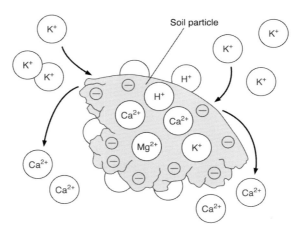

Figure 2.10 Cation exchange on the surface of a soil particle. Cations are bound to the surface of soil particles because the surface is negatively charged. Addition of a cation such as potassium (K^+) can displace another cation such as calcium (Ca^{2+}) from its binding on the surface of the soil particle and make it available for uptake by roots. (After Taiz and Zeiger, 1991.)

amount of exchangeable aluminium which is toxic to plant roots increases. Most trees seem to prefer soils in which the pH is around neutral ie ranging from 6.5 to 7.5 (Hartman *et al*, 2000). There are, however, some species eg sweetgum (*Liquidambar styraciflua*) that prefer more acid soils (6.0–6.5) and others eg acacia (*Acacia longifolia*), honey locust (*Gleditsia triacanthos*) and plane (*Platanus x acerifolia*) which prefer more alkaline soils (Watson and Himelick, 1997). Low pH favours the weathering of rocks and the release of ions such as K^+, Mg^{2+}, Ca^{2+}, and Mn^{2+}. At low pH, the salts present in the soil as carbonates, sulphates and phosphates are more soluble, increasing the likelihood of absorption by roots. In general, high rainfall and decomposition of organic material are major contributors to a lowering of pH. The soil pH can affect the growth of plant roots and soil micro-organisms. Root growth is generally favoured at slightly acidic pH values (5.5 to 6.5). Fungi generally predominate in the soil adjacent to the roots in the acid pH range, whereas at higher pH values bacteria become more prevalent.

2.7 Summary

- Soil consists of mineral and organic material, air and water. The soil is a growth medium for plant roots and a wide variety of soil organisms, some of which are closely associated with the roots. Nutrients and water that are essential for plant growth are provided by the soil. The organic fraction of soils contributes substantially to the global carbon stocks. This organic carbon comprises both living organisms as well as roots and the dead and decomposing remains of animals and plants deposited at the soil surface and within the soil.

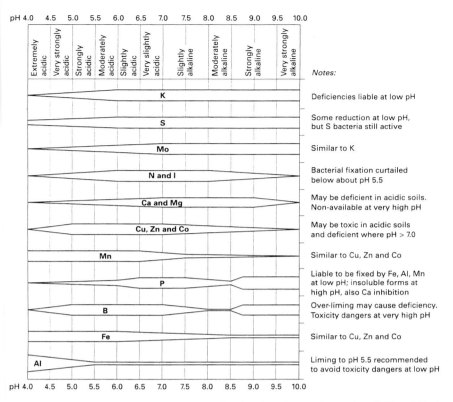

Figure 2.11 Influence of soil pH on the availability of nutrient elements in organic soils. The width of the bands indicates the degree of nutrient availability to plant roots. (After Landon, 1991.)

- The physical nature of soils, their texture and structure, have a major influence on their capacity to store, release and transmit water and nutrients to roots and to provide a suitable medium in which plant roots and other soil organisms can grow. Different soils eg sands, loams and clays have very different structures which influence the amount of water they can hold and how difficult it will be for plant roots to acquire that water.

- Changes in the water content of different soils influence the soil water potential at which water is held in the soil and the soil's hydraulic conductivity. These parameters will all influence the availability of soil water for plant roots.

- The mechanical strength of soils will depend on types of soil and their consolidation and compaction by external influences. The amount of water in soil will also influence its mechanical strength. The ability of roots to exploit soil depends on the mechanical strength of the soil. Cracks and channels created by a variety of means (eg shrinkage caused by drying or freezing and thawing, animal burrows and dead root channels) are important for root growth and entry of water and air into the soil.

- Normally when soils dry the associated changes in volume are small because air enters to fill the voids vacated by water. However, in some clay soils, shrinkage and cracking occurs on drying, and swelling will take place when the soil is rewetted. These volume changes have considerable implications to the integrity of buildings founded on clay soils that may be dried unevenly because of the presence of tree roots in proximity to parts of the structure.

- The structure of trees, and how this structure changes as the trees age, can influence the amount and delivery of rainfall to the soil. The entry of water into the soil is facilitated by a porous soil surface. An ideal type of soil surface for infiltration would be that found in natural forest soils which exhibit very high infiltration rates.

- Evaporation from bare soil proceeds at appreciable rates if the soil is wet and energy is available to sustain evaporation. Evaporation losses from bare soils can be reduced by limiting radiation received at the soil surface and promoting the entry of water to layers well below the surface.

- The degree of aeration of soils will be a critical factor for root growth. In surface soil horizons diffusion of oxygen into the soil and of carbon dioxide outwards usually means that conditions suitable for roots prevail. However, in deeper horizons in the soil the long diffusion pathway and the narrow pore spaces may mean that there are critically low levels of oxygen and high concentrations of carbon dioxide.

- A range of macro- and micronutrients must be available in soils for adequate plant growth. The cation exchange capacity of soil particles plays an important role in determining the availability of some plant nutrients. Anions tend to be freely available in the soil solution. The pH of soils has a large influence on the availability of some nutrients.

REFERENCES

Ashman, M.R. & Puri, G. 2002. *Essential Soil Science*. Blackwell Publishing, Oxford, UK. 198 pp.

Bradshaw, A.D., Hunt, B. & Walmsley, T. 1995. *Trees in the urban landscape: Principles and practice*. E & FN Spon, London, UK. 272 pp.

Brady, N.C. & Weil, R.R. 1999. *The Nature and Properties of Soils*. Prentice-Hall, New Jersey, USA. 881 pp.

Craul, P.J. 1992. *Urban soil in Landscape design*. John Wiley, New York, USA. 396 pp.

Hall, R.L. & Calder, I.R. 1993. Drop size modification by forest canopies: measurements using a disdrometer. *Journal of Geophysical Research*, 98 (D10), 18465–18470.

Hartman, J.R., Pirone, T.P. & Sall, M.A. 2000. *Pirone's Tree Maintenance*, 7th Edition. Oxford University Press, New York, USA. 545pp.

Hillel, D. 1998. *Environmental Soil Physics*. Academic Press, San Diego, USA and London, UK. 771 pp.

Hutchinson, I. & Roberts, M.C. 1981. Vertical variation in stemflow generation. *Journal of Applied Ecology*, 18, 521–527.

Kramer, P.J. & Boyer, J.S. 1995. *Water relations of plants and soils*. Academic Press, San Diego, USA and London, UK. 495 pp.

Landon, J.R. 1991. *Booker tropical soil manual: A handbook for soil survey and agricultural land evaluation in the tropics and subtropics*. Longmans Scientific, London, UK. 185 pp.

Marschner, H. 1995. *Mineral Nutrition of Higher Plants*. Academic Press, London, UK. 889 pp.

Pizzeghello, D., Nicolini, G. & Nardi, S. 2001. Hormone-like activity of humic substances in Fagus sylvaticae forests. *New Phytologist*, 151, 647–657.

Pizzeghello, D., Nicolini, G. & Nardi, S. 2002. Hormone-like activities of humic substances in different forest ecosystems. *New Phytologist*, 155, 393–402.

Roberts, J.M. 1999. Forests and Woodlands: An Ecohydrology Perspective. In: *Eco-hydrology: Plants and water in terrestrial and aquatic habitats* (Ed. by A. Baird and R. Wilby), pp. 181–236. Routledge, London, UK.

Taiz, L. & Zeiger, E. 1991. *Plant Physiology*. The Benjamin/Cummings Publishing Company, Redwood City, CA, USA. 565 pp.

Watson, G.W. & Himelick, E.B. 1997. *Principles and practice of planting trees and shrubs*. International Society of Arboriculture, Champaign, IL., USA. 199 pp.

White, R.E. 1997. *Principles and Practice of Soil Science*. Blackwell Science, Oxford, UK. 348 pp.

Wild, A. 1988. (Ed.) *Russell's Soil Conditions and Plant Growth*. Longmans, London, UK. 991 pp.

CHAPTER 3

The Growth and Functions of Roots

3.1 Introduction

The largest impacts that trees will face in the built environment are those that occur below ground. Trees are often grown in limited volumes of soil; the soil is often alien, differing markedly from a forest soil in crucial characteristics; water supply might be limited or indeed excessive; soil nutrient supplies may be lacking or unbalanced; aeration may be poor and valuable fungal associates may be absent. These and many other difficulties will be encountered by the trees' root systems and the ability of the roots to cope will often determine whether the tree flourishes, survives or fails. In addition to environmental impacts below ground the root system may be compromised by operations, such as excavation, that reduce its effective size. On the other hand the development of tree root systems and their function can have important influences on buildings, pavements and other structures, both directly and indirectly, usually by changing soil properties. In such circumstances, therefore, the form and function of the roots of different species will determine their suitability for planting or retention close to structures. A better understanding of the likely interactions of roots and the built environment will be available if there is a sound knowledge of the basic properties of roots and root systems, the form of root systems and how they function. This chapter examines the aspects of form and function of root systems of trees that have most relevance to their survival and performance in the built environment.

The basic functions of the root system are:

- uptake of water
- uptake of mineral nutrients
- transport of water and nutrients to the stem.
- support and anchorage of the tree.

Roots also supply certain hormones – **plant growth regulators** – to the shoot system, and roots commonly store materials such as starch and oils for subsequent use by the tree for growth. Roots form symbiotic relationships with a wide range of soil fungi, the fungi receive carbohydrates from the plant and facilitate the uptake of some nutrients and possibly water for the plant. Dead root material provides a considerable source of organic carbon as a substrate for the growth of soil micro-organisms.

3.2 Root growth

3.2.1 Growth processes

The root is usually the first organ to appear during seed germination. Traditionally, the young apex of a growing root has been divided into four zones: the root cap, the apical **meristem**, the zone of elongation, and the root hair zone or zone of maturation (Fig 3.1). However, except for the **root cap**, the boundaries of these zones overlap considerably. The cells of the apical meristem are expanding as well as dividing and therefore also lie within the **elongation zone**. Many cells within the elongation zone are also undergoing differentiation, and certain cells, such as root hairs, elongate in the **maturation zone**.

Cell division occurs in the **meristematic zone** both in the direction of the root cap and in the direction of the root base to form cells that will differentiate into tissues of the functioning

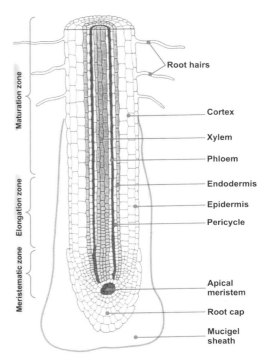

Figure 3.1 Diagrammatic longitudinal section of the apical region of the root. The meristematic cells are located near the tip of the root. These cells generate the root cap and the upper tissues of the root. In the elongation zone, cells differentiate to produce the xylem, phloem and cortex. Root hairs, formed in epidermal cells, are located in the maturation zone. (After Taiz and Zeiger, 1991.)

root. The root cap protects the delicate meristematic cells as the root moves through the soil and also secretes mucigel which surrounds the root tip. It is likely that the mucigel protects the root apex from drying, facilitates nutrient transfer to the root and also promotes interactions between the root and micro-organisms. Another important root function thought to occur in the root tip is the ability to respond to gravity and the associated signal to promote downward growth of roots – the gravitropic response.

As its name implies, the elongation zone is the site of rapid root growth, cells may continue to divide while they extend. After division and elongation have

TREE ROOTS IN THE BUILT ENVIRONMENT

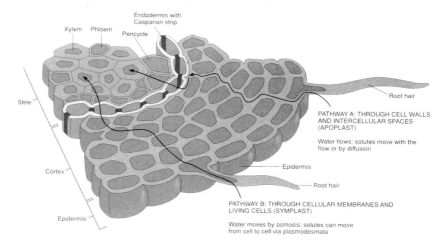

Figure 3.2 Pathways for water uptake by the root. Through the cortex, water may travel via the apoplast pathway, i.e. through cell walls or through cells, the symplastic pathway, which includes transport across membrane and within the cell space. At the endodermis, the apoplast pathway is blocked by the Casparian strip. Water entering the root's vascular system must cross the plasma membrane of the endodermis. (After Moore *et al*, 1998.)

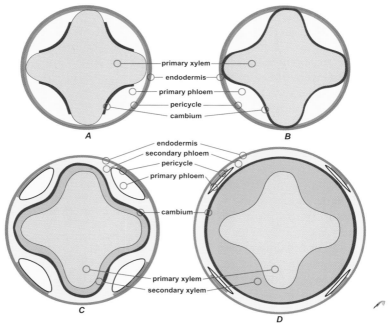

Figure 3.3 Diagrammatic representation of the development of the secondary growth in a root. **A**, at the completion of primary growth a row of procambium cells remains and a complete circle of pericycle is present. **B**, the procambium joins with the pericycle cells outside the xylem arms to form a continuous cylinder of vascular cambium. **C**, the vascular cambium forms secondary xylem internally and secondary phloem externally. The primary phloem is being pushed outward and a small amount of pericycle is still associated with it. **D**, a smooth circle of vascular cambium forms, producing secondary xylem and phloem. The primary xylem remains in the centre of the stem, the primary phloem has been crushed, and only a small amount of the pericycle remains.

ceased, cells undergo maturation, producing columns of cells of different types (Fig 3.1). Differentiation may actually begin much earlier, but the cells do not reach the mature stage until they reach this zone. Two regions of the root become distinguished, the **cortex** and the **stele** (Fig 3.2). The stele contains the vascular elements of the root: the **xylem** which conducts water and solutes to the shoot, and the **phloem** which transports **metabolites** from the shoot to roots. The stele is surrounded by the cortex, several cell layers in thickness, and the outermost layer of cells, the epidermis. Root hairs develop in this region, a clear indication that extension has ceased. If it had not, the root hairs would be destroyed as they were pulled through the soil. Root hairs are brittle, microscopic extensions of root epidermal cells which greatly increase the surface area of the root, thus providing greater capacity for absorption. Lateral or branch roots arise from cell divisions in the **pericycle** layer at the periphery of the vascular cylinder (the xylem and phloem elements) (Fig 3.1). They grow at right angles to the main vascular bundle, compressing the cortical cells and eventually breaking out of the epidermis.

The innermost cortical layer next to the stele is the endodermis. The walls of this endodermal layer become thickened with a deposition of a waxy substance, **suberin**, on the radial walls and transverse walls to form the **Casparian strip** (Fig 3.2). This is a hydrophobic structure which acts as a barrier to the movement of water and minerals through the cell wall ensuring that the transport pathway must pass through the plasma membrane and into the living cell. Formation of this suberised layer generally coincides with a change in the colour of the roots from white to pale brown. Solute movement at the endodermis must occur within living cells after transport through the plasma membrane.

A later stage in the development of some roots is the formation of secondary thickening due to the development of a layer of **cambium** just inside the endodermis and the laying down of an outer corky layer over the root surface (Fig 3.3). In the case of long-lived roots of trees this cambial layer may be active for decades to centuries.

3.2.2 The form, depth and extent of root systems

3.2.2.1 Root system form

The morphology of the root system is markedly dependent on the tree species. As a seedling the root system develops along a single root axis, the tap-root, which thickens as a result of secondary cambial activity. From this main root axis, lateral roots develop to form an extensively branched root system. The development of the root system in trees depends on the activity of the root apical meristem and the production of lateral root meristems.

The development of the architecture of the tree root system is strongly influenced by species (Toumey, 1929) but is considerably modified by a range of

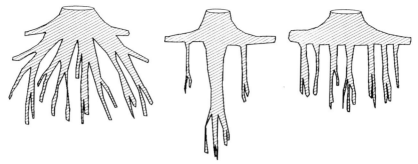

Figure 3.4 Diagram illustrating the three principal types of tree root system. *From left to right:* heart root, tap-root and surface root. (After Köstler *et al*, 1968.)

soil conditions which indicates that the form and spread of tree root systems exhibits considerable flexibility. Contrary to popular misconception, only a small proportion of species have a tap-root that persists as a major woody root into adulthood of the tree; in many species the dominance of the tap-root diminishes very early in the development of the root system (Sutton, 1980). Only in a few species eg oak, pine and fir is there a tendency to retain the tap-root form as older trees (Büsgen and Münch, 1929). The tap-root is largest immediately beneath the tree trunk but its diameter decreases sharply as secondary roots grow out from it (Perry, 1982). Biebelreither (1962, 1966) claimed that at 0.5 m depth the tap-root tends to be less than 50 mm diameter and has subdivided into many smaller roots when depths between 0.5 to 1.0 m have been reached. Many cultivated trees will have had their roots **undercut** prior to transplanting. Therefore they have a modified root system even if they might naturally have a tap-root.

Previous attempts to classify the root systems of different tree species into numerous shape categories has been frustrated by the considerable variability that is encountered even within a single species, so only broad generalisations about the shape of the root system can be made. Köstler *et al* (1968) identify three principal types of root system shape (Fig 3.4).

- The *heart root system*, which is formed by both large and small roots emerging diagonally from the trunk in all directions.

- The *tap-root system*, having a strong vertically directed main root originating from the underside of the trunk.

- A *surface root system*, which features large, horizontal, main lateral roots extending just under the soil surface, from which a number of large and small roots branch down vertically.

Although the three broad patterns that have been outlined here are useful to describe root system characteristics in general terms, a number of authors (eg Dobson and Moffat, 1993) have taken pains to warn against an inclination to rigidly classify species into one group or another. The characteristics of the

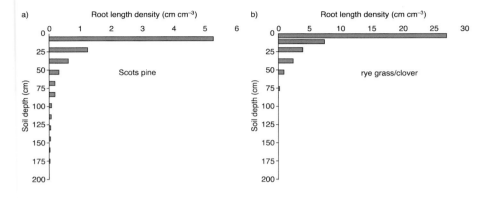

Figure 3.5 (a) The pattern of root length density with soil depth in a Scots pine plantation (after Roberts, 1976) and **(b)** below a grass/clover mixture (after Mackie-Dawson and Atkinson, 1991).

three forms are often not retained and many exceptions occur. A further issue that has been stressed is that the individual categories do not carry with them any intrinsic classification about the depth of the root system. For example, a surface root system may have vertical roots branching off it which grow as deep or deeper than those of a heart root or tap-root. The work of a number of early researchers has been summarised by Dobson and Moffat (1993) who stress the strong influence of soil conditions in modifying the form of adult root systems.

3.2.2.2 Root system depth

A further misconception about tree roots is that they occur typically in significant quantities at substantial depths (ie greater than 3 m) in the soil profile. There are cases where isolated roots have been found at depths much greater than this in deep and loose soils (Gilman, 1990), but from numerous studies involving comprehensive root excavations the indication is that typically as much as 90% of the tree root length occurs in the upper metre of soil. Fig 3.5a shows the vertical pattern of root length density over the upper two metres of soil in a Scots pine forest in Thetford, East Anglia (Roberts, 1976). Over 90% of the total root length is found in the upper metre of soil. The amount of root declines exponentially with depth and this overall pattern is typical of the many profiles of plant root distributions that have been described. What does differ between different types of vegetation is the sharpness of the decline with depth and therefore the fraction of the root system that is concentrated in the uppermost horizons of the soil. A comparison by Jackson *et al* (1996) showed that overall temperate broadleaves have 82% of their roots in the upper 50 cm of soil while conifers have 70%. For comparison, Fig 3.5b shows a vertical profile of root length density for a grass/clover mixture (Mackie-Dawson and Atkinson, 1991) and the contrast with the Scots pine profile is very clear. The exponential decline in root length density with depth is also evident

Table 3.1 Summary of data from the Kew Wind Blown Tree Survey (adapted from Gasson and Cutler, 1990) on maximum depths of roots in the root plates of wind blown trees. The number of trees having maximum root plate depths in the categories <0.5 m, 0.5–1.0 m, 1.0–1.5 m, 1.5–2.0 m and >2.0 m are shown.

Genus	Maximum root plate depth (m)					Total number of trees	Range of root plate depths (m)
	<0.5	0.5–1.0	1.0–1.5	1.5–2.0	>2.0		
Apple	1	2	4	0	1	8	0.45–2.70
Ash	0	10	14	4	3	31	0.75–2.80
Beech	5	28	52	14	4	103	0.10–2.80
Birch	4	13	13	1	1	32	0.10–3.00
Cedar	1	1	1	0	0	3	1.00–2.00
Cherry	0	0	3	3	0	6	1.00–1.55
Chestnut	1	6	14	1	2	24	0.20–2.19
Cypress	3	9	2	0	0	14	0.65–1.81
Douglas fir	1	3	1	0	0	5	0.30–1.45
False acacia	3	1	0	0	0	4	1.59–2.00
False cypress	2	3	2	1	0	8	0.85–1.30
Fir	1	4	4	3	2	14	0.25–2.17
Hawthorn	2	1	0	0	0	3	0.40–0.80
Hazel	1	1	0	0	0	2	0.35–0.75
Hickory	1	1	2	0	0	4	0.94–1.94
Holly	1	12	1	0	0	14	0.33–1.00
Honey locust	2	1	1	0	0	4	0.50–1.72
Hornbeam	0	12	7	0	1	20	0.50–2.10
Horse chestnut	0	4	2	0	0	6	0.50–1.40
Indian bean tree	4	1	0	0	0	5	0.62–1.21
Larch	1	8	11	3	1	24	0.30–2.20
Lime	1	6	12	4	3	26	0.12–2.60
Maple	0	15	14	2	0	31	0.50–1.82
Mulberry	1	1	1	0	0	3	0.81–1.50
Oak	4	39	62	31	9	145	0.30–2.05
Pine	2	8	16	5	1	32	0.40–3.00
Plane	2	1	0	0	0	3	0.80–1.00
Poplar	0	2	3	6	2	13	0.80–2.43
Rowan	3	4	3	0	0	10	0.40–1.35
Southern beech	2	1	6	1	0	10	0.33–1.58
Spruce	3	21	10	1	1	36	0.30–2.14
Tulip tree	1	0	1	2	0	4	0.93–2.00
Walnut	1	3	0	0	1	5	0.30–2.14
Willow	2	1	4	0	0	7	0.20–1.22
Yew	4	1	1	0	0	6	0.50–1.70
Others	4	19	6	3	0	32	0.30–1.75
Total number	64	243	273	85	32	697	0.10–3.00
Percentage of total	9	35	39	12	5	100	

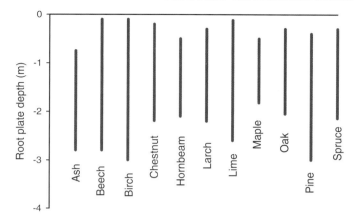

Figure 3.6 Variation in root plate depth for a number of species. (After Gasson and Cutler, 1990.)

but overall the grass/clover roots are located over much less depth of soil. However, the density of the roots in the surface horizons is up to five times that of the woodland. The dense surface rooting in short vegetation, and particularly below grassland, has important implications for establishing young trees in the face of below-ground competition from weeds or surrounding vegetation (Section 5.5.2).

There are a number of reasons why the roots of plants, trees included, are predominately in the upper layers of the soil. Firstly, it is in the surface horizons that the root system will acquire most nutrients from decaying organic material and need not expend resources unnecessarily to develop deep roots unless it is to acquire a ready supply of water when supply from rainfall is irregular. As we will see later (Section 3.5) deep roots play only a small role in providing stability for trees against wind and this tends to be in the tap-rooted species, which are, however, less common. The other main reason why root density declines with depth in the soil is largely to do with the physical limitations of the soil at depth that make it a relatively difficult environment to exploit. Normally, soil bulk density increases with depth in the soil and the non-capillary pore space declines (Section 2.2.3). These factors will mean that there is increased mechanical impedance to root growth deeper in the soil and there is a limit created by the diffusion of oxygen necessary for adequate root function deep in the soil.

Generally trees root deeper than shorter vegetation and there are records of extremely deep roots being found associated with trees growing in areas with limited rainfall (eg Stone and Kalisz, 1991). Normally, however, rooting depths of trees are quite modest. Table 3.1 (Dobson and Moffat, 1993) interprets the data on root plate dimensions of wind-blown trees published by Gasson and Cutler (1990). Despite the need for caution, because some roots may have been broken off at ground level during the damage by wind, the results show that no trees had roots below 3 m and only 5% had rooting depths greater than 2 m. There is, however, considerable variation in the depth of

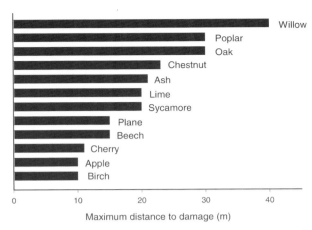

Figure 3.7 Variation in maximum distance to indirect building damage for a range of tree species. (After Cutler and Richardson, 1989.)

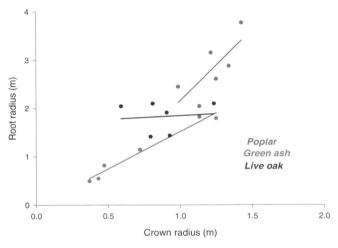

Figure 3.8 Variation in the relationship between crown radius and root radius in three tree species. (After Gilman, 1989.)

rooting within individual species. Fig 3.6 shows the range of root plate depths based on the data from Gasson and Cutler (1990). The span of root depths for any particular species is large and obscures any species differences that might exist.

3.2.2.3 Root system extent

For studies of water and nutrient supply in forests there has been a long-standing need to describe rooting depths of trees and a great deal of information has accumulated (eg Stone and Kalisz, 1991; Canadell *et al*, 1996; Polomski and Kuhn, 1998). For trees growing in forests, the lateral extent of individual root systems has far less significance and consequently there is much less information available.

In terms of requirements for trees in the built environment this lack of information is unfortunate because it is often the case that the lateral extent of roots is a particularly important consideration. For example, in defining protection zones where there is excavation/construction close to trees (Section 8.4.1), a valuable piece of information would be the likely lateral extent of the roots of different species and how this varies with tree age and vigour. Furthermore, there is the need to understand the risk to buildings founded on shrinkable clay soils which might deform when water is abstracted by tree roots. It is from studies of damage to buildings and the implication, albeit circumstantial, of which tree and species is involved and its distance from the building, that idea of root extent has been derived (see Section 10.3.6). Using data presented by Cutler and Richardson (1989), Fig 3.7 shows the lateral extent of roots that have been implicated with building damage. From this type of information it is clear that large species differences exist but it is also the case that the horizontal extent of tree roots substantially exceeds the perimeter or '**dripline**' of the crown.

Numerous studies involving excavations and soil coring in forests, orchards and nurseries indicate that roots extend well beyond the 'dripline' and are not concentrated there (Hodgkins and Nichols, 1977; Stout, 1956). There is a great deal of variation between species in the extent to which their roots extend beyond the dripline (Gilman, 1989, 1990). Figure 3.8 (Gilman, 1989) shows that there is a good relationship between crown spread and root radius but the relationship tends to be very species specific. Roots extending furthest from the tree trunk are usually found in the soil surface. Results presented by Coile (1937) suggest that the maximum extent of the tree roots is reached before the canopy has completed expanding, suggesting that the ratio of root spread to crown spread may decrease as trees become older.

An important aspect of root growth and development is that it is dynamic and highly dependent on the soil environment. Given suitable conditions, plant roots can grow continuously (but this is balanced by death of roots – see below). However, the proliferation of roots depends on the availability of water and nutrients in their microenvironment. Root growth and proliferation will be greatest in soil regions that are rich in water and minerals.

3.2.3 The periodicity and rates of root growth

A wide variation exists in the patterns of root growth activity shown by trees in temperate conditions (Gilman, 1990). There are no reports of vigorous root growth activity by trees in winter but the distribution of the peaks of activity at other times of the year shows wide variation. In a large number of species root growth begins in spring before shoot growth (Atkinson, 1980; Lyr and Hoffman, 1967) and a second smaller peak occurs in the autumn after all shoot growth has stopped. Most authors interpret this pattern to indicate competition for photosynthetic products between shoots and roots. However, this is not a universal pattern and in some species root growth only begins after leaf expansion has been completed and ends before leaf fall with some species showing pronounced peaks in midsummer (Lyr and Hoffman, 1967). Overall, it can be concluded that root growth is curtailed by temperature in the winter, and in summer dry soil conditions may reduce root growth. However, the amount of data available is insufficient to identify very clear differences in growth patterns of different species.

Typical root growth rates of around 10 mm day^{-1} have been reported for tree roots (Kramer and Boyer, 1995). This is a modest value compared to grasses and cereals which can extend at five times that rate. If temperatures are not critically low, ie below ~5°C, roots will tend to grow more at night than during the day (Lyr and Hoffman, 1967). This is to be expected as extension growth of all plant parts will be higher at night when their internal **water stresses** are least.

3.2.4 How long do roots live?

Some of the large structural roots of mature trees could be as old as the individual tree itself. However, unlike the trunks of temperate trees, the major structural roots do not necessarily possess a full complement of annual growth rings and even two portions of the same structural root, in close proximity to each other, may have different numbers of annual rings suggesting that the cambium has been differentially active.

The many fine roots of trees are much more short-lived than structural roots, having a life span ranging from 10 days to over a year (Eissenstat and Yanai, 1997). The life span is shorter for roots produced in spring and autumn and fine roots produced near the soil surface live longer than those deeper in the soil (Hendricks and Pregitzer, 1992; Schoettle and Fahey, 1994). So far there is little clear evidence of how fine root production changes as trees age (Ryan *et al*, 1997).

There are number of important implications of the dynamics and turnover of fine roots of trees:

• The benefits to trees of fine roots include exploration and capture of nutrient resources and moisture from unexploited parts of the soil.

• The death and decay of fine roots and the release of nitrogen and carbon are essential for nutrient cycling and the metabolism of soil organisms.

• The production of fine roots can be a substantial part of the net primary production (NPP) of a tree. NPP is the product of **photosynthesis** available for allocation to growth or storage after respiration has been accounted for. The fraction of NPP assigned to fine root production, including the support of mycorrhizae, can range from as little as 10% but can be as high as 60%.

• Lower percentage allocations to fine root production are usually observed in forests growing on soils well supplied with nutrients and water.

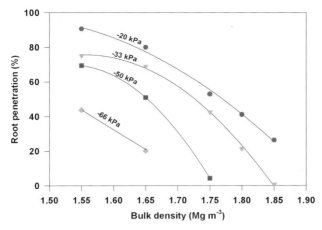

Figure 3.9 The effect of soil bulk density on the penetration of the seedling roots of cotton through layers of fine sandy loam at different water potentials ranging from -20 kPa (moist) to -66 kPa (dry). (After Taylor and Gardner, 1963.)

- There is a production and maintenance cost associated with the population of fine roots in the soil. Cost-benefit analyses have been conducted for fine roots in soil to determine the life span that could maximise root efficiency, defined as the amount of nutrient acquired per unit of carbon expended. Analyses indicate that roots would have long life spans if they have low maintenance respiration or are located in favourable patches of nutrient rich soil. High temperature enhances respiration so an example of where fine roots would be expected to have short life spans would be in nutrient poor soils experiencing high temperatures (Eissenstat and Yanai, 1997).

3.2.5 Soil mechanical resistance and root growth

Roots increase in length because new cells in the actively growing zone near the root tip grow, increase in volume and force the tip forward. Root elongation in soils is possible only to the extent to which the root pressure exceeds the mechanical impedance of the soil (Bennie, 1991). Roots cannot reduce their diameter to enter small pores.

Roots exert a measurable pressure, both forwards and outwards, which can be measured and has been found to be in the range 0.7 to 2.5 MPa (Gregory, 1988). The mechanical forces in the soil that oppose root penetration will be difficult to determine directly and exactly. Nevertheless, it is possible to gauge the likelihood that roots will penetrate soil from characteristics of the soil which can be measured directly, eg soil bulk density and the resistance to entry into the soil of a probe using a known applied force (**penetrometer**). However, it is possible to appreciate that neither of these types of measurements can provide direct information on other soil properties that also influence the ability of roots to exploit the soil. The continuity of soil pores and the planes of weakness in soil that roots can exploit will also be important.

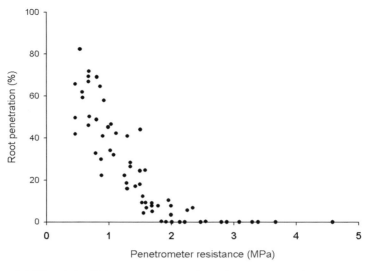

Figure 3.10 The relationship between root penetration and penetrometer resistance. (After Taylor *et al*, 1966.)

As the bulk density of soil increases, its pore space and particularly the space occupied by large pores is reduced. In any soil, then, the extent to which root penetration is restricted will vary closely with bulk density but this will vary from soil to soil. Additionally, if the water content of the soil varies the relationship between bulk density and root penetration will vary because the strength of the soil will vary with its wetness. When soils are wet there is less frictional resistance between soil particles, which can then be dislodged more readily by roots. Fig 3.9 gives an example of the decrease in root penetration with increasing bulk density and how this relationship changes from wet to dry soil.

Penetrometers are devices which measure the force required to drive metal probes into the soil. They have been used very often to gauge the resistance which soil offers to the entry by roots. Even though penetrometers have been constructed with fine tips which mimic the shape and diameter of root apices, the devices cannot emulate the important features of root tips – their flexibility and their ability to deform when they come into contact with resistant soil. Nevertheless, penetrometers have been useful in establishing relationships between soil strength and root penetration. There is an exponential decrease in root growth as soil strength increases. Figure 3.10 shows that penetration of roots into soil is reduced by a half at penetrometer resistances of around 0.7 MPa and effective root growth ceases at a soil strength between 2.0 and 2.5 MPa (Russell, 1977; Greacen and Sands, 1980). However, there can be species differences. Taylor and Ratliff (1969) showed that root elongation of cotton effectively ceased at 2.0 MPa but in peanuts elongation was not reduced to the same extent as in cotton until the penetrometer resistance was above 3.0 MPa.

Unfavourable soil conditions can further reduce root growth pressure. Low oxygen concentrations and temperature and soil compaction all reduce root

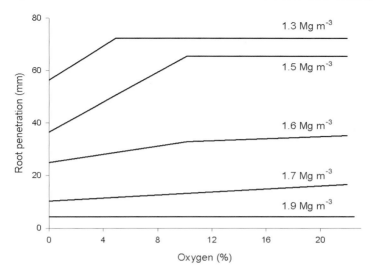

Figure 3.11 The effect of oxygen level and soil bulk density on the depth of cotton root penetration into a compacted sub-soil layer. (Rendig and Taylor, 1989.)

growth pressure (Greacen, 1986). Fig 3.11 shows that as soil oxygen is reduced the capacity for root penetration into soil begins to be reduced at soil bulk densities which are not restrictive when oxygen is plentiful. A root must be well anchored in firm soil to exert its maximum pressures or distortion and buckling of the root will occur (Dexter, 1986).

When soils are compacted, the bulk density increases and the soil pore volume is reduced, mainly by reduction of the size of the larger pores. The mechanical forces necessary for deformation and displacement of soil particles by roots becomes limiting, and root elongation rates decrease. There may be various reasons for differences in root response to soil strength between plant species, the difference in average diameter of the root being one of them (Bennie, 1991). Soil compaction also affects root growth indirectly because of changes to the soil water regime, nutrient flow and because of changes in aeration.

When soil water content is low, mechanical impedance of the soil increases and root elongation growth is inhibited, which further limits nutrient supply to the root surface by diffusion. However, root hair growth is strongly enhanced at low soil water content (Mackay and Barber, 1985, 1987) and this might, in part, compensate for any decrease in surface area from impeded elongation growth of the root axis. The formation of lateral roots is also enhanced. These are produced closer to the root apex with a higher density per unit root length. When only one compacted layer occurs in the soil a reduction in root growth in the zone of high soil strength is often compensated for by higher growth rates in loose soil above or below the compacted zone.

The decrease which occurs in the rate of root elongation in response to increasing soil strength is correlated with an increase in root diameter, mainly

Figure 3.12 Seasonal patterns of starch deposition and mobilisation in trees. Maximum starch accumulation is shown in black, large amounts by hatching, and small amounts by stippling; clear parts indicate traces only or no starch.
Beech (*Fagus sylvatica*) in Europe.
1 = just before leaf emergence,
2 = leaf unfolding,
3 = midsummer,
4 = just before leaf fall and
5 = conversion of starch to soluble carbohydrates in winter. (After Gaumann, 1935.)

because of the greater radial expansion of cortical cells under these conditions (Atwell, 1990). Inhibition of root elongation is not necessarily correlated with inhibited uptake of mineral nutrients. In compacted soils the contact between roots and soil increases and therefore also the delivery rate for mineral nutrients, as indicated, for example, by higher uptake rates per unit length of nitrate and phosphorus. Despite the various compensatory reactions of root systems in compacted soils, plants usually grow poorly in soils of high bulk density. Insufficient water and nutrient supply might play a role, but often shoot growth and transpiration are first reduced, regardless of the plant nutrient and water status. In compacted soils shoot growth is also often more depressed than root growth, suggesting root-derived hormonal signals are increased in response to soil compaction.

In compacted soils at a given bulk density the effect of compaction can be even greater in wet compared with dry soils, suggesting that factors other than mechanical impedance are involved. Likely candidates are oxygen deficiency or elevated concentrations of ethylene. Inhibition of root extension in compacted soils is therefore brought about by various factors. In dry soils increase in mechanical impedance and decrease in soil water potential may be most important, and in wet soils oxygen deficiency and accumulation of ethylene and other phytotoxins are the main factors.

A further consequence of mechanical impedance of soil is an increase in the release of organic carbon rhizodeposition into the soil. Rhizodeposition is very variable but can account for as much as 70% of the net carbon in some trees, eg Douglas fir (Lynch and Whipps, 1990). **Rhizodeposition** is increased by various forms of stress, which in addition to mechanical impedance could be anaerobic soil, drought or mineral nutrient deficiency (Lynch and Whipps, 1990).

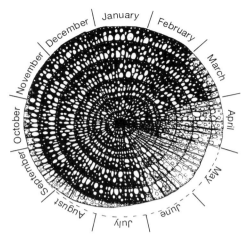

Figure 3.13 Starch deposition and mobilisation in the root wood of sugar maple (*Acer saccharum*) throughout the year. Tissues containing starch are black. (From Wargo, 1979.)

Increase in soil bulk density from 1.2 to 1.6 g cm^{-3} drastically depresses root length of maize but the allocation of photosynthates to the roots remains similar (~40% of net photosynthesis), leading to an increase in consumption of photosynthate per unit root length by a factor of two. During drought, the production of mucigel is particularly noticeable and substantial quantities of soil particles may adhere to the roots, but the relevance of this for water uptake is not clear.

3.2.6 Storage of food reserves in roots

Fig 3.12 illustrates the seasonal fluctuations in starch storage in a beech tree. The stored carbohydrates in the roots, along with those from other parts of the tree structure are emptied shortly before the leaves begin to unfold in the spring. The assimilates are transferred to the buds and later to the young shoots. Allocations later go to flower production if this follows leaf emergence, and next the cambium receives materials as the tree begins to increase in girth. Later in the season materials are used for formation of buds and, finally, the replenishment of starch stores in the roots, trunk and branches occurs. The seasonal changes in starch stored in a root are depicted in Fig 3.13.

3.2.7 Roots and hormones

Plant hormones, also known as plant growth regulators, are usually defined as substances synthesised in one part of the plant that in very low concentrations have important physiological effects in some distant parts. **Auxins**, for example indole acetic acid (IAA), are produced in buds and young leaves, transported down through the plant and can influence root growth, differentiation and branching. **Cytokinins** and **gibberellic acid** synthesised in the roots have important effects on shoot growth (Marschner, 1995). A further role for roots as a production site for hormones which influence behaviour in foliage is the production of **abscisic acid** (ABA). ABA levels have been shown to increase in xylem sap and leaves in response to increased soil drying. However, there is much research to be done and clear evidence that ABA has a major role to play in signalling soil water deficits to foliage in large, adult trees remains to emerge.

3.2.8 Soil aeration and roots

If temperatures are low and/or plants are dormant or relatively inactive the respiratory requirements of roots and soil organisms for oxygen are low and limited aeration may be relatively harmless. However, at higher temperatures (above 20°C), oxygen consumption by plant roots, soil fauna and soil micro-organisms can deplete the soil of oxygen in a very few days. Under such conditions the growth and survival of many plants is compromised. Waterlogging (or anaerobiosis) inhibits root growth and the synthesis and export to the shoots of cytokinins and **gibberellins**. The rapid decline in leaf growth and reduction in stomatal closure in response to flooding, however, is not caused by lower cytokinin export from the roots but by elevated abscisic acid levels in the leaves.

The accumulation of ethylene in soils as well as in roots becomes increasingly important as oxygen concentrations in the soil atmosphere falls below 9%. Because of the much lower diffusion rates of gases in water compared with air, the water film around roots which would prevail in waterlogged conditions traps ethylene in the root tissue. The resulting increase in ethylene concentration within root tissue has a number of effects on root growth and morphology, simultaneously triggering anatomical changes in the root tissue and the export of inhibitory plant growth regulators.

Some plants, including a few trees, are well adapted to resist oxygen deficiency in the root zone. As a rule flooding-tolerant species (eg Lodgepole pine, Swamp cypress) develop an extended **aerenchyma** in the roots. The aerenchyma contains prominent air spaces in the root cortex which are stimulated by waterlogging. The aerenchyma is formed in the root cortex by cell wall separation with or without collapse of the cell walls. In most instances there is a close correlation between flooding tolerance and the size of the aerenchyma. Oxygen transport to submerged roots by diffusion is not very effective over long distances. For efficient long-distance transport in the aerenchyma from shoots to roots other mechanisms are required such as pressurised gas transport driven by temperature gradients between aerated parts (leaves, stems) and submerged parts. This mechanism is thought to be particularly effective, for example, in flooding tolerant species, such as alder compared to intolerant species eg beech. Table 3.2 gives an indication of the tolerance of different tree species to poor soil aeration.

3.2.9 Soil temperature and roots

Soil temperature not only directly affects the rates of physiological reactions but also may have indirect effects on soil biological activity through temperature-mediated differences in diffusion rates, weathering of minerals

Table 3.2 Characteristics of root systems of mature European broadleaved and coniferous tree species growing on well aerated, sandy soils. Such soils present minimum resistance to root penetration. The ability of roots to penetrate into compact or stony soils, and to tolerate poor soil aeration is also shown. Scientific names of tree species may be found in Appendix 2. (Data adapted from Biebelriether, 1966 and Köstler *et al*, 1968.)

Species	Typical root system architecture	Typical root depth (m)	Mechanical root penetration	Tolerance to O₂ deficit
Ash	Surface root	1.1	Medium	Medium-high
Aspen	Surface root	1.3	High	High
Birch	Heart root	1.8	Medium	Low
Beech	Heart root	1.3	Low	Low
Common alder	Heart/surface root	2.0	High	High
Corsican pine	Tap-root	–	Medium	–
Douglas fir	Heart root	2.0	High	Medium-low
English oak	Tap-root	1.5	High	High
European larch	Heart root	2.0	High	Medium
Hornbeam	Heart root	1.6	Medium	Medium
Japanese larch	Heart root	–	Medium	Medium
Lime	Heart root	1.3	Low	Low
Norway maple	Heart root	1.0	–	Medium
Norway spruce	Surface root	2.0	Low	Very low
Red oak	Heart root	1.6	Medium	Medium-high
Scots pine	Tap-root	2.1	High	Medium
Sessile oak	Tap-root	1.5	High	High
Silver fir	Tap-root	2.0	High	High
Sycamore	Heart root	1.3	Low	Low
White pine	Surface root	1.7	Low	Very low

and **redox potentials**. Root growth is often limited by low or high temperatures. The temperature optimum varies among species and tends to be lower for root growth than for shoot growth. Compared to root zone temperatures that are above the optimum, much more detailed information is available on effects of low, sub-optimal, temperatures on root growth and development. Typically, at low temperatures root growth is retarded, the roots become shorter and thicker and lateral root formation, particularly, is depressed.

A fall in the elongation rate of roots at low temperatures is caused by a decrease in cell wall extensibility of the cells in the extension zone, not a loss of turgor. Lowering of root zone temperature can be followed by an increase in abscisic acid in the leaves and also a decrease in export of cytokinins from the roots.

Plant root systems are particularly sensitive to changes in soil temperature; a rise in soil temperature of as little as a degree Celsius can markedly stimulate both root and shoot growth and plant nutrient uptake. The mechanisms of growth effects due to changes in soil temperature are complex and include changes in water uptake, nutrient absorption, the budget of growth-related substances, and the temperature of the root apical meristem. Soil temperature also influences the partitioning of **photoassimilates** within the soil plant system, particularly with regard to root respiration which markedly increases with soil temperature. To add further to these complications, temperature will not only affect the amount of carbon entering the soil from the plant root, but will also change the nature of the carbon supply. Because the **rhizosphere** microflora are dependent on this supply of carbon, soil temperature is, therefore, a fundamental control of the interaction between plant roots and the soil microbial biomass. The effect of changing soil temperature on this control, however, varies enormously with plant species, growth stage and other interacting factors such as soil moisture and pH.

Soil temperature is an important factor in terms of the distribution and activity of the soil animals which are sensitive to overheating and will migrate deeper into the soil to avoid high temperatures. This is largely because of the excessive respiratory oxygen demand associated with high temperatures. It should be emphasised that soil temperature often interacts with other factors such as soil moisture to regulate biological activity. A rise in soil temperature, for example, can only have a marked stimulatory effect on soil biological activity if the moisture status of the soil is not limiting the activity. Similarly, rewetting of a drought-affected soil will only stimulate biological activity when temperatures permit.

3.3 Roots and water uptake

3.3.1 Uptake mechanisms

The main driving force for water uptake by trees arises in the leaves. When light levels are sufficiently high, the pores **(stomata)** in the leaf surfaces open to allow carbon dioxide (CO_2) to diffuse in, an essential part of the process of photosynthesis. Inevitably, because the air surrounding the leaves is less humid than the almost saturated atmosphere inside the leaf, transfer of water vapour from inside the leaves to the atmosphere occurs. This is the process of transpiration. Because molecules of water form strong cohesive links to each other, evaporation from the internal leaf surfaces creates a continuous column of water, moving upwards along a **potential gradient** through the tree. In actively transpiring trees the most negative water potential values occur in the leaves (values as low as -1.5 to -2.0 MPa have commonly been measured in the leaves of adult trees in summer in the UK) and the least negative at the root surface. Nevertheless, the water potential at the root surface is more negative than the potential with which water is held in the soil. This potential gradient causes water to enter the root from the soil. We discuss water movement into, through and out of the tree further in Section 6.2.1.

When a soil dries out sufficiently, the water potential (ψ) – see Box 2.2 – may fall below the point at which roots can extract water from it. This point will vary with different tree species and of course there will be variation in the water potential in different parts of the soil profile. Roots will perhaps still be able to extract water from some regions whereas in other places the soil water potential is too low and water is not available.

As plant roots absorb water from the soil, they deplete the soil of water near the root surface. This reduction in the value of ψ in the water near the root surface establishes a pressure gradient with respect to nearby soil with higher ψ values. Because the water-filled pore spaces in the soil are interconnected, water moves through these channels down the pressure gradient to the root surface.

As water is removed from the soil by transpiring plants, the soil water potential approaches the lowest water potential that can be developed in the tree. Absorption decreases because of the decreasing **water potential gradient** between soil and roots, the water lost by transpiration is not replaced, and stomatal closure occurs. Also, as the soil dries, resistance to water movement towards the roots increases because of loss of continuity in capillary columns and possibly because of decreasing contact between soil and roots.

High salt concentrations in soils and their accumulation at the root surface will create a low water potential which will reduce water absorption of the root by decreasing the gradient in water potential from the soil to the roots. Low soil temperatures increase the resistance to water flow through the roots.

In some circumstances water can enter roots by osmosis. Root systems of slowly transpiring plants in moist, well-aerated soil sometimes behave like osmometers because the accumulation of solutes in the root xylem has a lower potential than the soil water. This results in the development of root pressure, and the 'bleeding' from wounds observed in spring in trees such as birch and maple is an example of root pressure caused by osmosis. However, osmotic pressures of sufficient magnitude to enable water to be raised to the tops of adult trees are unlikely to develop. Later in the season, rapid sap flow sweeps out most of the solutes, making the osmotic process largely inactive, and water absorption is brought about principally by the tension or reduced water potential in the xylem sap as described initially in this section. Thus in rapidly transpiring trees, water is pulled in through the roots and up to the transpiring leaves.

3.3.2 Sites of uptake

The traditional view of water and nutrient uptake by tree roots is that uptake is concentrated in the young new, white zone close to the root tip. This interpretation may hold in some species for both water and nutrients or at least specific ions. As roots grow older they become increasingly suberised ie covered with a cork-like material, and therefore less **permeable** to minerals and water. However, it seems probable that mineral and water absorption by trees must involve suberised roots substantially because the unsuberised root surface is usually inadequate to support all of the requirements of a tree. Fractures in the suberised cork layer in mature roots do occur and may allow entry of water and nutrients (Kramer and Bullock, 1966; Chung and Kramer, 1975). Particularly in recent years, with the additional insight provided by modern techniques such as magnetic resonance imaging, some agreement seems to have emerged that water uptake may occur in both the unsuberised and suberised regions of roots. In trees the suberised roots constitute the major fraction of the root system although rates of uptake may be less than observed in the newly formed zones of roots. Intimate contact between the surface of the root and the soil is essential for effective water absorption by the root. This contact is likely to be most intimate at root tips because of the growth of root hairs into the soil. The possible influence of mycorrhizal infection of roots to nutrient and water uptake is discussed in Section 3.4.2.1.

3.4 Roots and nutrient uptake

3.4.1 Uptake processes

There has been considerable research aimed at identifying the zones along roots where nutrient uptake occurs. Unfortunately, little of this research has been done on trees let alone mature trees. However, in cereals, uptake of a range of nutrients occurs over the whole root surface while uptake of some ions, eg calcium, is restricted to the root apex (eg Clarkson and Hanson, 1980).

The nutrients absorbed by roots are in the form of cations (positively charged ions) eg calcium, magnesium and potassium, and anions (negatively charged ions) eg phosphate, nitrate and sulphate.

The process of nutrient uptake consists of four steps:

- movement of ions from the soil to the root surface
- ion accumulation in root cells
- the movement of ions from the root surface to the xylem
- **translocation** of ions from the roots to the shoots.

Ions arrive at the root surface by three means (Fig 3.14). Mass flow of ions in water moves to the root surface as part of the process of soil water uptake; diffusion of ions can occur if gradients occur in the soil; finally, roots can grow towards new sources of nutrients – root interception of nutrients. Certain ions such as nitrate are very mobile in soil and are readily transported with the movement of water. Other ions, phosphorus being an important example, can only diffuse slowly through soils and are rapidly depleted in the zones near to roots. It is only by extension of the root system into previously unoccupied soil volumes that new resources of these immobile nutrients can be acquired. The only very local availability of some resources close to roots means that it is

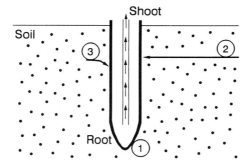

Figure 3.14 Schematic presentation of the movement of mineral elements to the root of a tree.
(1)   Root interception: soil volume displaced by root volume.
(2)   Mass flow: transport of bulk soil solution along the water potential gradient, driven by transpiration.
(3)   Diffusion nutrient transport along the concentration gradient. • = available nutrients.
(After Marschner, 1995.)

important to distinguish between the rooting zone, which is the depth profile over which roots occur, and the rhizosphere, which is the cylinder around individual roots which contains resources which the root can exploit and into which roots can exude materials. Table 3.3 illustrates the requirements of crops for different important nutrients and what amounts are supplied by root interception, mass flow and diffusion. A very large proportion of the nitrogen is supplied as mass flow in the transpiration stream whereas all the phosphorus is supplied by diffusion. The case of magnesium is important to note. More magnesium is supplied to the plant by mass flow than the plant requires and the excess will accumulate at the root surface. The implication of this phenomenon will be discussed in relation to salinity effects in Chapter 7.

Uptake of ions by roots can be 'passive' or 'active'. Passive transport does not depend on the tree's metabolism and is non-selective for ions except that cations are favoured. On the other hand, active transport requires the plant to expand energy; it is strongly influenced by the root metabolism and as such will be affected by factors such as temperature and aeration. The transport process involves ions being attached to carrier proteins which transfer them across cell walls radially through the root and into the xylem sap. Active transport is highly selective in cation and anion absorption.

Table 3.3   Nutrient demand of a maize crop and estimates of nutrient supply from the soil by root interception, mass flow, and diffusion. (From Barber, 1995.)

	Demand $(kg\,ha^{-1})$	Estimates of amounts $(kg\,ha^{-1})$ supplied by		
		Interception	Mass flow	Diffusion
Potassium	195	4	35	156
Nitrogen	190	2	150	38
Phosphorus	40	1	2	37
Magnesium	45	15	100	0

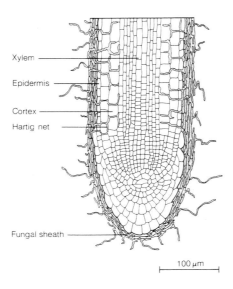

Xylem

Epidermis

Cortex

Hartig net

Fungal sheath

100 µm

Figure 3.15 A root infected with ecto-trophic mycorrhizal fungi. In the infected root, the fungal hyphae surround the root to produce a dense fungal sheath and penetrate the intercellular spaces of the cortex to form the Hartig net. The total mass of fungal hyphae is comparable to the root mass. (After Taiz and Zeiger, 1991.)

3.4.2 Fungal associations

3.4.2.1 Mycorrhizae

Foraging efficiency of tree roots can be increased, especially in soils of low fertility, by increasing the root:shoot ratio, and by supplementing the interface area by the hyphal component of mycorrhizae, the symbiotic associations of fungi and roots which exist in the majority of woodland plants (Packham *et al*, 1992). Most trees in northern temperate regions, together with southern hemisphere genera such as *Nothofagus* and *Eucalyptus*, possess sheathing (ectotrophic) mycorrhizae (Fig 3.15). These develop as a blanket of **hyphae** over the surface of short fine roots, in which the production of root hairs is suppressed (Allen, 1991). Hyphae radiate out from the sheath into the soil either as individuals or, in some species, as aggregated cords called rhizomorphs. Inside the root, a complex system of branching hyphae (the Hartig net) constitutes a considerable area for exchange of materials with the root cortical cells. An individual tree may support several species of fungi, many of which give a characteristic form to the infected roots. Beech and birch roots and those of many conifers are often much branched, but in other species are club-shaped. **Ectomycorrhizae** are common on trees, including members of the family Pinaceae (pine, fir, spruce, larch, hemlock), Fagaceae (oak, beech, chestnut), Betulaceae (birch, alder), Salicaceae (willow, poplar). Several of the fungi involved have large fruiting bodies, such as those of the conspicuous fly agaric (*Amanita muscaria*, often associated with birch or pine), ceps (*Boletus* spp) and earthballs, or of *Tuber*, the truffle.

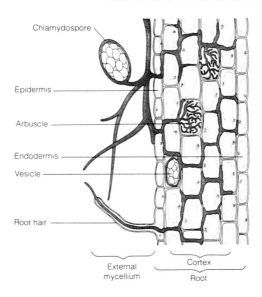

Figure 3.16 The association of vesicular-arbuscular mycorrhizal fungi with a section of a plant root. The external mycelium can bear reproductive spores and extend out from the root into the surrounding soil. The fungal hyphae grow into the intercellular wall spaces of the root cortex and penetrate individual cells. As they extend into the cell, they do not break the plasma membrane or the tono-plast of the host cell. Instead the hypha is surrounded by these membranes as it occupies intercellular space. In this process, fungal hyphae may form ovoid structures known as vesicles or branched structures known as arbuscules. The arbuscules participate in nutrient ion exchange between the host plant and the fungus. Arbuscules develop and proliferate following the penetration of the hyphae into the cortical cells. (After Taiz and Zeiger, 1991.)

Vesicular-arbuscular (V-A, or sometimes termed endotrophic) mycorrhizae do not normally affect root appearance. A coarse, branching **mycelium** in the soil is connected at entry points on the root surface to hyphae in the root cortex. The hyphae produce storage **vesicles** and intracellular **arbuscules**, whose fine branches are probably the main sites of nutrient exchange (Fig 3.16). In angiosperm tree genera, V-A fungi have been found associated with *Liquidambar, Liriodendron, Acer, Alnus* and *Populus*. They also occur in gymnosperm genera *Cupressus, Thuja, Taxodium, Juniperus* and *Sequoia*. Allen (1991) reports that some tree genera host both types of mycorrhizae at the same time eg *Populus* and *Salix*. It seems as if the initial colonising fungus is vesicular-arbuscular followed by ectomycorrhizal fungi invading later.

Hyphae not only exploit a greater volume of soil than the roots alone, but also store nutrients which subsequently can be passed to the tree. This is especially significant with nutrients such as phosphorus, where availability in the soil solution varies seasonally. There is some evidence (Alexander, 1989) that certain mycorrhizae may be directly involved in decomposition, but the majority seem to depend on their tree associate for carbon compounds. The metabolic costs to the tree may be high (15% of the net primary production of certain pines is diverted into mycorrhizal biomass) but presumably this is compensated for by the more efficient utilisation of soil nutrients.

Many species of tree seedlings have been shown to grow more quickly when infected with mycorrhizal fungi, especially in nutrient-poor soils. There is also evidence of reduced susceptibility to **pathogens**, such as *Phytophthora cinnamomi*, and of a greater tolerance of adverse soil conditions, such as low pH, toxic chemicals and water stress. Attempts to establish trees on derelict sites, such as mining spoil heaps, highlight the importance of mycorrhizae. Natural infection can be supplemented by importing soil or seedlings from healthy stands, but increasing attention is being given to the possibility of inoculating cultures of selected species of ectotrophic fungi in nursery beds or the compost of potted seedlings.

While the evidence that ecto- and endotrophic mycorrhizae have important roles to play in enhancing nutrient uptake, particularly phosphorus, by trees, the other advantages of infection are less well-established. Table 3.4 (Killham, 1994) indicates the range of responses of plant hosts to infection by mycorrhizal fungi. Many of these responses are isolated reports and few are for woody species; commonly the studies have been made on young plants. There is some evidence to suggest that the fungal mycelia growing outside roots infected with ectomycorrhizal fungi play a role in the absorption and transport of water as soil water potential declines (eg Dixon *et al*, 1983; Walker *et al*, 1982; Walker *et al*, 1989). This influence of ectomycorrhizal infection should contribute to drought tolerance and **water balance** of trees whose roots are infected with ectomycorrhizae. On the other hand, there are reports showing no effect of ectomycorrhizal infection on plant water relations (eg Sands *et al*, 1982; Coleman *et al*, 1990). Sands and Theodorou (1978) found a greater resistance to water flow in the soil plant pathway when *Pinus radiata* were colonised by ectomycorrhizae than when they were not colonised. Rhizomorphs of ectomycorrhizal fungi have been shown to transport water from the soil to tree roots. Boyd *et al* (1986) cut rhizomorphs connecting mycorrhizal seedlings of *Pinus sylvestris* to moist soil and found that transpiration declined almost instantaneously. Lamhamedi *et al* (1992) infected seedlings of *Pinus pinaster* with different genetic strains of the fungus *Pisolithus tinctorius*. The individual strains produced rhizomorphs of distinctly different diameters and vigour. Seedlings infected with the strains that had the most extensive and thickest rhizomorphs developed the highest water potentials, ie least water stress, in the foliage. The weight of evidence is that increased water uptake associated with infection by **vesicular-arbuscular mycorrhizae** is a consequence of improved nutrient uptake and plant growth rather than due to a direct effect on root water uptake (Smith and Read, 1997). The possibility that mycorrhizal infection might enhance water uptake and/or improve drought tolerance of adult trees requires much more study. A particularly useful website providing further information about mycorrhizae associated with trees is www.ffp.csiro.au/research/mycorrhiza/index.html

3.4.2.2 Nitrogen fixation

The process by which atmospheric nitrogen, N_2, is reduced to NH_4^+ is called nitrogen fixation. Bacteria or other microbes associated symbiotically with

Table 3.4 Known plant host responses to mycorrhizal fungal infection. (After Killham, 1994.)

Host response	Mycorrhizal association	Reference
* N-uptake	ectomycorrhizae	Rygiewicz *et al*, 1984
* P-uptake	ectomycorrhizae	Bowen, 1973
	endomycorrhizae	Hayman & Mosse, 1972
* K-uptake	ectomycorrhizae	Lamb & Richards, 1971
	and endomycorrhizae	
* S-uptake	endomycorrhizae	Rhodes & Gerdemann, 1978
* root phosphatase	ectomycorrhizae	Bartlett & Lewis, 1973
* trace and minor	ectomycorrhizae	Bowen, 1973
element uptake	endomycorrhizae	Killham, 1985
* drought tolerance	ectomycorrhizae	Bowen, 1973
	endomycorrhizae	Safir *et al*, 1971
* resistance to extreme temperatures	endomycorrhizae	Marx & Krupa, 1978
* heavy-metal tolerance	endomycorrhizae	Bradley *et al*, 1981
* resistance to soil toxins	endomycorrhizae	Marx & Krupa, 1978
* resistance to soil-borne pathogens	ectomycorrhizae and endomycorrhizae	Marx, 1973 Graham & Menge, 1982
* root longevity	ectomycorrhizae and endomycorrhizae	Smith & Read, 1997
inter-plant nutrient transfer	ectomycorrhizae and endomycorrhizae	Read *et al*, 1985
* N_2-fixation (legumes and other hosts only)	ectomycorrhizae and endomycorrhizae	Bowen, 1984

* indicates increased host response

roots, especially legumes eg clover are the most common and important nitrogen fixers. Non-legumes that are able to fix N_2 are far less common, but do include some trees and shrubs eg *Alnus* (alder), *Elaeagnus* and *Ceanothus*. In these cases the organisms inhabiting nodules on the tree roots and responsible for N_2 fixation are usually **actinomycetes** of the genus *Frankia*.

3.5 Roots and tree stability

In addition to their role in taking up essential resources for growth from soil, roots provide anchorage for trees, ensuring that they remain upright. The resistance

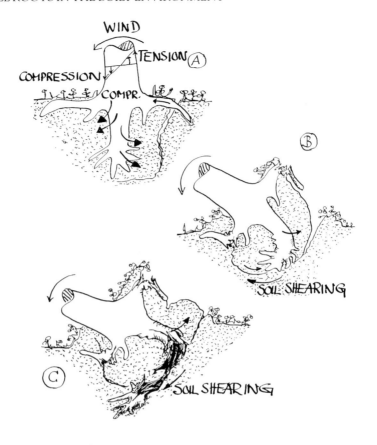

Figure 3.17 Windthrow of a tap-rooted tree.
(A) Soil cracks develop.
(B) Depending on the number of lateral roots, a root ball, which can vary in size, rotates and comes out of the ground.
(C) A long tap-root may break at the surface of the root ball.
(After Mattheck and Breloer, 1994.)

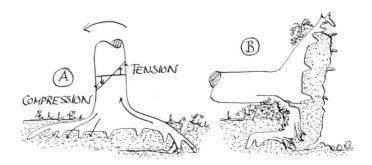

Figure 3.18 Windthrow of a shallow-rooted tree.
(A) Soil cracks develop and roots slide.
(B) The root plate tears out and tips over with almost no shearing.
(After Mattheck and Breloer, 1994.)

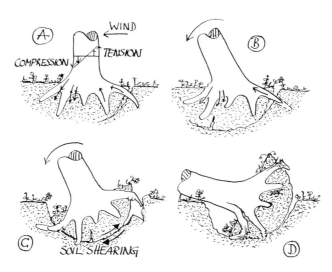

Figure 3.19 The development of windthrow over time in a heart-rooted tree.
(A) Soil cracks develop,
(B) roots pull out,
(C) the root/soil ball slides and
(D) roots break at the surface of the root ball and at the butt.
(After Mattheck and Breloer, 1994.)

of trees to being blown over by the wind is provided mostly by the large roots close to the base of the tree. Detailed analysis by Mattheck and Breloer (1994) suggest that little contribution to tree stability is offered by roots distant from the bole of the tree, nor by very deep roots.

The mechanisms of structural failure of tree root systems under loading from wind were reviewed by Mattheck and Breloer (1994). They distinguished between the anchorage properties of the three principal forms of tree root system architecture, the surface, heart root and tap-root systems (Fig 3.4). Failure of tap-root systems occurs when wind loading on the tree causes the soil to crack near the base of the trunk. Lateral movement of the tree then increases and the tap-root eventually snaps (Fig 3.17). Failure of surface root systems occurs when lateral roots on the windward side of the tree slide out of the soil as tension in the stem increases and cracks in the soil appear; the tree falls when laterals on the opposite side of the tree bend and open like a hinge (Fig 3.18). Failure of a heart root system follows a similar mechanism, although additional anchorage is provided by the shear strength of soil around the **root-ball** (Fig 3.19). This advantage gives heart root systems greater mechanical strength than tap-root or surface root systems, but is lost in wet soils because shear strength declines as soil becomes wetter. This is why the danger of trees falling is highest during wind storms with heavy rain (Gibbs and Greig, 1990; Mattheck and Breloer, 1994).

A concept that has been developed by Mattheck (1990) and discussed by Wood (1995), for example, is the adaptive growth hypothesis. In the case of roots that contribute to tree stability, this concept implies that the growth of different parts of the cross-section of a lateral root will be in response to perceived tensions and compressions ie the growth will be adaptive. An important consequence of adaptive growth is the likelihood that the support capacity of a root system has little redundancy in the event that parts of the root system are damaged or removed or the wind loading is increased. In practical terms this means that there is a danger that root cutting can compromise the support function of roots and increase the risk of trees blowing over during periods of strong wind. Equally, changing the level of shelter provided to a tree, eg by removing neighbouring trees, can create a loading to which the roots, which provide stability to the remaining tree (or trees), are not yet adapted. Particularly, in an urban environment, any practices that compromise tree stability would pose an unacceptable danger to life and property.

3.6 Summary

- The key functions of the roots of trees are to acquire nutrients and water and transmit these to the other parts of the tree. The roots support the tree, provide a store for food reserves and produce plant growth regulators.

- The traditional view has been that root systems of isolated trees extend to great depths and their lateral growth is restricted to the distance over which the canopy extends. This view is not supported by observations. The majority of the root system of trees is found in the upper 1 m of soil but can extend substantially beyond the dripline of the canopy.

- The structural parts of the root system of a tree are long-lived, perhaps spanning the whole life of the tree. In contrast, the fine roots of a tree are short-lived, having a life span ranging from as little as 10 days to over 12 months. The growth of new fine roots is important for trees as it allows them to explore and exploit untapped water and nutrient resources in the soil. The carbon allocation to support new fine roots can be a substantial fraction of the net production of trees, particularly in resource-limited soils.

- The uptake of water and nutrients by roots is highest at the new tips of growing roots. The evidence that uptake occurs in older parts of roots, particularly in adult trees, requires further detailed study. In most circumstances the water uptake by roots occurs because water loss from the foliage creates a water potential gradient down through the tree which is exerted on the soil at the root surface. Water uptake by tree roots will be sustained as long as a water potential gradient occurs between the root and the soil.

- Nutrient uptake by roots occurs by one of three mechanisms: root interception, diffusion and mass flow. The mobility of certain elements, particularly phosphorus, is low in soils and their supply to the plant will be determined by root growth and diffusion. The movement of some ions, eg nitrate, will depend almost completely on rates of transpiration.

- Carbohydrate reserves in roots can be mobilised and contribute substantially to support tissue growth at a range of sites in the tree. Stores of food reserves are replenished towards the end of the annual growth season when size growth, flowering and fruiting of the tree has ceased.

- Observations in a range of plants demonstrate the importance of roots as a source of plant growth regulators. The efficacy of plant growth regulators in adult trees remains to be demonstrated.

- Root growth is limited by the mechanical strength of soils which are naturally consolidated or have been compacted. Root growth will be substantially reduced at soil strengths between 0.7 and 1.0 MPa and is completely curtailed by soil strengths around 2.0 MPa.

- Mycorrhizal associations with tree roots have important consequences for the improved supply of nutrients, particularly phosphorus, to roots. A wide range of plant processes have been shown to be affected by the presence of mycorrhizae. Unfortunately much of the research has been restricted to individual species in experimental situations. More study is required of the relationship between mycorrhizal infection and the possibility of substantial improvements in drought resistance and water uptake by adult trees in field situations.

- The ability of trees to withstand wind forces is provided by the main structural roots close to the base of the tree. There are different mechanisms of failure for roots with different form. The development of structural roots that give trees stability is adapted to stresses and strains experienced during growth. Reduction in size of a root system or an increase in wind loading will make a tree, at least temporarily less able to resist stresses and strains.

REFERENCES

Alexander, I. 1989. Mycorrhizas in tropical forests. In: *Mineral Nutrients in Tropical Forest and Savanna Ecosystems* (Ed. by J. Proctor), pp. 169–188. Blackwell Scientific, Oxford, UK.

Allen, M.F. 1991. *The Ecology of Mycorrhizae.* Cambridge University Press, Cambridge, UK. 184 pp.

Atkinson, D. 1980. The distribution and effectiveness of the roots of tree crops. *Horticultural Reviews*, 2, 424–490.

Atwell, B.J. 1990. The effect of soil compaction on wheat during early tillering. I. Growth, development and shoot structure. *New Phytologist*, 115, 29–35.

Barber, S.A. 1995. *Soil Nutrient Bioavailability: A Mechanistic Approach.* 2nd Edition. John Wiley, New York, USA. 414 pp.

Bartlett, E.M. & Lewis, D.H. 1973. Surface phosphatase activity of mycorrhizal roots of beech. *Soil Biology and Biochemistry*, 5, 249–257.

Bennie, A.T.P. 1991. Growth and mechanical impedance. In: *The Plant Root, the Hidden Half* (Ed. by Y. Waisel, A. Eshel and U. Kafkafi), pp. 393–414. Marcel Dekker, New York, USA.

Biebelriether, H. 1962. Research on roots of firs and oaks in middle Swabia. *Forstwissenschafliches Centralblatt*, 81, 230–247.

Biebelriether, H. 1966. Root development of some tree species in relation to soil properties. *Allgemaine Forst Zeitschrift*, 21, 805–818.

Bowen, G.D. 1973. Mineral nutrition of mycorrhizas. In: *Ectomycorrhizae – Their Ecology and Physiology* (Ed. by G.C. Marks and T.T. Koslowski), pp. 151– 205. Academic Press, London, UK.

Bowen, G.D. 1984. In: *Nutrition of Plantation Forests* (Ed. by G.D. Bowen and E.K.S. Nambiar), pp. 147–179. Academic Press, London, UK.

Boyd, R., Furbank, R.T. & Read, D.J. 1986. Ectomycorrhiza and the water relations of trees. In: *Physiological and Genetical Aspects of Mycorrhizae* (Ed. by V. Gianinazzi-Pearson and S. Gianinazzi), pp. 689–693. INRA, Paris, France.

Bradley, R., Burt, A.J. & Read, D.J. 1981. Mycorrhizal infection and resistance to heavy metal toxicity in *Calluna vulgaris*. *Nature*, 292, 335–337.

Büsgen, M. & Münch, E. 1929. *The Structure and Life of Forest Trees.* Chapman and Hall, London, UK. 436 pp.

Canadell, J., Jackson, R.B., Ehleringer, J.R., Mooney, H.A., Sala, O.E. & Schulze, E.-D. 1996. Maximum rooting depth of vegetation types at the global scale. *Oecologia*, 108, 583–595.

Chung, H.H. & Kramer, P.J. 1975. Absorption of water and ^{32}P through suberised and unsuberised roots of loblolly pine. *Canadian Journal of Forest Research*, 5, 229–235.

Clarkson, D.T. & Hanson, J.B. 1980. The mineral nutrition of higher plants. *Annual Review of Plant Physiology*, 31, 449–456.

Coile, T.S. 1937. Distribution of forest tree roots in North Carolina Piedmont soils. *Journal of Forestry*, 36, 247–257.

Coleman, M.D., Bledsoe, C.S. & Smit, B.A. 1990. Root hydraulic conductivity and xylem sap levels of zeatin riboside and abscisic acid in ectomycorrhizal Douglas fir seedlings. *New Phytologist*, 115, 275–284.

Cutler, D.F. & Richardson, I.B.K. 1989. *Tree Roots and Buildings*, Longmans, London, UK. 71 pp.

Dexter, A.R. 1986. Model experiments on the behaviour of roots at the interface between a tilled seed-bed and a compacted subsoil. I. Effects of seed-bed aggregate size and sub-soil strength on wheat roots. *Plant and Soil*, 95, 123–133.

Dixon, R.K., Pallardy, S.G., Garrett, H.E. & Cox, G.S. 1983. Comparative water relations of container-grown and bare-root ectomycorrhizal and non-mycorrhizal *Quercus velutina* seedlings. *Canadian Journal of Botany*, 61, 1559–1565.

Dobson, M.C. & Moffat, A.J. 1993. *The Potential for Woodland Establishment on Landfill Sites*. Department of the Environment. HMSO, London, UK. 88 pp.

Eissenstat, D.M. & Yanai, R.D. 1997. The ecology of root lifespan. *Advances in Ecological Research*, 27, 1–60.

Gasson, P.E. & Cutler, D.F. 1990. Tree root plate morphology. *Arboricultural Journal*, 14, 193–264.

Gaumann, E. 1935. Der stoffhaushalt der buche (*Fagus sylvatica*) im laufe eines jahres. *Berichte Schweiz Bot. Ges.*, 44, 157–334.

Gibbs, J.N. & Greig, B.J.W. 1990. Survey of parkland trees after the Great Storm of October 16, 1987. *Arboricultural Journal*, 14, 321–347.

Gilman, E.F. 1989. Predicting root spread from trunk diameter and branch spread. *Arboricultural Journal*, 13, 25–32.

Gilman, E.F. 1990. Tree root growth and development. 1. Form, spread, depth and periodicity. *Journal of Environmental Horticulture*, 8, 215–220.

Graham, J.H. & Menge, J.A. 1982. Influence of vesicular–arbuscular mycorrhizae and soil phosphorus on take-all disease of wheat. *Phytopathology*, 72, 95–98.

Greacen, E.L. 1986. Root responses to soil mechanical properties. *Transactions of the 13th congress of the International Society of Soil Science*, pp. 20–47.

Greacen, E.L. & Sands, R. 1980. Composition of forest soils – a review. *Australian Journal of Soil Research*, 8, 163–189.

Gregory, P.J. 1988. Growth and functioning and plant roots. In: Russell's *Soil Conditions and Plant Growth* (Ed. by A. Wild), pp. 113–167. Longmans, London, UK.

Hayman, D.S. & Mosse, B. 1972. Plant growth responses to vesicular-arbuscular mycorrhiza. III. Increased uptake of labile P from soil. *New Phytologist*, 71, 41–47.

Hendricks, R.L. & Pregitzer, K.S. 1992. The demography of fine roots in a northern hardwood forest. *Ecology*, 73, 1094–1104.

Hodgkins, E.J. & Nichols, N.G. 1977. Extent of main lateral roots in natural longleaf pine as related to position and age of tree. *Forest Science*, 23, 161–166.

Jackson, R.B., Canadell, J., Ehleringer, J.R., Mooney, H.A., Sala, O.E. & Schulze, E.-D. 1996. A global analysis of root distributions for terrestrial biomes. *Oecologia*, 108, 389–411.

Killham, K. 1985. Vesicular-arbuscular mycorrhizal mediation of trace and minor element uptake in perennial grasses: relation to livestock herbage. In: *Ecological Interactions in the Soil: Plants, Microbes and Animals* (Ed. by A.H. Fitter), pp. 225–233. BES Special Publication 4. Blackwell, Oxford, UK.

Killham, K. 1994. *Soil Ecology*. Cambridge University Press, Cambridge, UK. 242 pp.

Köstler, J.N., Bruckner, E. & Biebelriether, H. 1968. *Die wurzeln der waldbaum*. Paul Parey Verlag, Hamburg, Germany.

Kramer, P.J. & Boyer, J.S. 1995. *Water relations of plants and soils*. Academic Press, New York, USA. 495 pp.

Kramer, P.J. & Bullock, H.C. 1966. Seasonal variations in the proportions of suberized and unsuberized roots of trees in relation to the absorption of water. *American Journal of Botany*, 53, 200–204.

Lamb, R.J. & Richards, B.N. 1971. Effect of mycorrhizal fungi on the growth and nutrient status of slash and radiata pine seedlings. *Australian Forestry*, 35, 1–7.

Lamhamedi, M.S., Bernier, P.Y. & Fortin, J.A. 1992. Hydraulic conductance and soil water potential at the soil root interface of *Pinus pinaster* seedlings inoculated with different dikaryons of *Pisolithus* sp. *Tree Physiology*, 10, 231–244.

Lynch, J.M. & Whipps, J.M. 1990. Substrate flow in the rhizosphere. *Plant and Soil*, 129, 1–10.

Lyr, H. & Hoffman, G. 1967. Growth rates and growth periodicity of tree roots. *International Review of Forest Research*, 2, 181–236.

Mackay, A.D. & Barber, S.A. 1985. Effect of soil moisture and phosphate level on root hair growth of corn roots. *Plant and Soil*, 86, 321–331.

Mackay, A.D. & Barber, S.A. 1987. Effect of cyclic wetting and drying of a soil on root hair growth of maize roots. *Plant and Soil*, 104, 291–293.

Mackie-Dawson, L.A. & Atkinson, D. 1991. Methodology for the study of roots in field experiments and the interpretation of results. In: *Plant Root growth:*

an ecological perspective (Ed. by D. Atkinson), pp. 25–47. Blackwell Scientific Publications, Oxford, UK.

Marschner, H. 1995. *Mineral nutrition of higher plants.* Academic Press, London. 889 pp.

Marx, D.H. 1973. Mycorrhizae and feeder root diseases. In: *Ectomycorrhizae – Their Ecology and Physiology* (Ed. by G.C. Marks and T.T. Koslowski), pp. 351–382. Academic Press, London, UK.

Marx, D.H. & Krupa, S.V. 1978. Ectomycorrhizae. In: *Interactions between Non-pathogenic Soil Microorganisms and Plants* (Ed. by Y.R. Dommergues and S.V. Krupa), pp. 373–400. Elsevier, Amsterdam, The Netherlands.

Mattheck, C. 1990. Engineering components grow like trees. *Material-wissenschaft und Werkstofftech*, 21, 143–168.

Mattheck, C. & Breloer, H. 1994. *The body language of trees: a handbook for failure analysis.* Research for Amenity Trees No. 4, TSO, London, UK. 240pp.

Moore, R., Clark, W.D. & Vodopich, D.S. 1998. *Botany*, 2nd Edition, WCB/McGraw-Hill, New York, USA. 919 pp.

Packham, J.R., Harding, D.J.L., Hilton, G.M. & Stuttard, R.A. 1992. *Functional Ecology of Forests and Woodlands.* Chapman and Hall, London, UK. 408 pp.

Perry, T.O. 1982. The ecology of tree roots and the practical significance thereof. *Journal of Arboriculture*, 8, 197–211.

Polomski, J. & Kuhn, N. 1998. *Wurzelsysteme.* Paul Haupt Verlag, Bern, Switzerland. 290 pp.

Read, D.J., Francis, R. & Finlay, R.D. 1985. Mycorrhizal mycelia and nutrient cycling in plant communities. In: *Ecological interactions in soil: plants, microbes and animals* (Ed. by A.H. Fitter), pp. 193–217. BES Special Publication 4. Blackwell, Oxford, UK.

Rendig, V.V. & Taylor, H.M. 1989. Physical environmental effects (root growth and distribution). In: *Principles of soil-plant interrelationships*, pp. 50–65. McGraw-Hill Publ. New York, USA.

Rhodes, L.L. & Gerdemann, J.W. 1978. Influence of phosphorus nutrition on sulphur uptake by vesicular-arbuscular mycorrhizae of onions. *Soil Biology and Biochemistry*, 10, 361–364.

Roberts, J.M. 1976. A study of the root distribution and growth in a *Pinus sylvestris* L. (Scots pine) plantation in East Anglia. *Plant and Soil*, 44, 607–621.

Russell, R.S. 1977. *Plant Root Systems: Their Function and Interaction with the Soil.* McGraw-Hill, London, UK. 298 pp.

Ryan, M.G., Binkley, D. & Fownes, J.H. 1997. Age-related decline in forest productivity: pattern and process. *Advances in Ecological Research*, 27, 213–262.

Rygiewicz, P.T., Bledsoe, C.S. & Zasoski, R.J. 1984. Effects of ectomycorrhizae and solution pH on ^{15}N nitrate uptake by coniferous seedlings. *Canadian Journal of Forest Research*, 14, 893–899.

Safir, G.R., Boyer, J.S. & Gerdemann, J.E. 1971. Nutrient status and mycorrhizal enhancement of water transport in soybean. *Science*, 172, 581–583.

Sands, R., Fiscus, E.L. & Reid, C.P.P. 1982. Hydraulic properties of pine and bean roots with varying degrees of suberisation, vascular differentiation, and mycorrhizal infection. *Australian Journal of Plant Physiology*, 9, 559–569.

Sands, R. & Theodorou, C. 1978. Water uptake by mycorrhizal roots of radiata pine seedlings. *Australian Journal of Plant Physiology*, 5, 301–309.

Schoettle, A.W. & Fahey, T.J. 1994. Foliage and fine root longevity in pines. *Ecological Bulletin*, 43, 136–153.

Smith, S.E. & Read, D.J. 1997. Microbial symbiosis. 2nd Edition. Academic Press, London, UK. 605 pp.

Stone, E.L. & Kalisz, D.J. 1991. On the maximum extent of tree roots. *Forest Ecology and Management*, 46, 59–102.

Stout, B.B. 1956. Studies of the root systems of deciduous trees. *Black Forest Bulletin*, 15, 1–45.

Sutton, R.F. 1980. Root system morphogenesis. *New Zealand Journal of Forest Science*, 10, 265–292.

Taiz, L. & Zeiger, E. 1991. *Plant physiology*. The Benjamin/Cummings Publishing Company, Redwood City, CA, USA. 565 pp.

Taylor, H.M. & Gardner, H.R. 1963. Penetration of cotton seedling taproots as influenced by bulk density, moisture content and strength of soil. *Soil Science*, 96, 153–156.

Taylor, H.M. & Ratliff, L.F. 1969. Root elongation rates of cotton and peanuts as a function of soil strength and water content. *Soil Science*, 108, 113–119.

Taylor, H.M., Roberson, G.M. & Parker, J.J. 1966. Soil strength-root penetration relations for medium to coarse textured materials. *Soil Science*, 102, 18–22.

Toumey, J.W. 1929. Initial root habit in American trees and its bearing on regeneration. *International Congress on Plant Science Proceedings*, 1, 713–728.

Walker, R.F., West, D.C. & McLaughlin, S.B. 1982. *Pisolithus tinctorius* ectomycorrhizae reduce moisture stress of Virginia pine on a southern Appalachian coal spoil. In: *Proceedings of the Seventh North American Forest Biology Workshop* (Ed. by B.A. Thielges), pp. 374–383. University of Kentucky, Lexington, USA.

Walker, R.F., West, D.C., McLaughlin, S.B. & Amundsen, C.C. 1989. Growth, xylem pressure potential and nutrient absorption of loblolly pine on a reclaimed surface mine as affected by an induced *Pisolithus tinctorius* infection. *Forest Science*, 35, 569–581.

Wargo, P.M. 1979. Starch storage and radial growth in woody tissues of sugar maple. *Canadian Journal of Forest Research*, 9, 49–56.

Wood, C.J. 1995. Understanding wind forces on trees. In: *Wind and Trees* (Ed. by M.P. Coutts and J. Grace), pp. 133–164. Cambridge University Press, Cambridge, UK.

CHAPTER 4

Urban Soils for Amenity Trees

4.1 Soils in the urban environment

Soils in urban areas are subject to a great variety of disturbances not found outside of the built environment (Craul, 1992). Building and landscaping frequently require reshaping of terrain through the alteration of slopes or infilling of gullies and valleys, entailing the removal, transfer and re-spreading of large quantities of soil materials, either within a site or between sites. Demolition or refurbishment of buildings and other structures has created large volumes of rubble, wood, glass, plastic and metal that have been buried in the urban landscape, sometimes over many centuries. Urban soils are also particularly prone to contamination by chemical pollutants, because of deposition of atmospheric pollutants, disposal of industrial waste or use of de-icing salt on roads and footways. The structure and composition of soils has, consequently, been modified in urban areas by human activity and the chemical, physical and biological properties of urban soils differ substantially from those of forest and agricultural soils.

A defining feature of urban soils is a surface layer formed by mixing, filling or contamination, because of human activity during urban development (Craul, 1985). In addition, urban soils typically exhibit very high vertical and spatial heterogeneity in comparison with more natural soils (Craul, 1985, de Kimpe and Morel, 2000). Properties of forest and agricultural soils tend to change gradually from one layer to the next, although abrupt changes can occur, for example in soil texture. Such abrupt discontinuities in soil properties are common in urban soils, as a result of past construction and landscaping.

During a typical construction project the topsoil is first scraped away and the exposed subsoil is reshaped to create desired slopes and level areas, a process resulting in considerable mixing and compaction of soil layers. Hard fill consisting of rubble, gravel and other waste materials may then by used where necessary and covered with subsoil material or other soil brought from another site. Finally, after completion of the project, topsoil is re-spread over the site to facilitate landscaping, using either the original material or other soil brought from elsewhere. This reconstituted topsoil will have undergone considerable mixing and its structure will have been substantially destroyed. The resulting soil profile, which might look something like Fig 4.1, will be drastically different from a nearby natural soil. Layers in the profile are likely to have

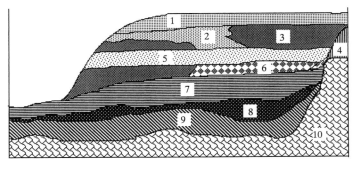

1 - sandy loam fill
2 - silty loam fill
3 - plastic clayey fill
4 - deep clay
5 - sandy fill

6 - refuse of concrete blocks
    and rotten debris
7 - alluvium
8 - organic layers
9 - weathered rock
10 - bedrock

Figure 4.1 The vertical and spatial variability of an urban soil. (After Craul, 1992.)

sharply contrasting texture, structure, organic matter content, pH and bulk density, as well as consequent differences in aeration, water-holding capacity and fertility (Craul, 1985). Conditions for root growth may be good in some layers, but very poor in others. Water may move rapidly through some parts of the profile, but only very slowly through others, creating possibly severe drainage problems at the interfaces between layers.

The nature of variability and extent of disturbance in urban soils depends on historical changes in land use, both before and after urban development. Soil disturbance tends to increase with proximity to city centres, creating gradients in soil properties between rural, suburban and urban areas (McDonnell *et al*, 1993). Several cycles of redevelopment may have occurred at old sites in urban centres, creating a highly complex soil environment. Degradation resulting from soil modification causes a variety of problems for tree growth and establishment, which tend to become more severe at heavily urbanised sites. Avoidance, diagnosis or remediation of these problems requires an understanding of the physical, chemical and biological properties of urban soils and their influence on root growth and function.

4.2 Physical properties of urban soils

4.2.1 Soil texture

The texture of soil is determined by the relative proportions of sand, silt and clay particles in the mineral fraction of the soil, as shown in the textural triangle in Fig 2.3. The complex history of land uses, mixing and infilling typical for urban soils means that particle size distribution can vary widely within the same profile. Discrete layers or pockets of soil may occur with highly dissimilar distributions of particle size. For example, a layer of masonry rubble created by building demolition or the addition of hard core to soil at a site may be adjacent to a layer of clay. Similarly, loam placed around the root-ball of a tree planted in a tree pit at the roadside may be surrounded by highly compacted, coarse base material beneath the paved surface. Such textural discontinuities can impede movement of water through soil (Craul, 1985).

4.2.2 Soil porosity and soil structure

Diameters of soil pores range from several millimetres down to less than 0.1 mm, or one-ten thousandth of a millimetre (Brady and Weil, 1999). Pores larger than about 0.1 mm in diameter are classed as macropores. These pores enable rapid movement of water and air through soil and, consequently, they help to ensure that soils are well-drained and well-aerated. Plant roots generally proliferate through networks of macropores. Smaller pores – the **micropores** – retain water which plants can use, and accommodate root hairs, fungi and bacteria, which are essential for the uptake and cycling of plant nutrients.

Distributions of pore sizes in soil are determined, in part, by soil texture, because the size of spaces between particles depends on particle size. Pores between clay particles may be as small as 0.001 mm in diameter, while those between sand particles are likely to be at least ten times that dimension. Pore space in soil is also determined by structural formations created by aggregation of individual particles because of cohesive forces between clay particles and the binding qualities of organic matter. Micropores occur within aggregates, but pores between aggregates are generally macropores. Well-structured soils with good aggregation thus contain a wide range of pore sizes able to fulfil a broad range of important functions. Large pores are also created by burrowing of earthworms and other soil-dwelling animals, decay of old roots and cracking resulting from cycles of wetting and drying or freezing and thawing.

In urban environments, human activity and reduced organic matter content tend to destroy good soil structure. Mixing, moving and re-spreading of soils results in at least partial loss of soil structure (Rimmer, 1991; Craul, 1992), as aggregates are broken up and compressed. Low input of organic matter to urban soils, because organic litter (such as fallen leaves) is often removed from the soil surface for disposal, also results in loss of soil structure, as the decay products of organic matter are needed to maintain soil aggregation. Loss of vegetation cover from soils, even for short periods, can result in erosion of topsoil, exposing deeper soil layers that often have poor structure. The loss of aggregation and breakdown of structure in urban soils results in a reduction in the proportion of the pore volume made up by macropores. Loss of macropore space restricts drainage and aeration and impedes the development of root systems.

Perhaps the most serious threat to soil structure in urban settings is soil compaction because of physical activities on the surface. Pedestrian traffic and vehicle movement cause soil compaction. However, construction activities can be responsible for severe soil compaction over extensive areas, often when the soil water content is most conducive to compaction. Soil compaction on construction sites is not easily rectified and it is frequently a major impediment to the establishment and maintenance of healthy trees on development sites.

4.2.3 Soil compaction

If a load is applied to soil, compaction occurs when particles are forced into closer contact (Hillel, 1998). Air is expelled from the soil volume and pore space is reduced, with many macropores and large micropores compressed into smaller pores (Brady and Weil, 1999). The reduction in pore space in compacted soils results in increased bulk density. Deformation of soil because of the passage of vehicles or machinery across the soil surface is a common cause of compaction, although any loading of the soil surface can lead to compaction. Other causes of soil compaction common in the urban environment include pedestrian movement along unpaved footpaths and recreational activities in parks and on playing fields. Urban soils are also prone to compaction because of vibration, which can shake particles into more tightly packed arrangements, especially in street-side locations and near railways or underground tunnels (Craul, 1992; Brady and Weil, 1999).

Activities associated with construction cause severe soil compaction. Soils are intentionally compacted when preparing roadbeds or building foundations, to prevent subsequent damage to structures and pavements because of uneven **settlement** of the soil (Brady and Weil, 1999). Intentional compaction is achieved using specialised equipment such as heavy rollers. When compacting soils for construction, engineers aim to attain bulk densities that are close to the maximum possible. The bulk density of a soil compacted by a given force depends on soil texture and moisture content, with the maximum bulk density occurring when soils are compacted at the optimum moisture content, as shown in Fig 4.2. In soils drier than the optimum, frictional resistance and bonding between particles constrains compaction; at water contents higher than the optimum, the incompressibility of water prevents particles from being forced together, and bulk density under a given load is then less than the maximum (Craul, 1992; Hillel, 1998). The Proctor test is a standard test used by construction engineers to determine maximum bulk densities (**Proctor density**) for soils and optimum water contents for compaction (Hillel, 1998). Specifications used by contractors for site preparation typically stipulate that soil is compacted to 95% of the maximum bulk density, as defined by the Proctor test (Hillel, 1998).

A research project commissioned initially by the Highways Agency and subsequently administered by Transport for London was conducted by a consortium lead by Richards, Moorehead and Laing Ltd, (RML). A principal aim of the project was to examine to what extent structural tree soils, eg Amsterdam Tree Soil, can be compacted sufficiently to provide the engineering requirements of soils to adequately support roads and pathways while still enabling sufficient root growth for satisfactory tree growth.

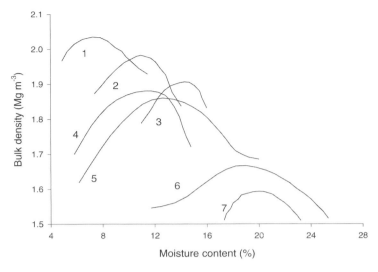

Figure 4.2 A family of soil moisture-compaction curves.
(1) A well-graded coarse to fine sand;
(2) very fine sandy loam;
(3) a clay till;
(4) a sandy clay;
(5) a clay till;
(6) an alluvial silt;
(7) a sandy clay loam.
(After Craul, 1992.)

In the UK, the required strength of soils below pavements uses values of the **California Bearing Ratio** (CBR) to specify the strength of sub-bases which should have a CBR of 30% or more, and subgrades having a CBR of 15% or more (Department of Transport, 1994). The CBR is the ratio of the force required to achieve a given penetration of a prescribed piston into a soil to the force required to produce the same penetration into a standard sample of crushed rock.

Because of the practical difficulties of measuring CBR rapidly and routinely, the RML project (RML 2002) has compared determinations of CBR with readings using a dynamic cone penetrometer (DCP). Good statistical correlations have been obtained enabling the simpler DCP measurements to be used to evaluate the degree to which the soils in experimental tree planting plots have approached the required CBR value after compaction. It is difficult to relate values from a DCP to soil resistance values determined using other types of penetrometers which measure the resistance to the gradual turning and pushing of a probe into the soil. Good relationships are usually observed between the mechanical strength of the soil determined from such penetrometer measurements, root growth and soil bulk density (Bengough *et al*, 2001). The compaction of non-structural soils to CBR values sufficient to meet current specifications will produce bulk density values which will substantially exceed those found limiting to root growth.

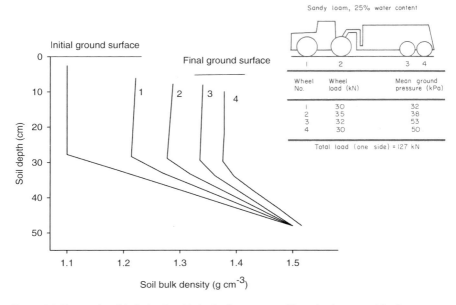

Figure 4.3 Changes in soil bulk density with depth after passage of four wheels on one side of a tractor and trailer. (After Smith, 1987.)

Severe compaction of soil also occurs on construction sites as an unintended consequence of other activities (Randrup and Dralle, 1997). Movement of heavy machinery and storage of materials cause compaction on construction sites, and unless carefully planned and controlled, they can result in long-term damage to the capacity of a site to support the growth of trees. It is very important to realise that a major contribution to soil compaction occurs in the first passes of vehicles over the ground. Fig 4.3 shows the increase in soil bulk density in an agricultural soil with a single pass of a tractor and trailer and that a major fraction of the compaction occurs when only two wheels have passed over the ground (Smith, 1987). Building works often require many months to complete, possibly starting with demolition or site clearance, entailing perhaps hundreds or thousands of vehicle or machinery movements across the site, sometimes during the wettest months of the year. If routes for traffic are not strictly controlled, all soil at a site can quickly become severely compacted by roaming vehicles. Subsequent landscaping and tree planting at the site will then be detrimentally affected by the impacts of soil compaction on soil properties and root growth.

4.2.3.1 Impacts of soil compaction on porosity

The direct impacts of compaction are loss of pore space and an increase in bulk density. The data in Table 4.1, taken from a laboratory study on forest soils (Foil and Ralston, 1967), demonstrate the impact of compaction on **porosity**. As compaction increased, bulk density increased in each textural class and the proportion of large pores fell. When compaction occurs, the reduction in porosity predominantly results, therefore, from destruction of macropores,

Table 4.1 Effects of compaction treatments on physical characteristics of soil. (Source: Foil and Ralston, 1967.)

Soil	Compaction treatment	Bulk density ($Mg\,m^{-3}$)	Porosity (% by volume) Total	Macropores
Loamy sand	undisturbed	1.07	57.3	25.6
	light ($3.5\,kg\,cm^{-2}$)	1.27	47.5	11.6
	medium ($7.0\,kg\,cm^{-2}$)	1.34	47.4	9.5
	heavy ($10.5\,kg\,cm^{-2}$)	1.33	48.4	9.2
Loam	undisturbed	1.06	52.8	12.9
	light ($3.5\,kg\,cm^{-2}$)	1.20	56.1	6.7
	medium ($7.0\,kg\,cm^{-2}$)	1.19	54.6	5.3
	heavy ($10.5\,kg\,cm^{-2}$)	1.38	50.5	4.1
Clay	undisturbed	1.31	49.2	8.1
	light ($3.5\,kg\,cm^{-2}$)	1.43	48.7	3.3
	medium ($7.0\,kg\,cm^{-2}$)	1.48	45.2	2.4
	heavy ($10.5\,kg\,cm^{-2}$)	1.49	51.2	2.5

which are highly important for drainage. Compacted soils are, consequently, more prone to waterlogging (Brady and Weil, 1999). Reduced pore size also causes decreased infiltration of water at the soil surface. This may be exacerbated by the formation of crusts at the surface, which result from the accumulation in pores of fine particles from crushed soil aggregates. Reduction of porosity generally causes reduced water-holding capacity, although in very loose soil, the increase in micropore space can improve water retention. Loss of macropores also restricts aeration, because diffusion of gases occurs more slowly through fine micropores.

4.2.3.2 Impacts of compaction on bulk density

Bulk densities of between 1.7 and 2.2 $Mg\,m^{-3}$ were found for soils under turf in central Washington DC subject to very high pedestrian traffic (Patterson, 1977). Densities for less disturbed soils were less than 1.6 $Mg\,m^{-3}$ (Craul, 1994). An example of the effects of soil compaction on development sites during construction is given in Fig 4.4. Mean bulk density at 11 sites increased from 1.03 to 1.56 $Mg\,m^{-3}$ after completion of construction, in areas where compaction was unintentional and not necessary for engineering purposes (Alberty *et al*, 1984). These densities were found for soils available for landscaping and tree planting and are in the range at which root growth can be restricted.

4.2.3.3 Impacts of compaction on root growth

Growth of roots is restricted in compacted soils. Destruction of macropores reduces the number of pathways for root proliferation and increased soil strength causes mechanical impedance of root elongation (Brady and Weil,

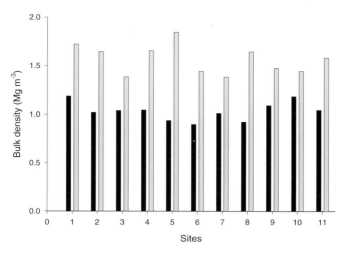

Figure 4.4 Bulk densities of soil from construction sites *(grey)* and adjacent, undisturbed areas *(black)*. (After Alberty *et al*, 1984.)

1999; Kozlowski, 1999). Roots are unable to enter pores narrower in diameter than the root cap, unless they can exert sufficient pressure to displace soil particles and widen pore openings. In compacted soil, the pressure required to displace particles is higher than in more loosely packed soil because of increased mechanical strength when particles are forced together. Thus, as soils are compacted and their bulk densities increase, root growth is reduced.

Bulk densities which restrict root growth vary with soil texture and soil wetness, because of their effects on soil strength. Soil strength is higher in drier soils and those containing more clay. At a given bulk density or level of compaction, therefore, resistance to root growth is more severe in drier soil and clay soil (Day and Bassuk, 1994; Brady and Weil, 1999). In general, penetration of wet soils by growing roots is limited in clay soils at bulk densities above approximately 1.45 Mg m^{-3}, but above 1.85 Mg m^{-3} in sandy soils (Brady and Weil, 1999; Kozlowski, 1999), although the capacity of roots to overcome mechanical impedance varies among species (Kozlowski, 1999). In drier soil, restriction of growth would occur at lower densities. Variation in bulk densities restrictive to root growth, as a result of the effects of soil wetness, texture and plant species, has made it difficult to develop definitive guidelines on acceptable bulk densities for soils used in landscaping (Alberty *et al*, 1984).

There are two important issues in the rooting behaviour of trees when woodland is the proposed after-use on landfill sites. Firstly, the roots must not invade and disrupt the clay cap seal to the landfill but, secondly, the topsoil laid on top of the clay cap must not be too compact to limit tree root growth. Information presented by Dobson and Moffat (1993), Bending and Moffat (1997) and Dobson and Moffat (1999) indicates that roots are unable to exploit soils which have a bulk density of 1.8 g cm^{-3} and above. This means that the clay cap seal to the landfill must be at least this value. Dobson and

Moffat (1993) recommend that for adequate tree growth on a closed landfill the soil bulk density of the soil in the upper 0.5 m should not exceed 1.5 g cm^{-3} and should not exceed 1.7 g cm^{-3} between 0.5 and 1m.

Reduced root elongation can result in lower total root lengths for plants. If, however, soil on one side of a plant is compacted by vehicle traffic, for example, the reduction in root growth may be mitigated by compensatory growth in soil free from traffic (Unger and Kaspar, 1994). Similarly, compaction may result in a clumped root distribution, as root proliferation may be restricted to cracks or old root channels that persist between very dense, compacted soil blocks (Passioura, 1991). Regardless of whether compaction results in reduced total root length or modified root distribution, the ability of the root system to extract water and nutrients is diminished, as movement of resources to the root must then occur over longer distances, which requires more time (Passioura, 1991).

4.2.4 Soil aeration

Healthy functioning of roots requires oxygen (O_2) for aerobic respiration. Sugars produced by photosynthesis are translocated from leaves to roots and the energy they contain is released by respiration, to support root growth and essential functions such as mineral uptake, maintenance of cell membranes and cell synthesis. Carbon dioxide (CO_2) is a by-product of aerobic respiration. Root health is dependent, consequently, on adequate transport of gases through soil, to deliver O_2 to roots and to remove CO_2 from the soil.

Gas transport through soil occurs by diffusion, along pathways of interconnected pores. Soil aeration can thus be reduced by any changes in soil properties which restrict the continuity of pores. As connections between pores are closed and continuity reduced, pathways for diffusion become more tortuous, meaning that twists and turns make diffusive pathways longer and less direct.

The principal causes of reduced soil aeration are soil compaction and waterlogging. Compaction of soil destroys soil structure and reduces macroporosity, forcing gas transport to follow more tortuous pathways through smaller pores. Rates of diffusion are consequently lower in compacted soil, which results in lower concentrations of O_2 and higher concentrations of CO_2 in soil air as respiration by roots and soil organisms depletes O_2 and causes accumulation of CO_2. High moisture contents in soils reduce aeration because diffusive pathways are closed by water-filled pores and, crucially, the rate of diffusion of gases is approximately 10,000 times slower in water than in air (Hillel, 1998).

In urban soils, aeration is also commonly reduced by the addition of fill at the soil surface, when soil levels are changed during construction, and by covering of the surface by buildings and hard surfaces. Yelenosky (1963) compared the composition of soil air under a 0.3–1.0 m layer of clay fill, a newly paved roadway and in an adjacent, undisturbed forest. Gas concentrations at 1 m depth in the undisturbed soil were never lower than 18% (by volume) for O_2 or higher than 2% for CO_2, in comparison to atmospheric concentrations of 21% and 0.03%, respectively. In the year after paving of the roadway with asphalt, the O_2 concentration in the underlying soil was 4% and the CO_2 concentration was 15%. Aeration was most severely restricted beneath the clay fill, where concentrations of O_2 were as low as 3% and CO_2 as high as 19%. Such poor aeration of soils can severely restrict root growth and function, and thus the addition of fill or covering of the soil with hard surfaces or buildings can seriously damage the root systems of established trees.

It is difficult to define a critical threshold for O_2 concentration in the soil, as there are variations in demand for O_2 by roots and soil microbes at different times of year and in tolerance among tree species to low O_2 levels in the root zone. Tolerance of low O_2 concentrations also increases at lower temperatures (Stolzy, 1974). In general, O_2 concentrations in soil below 10% have been shown to restrict root growth (Patterson, 1977; Day and Bassuk, 1994), while root growth stops at concentrations of about 3% (Kozlowski and Davies, 1975). An inadequate supply of O_2 impairs root growth and function because respiration becomes anaerobic, which is inefficient and does not release enough energy to maintain essential physiological processes in root tissue. As a consequence, uptake of water and nutrients by the root system decreases, causing reduced photosynthesis in the shoots and potentially causing decline of the tree.

Threats to trees from poor aeration caused by soil compaction are similar to those caused by flooding. Tolerance to poor soil aeration varies among tree species. In general, conifers are injured more by poor aeration than broadleaved trees, while some genera, such as willow (*Salix* spp), are adapted to flooded conditions and are tolerant of extended periods of poor aeration. Table 4.2 presents groups of species tolerant and intolerant to soil compaction and also species with intermediate tolerance (Craul, 1992).

4.2.5 Soil water

4.2.5.1 Infiltration

Infiltration refers to the entry of water, from rainfall, snow melt or irrigation, into soil at the surface. Infiltration rates depend on the physical properties of the soil profile and its initial wetness and water potential, unless an impediment to the entry of water exists, such as paving or a soil crust.

Rates of water movement in soil are determined by the hydraulic conductivity, which is a measure of the ease with which water moves through soil, and gradients in soil water potential. When soil is initially wetted, infiltration rates are high because saturation of the top few millimetres of soil creates a large gradient in water potential near the surface. Infiltration rates then gradually decline and approach a steady value as water percolates downwards and dissipates the potential gradient. Infiltration rates are generally higher for more

Table 4.2 Tree species and their resistance to soil compaction. (After Craul, 1992.)

Resistant

Acer negundo	Box elder	Salix spp	Willow
Fraxinus pennsylvanica	Green ash	Ulmus americana	American elm
Gleditsia triacanthos	Honey locust	Ulmus rubra	Red elm
Populus deltoides	Eastern cottonwood	Crataegus spp	Hawthorns
Quercus bicolor	Swamp white oak	Quercus macrocarpa	Burr oak
Ostrya virginiana	Hop hornbeam		

Intermediate

Acer rubrum	Red maple	Liquidambar styraciflua	Sweetgum
Acer saccharinum	Silver maple	Celtis occidentalis	Hackberry
Acer platanoides	Norway maple	Nyssa sylvatica	Black gum
Carya ovata	Shagbark hickory	Quercus rubra	Red oak
Platanus x acerifolia	London plane	Tilia americana	Basswood
Quercus palustris	Pin oak		

Susceptible

Acer saccharum	Sugar maple	Pinus nigra	Austrian pine
Pinus strobus	White pine	Fraxinus americana	White ash
Picea pungens	Blue spruce	Betula papyrifera	Paper birch
Quercus alba	White oak	Sorbus aucuparia	Mountain ash
Pinus resinosa	Red pine	Acer palmatum	Japanese maple

coarsely textured soils, as for example in Table 4.3, because water moves more rapidly through the larger pores of these soils, which are filled as the water penetrates the soil.

Macropores also enable rapid entry of water into soil (Beven and Germann, 1982). Consequently, infiltration is improved where good soil structure exists and especially where soils contain old root channels, cracks or high populations of burrowing animals, including earthworms, ants and moles (Ehlers, 1975; Beven and Germann, 1982; Kladivko et al, 1986). In untilled soil, earthworm channels with diameters of 2–11 mm have been found to reach depths of 1.8 m, providing pathways for very rapid infiltration to well below the surface layer of soil (Ehlers, 1975). In addition to creating channels through soil, earthworms leave casts of organic material that increase the structural stability of soil aggregates (Kladivko et al, 1986). As a result, earthworm activity has a substantial impact on the quantities of water infiltrating soil (Fig 4.5).

Table 4.3 Steady infiltration rates for different soil types. (*Source*: Hillel, 1998.)

Soil type	Steady infiltration rate (mm h^{-1})
Sands	>20
Sandy and silty soils	10–20
Loams	5–10
Clayey soils	1–5

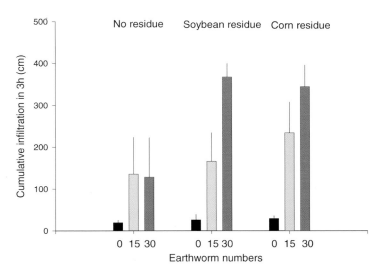

Figure 4.5 Effect of 0, 15 and 30 earthworms per pot and no residue, soybean or corn residue on cumulative infiltration in 3 hours in Raub soil (silty-loam) in 16 l pots. Standard deviations are represented by a vertical line on each column. (After Kladivko *et al*, 1986.)

There is also an added influence of crop residues on infiltration. Crop residues are normally left in place in zero or low-tillage agriculture.

The presence in the soil of layers with contrasting texture, especially pans, also affects infiltration (Hillel, 1998). Where a coarse soil overlies a finely textured layer with a much lower hydraulic conductivity, infiltrating water initially moves rapidly through the coarse soil, but slows when the wetting front reaches the finer sublayer. Further downward penetration of the wetting front is then impeded by the lower conductivity of the finer soil. If the duration of infiltration is sufficient, the soil just above the impeding layer can become saturated, creating a waterlogged zone, or **perched water table**.

Infiltration can also be impeded where a finely textured soil overlies a coarse layer. During infiltration, soil at the wetting front is not saturated and has a negative water potential, meaning it is held in the pores under suction. When the wetting front reaches the interface between layers, the larger pores of the coarse sublayer cannot fill with water until the water potential in the finer soil

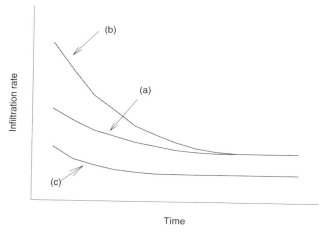

Figure 4.6 Infiltrability as a function of time in **(a)** a uniform soil, **(b)** a soil with more permeable upper layer, and **(c)** a soil with a surface crust. (After Hillel, 1998.)

increases, reducing the suction retaining water in the finer pores. As a result, if the contrast in texture between layers is large, as for example where a clay overlies coarse sand or gravel, infiltration is impeded until the soil just above the interface is saturated or nearly saturated.

Crusting at the soil surface creates a further major impediment to infiltration. Soil crusts develop because of the breakdown of soil aggregates under the impact of raindrops. Clay particles dispersed from the aggregates clog the pores at the surface and are cemented together as the soil dries, creating a thin, structureless crust with much lower hydraulic conductivity than the soil beneath. The crust acts as a seal over the soil, severely reducing infiltration rates, as shown in Fig 4.6. Vegetation protects soils from crusting by intercepting rainfall and reducing the velocities of impacting raindrops (Hillel, 1998).

4.2.5.2 Infiltration in urban soils

Properties typical of urban soils tend to reduce infiltration rates. Loss of pore space because of soil compaction causes reduced infiltration, as does loss of soil structure and macroporosity (Craul, 1985). Macroporosity, and therefore infiltration, is also diminished in urban soils because of reduced populations of earthworms (Pizl and Josens, 1995) and other burrowing soil organisms. Heterogeneity in soil texture, common in urban environments as a result of historical changes in land use and infilling with clays, gravel or masonry rubble, reduces infiltration because of textural discontinuities at interfaces between layers or pockets of soil with contrasting properties. The consequence of impeded infiltration in urban soils is increased runoff from the surface, particularly when rainfall is heavy. Surface runoff, which in the urban environment is likely to be diverted to drains and sewers, means less water is stored in the soil for use by trees and other vegetation.

Runoff from urban surfaces is also enhanced because of impedance of infiltration by sealing of the soil. Sealing may result from crusting of soils left bare of vegetation, even for short periods, which may be common on development sites, wasteground or in parkland subject to high levels of pedestrian traffic. Paving and buildings restrict infiltration and increase runoff over wide areas of the urban landscape and usually cover a high proportion of the root systems of roadside trees. Surfaces of urban soils are also prone to sealing by the deposition of petroleum-based aerosols, particulates and other pollutants, which cause soils to become hydrophobic (Craul, 1985). Entry of rainwater at the surface is then reduced because oily soil particles repel water droplets, preventing their entry into pores. This is a particular problem for trees growing adjacent to streets.

4.2.5.3 Water-holding capacity

The capacity of a soil to store water for use by plants is the quantity of water retained in the soil between field capacity and the **permanent wilting point**. Field capacity is the water held in a soil after the macropores in a saturated soil have drained under gravity (see Fig 2.6). Water retained in the soil against gravity is held in smaller pores under suction, at negative water potentials. Water in very fine micropores is held under very strong suction, at water potentials that are too low (too negative) for it to be extracted by plant roots. Most plants cannot take up water at potentials lower than –1.5 MPa. This is known as the permanent wilting point, because plants wilt if all water remaining in a soil has a lower potential. Only water held in soil between field capacity and the permanent wilting point is available to plants.

Because pore sizes and the distribution of pore sizes in soils are determined by soil texture, the available water-holding capacity of soils is dependent on texture, as shown in Figure 2.6. Loams and silt loams have the highest capacity to retain water for use by plants. Sands have lower water-holding capacities because they have a high proportion of large pores that drain rapidly under gravity. Clays retain the most water after drainage, but a high proportion is held in very small pores at water potentials below the wilting point, rendering it unavailable to plants. Water-holding capacity of soils is also higher in soils containing more organic matter (Brady and Weil, 1999).

Disturbance of soil in urban environments can be expected to reduce its water-holding capacity. Compaction reduces pore space in soils and therefore reduces water-holding capacity, although compaction of loose soils can increase water availability to plants if pore size distribution then favours water retention above the wilting point. Typically, however, compaction increases the proportion of very fine micropores, resulting in lower availability of water to plants because more water is held below the permanent wilting point. Use of clay fills will reduce available water-holding capacity for the same reason. Very coarse fills, such as gravel, drain almost entirely under gravity and thus retain very small amounts of water for use by plants. Lower organic matter content, typical of urban soils, also results in lower water-holding capacities.

4.2.5.4 Soil water movement and drainage

Well-structured soils and sandy soils drain easily because, at high soil water contents, water moves quickly though macropores, giving them high hydraulic conductivities. Unstructured clay soils have hydraulic conductivities at saturation more than 1000 times lower (Hillel, 1998) and thus they drain much more slowly, because their pore size distribution is dominated by micropores. Any soil disturbance that destroys structure and causes compaction thus reduces drainage and leaves soils prone to waterlogging.

Textural discontinuities in soils can also result in waterlogging, because of the properties of soil water movement at the interfaces between soils with contrasting textures (see Section 4.2.5.2). Textural discontinuities may occur between soil layers and where pockets of soil are surrounded by soil with a different texture. The latter situation is common in urban tree pits (Craul, 1985). For example, drainage from a tree pit dug in a compacted clay soil and backfilled with a high quality loam will be poor because the very low hydraulic conductivity of the clay will permit only very slow seepage of water out of the tree pit. During rainy periods, or if the soil is irrigated too frequently, the tree pit can easily become waterlogged. Aeration of the soil in the tree pit would then be severely reduced, causing impaired functioning of the root system of the tree planted in the tree pit.

A tree pit in a coarse gravel, which is the usual base for load-bearing surfaces, is also prone to waterlogging because of poor drainage. Drainage from loamy backfill in the tree pit will not occur until the water potential is high enough for water retained under suction in the finer pores of the backfill to be released into the larger pores of the gravel. The required water potential will not be reached until the backfill is saturated or nearly saturated, if there is a large contrast in texture between the two soils. As a consequence, tree pits in gravelly soil are prone to waterlogging, like those in clay soils, though for different reasons. Craul (1985) called the effect of textural discontinuities on drainage from tree pits the 'teacup effect'.

4.2.6 Soil temperature

Soil temperature depends on the **energy balance** at the surface and the conduction of heat down into the soil. Surfaces that absorb high amounts of solar radiation become hotter, especially when dry, as energy cannot then be dissipated by evaporation. Surfaces of pavements and buildings reach high temperatures, unless shaded from direct sunlight. For example, Kjelgren and Montague (1998) measured temperatures of 55–60°C on the surface of an asphalt pavement, but because of evapotranspiration, an adjacent turf surface was 25°C cooler. High densities of asphalt, concrete and masonry surfaces in towns and cities are consequently an important cause of the phenomenon of the urban heat island, which results in air temperatures in cities as much as 12°C warmer than surrounding rural areas on cloudless days (Oke, 1987).

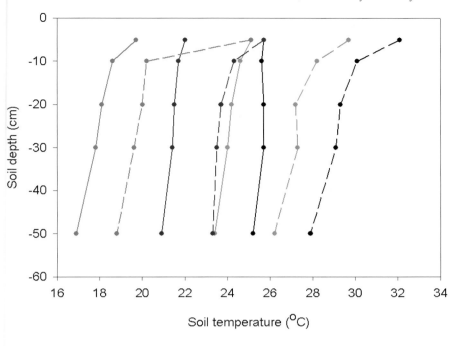

Figure 4.7 Mean root-zone temperature at different sites in Lafayette, Indiana in July 1985 (after Graves and Dana, 1987). Native woodland (•), Urban non-street (•), Suburban street (•) and Urban street (•). Mean values are presented as a solid line and maximum values as a broken line.

Temperatures in the soil beneath hard surfaces also tend to be warmer in summer. Graves and Dana (1987) compared soil temperatures beneath four surfaces in the mid-Western USA. The mean temperature for the top 0.5 m of soil was 4°C warmer beneath concrete footways than nearby lawn and 7°C warmer than soil beneath woodland outside the city (Fig 4.7). The maximum temperature beneath the concrete surface was 32.1°C, but only 25.7°C beneath the urban lawn and 25.1°C beneath the woodland. Soil temperatures were coolest for the woodland because of shading of the surface by trees and evapotranspiration.

High soil temperatures cause changes in the physiology of root tissue that impair the functioning of root systems (Gur *et al*, 1976). In controlled experiments, soil temperatures above 30°C for extended periods have been found to reduce root and shoot growth of trees (Graves *et al*, 1989), although some species and cultivars have more tolerance of high temperatures in the root zone than others (Wilkins *et al*, 1995). Detrimental effects of soil temperature on tree growth may be worse if high temperatures are combined with other stresses, such as drought (Graves, 1998). Thus, trees growing at locations surrounded by concrete and asphalt may be prone to impaired health and reduced vigour because of high soil temperatures, particularly in warm climates, or during hot spells in summer.

4.3 Chemical properties of urban soils

The chemical properties of soils have been extensively researched, but largely for rural soils, in the context of agriculture, forestry or natural plant communities. Very little is known about the chemistry of urban soils, except in relation to contamination by salt or pollutants. Knowledge of nutrient availability in urban soils is very limited, which has perhaps resulted in the common assumption that urban soils are nutrient poor, although this is not always the case (Pulford, 1991). There is more understanding of the problems created in urban soils by interrupted cycling of organic matter (Craul, 1985). Urban vegetation is often sparse and quantities of litter returned to the soil therefore small. Any organic material which does accumulate is usually collected and discarded as waste (Craul, 1985). Lack of organic matter cycling in urban soils has implications for soil structural stability, because soil aggregation is improved by organic matter, as well as soil fertility and soil biology.

4.3.1 Fertility of urban soils

Most studies of fertility in degraded or industrial soils have concluded that the major nutritional limitation on plant growth is lack of nitrogen (Pulford, 1991). Most nitrogen in soils (>90%) exists in organic form and is unavailable to plants. Microbial action mineralises organic nitrogen into ammonium (NH_4^+) and nitrate (NO_3^-), which can be taken up by plant roots. Without an adequate pool of organic nitrogen, however, mineral nitrogen is quickly depleted in soils and nitrogen deficiency in plants results. Low organic matter content is typical of urban soils and thus nitrogen is commonly the nutrient most limiting to growth.

Phosphorus is most likely to limit growth when nitrogen availability is adequate. Phosphorus compounds in soil have very low solubility because of chemical reactions in the soil, resulting in low availability to plants. However, phosphorus chemistry in urban soils is not well understood (Pulford, 1991). Uptake of phosphorus by many plants, including trees and shrubs, is aided by mycorrhizal fungi, as fungal hyphae are able to explore a much larger volume of soil than roots, enabling more uptake of immobile nutrients. Where soil conditions inhibit growth of mycorrhizae, therefore, phosphorus deficiency is more likely. Additionally, because phosphorus has low mobility in soil, it is generally concentrated in upper soil layers; thus, stripping of topsoil during urban development can cause phosphorus deficiency (Craul, 1992).

The availability of other macro- and micronutrients in urban soils does not usually limit plant growth (Pulford, 1991; Craul, 1992), although potassium deficiency can also result from stripping of topsoil (Harris *et al*, 1999). However, deficiencies in any nutrient may arise because of local conditions at a site, or in soil mixes in planting containers. These can be diagnosed by examination of foliage for deficiency symptoms (see Harris *et al*, 1999) and by soil testing. Nutrient management plans should be developed to avoid nutrient deficiencies, prescribing appropriate addition of slow-release fertilisers as required.

4.3.2 Soil pH

The pH of soil is determined by the chemistry of the parent material, the composition of present and previous vegetation and any amendments added to soil. Urban soils may be acid or alkaline, but in general, there is a tendency for them to have higher pH than rural soils. There are three principal reasons for this: first, the use of calcium or sodium chloride as de-icing compounds in winter on roads and footways; second, irrigation water is often enriched with calcium; and, third, soil pH is elevated by the release of calcium by the weathering of building rubble and the surfaces of buildings and concrete structures (Craul, 1985).

4.3.3 Soil contamination

Urban soils are subject to contamination by a variety of pollutants. These include de-icing salts, mineral and organic pollutants, particularly on former industrial sites, and heavy metals. The implications of soil contamination for urban trees are discussed in Chapter 7.

4.4 Biological properties of soils

A handful of soil may contain billions of living organisms, including earthworms, nematodes, protozoa, bacteria, algae, actinomycetes and fungi (Harris *et al*, 1999). These organisms exist in a complex web of life that is vital to the growth and survival of larger plants and animals. Soil organisms decompose organic matter, fix atmospheric nitrogen, transform nitrogen between organic and mineral forms, assist plants with nutrient uptake, or cause pathogenic or parasitic infections. Soil organisms fulfil a myriad of functions, which may have positive and negative effects on plants. Earthworms are readily seen in soil and improve soil quality by digesting organic matter and mixing and aerating the soil. Other prominent soil organisms are mycorrhizae, which form symbiotic relationships with roots of most plant species.

The biology of urban soils has been widely studied, but most reports indicate that they contain reduced numbers of organisms, as well as reduced biomass and species diversity (Harris, 1991). Generally, more disturbed or polluted soils have the poorest inventory of organisms. For example, Pizl and Josens (1995) found that the density and biomass of earthworms decreased between the suburbs of Brussels and the city centre, and the fall in the population of earthworms was correlated with increased soil pollution by heavy metals.

4.5 Engineering soils for urban trees

4.5.1 Conflict over urban soils: biology vs engineering

Incorporation of vegetation in urban landscapes commonly necessitates that soil serves a dual purpose. Away from parks and gardens, urban soils must provide a load-bearing base for buildings, roads and footways. For trees and shrubs to grow alongside this infrastructure, however, urban soils must also provide a medium suitable for root growth. There is a conflict inherent in the use of soil as both an engineering and biological substrate, as the properties required of soil in each role are divergent. As a biological medium for root growth, soils ideally have a low bulk density, with maximum values varying between about 1.45 Mg m^{-3} for clay and 1.85 Mg m^{-3} for sand, depending on soil texture. The distribution of pore size should provide adequate storage capacity for plant-available water, but also good drainage and aeration. This requires pore sizes in the range of macropores as well as micropores, and therefore good soil structure and aggregation. Fertility of the soil should be sufficient to provide adequate amounts of the macro- and micronutrients required for growth, at least with the addition of fertilisers.

As an engineering substrate, in contrast, soils must be compacted to within at least 95% of their **peak bulk density**, to prevent future settling under loads from buildings and traffic. The process of attaining such high bulk densities destroys soil structure and results in a soil environment that is highly unsuited to root growth. Beneath a typical footway, for example, the subgrade (Fig 4.8) is formed by compaction of existing soil, which is then largely impenetrable to root growth and significantly reduces drainage, unless a high proportion of sand is present. Above the subgrade, and immediately beneath the pavement, is a base layer of well-compacted granular material, which provides structural stability. The base layer is composed of sand or gravel, with little silt or clay, and thus has a very low capacity to retain nutrients or plant-available water (Bassuk *et al*, 1998).

Planting trees in compacted soil near infrastructure has conventionally been accomplished by placing trees in tree pits dug out of the compacted material (Fig 4.8). As the soil surrounding the planting pit is so hostile to root growth, the rooting volume available to the tree is largely restricted to the confines of the pit (Kristoffersen, 1999). The dimensions of a conventional tree pit are typically about 1.2 x 1.2 m square and 0.6 m deep, giving a total rootable volume of 0.86 m^3 (Craul, 1992). It is important to realise that a tree pit of this volume is conservative and is very unlikely to provide the water requirements of trees of substantial size. Published estimates of the volume of soil required to meet the demand of a mature tree for water and nitrogen are based largely on empirical evidence and vary over a broad range. Lindsey and Bassuk (1992) estimated from an empirical relation between evaporation and tree size that a soil volume of at least 5 m^3 is needed to sustain water use by a 'typical specimen tree' through the summer. Others have suggested higher estimates, including 8.5 m^3 (Urban, 1989), 43 m^3 (Kopinga, 1991) and, for very large trees, 200 m^3

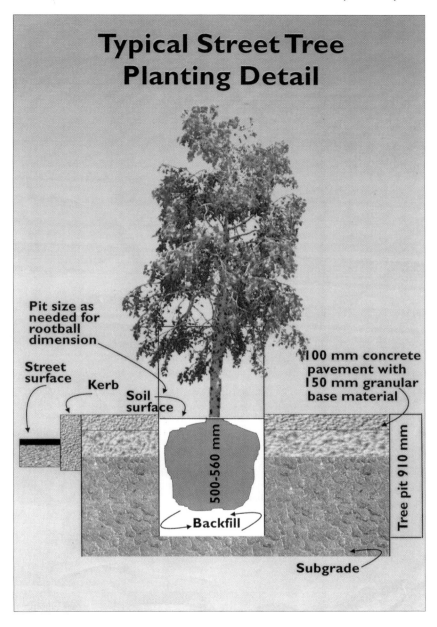

Typical Street Tree Planting Detail

Pit size as needed for rootball dimension

Street surface

Kerb

Soil surface

100 mm concrete pavement with 150 mm granular base material

500-560 mm

Backfill

Tree pit 910 mm

Subgrade

Figure 4.8 Profile of a conventional tree pit in a compacted subgrade beneath a pavement. (After Bassuk, 2001.)

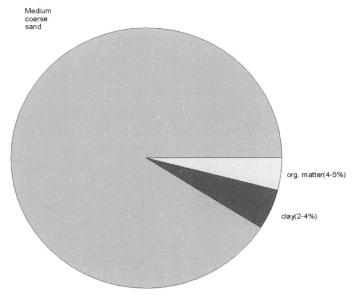

Medium
coarse
sand

org. matter(4-5%)

clay(2-4%)

Figure 4.9 The composition of Amsterdam Tree Soil. (After Couenberg, 1994.)

(Helliwell, 1986). Despite such uncertainty about the size of adequate rootable volumes, it is clear that the soil volume provided by a conventional tree pit alone is vastly inadequate. The consequences of restricted rootable volume on tree health are commonly observed in towns and cities: dieback and death of the tree as the demand for water and nutrients by the crown outstrips the capacity of the suppressed root system for supply (Krizek and Dubik, 1987; Kopinga, 1991; Schwets and Brown, 2000).

To reduce constraints on the health and survival of urban trees imposed by a poor rooting environment, a balance must be struck between the role of soil as a biological growth medium and an engineering substrate. One approach to achieving this balance is to use specially composed soil mixes that retain the qualities needed for root growth when compacted to densities demanded in engineering specifications.

4.5.2 Amsterdam Tree Soil

Amsterdam Tree Soil is a soil mix developed in The Netherlands in the 1970s following concerns about the decline of street trees in Amsterdam because of unfavourable soil conditions for tree root growth (Couenberg, 1994). The mixture is predominantly sand, with small amounts of organic matter (4–5% by weight) and clay (2–4%) (Fig 4.9). The sand must be a medium coarse sand, free of salts, with a median particle size of 220 μm. It must have a relatively uniform distribution of particle sizes, which is specified by a D60/D10 ratio of >2.5. This is the ratio of the diameters at which 60 and 10% of material passes through a sieve, with a high value indicating a low content of fine particles. The mix must contain only 2–4% clay (particles <2 μm in diameter). This

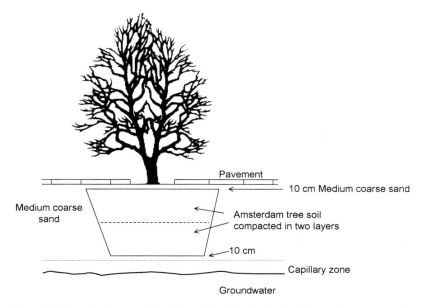

Figure 4.10 Current underground basic tree pit design in Amsterdam. The medium coarse sand surrounding the Amsterdam Tree Soil is compacted to >90% Proctor density. The tree pit is extended underneath the pavement. (After Couenberg, 1994.)

ensures that pores between sand grains are not clogged by small particles after mixing and prevents excessive compaction during installation. The organic matter content of the mix must not exceed 5%, otherwise excessive settling may occur after compaction. The organic matter and clay present in the mix add capacity for nutrient and water retention (Couenberg, 1994).

The components of Amsterdam Tree Soil are blended in a heavy-duty industrial mixer prior to installation. It is installed to depths of not more than 1 m, as aeration is too poor for root growth if used at greater depths. When installed, compaction is specified in terms of **penetration resistance**, rather than relative to maximum bulk density by the Proctor test. Penetration resistance after compaction must be 1.5–2.0 MPa. This is the pressure required to push the standard tip of a cone penetrometer into the soil. For Amsterdam Tree Soil, this is equivalent to compaction to 70–80% of peak density. At such a density, root growth is not impeded. However, this is a lower density than normally specified for **load-bearing soils**, which is normally 95% of the peak density. At the more limited level of compaction, Amsterdam Tree Soil has successfully been used to construct tree pits below footways and parking for light vehicles (Couenberg, 1994, 1998). Thus, Amsterdam Tree Soil is a compromise between the biological and engineering requirements of urban soils. It cannot be used as an alternative base for pavements or foundations, but it does enable installation of larger tree pits in built-up areas than is conventionally possible. Use of Amsterdam Tree Soil allows a wider overlap to be used between the tree pit and the surrounding pavement, as shown by the design of a basic tree pit used in Amsterdam (Fig 4.10).

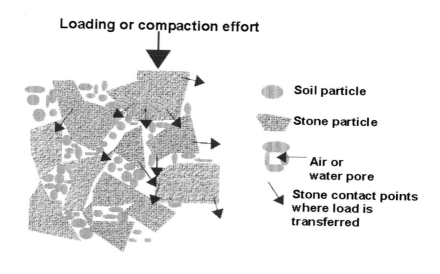

Loading or compaction effort

Soil particle

Stone particle

Air or
water pore

Stone contact points
where load is
transferred

Figure 4.11 Schematic of the Cornell University structural soil showing the load-bearing matrix formed by the stone component, with soil occupying the voids between the stones (after Grabosky *et al*, 1998).

4.5.3 Structural soil

Structural soils were developed during the 1990s at Cornell University in the United States (Grabosky and Bassuk, 1995) and in Europe, notably in Denmark (Kristoffersen, 1998). Structural soil mixes combine crushed stone and soil. The crushed stone forms a load-bearing matrix, with the soil filling the voids between stones, to create viable space for roots (Fig 4.11). Structural soil is intended for use as a sub-base under footways and roadways carrying light vehicular traffic, not just as a tree pit backfill. It should be able to withstand loading from emergency and maintenance vehicles. It thus enables sub-bases under paving to fulfil the dual role of engineering substrate and biological growth medium.

4.5.3.1 CU soil

The stone component of the **Cornell University structural soil** is an angular crushed stone with dimensions in the range of 1.5–2.5 cm and not more than 10% passing a 1.25 cm sieve. The soil component is preferably a clay loam, with 2–5% organic matter by dry weight. The soil and stone are mixed prior to installation with a rotary mixer. A small amount (0.025%) of **polyacrylamide (hydrophilic gel)** is added during mixing. Hydrogels are capable of absorbing many times their own weight of water and then allowing this to be released as part of root water uptake. The normal use of hydrogels is as a soil additive used to increase the water storage capacity of the soil. In the case of the addition of hydrogels to structural soils, the aim is also to provide a **tackifier** that prevents separation of the soil and stone during transportation, handling and installation.

Further information about hydrogels is given in relation to the establishment of young trees in Chapter 5.

An appropriate ratio of soil to stone is critical to successful use of structural soil. If the volume of soil used in the mix exceeds the volume of voids in the stone matrix, soil will prevent formation of a stable stone skeleton after compaction, as soil would then impede locking of one stone against another (Grabosky *et al*, 1998). The proportion of soil in the mix should be in the range of 13–22% by dry weight. The optimum soil content within this range depends on the actual size and shape of the stones and hence the volume of voids in the matrix (Grabosky *et al*, 1998).

During installation, the stone-soil mix is compacted to within 95% of peak bulk density. The soil within the mix is protected from compaction by the stone skeleton, remaining largely uncompacted. The California Bearing Ratio (CBR) of the compacted mix is ≥50. The CBR is a standardised measure of the load-bearing capacity of materials used in pavements. Values for acceptable materials for use as pavement bases range from 40 to 80. The CU Structural Soil is consequently suitable for use under paved surfaces (Grabosky and Bassuk, 1996).

The capacity of the structural soil mix to retain water for use by plants was necessarily limited by the low proportion of soil in the mix. Water retention was improved by the hydrogel, at least close to field capacity, and a mixture containing 16.6% (by dry weight) soil had an available water-holding capacity of $0.128 \ m^3 \ m^{-3}$, or 12.8% by volume (Grabosky and Bassuk, 1996). This was similar to a sandy loam soil (Brady and Weil, 1999). Aeration of structural soil beneath concrete pavement was good, with concentrations of O_2 well above 10% at a range of depths (Fig 4.12(a)). In comparison, O_2 concentrations in the compacted subgrade of a standard profile beneath a concrete pavement were much lower, reaching 3% and lower at depths which had become saturated because of poor drainage (Fig 4.12(b)) (Grabosky *et al*, 2000). The fertility of the mix is determined by the nutrient status of the soil component and can be improved by addition of fertilisers, as required according to soil testing.

Use of a structural soil to form a sub-base beneath a pavement is shown in Fig 4.13. The structural soil provides a vastly expanded rootable volume in comparison to the conventional tree pit in a compacted subgrade (Fig 4.8). If used in construction of a footway, structural soils enable tree roots to utilise the entire volume of sub-base, between the kerb and adjacent structures. Trees are planted directly into structural soil, to avoid creating an interface with the backfill of a tree pit. Roots grow well in structural soil, following pathways through the soil within the stone matrix. In a comparison of tree growth in pavements constructed using a standard compacted subgrade or structural soil, root lengths per tree were significantly higher in structural soils for two out of three species (Fig 4.14). Shoot extension for these trees was significantly improved in the structural soil (Fig 4.15) (Grabosky *et al*, 2000).

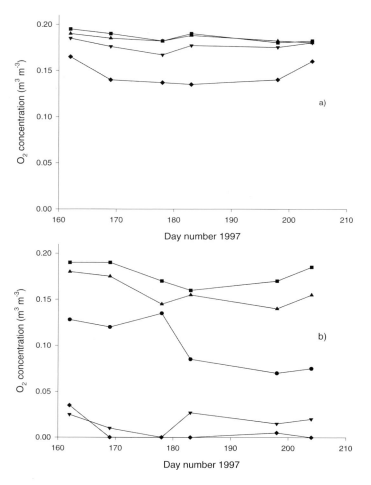

Figure 4.12 Concentration of O_2 in the soil atmosphere at depths of 12.7 (—■—), 25.4 (—▲—), 38.1 (—●—), 50.8 (—▼—) and 63.5 cm (—◆—) in a pavement base profile using **(a)** structural soil and **(b)** a conventional compacted subgrade. (After Grabosky *et al*, 2000.)

4.5.3.2 Testing of structural soils in Denmark

Structural soil mixes were also independently developed and evaluated in Denmark during the 1990s. In Danish tests, the load-bearing matrix was formed using crushed granite, brick or lava. The stone and soil were mixed during installation, by compacting the stone component in 15–25 cm layers and then filling the voids either by watering soil into the stones or by sweeping dry soil over the compacted surface (Kristoffersen, 1998). The soil content of the mixtures was about 30% by volume. Above and below-ground growth of Norway maple (*Acer platanoides*), ash (*Fraxinus excelsior*) and lime (*Tilia x vulgaris*) was compared for trees growing in topsoil, structural soils and compacted sandy-loam subsoil, gravel and a sand-humus mix similar to Amsterdam Tree Soil (Kristoffersen, 1999). The topsoil, with a bulk density of

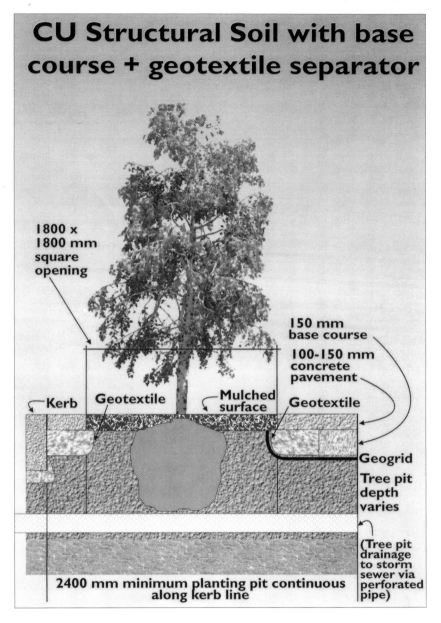

CU Structural Soil with base course + geotextile separator

1800 x 1800 mm square opening

150 mm base course

100-150 mm concrete pavement

Kerb   Geotextile   Mulched surface   Geotextile

Geogrid

Tree pit depth varies

(Tree pit drainage to storm sewer via perforated pipe)

2400 mm minimum planting pit continuous along kerb line

Figure 4.13 Profile of a tree pit and pavement base using structural soil. (After Bassuk, 2001.)

73% of the peak value, provided optimum below-ground conditions for root growth. The subsoil treatment was compacted to 85% of peak density to represent typical conditions after building construction (Randrup and Dralle, 1997). The gravel was compacted to peak density to represent a normal base course for pavement. The sand-humus mix was compacted to 80% of peak density, as recommended for Amsterdam Tree Soil.

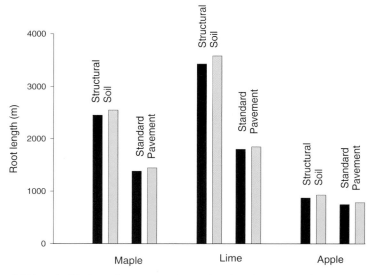

Figure 4.14 Length of 0–2 mm diameter roots (■) and total root length (■) of three species (maple, *Acer campestre*; lime, *Tilia cordata* 'Olympic' and crab apple, *Malus* 'Adironack') in two different pavement profiles. (After Grabosky *et al*, 2000.)

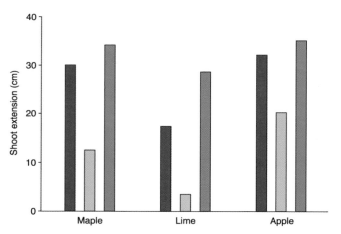

Figure 4.15 Shoot extension of three tree species (*see* Fig. 4.14) growing in structural soils (■), standard pavement soil (■) and an agricultural soil control (■). (After Grabosky *et al*, 2000.)

Root growth outside of the original root-ball for each soil, two years after planting, is shown in Fig 4.16. Root growth was severely reduced in the compacted gravel, subsoil and sand-humus mix relative to the topsoil treatment. In the three structural soils, however, root growth was not significantly different or was better than in the topsoil. Norway maple was most sensitive to a poor soil environment and ash was most tolerant. Height growth of the tree crowns was similarly affected by the different treatments (Fig 4.17) (Kristoffersen, 1999). Growth in a fourth structural soil containing concrete (data not shown) was reduced because of very high soil pH resulting from weathering of the lime in the concrete.

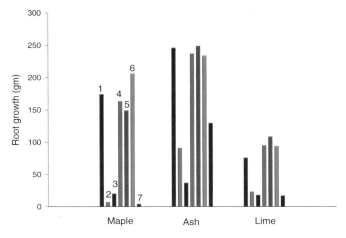

Figure 4.16 Root growth of three tree species (maple, *Acer platanoides* 'Emerald Queen'; ash, *Fraxinus excelsior* 'Westhof's Glory' and lime, *Tilia x vulgaris* 'Pallida') in topsoil **(1)**, compacted subsoil **(2)**, gravel **(3)**, and three structural soils composed of granite **(4)**, lava **(5)** or brick **(6)**, and a sand mix **(7)**. (After Kristoffersen, 1999.)

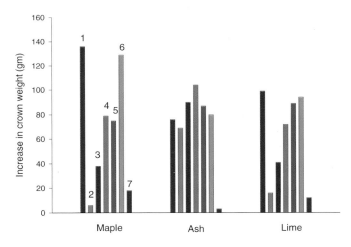

Figure 4.17 Crown growth of three tree species (*see* Fig. 4.16) in topsoil **(1)**, compacted subsoil **(2)**, gravel **(3)**, and three structural soils composed of granite **(4)**, lava **(5)** or brick **(6)**, and a sand mix **(7)**. (After Kristoffersen, 1999.)

Reduced root growth in the compacted subsoil was attributed to poor drainage and frequent waterlogging, which also occurred for prolonged periods in the sand-humus mix. The gravel was well-drained and reduced root growth was attributed to mechanical impedance. Tree performance in the structural soils made from granite, brick or lava was good, and there have been no observations of problems caused by limited load-bearing capacity, frost heave or settling at more than 30 sites in Denmark where these structural soils have been installed (Kristoffersen, 1998).

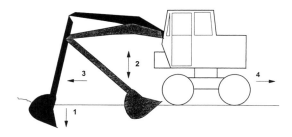

Figure 4.18 Subsoiling using a mechanical excavator. **(1)** The bucket is lowered to the required depth. **(2)** The bucket is lifted up and shaken. **(3)** The soil is dropped back into the hole. **(4)** The excavator reverses. (After Rolf, 1994.)

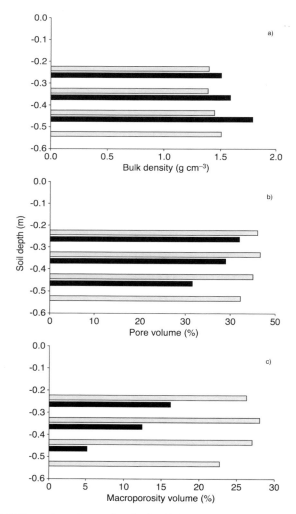

Figure 4.19 Comparison of properties of soils which were subsoiled (grey) and compacted (black) 18 months previously. **(a)** Mean bulk densities, **(b)** pore volume (% by volume) and **(c)** macroporosity (pores greater than 0.03 mm) (% by volume). (After Rolf, 1991.)

Structural soils have considerable potential to improve conditions for root growth for trees planted in the vicinity of paved surfaces and to therefore increase the viability of amenity trees in the built environment. However, long-term observations of tree growth and maturation in structural soils are needed, as is an evaluation of the properties controlling the movement and storage of water in structural soils. This would enable design of soil water management plans for trees in structural soils.

4.6 Improving tree root growth in urban soils

Where the survival of urban trees is threatened by poor quality soil, there are a number of options available to improve root growth and function. Some of these must be implemented prior to planting, during site preparation. Others may be applied to established trees. Some are ancient and others have been developed only during the last decade.

4.6.1 Compaction alleviation by subsoiling

Soil compaction on development sites after completion of construction is a widespread problem. If trees are planted into compacted soils during landscaping, they frequently fail to thrive because of restricted root growth. Physical properties of the soil may be improved, however, if the soil is broken up prior to planting. Rolf (1991, 1994) demonstrated the use of a mechanical excavator to break up the soil to a depth of approximately 50 cm. In a controlled experiment, soil physical properties and growth of trees over a four-year period were compared in plots on a sandy loam soil subjected to different treatments. Untreated arable land, with a plough **pan**, served as a control. Soils were compacted at the surface by driving wheeled machinery repeatedly over the soil. Subsoil compaction was imposed by the same means, but after stripping the top 30 cm of soil; topsoil was replaced after subsoil compaction. Subsoiling was implemented by using the bucket of a mechanical excavator to lift soil from the ground, and then replace it, after light shaking, as illustrated in Fig 4.18.

Subsoiling reduced the bulk density and increased the **porosity** of compacted soil (Fig 4.19(a) and (b)). Macroporosity was also improved by subsoiling, with treatment effects still evident after 18 months (Fig 4.19 (c)). Thus infiltration, drainage and aeration should have been improved by subsoiling (Rolf, 1991). Four years after subsoiling, biomass for a range of species was higher for subsoiled plots than compacted plots (Fig 4.20). Subsoiling thus provides a means of reducing the impacts of soil compaction on the establishment and growth of trees. However, to avoid damaging roots, subsoiling should not be carried out close to existing trees.

Considerable care should be taken to avoid compacting soil placed for landscaping or, for example, when covering landfill caps (Dobson and Moffat,

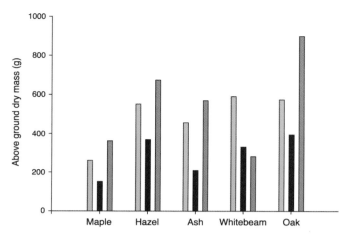

Figure 4.20 Effect on the biomass of five tree species (maple, *Acer platanoides*; hazel, *Corylus avellana*; ash, *Fraxinus excelsior*; whitebeam, *Sorbus intermedia* and oak, *Quercus robur*) growing in an arable control soil (■), a sandy loam with a compacted subsoil (■) and a subsoiled treatment (■) four years after treatment. Differences between subsoiled and compacted plots were significant except for the whitebeam plots. (After Rolf, 1994.)

1993). The means used to place the soil will have a substantial effect on the degree of compaction and its influence on subsequent tree growth. 'Loose-tipping' is a technique that can almost entirely prevent soil compaction (Department of the Environment, 1986) and is strongly recommended as a site preparation for an after-use involving forestry and woodland creation or individual tree planting (Dobson and Moffat, 1993). Fig 4.21 shows a sequence of procedures for 'loose-tipping' of soil above the clay seal of a landfill. The approach is, however, applicable wherever ground is prepared for tree planting. Obviously, the size of plant used in the operations may differ, but the aim of not compacting the tipped soil will be common.

Figure 4.21 Loose tipping of soil at a landfill site. (1) Soil materials brought in by dump truck running over the cap. (2) Soil materials tipped in heaps onto cap. (3) Soil materials spread and levelled by excavator working from cap surface. (After Dobson and Moffat, 1993.)

4.6.2 Backfilling of tree pits

Day *et al* (1995) showed that the impacts of soil compaction on tree establishment after transplanting could also be mitigated by improving the quality of the soil used for backfilling the tree pit. For soils compacted by heavy machinery, they found that amendment of soil backfill with 50% (by volume) sphagnum peat moss significantly increased second and third year shoot growth

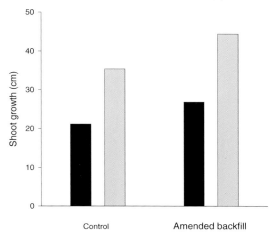

Figure 4.22 New shoot growth of pears (*Pyrus calleryana* 'Redspire') for the second (■) and third (▦) year after planting in a control soil and with an amended backfill. (After Day *et al*, 1995.)

of Callery pear (*Pyrus calleryana*) (Fig 4.22). However, establishment of sugar maple (*Acer saccharum*) in the same trial was not improved by amending backfill. Others have found that amendment of soil has little or no benefit on tree establishment (Day and Bassuk, 1994), and even untreated soil conditions in these tests were not impaired by compaction. Amendment of backfill does create an interface between the tree pit and surrounding soil that may impede redistribution of soil water. Consequently, care must be taken to avoid either drought or waterlogging in the tree pit.

The incorporation of organic matter, such as leaf litter or compost in the tree pit soil will have benefits to the tree. There will be an improvement in soil structure that will benefit water storage and aeration and the organic matter will provide a source of nutrients. There is, however, a temptation to incorporate excess organic material. This should not exceed 5% of the total soil volume in the tree pit (Craul, 1992). With excess organic matter there is a risk in time of serious soil settlement. This settlement may mean that the root-ball and the root collar are below soil level which may cause rotting of the trunk. Settlement of the soil will also dislodge structures, eg tree grills, placed on the soil surface close to the tree. If higher amounts of organic matter are required, the increase can be met by adding organic compost on the soil surface.

4.6.3 Mulching

Mulching of the soil with composted organic matter is a practice as old as gardening. There are a number of benefits of mulching to tree growth. These benefits are (1) conservation of moisture in the surface soil, (2) moderation of soil temperature, (3) reduction of soil compaction by traffic, (4) reduction of soil erosion, (5) improvements to soil structure and fertility, (6) protection of roots from mechanical damage, and (7) reduction of weed growth. Over time, mulching helps to rebuild soil structure and improve the root environment,

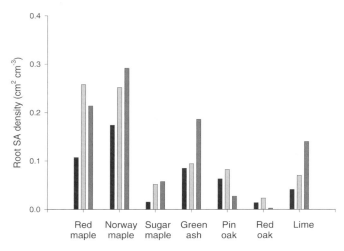

Figure 4.23 The effect of mulching with compost on root densities for seven species of 20-year-old trees. Densities (on a surface area basis - root SA) are shown for tree roots at 0–7.5 cm depth for soil under grass (■) and a mulch layer (■). Densities of roots in the mulch layer are also shown (■). (After Watson, 1988.)

promoting root growth. Watson (1988) added composted wood chips and leaves to the soil surface beneath 20-year old trees of a variety of species every second year over a five-year period. Six years after initiation of the treatment, mulching had created a layer of well-composted material 10–12 cm thick, and root density – expressed as surface area of root per unit volume of soil – was higher where soil was mulched (Fig 4.23). Root growth was also enhanced by proliferation of roots in the mulch layer itself. Thus, given adequate time and quantities of organic matter, mulching is an effective means of improving root growth of established trees.

Because mulching is perceived to have beneficial effects there is a danger to over-apply mulch. Excessive mulch leads to (1) poor gas exchange of the soil with the atmosphere, leading to root suffocation, (2) colonisation by rodents, which may forage on the roots, and (3) excess water around the roots because it cannot be evaporated, resulting in poor aeration of the roots. Mulch should not be spread deeper than 15 cm but 8 to 10 cm is probably optimal. Organic material such as compost or shredded leaves might be 8 cm deep while wood chips could be deeper, 10–12 cm. If decomposition of the material is slow the depth should be thinner.

4.6.4 Soil replacement

Where rapid results are required, eg where soil has been contaminated by a fuel spillage, poor quality soil can be removed and replaced. This can be accomplished by radial trenching, where soil is removed from trenches extending radially from the trunk (Fig 4.24) and replaced with soil with improved properties. The trenches are positioned to avoid damage to the major roots. Watson *et al* (1996) used a backhoe to dig four trenches around white oak

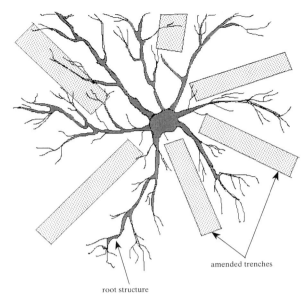

Figure 4.24 Radial trenching around a tree trunk for soil replacement. (After Watson, 1990.)

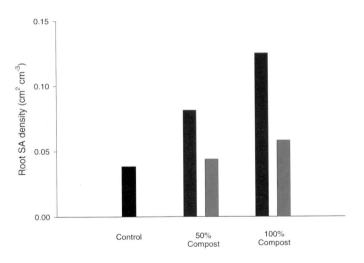

Figure 4.25 Root densities for white oak in an undisturbed, control soil (■) and within (■) and adjacent (■) to radial trenches in which soil was replaced by 50% or 100% compost. (After Watson *et al*, 1996.)

(*Quercus alba*) trees, beginning 3 m from the trunk, each 3 m long, 0.6 m deep and 0.35 m wide. The trenches were refilled with soil mixes containing either 50% or 100% compost (by volume). Four years after treatment, root density was consistently higher in the trenches than in untreated soil, with the increase significant for trenches refilled with 100% compost (Fig 4.25). Replacement of soil in radial trenches may thus provide a means of improving root growth of established trees suffering decline because of poor soil conditions.

Figure 4.26 Demonstration of removal of soil from around tree roots with an industrial vacuum system.

Figure 4.27 Using high-pressure water jet and soil vacuuming to expose services.

An alternative to radial trenching is to use high-pressure air or water to remove soil from around roots, leaving them intact (Smiley, 1999). Excavated soil can be vacuumed away using specialised equipment and removed from the site (eg DISAB, Fig 4.26, www.disab.se). This process has been used commercially in Switzerland (Watson *et al*, 1996), with soil surrounding the trees removed either from large pits or from a series of 0.1 m diameter holes spaced at intervals of 0.3–0.75 m. In both approaches, soil is removed to a depth of up to 0.6 m and replaced with a mix of sand, composted organic matter and fertiliser.

Hydraulic excavation uses water from fire hoses at a pressure of approximately 1000 bar (Gross, 1995). The soil around the roots forms a slurry and drains away or is removed using a pump or vacuum (Fig 4.27). Pneumatic excavation uses a lance delivering supersonic jet of compressed air to remove soil from roots (eg the air spade, www.air-spade.com). Air is supplied by a compressor and emerges from a specially engineered nozzle at over 2000 km h^{-1} (Figs 4.28 and 4.29). The air jet enters soil pores, where it rapidly expands and slows, blowing the pores apart (Harris *et al*, 1999). The system allows very rapid excavation and is supplied commercially for applications such as excavation of buried pipes and cables on construction sites. There is increasing interest in its use for excavation around tree roots when trenching for utility installation and also for investigations of root systems for tree management or research in arboriculture (eg Nathenson and Jarabak, 2001; Smiley, 2001a). The technique could provide a way of reducing the time and labour required for manual excavation around roots within the root protection zone (Rob Gross, Calistoga, California, *pers. comm.*). As such, it could make compliance with guidelines such as NJUG 10 a more routine task (see Chapter 8.4.2.2).

Soil from around roots that may or may not have been already loosened by high-pressure air or water can be removed with industrial vacuum systems designed for the purpose (Fig 4.26). Soil vacuuming has a number of important uses in connection with the soil and roots of trees in built environments. As well as permitting utilities to be installed without cutting roots, the vacuum technique can be used to remove contaminated or low quality soil.

Growth of large trees (>50 cm **dbh** (diameter at breast height)) in replaced and untreated soils at six sites in Switzerland was compared (Watson *et al*, 1996). Depth of rooting increased where soil was replaced, with rooting depth correlated with the depth of soil replacement. Rooting depth was 68% deeper in replaced soil than controls for *Tilia* spp and 37% deeper for

Figure 4.28 The 'Air Spade' used for soil excavation and decompaction around roots.

Figure 4.29 Root system exposed using the 'Air Spade'.

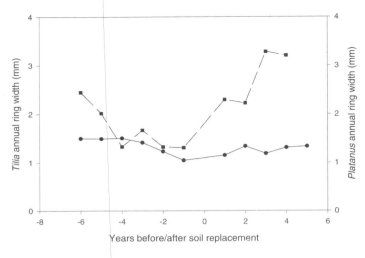

Figure 4.30 Trunk growth of *Tilia* sp (●) and *Platanus x acerifolia* (■) trees before and after soil replacement treatment. (After Watson *et al*, 1996.)

Figure 4.31 Using 'Terravent' high-pressure air decompaction equipment, Wallingford, Oxfordshire. The oak tree was planted in April 1887 to commemorate the golden jubilee of Queen Victoria.

London plane (*Platanus x hispanica*). Trunk growth before and after treatment was measured by examination of annual ring widths. Prior to treatment, trunk growth was declining (Fig 4.30), but increased after soil replacement. The changes in growth rate were not statistically significant, but trends in the data were supported by visual improvement in tree condition (Watson *et al*, 1996).

4.6.5 Air injection

Injection of high-pressure air into soil, to create cracks and fissures, has been advocated as a means of relieving soil compaction and associated problems

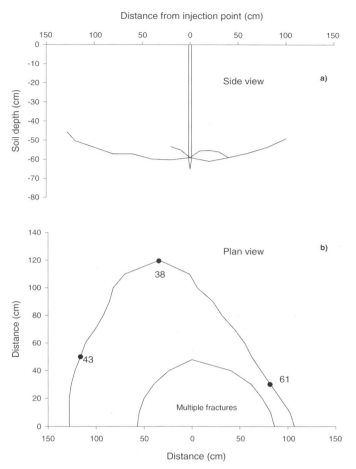

Figure 4.32 (a) Side view of the fracture pattern produced by the 'Terralift' in a sandy clay loam hill site. **(b)** Plan view of the fracture pattern. Values shown are the depths (cm) to the fracture plane. A single discharge at 60 cm was filled with 6.8 l of vermiculite. (After Smiley *et al*, 1990.)

with aeration and drainage. Several systems are commercially available, but research into the benefits of air injection for tree growth has produced mixed results.

Air under pressures of, typically, 6 to 20 bars is discharged into the soil at depths of up to about 0.75 m, through a spike inserted into the soil (Fig 4.31). The short burst of air causes displacement of soil, creating fissures. Fill material such as styrofoam beads, perlite or vermiculite can also be injected, in theory to keep fissures open.

The extent of fissuring was tested by Smiley *et al* (1990) in a comparison of the 'Terralift' ('Terravent') (R.E. Jarvis Co., Fayville MA, USA) and 'Grow Gun' (Grow Gun Corp., Arvada CO, USA) machines. Both produced a single saucer-shaped fracture close to the maximum depth of the injection spike, with

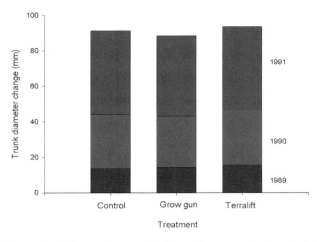

Figure 4.33 Annual trunk diameter increment for *Pyrus calleryana* growing in untreated compacted clay loam (control), or after air injection using the 'GrowGun' or 'Terralift'. (After Smiley, 1994.)

a very limited amount of vertical cracking (Fig 4.32). The area of fracture was 4.3 m^2 for the Terralift and 1.8 m^2 for the Grow Gun. The extent of fissuring was limited because overlying soil was lifted by the discharge of air and redeposited in its original position. Soil was not pulverised or broken up by the escaping air. As a consequence, neither machine reduced bulk density in compacted test plots and any impact on aeration was localised around the fissures (Smiley *et al*, 1990). The improvement in tree growth following attempts to decompact soil using air injection is variable. Growth of trees on compacted clay loam soil was not improved by air injection over three growing seasons (Fig 4.33) (Smiley, 1994). Hodge (1993) reported improvements in shoot growth of birch on a compacted sandy loam soil but was ineffective in halting the decline of sweet chestnut on a compacted clay loam soil.

Rolf (1992) also reported improvements in soil physical properties of compacted soil treated with air injection using the Terralift machine. Air was discharged at a spacing of 1 m, to ensure overlap between fracture zones. Bulk density of a compacted sandy loam was significantly reduced by air injection, even 18 months after treatment, by between 6 and 19%. Macroporosity was increased at depths of 20–50 cm, and as a result saturated hydraulic conductivity and soil aeration improved. Resistance to penetration, evaluated using a cone penetrometer was reduced by air injection, suggesting less mechanical impedance to root growth. However, identical tests on another site, with a loam over clay loam profile, showed no improvement in soil conditions (Rolf, 1992). Rolf concluded that improvements in soil physical conditions in sandy soils can be obtained using air injection, but that for clay soils, the benefits of air injection were questionable. A recent report (Anon, 2000) describes unspecified improvements in tree growth at the Royal Botanic Gardens, Kew following the use of Terravent air injection. It is relevant that the soils dealt with are sandy and is therefore in line with the trend described by Hodge (1993) and Rolf (1992).

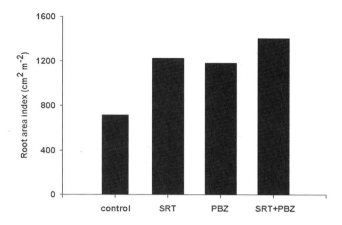

Figure 4.34 Root surface area per unit ground area for white oaks left untreated (control), with a soil replacement treatment (SRT), treated with paclobutrazol (PBZ) or a combination of soil replacement and paclobutrazol. (After Watson 1996.)

The effectiveness of air injection in relieving below-ground constraints on tree growth thus depends, in part, on soil texture. Soil water content at the time of injection is also important, as the plasticity of the soil determines how fissures are propagated through the soil (Hodge, 1991). If the soil is too dry, it fractures easily and the air escapes quickly to the surface. If the soil is too wet, it is highly plastic and tends to slump back to its original position directly after injection. The moisture conditions required for optimum plasticity are unknown, but will vary substantially between soils. Thus, effective use of air injection to improve physical conditions in the soil requires empirical testing of soil responses and frequently relies on the judgement and experience of operators (Hodge, 1991).

Air injection has been most effective where a thin, compacted layer of soil restricts drainage and impairs root growth because of frequent waterlogging. In this circumstance, fracturing of the soil layer by air injection improves drainage and prevents formation of a water table above the compacted layer. Improved aeration of the overlying soil results in more favourable conditions for root growth (Hodge, 1991). Thus, air injection can be a suitable remedy for poor soil conditions, but should be selectively applied to situations where diagnostic investigations at a site demonstrate that it is likely to address the cause of the problem (Hodge, 1991). Smiley (2001) believes that the results from soil fracturing with compressed gases do not give convincing evidence that it is a cost-effective way of dealing with soil compaction. Smiley believes that other measures such as cultivation in advance of root growth, radial trenching and air excavation (all dealt with above) are more effective than air injection in relieving compaction. Harris *et al* (1999) concluded that more research is needed to properly evaluate the various aeration practices.

4.6.6 Use of plant growth regulators

Paclobutrazol is a synthetic plant growth regulator that causes inhibition of gibberellin synthesis in plants. Gibberellins are chemical hormones that occur naturally in plants and stimulate elongation of stems. Inhibition of gibberellin synthesis has been shown to reduce shoot growth in many species and, as a result, paclobutrazol has been used by utility companies in the United States to reduce regrowth of trees under power lines (Watson, 1996). In the right concentrations, paclobutrazol has been found to stimulate root growth and increase root:shoot ratio (Swietlik and Miller, 1983; Watson, 1996). Thus, if applied to declining trees suffering from restricted root growth, it may help to re-establish a healthy root–shoot balance.

Watson (1996) applied paclobutrazol to mature white oaks (*Quercus alba*) suffering dieback. The 16 trees tested were from 50–70 cm dbh (diameter at breast height) and the paclobutrazol was applied to the soil within 20 cm of the base of the trunk in a dilute solution which delivered 0.8 g of active ingredient per centimetre of dbh. At three years after treatment, root density for treated trees was significantly improved and results of treatment with paclobutrazol were similar to the effects of soil replacement in radial trenches (Fig 4.34). Six years after treatment, treated trees had visibly improved vigour. Paclobutrazol thus offers a promising means of tackling dieback in mature trees suffering from restricted root growth, although there are uncertainties about rates of application and differences in response among species that need to be resolved through further research.

4.7 Summary

- Urban soils commonly differ substantially from soils in rural areas because of modification of their physical, chemical and biological properties as a result of mixing, filling and contamination. Soils in the built environment are typified by high heterogeneity, both laterally and vertically, because of historical changes in land use. Extent of soil disturbance tends to increase with proximity to city centres, creating gradients in soil properties, from higher to lower quality, between rural, suburban and urban areas.

- Human activities associated with urban development tend to destroy soil structure and cause soil compaction. The resulting increase in bulk density of soils is caused by the compression of larger pores, including macropores. Intentional compaction of soils is necessary for structural stability, but unintended compaction is commonly caused by vehicle and pedestrian traffic and creates a very poor environment for the growth of trees. Root growth in compacted soils is impeded by destruction of macropores and increased soil strength.

- Infiltration of water at the soil surface is reduced by degradation of soil structure, textural discontinuities between soil layers or pockets of soil, soil crusting and sealing of the surface by paving or building. Restriction of infiltration causes increased surface runoff and, therefore, reduced storage of water for use by trees. Destruction of macropores and textural discontinuities impede drainage, resulting in more frequent waterlogging of soil. The capacity of soils to retain plant-available water is reduced by compaction, infilling with clays or gravel and reduction in organic matter content. Soil aeration is reduced by loss of macropores, infilling or sealing of the surface and waterlogging. Soil temperatures are higher under pavement than lawn or woodland. The degraded physical properties typical of urban soils lead to impaired root function and tree health, potentially increasing tree mortality.

- Urban soils may have good fertility, although interrupted cycling of organic matter, because of sealing of the surface or disposal of leaf litter, can result in nitrogen deficiency. If nitrogen is not the nutrient most limiting to growth, phosphorus may be deficient. Stripping of topsoil during urban development can result in nutrient deficiencies. Fertilisers can be applied to improve soil fertility.

- Urban soils typically have reduced populations of soil organisms, including earthworms and important fungi. The biomass and species diversity of soil organisms is commonly reduced in urban soils.

- The conflict between use of soil in the built environment as both a biological growth medium and an engineering substrate must be overcome for trees to thrive in close proximity to infrastructure such as roads and buildings. Specially composed soil mixes can be used to improve the below-ground environment for trees where compaction of soils is required for structural stability, for example in the construction of pedestrian footways alongside roads. Amsterdam Tree Soil is a mix of sand and compost that has been used successfully beneath footways and parking areas for light vehicles, enabling enlargement of tree pits. Structural soils are composed of a stone-soil mix, with the stone component forming a load-bearing matrix. Soil fills the voids between stones, creating viable rooting space protected from compaction. Structural soils can be used to build sub-bases for pavements that are strong enough for light vehicular traffic and loading from emergency vehicles but allows tree planting as well.

- Remedial action can be taken to stimulate the growth of tree roots in urban soils with poor quality. Compaction can be alleviated prior to planting by subsoil tillage, for example with a mechanical excavator. Amendment of soil used to backfill tree pits with compost can improve tree growth during establishment. Given sufficient time, mulching around trees with compost helps to rebuild soil structure and improve root growth in compacted soils. If more immediate results are required, soil beneath trees can be replaced with compost, either in trenches radiating from the trunk or after vacuum-assisted excavation of roots. Injection of compressed air into soils causes fracturing of compacted soils, but is effective in improving conditions for root growth only when soil conditions are suitable, or when drainage and aeration can be enhanced by penetration of a thin layer of compacted soil. Growth of roots in mature trees can also be stimulated by the application of paclobutrazol, a synthetic plant growth regulator, to help restore a healthy root–shoot balance where root system size has been constrained by poor below-ground conditions.

REFERENCES

Alberty, C.A., Pellet, H.M. & Taylor, D.H. 1984. Characterization of soil compaction at construction sites and woody plant response. *Journal of Environmental Horticulture*, 2, 48–53.

Anon 2000. Sponsors help care for mature trees. *Kew*, Spring 2000, p 47.

Bassuk, N.L. 2001. Pers. comm.

Bassuk, N.L., Grabosky, J., Trowbridge, P. & Urban, J. 1998. Structural soil: an innovative medium under pavement that improves street tree vigor. In: *Proceedings of the 1998 Annual Meeting of the American Society of Landscape Architects*, pp. 183–185.

Bending, N.A.D. & Moffat, A.J. 1997. *Tree establishment on landfill sites: research and updated guidance*. Department of the Environment, Transport and the Regions, Forestry Commission, Edinburgh, UK. 53 pp.

Bengough, A.G., Campbell, D.J. & O'Sullivan M.F. 2001. Penetrometer techniques in relation to soil compaction and root growth. In: *Soil and Environmental Analysis*, 2nd Edition (Ed. by K.A. Smith and C.E. Mullins), pp. 377–403. Marcel Dekker, New York, USA.

Beven, K. & Germann, P. 1982. Macropores and water flow in soils. *Water Resources Research*, 18, 1311–1325.

Brady, N.C. & Weil, R.R. 1999. *The Nature and Properties of Soils, 12th Edition*. Prentice-Hall Inc., Upper Saddle River, NJ, USA. 881 pp.

Couenberg, E. 1994. Amsterdam tree soil. In: *The Landscape Below Ground* (Ed. by G.W. Watson and D. Neely), pp. 24–33. International Society of Arboriculture, Savoy, IL., USA.

Couenberg, E. 1998. Urban tree soil and tree-pit design. In: *The Landscape Below Ground II: Proceedings of an International Workshop on Tree Root Development in Urban Soils* (Ed. by D. Neely & G.W. Watson), pp. 189–202. International Society of Arboriculture, Champaign, IL., USA.

Craul, P.J. 1985. A description of urban soils and their desired characteristics. *Journal of Arboriculture*, 11, 330–331.

Craul, P.J. 1992. *Urban Soil in Landscape Design*. John Wiley & Sons, Inc., New York, USA. 396 pp.

Craul, P.J. 1994. Soil compaction on heavily used sites. *Journal of Arboriculture*, 20, 69–74.

Day, S.D. & Bassuk, N.L. 1994. A review of the effects of soil compaction and amelioration treatments on landscape trees. *Journal of Arboriculture*, 20, 9–17.

Day, S.D., Bassuk, N.L. & van Es, H. 1995. Effects of four compaction remediation methods for landscape trees on soil aeration, mechanical impedance and tree establishment. *Journal of Environmental Horticulture*, 13, 64–71.

de Kimpe, C.R. & Morel, J.L. 2000. Urban soil management: a growing concern. *Soil Science*, 165, 31–40.

Department of the Environment 1986. *Landfilling wastes*. Department of the Environment, Waste Management Paper No. 26. HMSO, London, UK.

Department of Transport 1994. *Design manual for roads and bridges. Volume 7, Pavement design and maintenance*, Department of Transport, London, UK.

Dobson, M.C. & Moffat, A.J. 1993. *The potential for woodland establishment on landfill sites*. Department of the Environment. HMSO, London, UK. 88 pp.

Dobson, M.C. & Moffat, A.J. 1999. Examination of tree and root performance on closed landfills in Merseyside. *Arboricultural Journal*, 23, 261–272.

Ehlers, W. 1975. Observations on earthworm channels and infiltration on tilled and untilled loess soil. *Soil Science*, 119, 242–249.

Foil, R.R. & Ralston, C.W. 1967. The establishment and growth of loblolly pine seedlings on compacted soils. *Soil Science Society of America Proceedings*, 31, 565–568.

Grabosky, J. & Bassuk, N.L. 1995. A new urban tree soil to safely increase rooting volumes under sidewalks. *Journal of Arboriculture*, 21, 187–201.

Grabosky, J. & Bassuk, N.L. 1996. Testing of structural urban tree soil materials for use under pavement to increase street tree rooting volumes. *Journal of Arboriculture*, 22, 255–263.

Grabosky, J., Bassuk, N.L., Irwin, L. & van Es, H. 1998. Structural soil investigations at Cornell University. In: *The Landscape Below Ground II: Proceedings of an International Workshop on Tree Root Development in Urban Soils* (Ed. by D. Neely and G.W. Watson), pp. 203–209. International Society of Arboriculture, Champaign, IL., USA.

Grabosky, J., Bassuk, N.L., Irwin, L. & van Es, H. 2000. Shoot and root growth of three tree species in sidewalk soil profiles: a pilot study. (*Manuscript*) 33 pp.

Graves, W.R. 1998. Consequences of high soil temperatures. In: *The Landscape Below Ground II: Proceedings of an International Workshop on Tree Root Development in Urban Soils* (Ed. by D. Neely and G.W. Watson), pp. 27–35. International Society of Arboriculture, Champaign, IL., USA.

Graves, W.R. & Dana, M.N. 1987. Root-zone temperature monitored at urban sites. *HortScience*, 22, 613–614.

Graves, W.R., Dana, M.N. & Joly, R.J. 1989. Root-zone temperature affects water status and growth of red maple. *Journal of the American Society of Horticultural Science*, 114, 406–410.

Gross, R. 1995. Construction applications of hydraulic soil excavation. In: *Trees and Building Sites* (Ed. by G.W. Watson and D. Neely), pp. 177–184. International Society of Arboriculture, Champaign, IL., USA.

Gur, A., Bravdo, B. & Hepner, J. 1976. The influence of root temperature on apple trees. III. The effect on photosynthesis and water balance. *Journal of Horticultural Science*, 51, 203–210.

Harris, J.A. 1991. The biology of soils in urban areas. In: *Soils in the Urban Environment* (Ed. by P. Bullock and P.J. Gregory), pp.139–152. Blackwell Scientific Publications, Oxford, UK.

Harris, R.W., Clark, J.R. & Matheny, N.P. 1999. *Arboriculture: Integrated Management of Landscape Trees, Shrubs and Vines*. Prentice Hall, Upper Saddle River, NJ., USA. 687 pp.

Helliwell, D.R. 1986. The extent of tree roots. *Arboricultural Journal*, 10, 341–347.

Hillel, D. 1998. *Environmental Soil Physics*. Academic Press, San Diego, USA. 771 pp.

Hodge, S.J. 1991. Improving the growth of established amenity trees: site physical conditions. Arboricultural Research Note, 102/91/ARB. Arboricultural Advisory & Information Service. Farnham, UK. 4 pp.

Hodge, S.J. 1993. Compressed air injection around amenity trees. Arboricultural Research Notes, 113/93/ARB. Arboricultural Advisory & Information Service. Farnham, UK. 4 pp.

Kjelgren, R.K. & Montague, T. 1998. Urban tree transpiration over turf and asphalt surfaces. *Atmospheric Environment*, 32, 53–41.

Kladivko, E.J., Mackay, A.D. & Bradford, J.M. 1986. Earthworms as a factor in the reduction of soil crusting. *Soil Science Society of America Journal*, 50, 191–196.

Kopinga, J. 1991. The effects of restricted volumes of soil on the growth and development of street trees. *Journal of Arboriculture*, 17, 57–63.

Kozlowski, T.T. 1999. Soil compaction and growth of woody plants. *Scandinavian Journal of Forest Research*, 14, 596–619.

Kozlowski, T.T & Davies, W.J. 1975. Control of water balance in transplanted trees. *Journal of Arboriculture*, 1, 1–10.

Kristoffersen, P. 1998. Designing urban pavement sub-bases to support trees. *Journal of Arboriculture*, 24, 121–126.

Kristoffersen, P. 1999. Growing trees in road foundation materials. *Arboricultural Journal* 23:57–76.

Krizek, D.T. & Dubik, S.P. 1987. Influence of water stress and restricted root volume on growth and development of urban trees. *Journal of Arboriculture*, 13, 47–55.

Lindsey, P. & Bassuk, N.L. 1992. Redesigning the urban forest from the ground below: a new approach to specifying adequate soil volumes for street trees. *Arboricultural Journal*, 16, 25–39.

McDonnell, M.J., Pickett, S.T.A. & Pouyat, R.V. 1993. The application of the ecological gradient paradigm to the study of urban effects. In: *Humans as Components of Ecosystems* (Ed. by M.J. McDonnell and S.T.A. Pickett), pp. 175–189. Springer-Verlag, New York, USA.

Nathenson, R. & Jarabak, A. 2001. The evolution of air tools for use in arboriculture. *Tree Care Industry*, May 2001.

Oke, T.R. 1987. *Boundary Layer Climates*, Second Edition. Methuen & Co., London, UK. 435 pp.

Passioura, J.B. 1991. Soil structure and plant growth. *Australian Journal of Soil Research*, 29, 717–728.

Patterson, J.C. 1977. Soil compaction – effects on urban vegetation. *Journal of Arboriculture*, 3, 161–1.

Pizl, V. & Josens, G. 1995. Earthworm communities along a gradient of urbanization. *Environmental Pollution*, 90, 7–14.

Pulford, I.D. 1991. Nutrient provision and cycling in soils in urban areas. In: *Soils in the Urban Environment* (Ed. by P. Bullock and P.J. Gregory), pp. 119–138. Blackwell Scientific Publications, Oxford, UK.

Randrup, T.B. & Dralle, K. 1997. Influence of planning and design on soil compaction in construction sites. *Landscape and Urban Planning*, 38, 87–92.

Richards, Moorehead & Laing Ltd. 2002. *Trees in Streets*, Final Report for Transport for London, Ruthin, UK. 43pp. http://rmlconsult.com/a catalog/reports.html

Rimmer, D.L. 1991. Soil storage and handling. In: *Soils in the Urban Environment* (Ed. by P. Bullock and P.J. Gregory), pp. 76–86. Blackwell Scientific Publications, Oxford, UK.

Rolf, K. 1991. Soil improvement and increased growth response from subsoil cultivation. *Journal of Arboriculture*, 17, 200–204.

Rolf, K. 1992. Soil physical effects of pneumatic subsoil loosening using a Terralift soil aerator. *Journal of Arboriculture*, 18, 235–240.

Rolf, K. 1994. Soil compaction and loosening effects on soil physics and tree growth. In: *The Landscape Below Ground: Proceedings of an International Workshop on Tree Root Development in Urban Soils* (Ed. by G.W. Watson and D. Neely), pp. 131–148. International Society of Arboriculture, Savoy, IL., USA.

Schwets, T.L. & Brown, R.D. 2000. Form and structure of maple trees in urban environments. *Landscape and Urban Planning*, 46, 191–201.

Smiley, E.T. 1994. The effects of soil aeration equipment on tree growth. In: *The Landscape Below Ground: Proceedings of an International Workshop on Tree Root Development in Urban Soils* (Ed. by G.W. Watson and D. Neely), pp. 207–210. International Society of Arboriculture, Savoy, IL., USA.

Smiley, E.T. 1999. Air excavation, the next arboricultural frontier. *Arbor Age*, 20, 8–10.

Smiley, E.T. 2001a. Air excavation to improve tree health. *Tree Care Industry*, May 2001.

Smiley, E.T. 2001b. Terravent: soil fracture patterns and impact on bulk density. *Journal of Arboriculture*, 27, 326–330.

Smiley, E.T., Watson, G.W., Fraedrich, B.R. & Booth, D.C. 1990. Evaluation of soil aeration equipment. *Journal of Arboriculture*, 16, 118–123.

Smith, D.L.O. 1987. Measurement, interpretation and modelling of soil compaction. *Soil Use and Management*, 3, 87–93.

Stolzy, L.H. 1974. Soil atmosphere. In: *The Plant Root and its Environment* (Ed. by E.W. Carson), pp. 335–361. University Press of Virginia, Charlottesville, VA., USA.

Swietlik, D. & Miller, S.S. 1983. The effect of paclobutrazol on growth and response to water stress of apple seedlings. *Journal of the American Society of Horticultural Science*, 108, 1076–1080.

Unger, P.W. & Kaspar, T.C. 1994. Soil compaction and root growth: a review. *Agronomy Journal*, 86, 759–766.

Urban, J. 1989. New techniques in urban tree planting. *Journal of Arboriculture*, 15, 281–284.

Watson, G.W. 1988. Organic mulch and grass competition influence tree root development. *Journal of Arboriculture*, 14, 200–203.

Watson, G.W. 1990. Tree growth revisited. *Golf Course Management*, 58(6) 8–25.

Watson, G.W. 1996. Tree root system enhancement with paclobutrazol. *Journal of Arboriculture*, 22, 211–217.

Watson, G.W., Kelsey, P. & Woodtli, K. 1996. Replacing soil in the root zone of mature trees for better growth. *Journal of Arboriculture*, 22, 167–173.

Wilkins, L.C., Graves, W.R. & Townsend, A.M., 1995. Responses to high root-zone temperature among cultivars of red maple and Freeman maple. *Journal of Environmental Horticulture*, 13, 82–85.

Yelenosky, G. 1963. Soil aeration and tree growth. *International Shade Tree Conference*, 39, 16–25.

CHAPTER 5
Establishment of Young Trees

5.1 Introduction

Establishment of trees in the built environment cannot be regarded as a routinely successful enterprise. The overall picture is that there are many dangers for a newly planted tree and in some cases the chances of survival are as little as 1 in 2. There is, however, considerable variation in the percentage survival of newly planted trees, when examined in terms of countryside, city or town and even from locality to locality within the same city (Bradshaw *et al*, 1995). The common perception might be that vandalism is the major cause of tree deaths in the built environment but surveys do not support this view. In a survey of the likely causes of tree deaths in northern cities of the UK Gilbertson and Bradshaw (1985) showed that, although vandalism did account for just over 15% of deaths, higher percentage losses, each reaching nearly 30%, were ascribed to the influence of weeds and to stress.

Figures, such as those given above, suggest that the chances of young trees thriving in the built environment depends very much on below-ground processes. Paramount among the needs of newly planted trees is the requirement to rapidly deploy an effective root system to acquire sufficient resources from the soil and to survive competition from weeds. In this chapter we discuss the types of trees that are typically planted in urban environments with comments on the relative merits of different sizes and the means by which they are raised. The major disruption and loss of significant parts of the root system during transplanting from the nursery into the final site is a major shock and potentially lethal for young trees. Preparing the tree for the shock can begin well before transplanting and mitigation can continue long afterwards.

5.2 Choice of material

5.2.1 Available stock

A wide variety of different sizes of nursery tree stock is available, with very different characteristics and costs. Fig 5.1 and Table 5.1 (after BSI, 1992 and Bradshaw *et al*, 1995 respectively) summarise the size range of trees that are available. It may seem the best option to purchase the largest and most

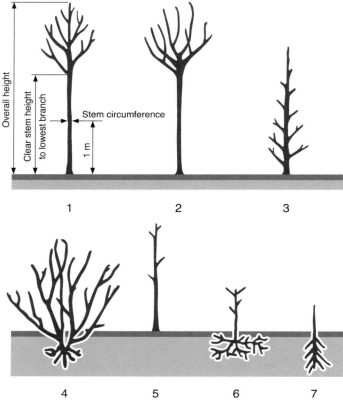

Figure 5.1 Stock types after BS 3936. **1** Standard with central leader; **2** Standard with branching head; **3** Feathered tree; **4** Multi-stemmed tree; **5** Whip; **6** Transplant 1+1 and **7** Seedling 2+0.

expensive type of stock that can be afforded but frequently this will not be the wisest decision, because of the problems associated with size increase. The difficulties and risks of failure associated with transplanting larger stock are nearly all to do with the lesser likelihood that the root systems of larger trees can survive major disruption, re-establish at the planting site and provide the needs of the tree, compared to smaller trees. Table 5.1 shows that there are distinct advantages and disadvantages attached to all types of stock and these have to be weighed up for a particular circumstance.

In urban plantings, the choice of standard trees is a compromise that satisfies the needs to provide an instant visual effect and a tolerance of the stresses of the urban environment. Extra heavy planting stock should only be used in prestige situations and where proper maintenance can be assured. In many situations smaller stock has great advantages in cost and better performance. In large-scale afforestation schemes small transplants are normally used. Economies of scale mean that problems with weeds and animal browsing can be dealt with more readily than could be the case with plants of this size in urban situations. The use of small trees (0.3–0.9 m tall) is therefore often promoted in a range of new urban woodland plantings (NUFU, 1998).

Table 5.1   The sizes of tree stock commonly available.
(After BS 3936, 1992; Bradshaw *et al*, 1995.)

Type	Size	Characteristics
Seedling, transplant, undercut	0.2–0.9 m (can be up to 1.25 m)	Very cheap. Easy to plant, readily stands stress of transplanting, but essential to provide weed control from beginning. Vulnerable to damage, must be protected or isolated from damage for 5–10 years. Only reasonable way to achieve large-scale plantings, although may take several years to create impact.
Whip	1.0–1.75 m (can be up to 2.0 m)	No side shoots. Cheap. Quite easy to plant, quickly recovers from stress of transplanting, but still requires good weed control. Requires protection or isolation from damage for at least 5 years. An impact achieved more quickly than with transplants.
Feather	1.25–2.5 m (can be up to 3.0 m)	Side shoots. Fairly cheap, easy to plant and recovers fairly quickly. But can suffer stress at establishment because there are more branches and usually larger than a whip. Must be well planted or can be loosened by wind.
Standard	2.0–3.5m	Normally specified by girth at 1 m. Expensive. Not all species can recover from transplanting stress. Careful handling and aftercare are important, weed control still essential for 3–5 years. Less susceptible to damage than smaller stock, but some protection or isolation still required. Normal method of achieving an immediate effect.
Heavy and extra-heavy standard	Above 3.5 m (girth 12–14, 14–16 cm)	More expensive. Stock must be specially prepared to withstand transplant stress, aftercare for at least 3 years essential. Even less susceptible to damage. A good way of achieving an immediate effect but a high risk of failure if aftercare is inadequate.

Table 5.1 *continued*

Semi-mature	Usually > 5 m	Very expensive. Stock has to be specially prepared for several years in advance. Requires special equipment for lifting and planting and elaborate steps have to be taken to ensure survival and recovery. Often considered for prestige schemes but there is a high risk of failure.
Cutting	0.25–0.30 m	Only applicable to species that root readily from cuttings (eg various willow and poplar species) but for these it is economical and reliable.
Seed	0.1–0.2 m in first year	A developing technique. Cheap and simple to use, appropriate for informal plantings. Weed control essential. Plants will be well-rooted.

Table 5.2 Stock types available for amenity tree establishment.

Stock type	Size and age	Predominant use
Bare-root	Seedling (1+0)	Forestry
	Transplant and whip 1/2+1/2,1+1,1+2)	Forestry
	Undercut (1/2u1/2, 1u1)	Forestry
	Feathered to standard	Amenity
Root-ball	Half-standard to semi-mature	Amenity
Container	Seedling (cell grown)	Forestry
	Container grown	Amenity

The use of seeds to establish trees and shrubs is a challenge, because seed germination will be haphazard so the place where the trees will emerge is not well defined. As well as all the other factors which influence small transplants, such as weeds, trampling and browsing, drought will play a major part in determining the survival of seedlings. Nevertheless, the costs are low and the root systems of plants should be well formed. Use of seeds might be considered in informal plantings at roadsides for example. A recent study from New Zealand (Watson and Tombleson, 2002) examined different degrees of stability against wind for young trees of Monterey pine (*Pinus radiata*) derived by different growing methods. A comparison was made between plants established after direct sowing, the use of **bare-root** seedlings and cuttings. The superiority of the

Table 5.3 Relative tolerance to transplanting of genera commonly used in the UK landscapes. (After Percival and Galloway, 2000.)

High	Intermediate	Low
Alnus	*Juglans*	*Betula*
Sorbus	*Prunus*	*Aesculus*
Tilia	*Fraxinus*	*Malus*
Salix	*Castanea*	*Carpinus*
Populus	*Crataegus*	*Acer*
Ginkgo	*Pyrus*	*Quercus*
Platanus		*Fagus*
Robinia		
Pinus		

plants from direct sowing was due to a greater preponderance of the biomass being allocated to the portions of the lateral roots close to the stem.

Woody plants are usually sold or transplanted as **bare-root, root-balled,** or container plants. Table 5.2 (Hodge, 1991) shows in which sector of tree planting the different types of rooted plants are typically used. There is an established convention indicating the previous management of bare-root plants eg 1+1 reports that the tree is two years old and has spent one year in the seed-bed and was then transplanted to the tree nursery where it has spent another year. U indicates that the trees in the nursery have been undercut to excise deep roots and encourage more compact root systems (see also Section 5.3.1). The most important aim in the management of young trees, whether bare-rooted, bagged or **containerised,** is to produce a tree with a compact, vigorous root system prepared for the time the tree is placed in its final growing position. In the seed-bed and nursery the natural tendency of young trees is to extend their roots widely to exploit available soil resources. By **wrenching** and undercutting, the root system of the tree is concentrated in a smaller soil volume.

5.2.2 Transplantability

5.2.2.1 Species

Based on published information, Percival and Galloway (2000) classified tree genera commonly planted in the UK into those with high, intermediate and low tolerance to transplanting and this information is reproduced as Table 5.3. This table does not differ fundamentally from a table in Hartman *et al* (2000) that includes species more commonly planted in North America. Certainly, there is good overall agreement in the sense of those genera that are highly tolerant and those highly intolerant of transplanting. Percival and Galloway (2000) point out that it is the faster growing genera (eg poplar, willow and alder) that are most tolerant of transplanting. Unfortunately there is little information about what variation in transplantability exists within a genus, in respect of ease or difficulty in transplanting.

An important factor that distinguishes between genera that usually transplant successfully and those that do not is the type of root system they possess. Struve (1990) believed that species with fibrous roots, eg green ash (*Fraxinus pennsylvanica*), grew better after transplanting compared to species with coarse roots, eg red oak (*Quercus rubra*). Hodge (1991) found that Struve's evidence is consistent with practical experience with some of trees commonly used in Britain. Ash (*Fraxinus excelsior*), wild cherry (*Prunus avium*), rowan (*Sorbus aucuparia*) and sycamore (*Acer pseudoplatanus*) have fibrous roots and are regarded as relatively easy to establish. However, fibrous roots are more likely to be desiccated between lifting and planting (see Sections 5.4 and 5.4.1). Trees with roots of Struve's coarse category, eg oak (*Quercus robur*), beech (*Fagus sylvatica*), and hornbeam (*Carpinus betulus*), are more difficult to establish. In these species a large number of root tips are lost when the plants are lifted, and slow regeneration of adventitious roots make these species prone to severe moisture stresses, especially when large stock with low root:shoot ratios are planted out.

There are exceptions to the trends described above. Birch (*Betula pendula*) has fibrous roots but it is difficult to establish (Hodge, 1991). Hodge suggests that species that regenerate new roots from large woody roots, are better able to establish than species which regenerate roots from small woody roots which are more likely to be lost at transplanting. A further explanation is that carbohydrate storage in birch is in the fine woody roots but in other species, eg lime, the larger woody roots are the main reservoirs (Abod and Webster, 1991).

Watson and Himelick (1997) suggested some steps to be taken prior to transplanting species with tap-roots, such as white oak, which is regarded as less easy to transplant successfully. The sequence is: 1) sever the tap-root at an early age to stimulate increased lateral root growth, 2) lateral roots are pruned for increased fine root development within the root-ball, 3) at transplanting a root-ball should be excavated to a depth that exceeds minimum standards, 4) prepare a favourable site to encourage new root growth, and 5) provide an extended period of maintenance, paying special attention to irrigation, to accommodate for the slow establishment of these trees.

5.2.2.2 Plant size

It is possible to transplant very large trees, and in some circumstances there may be a need to use trees of a substantial size to make an immediate impact in the landscape. In other circumstances there is a greater likelihood of success in transplanting if smaller trees are used rather than big ones. Given normal nursery practices and without constraints in the soil the root-ball of trees available for transplanting should be proportional to the crown size. However, larger trees will lose more root mass. Without specifying a tree genus, Hartman *et al* (2000) calculated that if trees of 5 cm and 15 cm in stem diameter were transplanted and if root spread resumed at around 45 cm per year the small tree would recover all the root system lost in transplanting in 2.5 years whereas the large tree would need 7 years to achieve the same recovery.

Physiological studies have shown that smaller trees suffer less water stress than larger trees. Distinct differences in leaf gas exchange and water relations between small and large transplants have been observed which indicate more effective root systems of the smaller plants. For example, Lauderdale *et al* (1995) showed that, for red maple, transplant size had a significant effect on physiological characteristics that might contribute to success after transplanting. It was shown that smaller transplants, initially having a stem diameter of 3.8 cm, had higher transpiration rates and **stomatal conductances** and less negative leaf water potentials than larger transplants, with stem diameters of 7.6 cm.

Although applying principally to bare-root trees, the site where a tree has been growing prior to transplanting can influence the likelihood of success when it is transplanted. In sandy, well-drained soils the root systems will tend to extend more horizontally and vertically than on sites with heavy soils. More roots will be lost during transplanting from a sandy site. Hartman *et al* (2000) suggest, therefore, that generally better success in transplanting should be expected when plants are moved from heavy to light soils compared to the reverse. They also suggest that large trees may not be the best option on poorly drained sites because the root-balls will be deeper and more likely to be influenced by the waterlogged zone at the bottom of the root-ball.

5.2.2.3 Quality of planting stock at the nursery

There are two main factors which determine the quality of planting material: 1) the quality of the stock and its treatment in the nursery and 2) the various treatments received by the stock between removal from the nursery soil and planting at the site. In both cases the major effects on plant quality are largely a function of impacts on the root systems of the trees and mean that the quality of stock arriving at the planting site can vary enormously. If the stock quality is poor it can lead to high failure rates and poor growth after establishment. The quality can be evaluated either on a morphological or physiological basis or perhaps both. On a morphological basis the quality of young planting stock is largely a result of growth conditions and management in the nursery. The physiological condition will also depend on the care received after lifting and transportation to the planting site, as well as the conditions the young trees experienced in the nursery.

The form and health of the root system of all types of trees is crucial to their successful future after planting. However, rather little concrete, quantitative guidance about the root systems of nursery trees can be found in the British Standard for nursery stock – BS 3936, Part 1 (BSI, 1992). The morphological characteristics of roots are dealt with in only four sentences of a rather general nature, and the standard makes no reference to physiological fitness. The

Table 5.4 Recommended minimum diameter and depth of root-balls for deciduous trees of various sizes. (After Hartman *et al*, 2000.)

Tree trunk diameter (cm)	Diameter of root-ball (cm)	Depth of root-ball (cm)
1.3–1.9	36	28
1.9–2.5	41	31
2.5–3.2	46	34
3.2–3.8	51	36
3.8–4.5	56	38
4.5–5.1	61	41
5.1–6.3	71	48
6.3–7.6	81	51
7.6–8.9	97	58
8.9–10.2	107	66
10.2–11.4	122	74
11.4–12.7	137	79
12.7–14.0	145	81
14.0–15.3	152	84

American standards for nursery stock (American Association of Nurserymen, 1997) are considerably more prescriptive in terms of the minimum acceptable root-ball diameters and depths for particular stem basal diameters. Similar information to the American Standard presented by Hartman *et al* (2000) is reproduced in Table 5.4.

5.2.2.4 Root morphology and successful establishment

The assessment of whether the root system has a satisfactory ratio with respect to the above-ground parts of the tree will determine the suitability of a tree for transplanting on a morphological basis. Root:shoot ratios on a dry weight basis are commonly used in an experimental context to evaluate the adequacy of the root system to supply the shoot. This measure is of course destructive, which limits its usefulness for routine assessment at the commercial scale. The ratio of the height of a tree to its stem diameter is a non-destructive measure that can be obtained quickly. The stem diameter is an indicator of the overall plant weight while the height might indicate the above-ground weight component but this will depend largely on the degree of branching. For the UK, in any case, there is not available for common amenity species, a table of plant parameters such as height/stem diameter ratios that are known to represent likely planting success. Should such tables exist they would provide a quantitative, morphological basis for routine assessment of stock quality.

Although not in themselves morphological characteristics, some indications of the suitability for transplanting can come from a life history of the trees prior to transplanting. Examples of these would be the degree of root pruning,

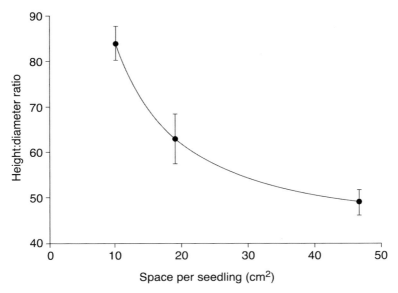

Figure 5.2 The relationship between height: diameter (root collar) ratio and nursery spacing of one-year-old container-grown white spruce seedlings. (After Burdett, 1990.)

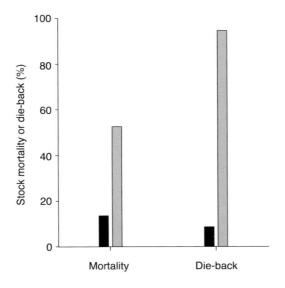

Figure 5.3 The effect of good (dark shading) and bad (grey shading) nursery conditions (water, fertiliser, weed control) on the mortality or dieback of otherwise similar stock in the year after transplanting. (After Bradshaw *et al*, 1995.)

transplanting and root wrenching. These features might be difficult to assess and quantify. The degree to which the root system exhibits circling roots may be easy to observe but not so if it occurs deep in the root-ball.

With standard trees, particularly, there is the strong possibility that the individuals have been grown too closely together. This practice will invariably result in trees with spindly elongated stems that will not be as well-suited to planting out conditions as stockier specimens. Fig 5.2 shows the marked influence of spacing in the nursery on morphology of seedlings. Stock raised under poor conditions, without fertiliser, water and weed control, can show very poor recovery after transplanting when measured in terms of survival and extension growth, compared to similar material raised in good conditions (Fig 5.3). A problem for managers of commercial tree nurseries must be the difficulty to predict future purchases of young tree stock. Therefore there is a risk of overstocking; stock remains too long in the nursery and becomes less suited to successful planting out.

Important defects that are likely to be associated with restricted growing conditions, particularly in containers, are kinking of major roots as well as circling roots. Those in the centre of the root-ball will be more difficult to detect and cut than those occurring at the periphery of the root-ball. Harris *et al* (1999) do not present a threshold for the amount of kinked or girdling roots that a tree might have without compromising its growth.

5.3 Improving the root system for transplanting

There are a number of strategies to improve the likelihood of successful transplanting. Firstly, because in **field-grown** trees, a substantial fraction of the more widely spread roots will be lost when the trees are dug up, attempts are made to increase the density of the roots in the zone intended for the root-ball. Secondly, attempts are made to encourage the roots to regenerate more effectively from the root system that remains after transplanting. A third strategy is to reduce the activity of above-ground growth that might direct resources to the root system or at least reduce demands on the root system. However, if severe pruning of the above-ground parts of the tree are carried out at the time of transplanting and coincides with a serious loss of roots, there may be a good root:shoot ratio but important food reserves could have been lost both above and below ground.

The need to make the root system denser, prior to transplanting, can apply to **container-grown** trees as well as field-grown trees. There are other special problems associated with the root systems of container-grown trees, such as circling or girdling roots, and these also need to be dealt with prior to transplanting. In regions where winter temperatures are below freezing for extended periods there is a risk of damage to the roots of container-grown trees especially when they are in bags or pots placed at ground level and not protected from frost. Root systems are regarded as less frost-resistant than above-ground tissue (Mityga and Lanphear, 1971; Sakai and Larcher, 1987).

Dumais *et al* (2002) examined the responses of container-grown plants to freezing temperatures. The species studied were white spruce (*Picea glauca*), black spruce (*P. mariana*) and jack pine (*Pinus banksiana*). The study showed that for the spruces there was as much as 50% root damage from freezing before water relations and growth were affected after planting out. With jack pine only 40% root damage produced increased water stress and growth reduction.

5.3.1 Root pruning

Root pruning is used routinely on seedlings and young plants growing in soil beds in amenity and forest tree nurseries. The aim is to control shoot vigour and produce planting stock with compact fibrous root systems well suited to transplanting. Common methods of root pruning are undercutting in which a tensioned steel blade is drawn horizontally through the soil, and wrenching, which uses a thicker blade set at a 20–30° angle to the horizontal to cut and break roots at and above the required depth. Possibly with undercutting and certainly with wrenching the soil above the blade will be loosened and lifted somewhat. Typically, the depth of the blade is set at around 20 cm below the surface. A large fraction of the published literature relating to root pruning in nurseries relates to studies on coniferous stock for forestry. Recent studies on broadleaves include studies using cherry, sweet chestnut, oak and sycamore by Hipps and his colleagues at Horticulture Research International at East Malling, who have carried out a comprehensive range of studies of the effects of root wrenching on nutrient contents, water relations, shoot growth and subsequent transplant success (Hipps *et al*, 1997, 1999, 2000).

Although there are a number of negative responses of undercutting and wrenching of seedlings and young plants these are usually temporary and no permanent adverse effects are incurred. Lowering of **shoot water potential** and stomatal conductance in both conifers and broadleaves following root pruning has been observed (van den Driessche, 1983; Rook, 1971; Hipps *et al*, 1997), but these recovered to control levels in some weeks. Because water stress will develop after root pruning, irrigation supplies should be made available. The impact of undercutting and wrenching on plant water stress will to a large extent depend on the depth at which pruning occurs. Clearly, if the soil level at which pruning occurs is deep, the amount of root pruned will be less but also less benefit might be obtained. Alternatively, if root pruning occurs at too shallow a depth the amount of root removed may be excessive and the levels of stress will be excessive.

Other environmental factors are also important. In addition to the need for adequate water supplies following root pruning, Geisler and Ferree (1984) believed that good root regeneration occurs when temperatures and light intensities are relatively high and there is good soil aeration. Root pruning can also affect the nutrient content of the young trees. Hipps *et al* (2000) showed that leaf nitrogen levels fall sharply after pruning of roots but levels also recovered within a few weeks.

Figure 5.4 Scheme for trenching around trees in the two years prior to transplanting. Year 1 trenches **A**, Year 2 trenches **B**. The tree sketched at the upper left shows the extent of root before pruning while that at the upper right illustrates the extent after pruning. (After Hartman *et al*, 2000.)

The timing of root pruning is important. There seems to be little benefit to be obtained by pruning while plants are dormant (Ranney *et al*, 1989). Typically, the best responses to root pruning have been obtained if the treatment is applied when shoot growth is most active. This leads to a beneficial redistribution of dry matter that increases root:shoot ratios whilst having a less severe drought stress impact which is more likely to occur later in the growing season. In UK conditions, early pruning (10 July) of sweet chestnut and cherry caused less drought stress than a pruning on 12 August (Hipps *et al*, 1999).

There are a number of ways that the root density in the root-ball zone of larger trees can be achieved. For trees as large as standards the method described by Hartman *et al* (2000) can be used (Fig 5.4). This involves digging trenches in two successive years before transplanting. In the spring or autumn a circular area around the tree at some distance from the trunk (approximately 5 cm for each cm of trunk diameter) is marked out. Three trenches, covering half of the circumference, are dug by hand, and all the exposed roots severed. One year later the remainder of the circle is trenched. The soil excavated on both occasions should be mixed with well-rotted manure, leaf mould or commercial compost before being backfilled into the trenches. Trenching and root pruning in this way will encourage abundant fine root development in the trenched zones. BS 4043, the British Standard recommendations for transplanting root-balled trees (BSI, 1989) illustrates a small, but perhaps significant difference to this method. A piece of root barrier material is placed vertically on the *inner* wall of the trenches, which are filled with inert, non-toxic material. The barrier would encourage roots to develop in the soil immediately adjacent to the trench, with the trenched zone playing no further role in the root development of the tree. In the case of either of the two approaches, the tree will be ready for moving one year after the second set of trenches has been dug. Had all the roots that were eventually cut been severed at the same time there would have been a great risk of the tree drying out. Trenching in phases allows the stress to be spread over a three-year period.

One approach to providing transplanted trees with root systems of adequate size is the use of tree spades. These are trailer or lorry-mounted frames with usually three or four hydraulic spades. The blades encircle the tree base and are forced hydraulically into the soil one by one, forming a root-ball when the blades meet below the tree. Roots up to 10 cm in diameter can be severed with sharp blades. An alternative is the 'Tree-Porter' that hydraulically hammers individual blades into the soil to cut the root-ball and form the transplanting container. The blades are locked together and the root-ball is lifted by crane for transport to the planting site. There have been very few direct comparisons of planting with a tree spade with other methods. Cool (1976) found that survival of bare-rooted transplants was 72% compared with 99% for tree-spade plantings. The maximum size of root-ball that can be dug up with tree spades that are routinely available are 3 m diameter and 1.35 m deep. There are reports from the USA of trees with much larger root systems being transplanted with tree spades (Harris *et al*, 1999).

www.natlshade.com/gianttreemoving.html gives examples of the transplanting of very large trees in the USA. Examples of moving large eucalypts and palms in Australia are obtainable at:
www.tradeaplant.com.au/Content/TreeCareTreeMoving.asp

Tree spade equipment is also used to excavate the tree pit, of identical size to the root-ball, into which the tree will be planted. The hydraulic spades are likely to produce a clean cut on the tree pit wall but particularly in clay soils there may be smearing and sealing of the walls of the tree pit. This smeared surface should be broken up to allow roots from the transplanted tree to exploit the soil outside of the tree pit.

Trees grown in containers comprise more than 60% of the stock planted as amenity trees in the UK (Seddon, 2001). Therefore any advantages or disadvantages of containers are particularly relevant. Young trees growing in containers will have more root length per unit volume than field-grown trees, and at the end of this section some ways to increase the rooting density and fibrosity further are discussed. However, there are a number of problems associated with containers and various approaches have been adopted to eliminate them. A particular problem of containers is the circling roots that grow around the wall of the pot. The persistence of these roots and their orientation will seriously threaten the welfare of the tree, even into adult life and should be eliminated sooner rather than later. Circling roots are discussed in more detail below. In the nursery, containers normally stand above ground. They will most likely be on sheeting of some sort to ensure drainage but restrict weed growth. The soil and roots can also be exposed to greater extremes of temperature than plants rooted in the ground. The soil in containers tends to be coarser than the soil at planting sites. This can cause a problem, as water will drain out very readily from the coarse container soil into the surrounding soil. An approach that will overcome the problems of trees blowing over and the extremes of temperature is to grow the trees in a pot sunk in the ground up to the soil level. The pot is usually located inside another pot of slightly larger diameter. Any roots growing between the pots are lost when harvested and this can cause some stress to the tree.

Sometimes the inner pot can be of a fibrous material that allows roots to grow into and through the pot wall. These can be readily pruned off by hand or may be pruned automatically with root tips entering the air gap between the inner and outer pots being desiccated and dying – air pruning. If this occurs well before the tree is planted, roots may proliferate immediately inside the wall of the pot. The air pruning of roots growing through small holes in pot walls is now exploited in pot designs. Some of these designs do not require the main pot to be buried within bigger diameter pots in the soil; the 'Air-pot' is an example. These pots have many fine holes in the pot wall. Roots venturing through these holes are air-pruned. A further development along these lines is the metal 'Spring Ring' which is a clamped sleeve, perforated by many small holes, enclosing the root mass. As with the 'Air-pot' air pruning of roots proliferating through the holes in the wall of the 'Spring Ring' occurs. This sleeve is removed prior to planting and can be reused.

Another approach that will help to some degree with the problem of the tree/pot blowing over, and to enhance the rooting space in the surface soils for young plants, is to use low-profile containers. The traditional approach to preventing trees blowing over, tying them in to a strained wire running through the nursery area, is still widely used. Watson and Himelick (1997) suggest that the shallow, wide root-balls produced in low-profile containers may be advantageous for planting on poorly drained sites. The traditional, taller container designs may be best for sites where soil water is readily available at depth.

5.3.2 Circling or girdling roots

A particular problem that is normally associated with young trees raised in containers, or even trees planted in root pits with smooth-sided boundary

Figure 5.5 An adult birch tree with a girdling root at ground level, Headington, Oxfordshire.

walls, is their tendency to circle the outside of the container (Watson and Himelick, 1997). This tendency has serious consequences as circling roots become girdling roots which strangle other parts of the root system and the stem, and when trees are transplanted into pits the tree is left with only a limited volume of soil that can be exploited. As trees mature the girdling roots may compromise tree stability and when they are on the surface they are vulnerable to damage (Fig 5.5). Although a number of techniques have been developed to prevent roots from circling around containers the problem still persists and trees growing in the landscape are still encountered with girdling or circling roots. It is a common procedure to cut these circling roots with several vertical slashes on the outside of the root-ball. Watson and Himelik (1997) also refer to 'butterflying' which is the creation of a deep vertical cut across the base of the root-ball and upwards into it. The two halves are then separated and spread across the bottom of the planting hole. A further problem may be that circling roots occur within the root-ball because the tree was previously transplanted from a smaller pot. Any treatment of circling roots needs to be aware of the prospect of additional circling within the root-ball.

Any cutting of the root-ball may cause stresses to the tree immediately prior to transplanting but that may be preferable to root circling. In nursery growing, attempts to prevent circling roots have involved vertical ribs built into the inner walls of plant containers. Another, chemical approach, uses copper hydroxide-based chemicals eg Spin Out®. This compound and others like it, which are painted or sprayed on the walls of containers, pots or barriers, inhibits root elongation and encourages the appearance of short root stubs where the roots meet the chemical.

Girdling roots are sometimes found in trees that have never been grown in pots, with Norway maple being more susceptible than other species (Watson and Clark, 2001). Watson and Clark suggest an explanation of the origin of girdling roots in transplanted trees. When a tree is dug in the nursery, and the large radiating primary roots are cut, new roots formed at the cut end grow in the same general direction as the original roots – these will not become girdling roots. However, existing secondary roots growing nearly perpendicular to the primary roots will grow more rapidly following the cutting of the primary roots. Any of the invigorated secondary roots located near to the tree trunk can become girdling roots. Watson and Clark (2001) presume that this tendency to produce girdling roots is a feature of transplanting of susceptible species such as Norway maple and is generally not a problem in forests which have regenerated from seeds.

5.3.3 Use of plant growth regulators

Root regeneration in deciduous and conifer seedlings may be promoted following transplanting by the prior application of plant growth regulators (auxins) as root sprays or dips. However, the exact effects are variable, depending on species, mode of application, type and concentration of auxin and environmental conditions (Kling, 1985). Davies *et al* (2002) examined the effect of the auxin, indole-3-butyric acid (IBA), on root development in two species with coarse roots, regarded as relatively difficult to transplant successfully, beech (*Fagus sylvatica*) and oak (*Quercus robur*). They found that IBA increased root initiation of beech seedlings but not in oak. As long as the IBA concentration exceeded 250 mg l^{-1} the duration of dipping was not critical. At a high concentration (2000 mg l^{-1}) many roots were initiated but many roots did not survive. Differences in response to auxins between species have been observed in other studies. Seaby and Selby (1990) found a large difference in response to another auxin, napthaleneacetic acid (NAA), in eight different conifer species.

The lack of any response in oak by Davies *et al* (2002) contrasts with results from other studies which show that auxins can promote root growth in other oak species (eg Cappiello and Kling, 1987; Struve and Rhodus, 1988; Struve and Arnold, 1986 and Struve and Moser, 1984). More relevant, using the same oak species as Davies *et al* (2002), and also alder, rowan and lime, Percival and Gerritsen (1998) found that three auxins, IBA, NAA and indole-3-acetic acid (IAA) alone and in combination promoted root and shoot growth in three-year-old containerised plants following root pruning. Auxins seem to offer a useful option for improving root development in young trees about to be transplanted but it would be valuable to understand the cause of variation in success that has been observed with the same species.

Paclobutrazol (PBZ) is a triazole derivative whose main mode of action is to disrupt the biosynthesis of gibberellic acids, naturally occurring plant growth regulators responsible for controlling shoot extension. There are many reports of the use of PBZ to limit above-ground growth of young amenity and forestry tree seedlings (Watson, 2001; Grossnickle, 2000). PBZ has also been used to limit shoot regrowth of pruned trees under overhead utility transmission lines (Burch *et al*, 1996). The distinct advantage of the use of PBZ at the establishment stage for young trees is that shoot growth is usually reduced and that the root:shoot ratio is therefore raised. This would be expected to improve the balance of the young tree in preparation for transplanting. There are also reports that applications of PBZ improve the water relations of young tree seedlings. There are direct effects of PBZ on root growth but the reports are conflicting (Grossnickle, 2000; Watson, 2001). Both the promotion and reduction of root growth has been reported, and there is a possibility that the concentration applied can be critical (van den Driessche, 1996; Watson, 2001). Watson (2001) found that PBZ reduced both shoot and root growth in American elm seedlings but nevertheless there was greater root extension from the original root system following the PBZ treatment. Because effects on shoot growth occurred sooner in root pruned plants, Watson assumed that root pruning prior to application of PBZ probably increased the speed of chemical uptake.

Because of the potential value of PBZ in providing the young tree with a root: shoot ratio more suitable for transplanting and countering plant water stress, it would be useful to understand how different responses to PBZ may depend on the amount applied and if other variables such as soil substrate are influential. Much of the research on PBZ has been done on seedling trees in North America, so it would be valuable to extend these studies to species used commonly in Europe and also to evaluate the influence of PBZ applied to the root systems of trees after transplanting.

5.3.4 Physiological attributes and successful establishment

The morphological properties of a young tree are clearly of considerable importance but alone they do not determine whether a tree will grow successfully. There is not necessarily a close relationship between morphological characteristics and planting out performance (Grossnickle, 2000). In the extreme case, a young tree may exhibit excellent morphological characteristics but in fact be dead!

In the forestry industries of many developed countries, considerable effort has gone into establishing testing programmes using physiological assessments of the viability and vigour of the young stock, including the root system, prior to transplanting. These physiological tests, which might also evaluate transport and storage impacts, are important because while a morphological trait, such as root:shoot ratio, will alter little from the time the tree is removed from the nursery to when it is planted, its physiology may have changed considerably. A number of the tests have been used to evaluate the quality of forestry nursery stock ready for transplanting (Table 5.5) and these have been discussed and evaluated by Kerr and Harper (1994), McEvoy and McKay (1997), McKay

Table 5.5 A range of stock quality tests based on physiological measurements. (Modified after Grossnickle, 2000.)

Stock quality tests	Purpose	Comments
Root growth capacity (optimum environment)	Measures seedling ability to regenerate new roots and an indirect measure of seedling physiological condition	Simple, relatively inexpensive, but requires up to 14 days to complete
Vigour test	Expose seedlings to a stress event and then measure subsequent seedling survival	Simple, inexpensive but long in duration
Shoot water potential	Measure of ψ as an indirect measure of root system capability to absorb water	Not applicable to broadleaves in winter, needs skilled operation, equipment has safety implications
Needle conductance, transpiration, or photosynthesis	Measurement of gas exchange as an indirect measure of root system capability to absorb water	Not applicable to broadleaves in winter, needs skilled operation
Infrared thermography	Measurement of needle temperature as an indirect measure of root system capability to absorb water	Requires skill to interpret, not applicable to broadleaves in winter
Root system water loss capability	Measurement of root system water loss under positive pressure as an indirect measure of root system integrity	Simple but may not discriminate slight damage due to lifting of seedling from physiological problems
Fine root electrolyte leakage	Measurement of root electrolytes as an indirect measure of root system integrity	Simple, cheap, applicable to broadleaves and conifers in winter. Requires about 2 days to complete a determination

Table 5.5 *continued*

Stock quality tests	Purpose References	Root growth capacity
Enzymatic activity	Determination of whether cell tissue is damaged or dead	Requires expensive laboratory facilities
Chlorophyll fluorescence	Direct measure of photosynthetic capacity and an indirect measure of seedling overall quality	Not applicable to broadleaves in winter, equipment relatively expensive but can also be used to test for other aspects eg salinity damage
Stress-induced volatile emissions	A measure of anaerobic respiration due to cell injury	Requires expensive laboratory facilities

(1997) and Grossnickle (2000). A substantial fraction of plants established in the built environment will be broadleaved, and deciduous in winter and therefore, will typically be leafless and dormant at the time when quality assessments would normally be made prior to planting out. A number of the physiological assessments require that the target plant should have functional foliage and not be deeply dormant. Therefore some of the tests are not appropriate for young broadleaf deciduous trees in mid-winter.

Physiological tests may require sophisticated laboratory facilities. Because large numbers of young plants are used annually in national and independent forestry enterprises, particularly in North America, economies of scale and centralised resources have allowed investment in sophisticated laboratory facilities for routine evaluation of batches of nursery stock. For small nurseries that supply relatively few plants for amenity planting, the investment costs for such facilities are unlikely to be justified.

Kerr and Harper (1994) used four criteria to evaluate the different assessment techniques and their relevance for broadleaf planting stock:

- There should be a strong relationship with planting out performance

- The test should be repeatable by different operators

- The test should be quick and simple

- Initial and running costs should be low.

Based on these criteria it is probable that the most suitable techniques to evaluate the quality of the root system of young nursery trees are **root growth potential** (RGP) and **root electrolyte leakage** (REL) (see Box 5.1 overleaf).

Box 5.1 Assessing the potential for roots to grow.

For root growth to occur, it is necessary that the root system is both viable and in a physiological state that allows growth. Variation in root growth potential or capacity (RGP) occurs seasonally in response to cultural treatments such as fertilisation, damage by drought or frosts, or from lifting, handling, and storage (Burdett, 1990). The test procedure (eg Tabbush, 1986; Cannell *et al*, 1990) entails placing a seedling into a root observation box made of 50 cm of plastic roof gutter filled with moist peat. A clear PVC cover is taped over the roots ie over the open side of the gutter. The observation boxes (perhaps 20 as replicates of a batch of seedlings) are placed at an angle of 30° from the vertical against sheets of hardboard or plywood so that the roots are in darkness and new roots grow along the PVC cover. Root growth potential is assessed by quantifying the initiation of new roots, usually the number of roots greater than 1 cm long, on each plant. The RGP test has shown a great deal of value with conifers but there have been studies that have not shown a relationship between RGP and field performance (references cited by Grosnickle, 2000). The major disadvantage of RGP as a measure of plant quality is that it usually takes around 10–14 days to complete in conifers; in dormant broadleaf species root growth will generally be slow so an RGP test may take even longer.

In contrast to the estimation of RGP, measurements of root electrolyte leakage (REL) is relatively rapid. McKay (1992) describes the protocol used with two-year-old plants of Sitka spruce and Douglas fir. The measurement requires that a 2-cm band of roots is cut about 10 cm from the root collar of sample plants. A sample of roots less than 2 mm in diameter amounting to around 0.5 g in fresh weight is taken for a determination. The sample is mixed with distilled water of known conductivity (measured with a conductivity meter) and the conductivity measured again after 24 hours. Finally, the sample is killed by autoclaving (pressure-cooking) at 110°C for 10 minutes followed by a further measurement of conductivity. The conductivity prior to autoclaving is expressed as a percentage of the value afterwards with the distilled water value subtracted from both the pre- and post-autoclave value. Clearly in terms of time and infrastructure requirements, the REL method has distinct advantages over the RGP method. For this particular measurement a control is necessary and there may be a difficulty in providing this on a routine basis.

Techniques such as RGP and REL have been developed mainly for use with young bare-rooted conifer transplants. Samples are taken from the large numbers of seedlings produced in the forestry nurseries. In the course of the testing the sampled plants are normally destroyed. Should physiological testing of young amenity trees be regarded as important there is a need to

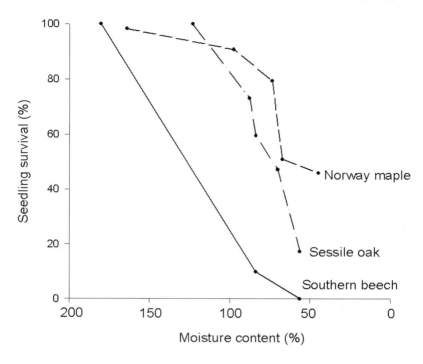

Figure 5.6 The relationship between moisture content at planting and the survival of seedlings of Norway maple (*Acer platanoides*), sessile oak (*Quercus petraea*) and southern beech (*Nothofagus obliqua*). (After Insley, 1979.)

develop these techniques for application to amenity transplants that will be far fewer in number and for which destruction of a sample might be considered an expensive and unacceptable option. There is also little experience of using a technique similar to REL on the root systems of containerised trees and development would be needed there.

5.4 Transplanting and desiccation

Much useful guidance in the handling and establishment of landscape plants will be found in JCLI (2002). When trees are dug up for transplanting, the loss of roots is a critical factor in determining survival after replanting as is the degree to which root regeneration occurs. However, there is the added problem that the degree to which the tree dries out, before some degree of establishment can occur, has a major impact on survival. Fig 5.6 (Insley, 1979) shows the requirement of the water content of young trees of three different species has to be high to ensure survival after transplanting. The nature of the risks of **desiccation** varies depending on whether the plant is bare-root stock, or grown in containers or with a root-ball enclosed in a bag, and whether the plant is an

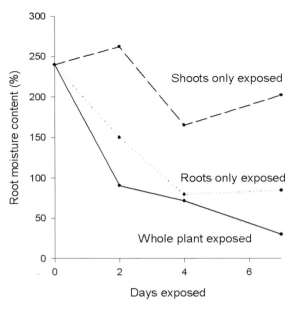

Figure 5.7 Changes in root moisture content over time of birch (*Betula pubescens*) seedlings subject to different amounts of protection. (After Insley, 1979.)

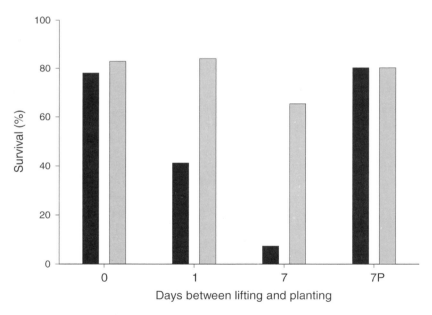

Figure 5.8 The survival of birch (*Betula pubescens*) (dark shading) and rowan (*Sorbus aucuparia*) (grey shading) subjected to different storage treatments prior to planting. 0, lifted and immediately replanted; 1, lifted and kept in store for 1 day before replanting; 7, lifted and kept in store for 7 days before replanting; 7P, lifted and kept in store with roots in polythene bag for 7 days before replanting. (After Dutton and Bradshaw, 1982.)

evergreen or leafless. The risks associated with the root system drying out apply to either evergreen or deciduous trees if the plants are bare-rooted.

Using data obtained by Insley (1979) for birch seedlings, Fig 5.7 shows the importance of reducing water loss from the root systems prior to transplanting. The best level of survival was found when the trees were completely covered with polythene between lifting and planting. Dutton and Bradshaw (1982) showed the need to replant quickly after digging up plants, unless elimination of desiccation losses between digging and replanting can be ensured (Fig 5.8). The study further illustrates that some species, eg rowan, are more tolerant to desiccation than others. The greater sensitivity of the fine roots of birch to drying out is also shown in Fig 5.8. Container-grown and root-balled plants are less at risk to the drying of the root system prior to transplanting than bare-rooted plants. There is also the additional risk of desiccation of the foliage of evergreen trees in winter and for deciduous trees if significant root establishment has not taken place before they leaf out.

5.4.1 Preventing desiccation

The risk of desiccation faced by young trees in the period after they are removed from the nursery and before they are planted out should not be underestimated. Prevention of water loss should be from the whole plant, not only the root system. Drying out of plants occurs quickly and can occur while in storage but especially if transported without covering in open vehicles. The transport of trees without covering in open-backed vehicles to a planting site, even in a brief journey, can cause severe desiccation and may negate careful prevention of water loss that might have occurred over several days.

5.4.1.1 Traditional methods

Young bare-rooted plants can be lifted through the winter period and stored at around 5 °C for several weeks in polythene sacks. The young plants can be transported in these sacks and transplanted directly. When plants are dug directly from the nursery they should be also kept in polythene sacks or wrapped in material such as hessian. It is important when reusing polythene sacks that they contain no traces of harmful chemicals or carry fungal infections. It is also important to realise that dry hessian sacking is far less effective in reducing desiccation of young plants than moist sacking. All efforts should be made to reduce desiccation and exposing the plants to excessively high or low temperatures but especially wind, which is often encountered when plants are transported in open-backed vehicles. For these reasons it is advisable to avoid placing the seedlings in direct sunlight. The same precautions also serve well for containerised trees or those with a bagged root-ball.

5.4.1.2 Root dips

Root dips are various different compounds in which the root system of the young tree is dipped prior to and in the transplanting process. The aim of using these compounds is either to provide the root system with a water-holding gel, which will provide a source of water for the roots or, for example, simply to coat the root system with a fine wet mud to minimise water loss. White (1990) has reviewed the use of the root dips and indicated that a benefit of using a root dip has not always been demonstrated and further studies are warranted.

5.4.1.3 Antitranspirants

Antitranspirants or **antidesiccants** are foliage sprays that reduce water loss through the leaf surfaces. There are a substantial number of products available marketed under evocative names (eg Wiltpruf, Leafshield, Moisturin, Vapor Gard, Folicote, Anti-Stress and Barrier). Antitranspirants are of two main types: (a) Film-type antitranspirants which produce a film on leaves, blocking stomatal pores or coating the cells inside the leaf with a waterproof film. The chemical nature of the sprays differs and they may be waxes, wax-oil emulsions, silicones, high molecular weight alcohols, resins, latexes or plastics. (b) Metabolic antitranspirants close the stomata chemically; they are now less common. The film-type antitranspirants form a thin protective film on the leaf surface that usually lasts for several weeks before weathering causes it to break up and disappear. It has been reported that some antitranspirants combined with the natural waxes in the stomatal pores of *Pinus resinosa* and formed an **impermeable** plug (Davies and Koslowski, 1974). Trials have also included metabolic antitranspirants which operate physiologically by inducing stomatal closure and in one case proved more effective than film-forming antitranspirants (Hummel, 1990).

Aside from questions of effectiveness, there are a number of possible problems with antitranspirants that were discussed by Koslowski and Davies (1975). They advocated caution in applying antitranspirants and recommended not applying high doses without running some trials on sample plants before full-scale usage. Some antitranspirants have been shown to have toxic effects on some species and not on others. Because antitranspirants prevent water loss from the leaves, high temperatures combined with strong sunlight can lead to heat injury of sprayed leaves. Another problem is that when trees that are in leaf are sprayed, while transpiration is curtailed by the sprays so also will be CO_2 uptake and growth may well be affected. In some cases, the permeability of antitranspirant films is greater for water vapour than for CO_2 (Koslowski and Davies, 1975).

Despite these problems, there are reports from several studies that indicate antitranspirants have a value in reducing stress after transplanting, even after summer planting (Watson and Himelick, 1997). On the other hand, there are reports, eg Castle (1983), which showed that spraying with an antitranspirant (Vapor Gard) had no short or long-term benefit for eight-year-old citrus trees. The alternative name for these types of products, antidesiccant, may be more appropriate as in many circumstances transplants (presumably leafless) of broadleaf species have been sprayed to delay drying out after transplanting. In the study reported by Englert *et al* (1993), 20 film-forming compounds were sprayed on bare-root transplants of red oak, Norway maple and Washington hawthorn (*Crataegus phaenopyrum*) at monthly intervals from September to April, and the desiccation stress, survival and plant performance were evaluated. The highest survival in the desiccation sensitive species, Washington hawthorn, was achieved with 'Moisturin'. A number of texts caution about relying on antidesiccants instead of adopting other practices such as irrigation, which is more likely to ensure the survival of the tree. The recommendations for transplanting root-balled trees in the British Standard BS 4043 (BSI, 1989) note that the benefit of antidesiccant sprays when transplanting evergreens, conifers or broadleaf trees in leaf is not yet proven. There is no recent research available to modify this observation.

5.4.2. Soil amendments

5.4.2.1 Peat and peat alternatives

Hodge (1995) reported on the performance of seven organic amendments on growth and survival of oak at three sites with differing soils (clay, chalk and silt). On the clay site three of the seven amendments improved survival but only two improved growth. In two cases growth was significantly poorer than the control at all three sites and this was associated with very high conductivity caused by the chemical content of the amendment. Hodge noted the high degree of variability in chemical and physical properties between the different amendments and also between different batches of the same product. One of the soil amendments tested by Hodge (1991) was a commercial peat compound which performed generally no better than other non-peat ameliorants.

In recent years, because of concerns about habitat destruction where sphagnum and sedge peat is extracted, there has been a trend in the reduction in use of natural peat in commercial plant production and as a soil ameliorant. Prestigious organisations in the UK eg the National Trust and the Eden Project are no longer using natural peat. The Consumers' Association published evidence that the quality of several peat substitutes can exceed that of natural peat. Their article, in *Gardening Which?*, does not provide details of the experimental procedures and statistical analysis (CA,2006). The plants that were used in the trials were those commonly used in patio planters and hanging baskets. Trees were not used in the tests. It would be valuable to repeat studies such as that of Hodge (1991) with present generation materials, such as those evaluated by the Consumers' Association.

5.4.2.2 Fertilisers

Nitrogen (N) is the element most likely to be needed by young trees for adequate growth. However, it is inadvisable to make heavy applications of nitrogen to a young tree at planting. The tree will not be able to exploit the fertiliser in the first year and root growth may be discouraged at the expense of shoot growth. However, this issue has conflicting evidence for it. While Hartman *et al* (2000) advise against applying nitrogen when transplanting trees, Harris *et al* (1999) believe the evidence that N is harmful because of excessive shoot growth at the expense of roots is not convincing. Dobson and

Moffat (1993) state that in conventional forestry, fertilisation is not recommended in the first two to three years after planting but there is evidence that on sites with poor nutrient status, fertiliser application has been useful. For example, Gilbertson *et al* (1987) applied N to birch and sycamore in a scheme to recolonise a china-clay waste dump and found 50% more root growth than shoot growth.

A small amount of fertiliser might be placed in the tree pit in the backfill soil 10 to 15 cm below the location of the root-ball. The use of slow release fertilisers is a useful option for providing the newly transplanted tree with a modest initial source of nutrients. Slow-release fertilisers can be:

• Slowly converted organic compounds

• Inorganic forms of low solubility such as magnesium ammonium phosphate

• Inorganic materials coated with plastic or sulphur or enclosed in plastic bags that govern the rate of release into the soil.

There is a price disadvantage of slow-release fertilisers. Harris *et al* (1999) estimated that proprietary slow-release fertilisers such as 'Apex' or 'Osmacote' are four to five times more expensive per unit of N than normal inorganic fertilisers.

The temptation to exploit surplus lawn fertiliser in tree planting should be resisted. It is likely to be supplemented with broadleaf herbicides with serious consequences for young trees.

5.4.2.3 Mycorrhizae

There seems to be no doubt that in most natural vegetation types, associations exist between plant roots and mycorrhizal fungi, and they seem to be universally present. As has already been mentioned in Chapter 3, in natural forests of temperate and boreal regions there is a strong association between the roots of most trees and either ecto- or **endomycorrhizal** fungi. The fungal symbiont, through its extensive hyphal network, takes up water and nutrients from the soil and transfers them to the root cortex. The fungus can also produce plant growth regulators affecting plant development, and the **mycelial mantle** of ectomycorrhizal symbiosis can protect the short absorbing roots against soil-borne pathogens.

There are several reviews of current knowledge concerning endomycorrhizal and ectomycorrhizal fungi and their use in forestry and horticulture (Kropp and Langlois, 1990; Smith and Read, 1997; Azcón-Aguilar and Barea, 1997). Particularly in the case of reforestation of logged forests either by regeneration or restocking and afforestation of new areas of degraded or damaged land, there are many accounts of the benefits to survival and subsequent growth of young trees, often in very harsh conditions. Of equal importance has been the accumulation of information about key factors that are likely to influence successful use of mycorrhizal fungi. There are many important findings that have come from the studies of mycorrhizae in forestry that seem to be equally applicable and relevant to any consideration to exploit mycorrhizal inoculation to enhance establishment and growth of young trees in urban situations.

There is a range of conditions that are optimal for the growth of mycorrhizae that mean that attempts to apply fungal inocula and expect benefits outside these ranges will produce disappointing results. The biggest benefits of the mycorrhizal infection of roots to tree growth has been observed when soil pH has not been too high ie between 4 and 5.5, with low or modest levels of nutrient and less than adequate amounts of soil water supply. There is little benefit to be expected by encouraging mycorrhizal infection when soil nutrients and water supply are already optimal. Equally, mycorrhizae will not thrive in soils with a naturally high pH, eg chalk or lime soils or soils in which the pH is high because of contamination by materials which raise the pH, eg mortar or plaster. In addition to highly fertile or moist/irrigated soils, other situations where application of mycorrhizal inoculation is not likely to be effective are (a) where there is substantial use of pesticides or herbicides, (b) where there is **anaerobic respiration**, eg flooded soils, or (c) where the problem for the tree is not a below-ground problem, eg a shade-intolerant tree being grown in shade (Findlay and Kendle, 2001).

A key feature of many studies of mycorrhizal fungi is the competition of the mycorrhizae with other soil microbes and a feature that should receive serious consideration in any applications of mycorrhizae in urban situations. The number of studies in which the practical benefits of applying mycorrhizal fungi to trees growing in urban situations have been examined are very much fewer than in the various types of forestry. One study is that by Garbaye and Churin (1996) who applied inocula of three different ectomycorrhizal fungi to the root pit when silver limes (*Tilia tomentosa*) were planted in Paris. Some of the observations in this study illustrate aspects of mycorrhizae referred to above. The benefits to the lime trees receiving mycorrhizal inoculation were only modest and short in duration. Shoot growth was greater in the second year after establishment and the leaves retained colour longer in the late summer. The authors acknowledge that because soil conditions were relatively good in any case, there were not expectations of large effects of the mycorrhizal inoculation. An important finding of this study was the decline in amounts of the inoculated mycorrhizae as time progressed. One of the mycorrhizal species (*Cenococcum geophilum*) that was inoculated had disappeared altogether by the end of the three-year study, while the concentration of the other two (*Laccaria laccata* and *Paxillus involutus*) decreased substantially. The competition of inoculated mycorrhizae with populations of resident soil microbes in urban soils is a key consideration and merits more research of the type advocated by Garbaye and Churin (1996). They indicated that a survey of the ectomycorrhizal symbionts occurring naturally with street trees in Paris was in progress and should serve as the basis for formulating future inoculations. This evidence from an urban study, which is supported by forestry literature, that competition with resident soil population of fungal types will determine the survival and efficacy of inoculated mycorrhizae is important. It means that applying commercial preparations of inocula with newly planted trees as a universal panacea for good growth is by no means guaranteed.

An important consideration is when to apply inocula of fungi to young trees. In the past, it was usual in traditional forest nurseries that were sufficiently close to forests to expect that sufficient amounts of spores would be released from fruiting bodies to inoculate the nursery. This might, however, be a fairly simplistic impression. Firstly, spore production can vary greatly from year to year so the effectiveness of infection of the nursery beds could be quite erratic. Secondly, studies have indicated that the fungi that produce the most effective symbiosis with mature trees are not necessarily those that are most beneficial to juvenile trees (Kropp and Langlois, 1990). The inoculation of the substrates in which young trees are grown in commercial nurseries of amenity trees may be difficult from outside sources as appropriate soils with sporulating fungi may be very distant. Also, when trees are grown in containers, many of the growing media, such as peat or other growing substrates will have been sterilised. Another factor that might mitigate against good mycorrhizal growth is that optimum fertiliser and water are usually provided at the nursery, and such optimum conditions are known to not favour mycorrhizal growth (eg Smith and Read, 1997).

The most suitable option for applying mycorrhizal supplements to trees would be at the time the tree is planted out. Fungal inoculation using spores is not as effective as applying cultures of the fungus in materials such as vermiculite. This can be injected into the root-ball or mixed with additional soil used to backfill the root pit. The solid inoculum may also be added later as an injection. Often the inoculum is added at the same time as nutrient supplements but there is considerable evidence that the influence of mycorrhizal infection on tree growth is better when nutrient levels are sub-optimal and pH is low. The use of mycorrhizal inoculations as an ameliorant of soil compaction effects is discussed in Chapter 9.

5.4.2.4 Hydrogels

Gel-forming or superabsorbent hydrophilic polymers (hydrogels) are soil conditioners developed to aid plant establishment during periods of water shortage. The polymers usually occur in one of three chemical types: (a) starch copolymers (b) polyvinylalcohols or (c) polyacrylamides. Forms of gels used in the past based on starch had a short life but several years of life can be expected from the more modern polymers such as the polyacrylamides, which is the type used most commonly at the present time. Water-absorbing polymers are least effective in the presence of soluble 'contaminants' and unfortunately, soil nutrients will fall into that category. Hydrogels have the largest increase in available water when mixed with infertile sand. They are least effective in a fertile, saline soil that is irrigated with hard water (ie high in Ca^+ and Mg^{2+}).

Even good quality tap water can reduce their effectiveness (Lamont and O'Conell, 1987). The high fertility that is usually expected of soils where the production and early growth of landscape trees occurs may reduce or even negate the hydration of hydrogels (Harris *et al*, 1999). Woodhouse (1989) and Bowman *et al* (1990) suggest that if soil solutions are rich in nutrients the capacity of the hydrogel to absorb water is reduced strongly. This factor is probably the biggest contributor to the occasions when only modest or no improvement has been detected when hydrogels have been used. Although there are manufacturers' claims that some polymers can absorb up to 500 times their own weight of distilled water, this capacity is decreased markedly in the presence of solutes.

There are a number of other circumstances when hydrogels would not be expected to show results. For example, it is clear that when water stress does not occur little benefit should be expected from the hydrogel. Equally, hydrogels cannot be effective if there is insufficient water available in the soil to hydrate them. Cross-linked polyacrylamide gels in particular seem to have certain 'salt-buffering' properties (Johnson, 1984a and b). This can reduce the phytotoxicity of salt (see Chapter 7). To achieve 100% hydration hydrophilic gels require longer than 2 hours of irrigation, and gel rehydration is much faster if the polymers are not fully dehydrated (Woodhouse, 1989). Therefore the effectiveness of the polymer will be influenced by the watering regimes.

A number of authors have reviewed the value of polymers in aiding the survival and growth of trees at the establishment phase, but unfortunately no overriding endorsement emerges. An early review by the UK Forestry Commission (Davies, 1987a) concluded that although polymers can markedly increase the available water capacity of soils, they proved to be of little or no use in sustaining the growth of newly planted trees (*Tilia, Fraxinus, Acer, Pinus* spp) and in some cases there were even deleterious effects. Other reports are somewhat more positive, however. Walmsley *et al* (1991) transplanted two-year-old bare-rooted sycamore in both pots and into the ground in coarse sand or peat. A 0.4% (by volume) addition of powdered polymer was added to a set of plants. The trees having polymer achieved the highest total weight and shoot weight gains but these differences were sometimes not significant. However, in all cases root weight was almost doubled in the plants receiving polymer compared to those without. Walmsley *et al* (1991) also showed that trees with polymers added to the soil did not wilt until one month whereas non-polymer plants wilted after two weeks. Winkelmann and Kendle (1996) aimed to resolve some of the conflicting results obtained previously in studies of the effectiveness of hydrophilic polymers in promoting plant establishment in two shrubs, *Deutzia* and *Ligustrum* (privet). These authors found (as did Woodhouse and Johnson, 1991) that there was an optimum application rate for the hydrogel, 'Broadleaf P4', and that higher application rates did not produce optimum growth. Promotion of growth occurred in pots but was not observed in the same treatments which had been planted out.

From their studies, Winkelmann and Kendle (1996) concluded that the effectiveness of polymers depended very much on the particular circumstances and there could be interactions with species, exploitable soil volumes and salinity. Positive as well as negative results could be achieved and dose rate was of critical importance as well as the watering frequency. Another important consideration was the growth parameter used to assess the effectiveness of the polymer. Some parameters showed significant effects of the polymer application while others did not. The overall conclusion on the possible value of hydrophilic polymers as an aid to the successful establishment of trees must be that it depends very often on particular circumstances and we are still not at a stage at which a protocol with universal applicability can be offered.

A few studies have evaluated the benefits or otherwise of incorporating polymers with structural soil mixtures (see also Chapter 4) to improve the capacity of the structural soil to hold water, and also to act as a sticking agent between the soil and the stone fractions. In a study at Cornell University, USA (Bassuk, 2001), polymer was added to the structural soil principally as a sticking agent and the aim was achieved. Another study in the UK (Richards, Moorehead and Laing Ltd, 2002)investigated the feasibility of providing a structural soil with adequate engineering strength to support load-bearing paving while still allowing tree water supply and growth. In this study, however, the addition of polymer (Broadleaf P4) or moler (a diatomaceous clay earth) was not a success because the inclusion of either prevented the compaction of the soil to the engineering standard required. The difference in success between the Cornell University and the UK study is most likely related to the size of the stone fraction. The size is substantially greater in the US experiment and the load-bearing properties come almost exclusively from stone to stone contact. In the UK study the stone and soil fractions were more intimately mixed and engineering strength comes from the mixture. The polymer is presumably preventing the compression of the mixture.

5.5 Care after transplanting

5.5.1 Irrigation

Fluctuations in water supply or higher atmospheric water demand in the nursery or at the planting site may adversely affect survival and later performance. Loss of young active roots at lifting and slow regeneration after planting out will make some species susceptible to dry soil conditions during establishment. Water stress has become the most frequent cause of dieback of amenity trees in Great Britain, accounting for 50% of all deaths with the majority occurring in the early years (Travers and Ireland, 1993). Often, a major contributing factor to these tree deaths will be a lack of an adequate supply of water for trees in the period after transplanting, and up until the water requirements of the tree can be met from the volume of soil exploited by roots, fed by rain without supplements from irrigation.

There is a need, therefore, to know the amounts of irrigation water that might need to be added. As with established trees which are discussed in detail in Chapter 6, there will be an uncertainty in the irrigation requirements because, as well as a varying evaporative demand controlled by the daily weather, the rooted volume and the available water storage in the rooted volume, there will be species differences over and above those caused by the amount of foliage borne by the tree. One of the major difficulties in estimating the exact water requirements of young transplanted trees is the large range of foliage amounts between a small transplant, perhaps a small whip, and a large standard. Nevertheless, for a number of reasons it is important to make a reasonable approximation of water needs. Sufficient water needs to be added to make a difference to survival or death and too much water could prove as harmful as too little. Also, there are significant costs and logistical difficulties associated with transporting and using large amounts of water, and these should be avoided.

There are large discrepancies between the perceptions of the water needs of young trees compared to actual measurements of transpiration loss. Information about apple trees provides a good example. Without offering the original reference, Thomas (2000) suggests that a young apple tree 2 m tall may use 7000 l in a summer. Assuming that the summer period extends for 200 days, this will mean that, on average, the daily water use is 35 l. Energy balance estimates of water use by apple trees of a similar dimension to the one discussed by Thomas (Thorpe *et al*, 1978) give a considerably smaller value, around 4.5 l day^{-1}. Values only slightly higher than those of Thorpe *et al* can be calculated from data presented by Brough *et al* (1982).

Using a model based on the work of Gilbertson *et al* (1987), Bradshaw *et al* (1995) have taken the approach that typical daily water use by young transplants will be between 1 and 3 litres and estimated the duration in days of the soil water supply given a range of rooted volume and available storage in that volume. A graphical illustration of calculations using their model is presented in Fig 5.9. The diagram shows, for example, that a tree transpiring 3 l of water per day growing in a rooted volume of 0.25m^3, that has an available water capacity of 10%, will use the available water in just over 8 days. At the other extreme a tree using 1 l of water per day, growing in 1 m^3 of soil with 30% of its volume being available water may sustain transpiration for 300 days. Box 5.2 gives detail of the calculations provided by Bradshaw *et al* (1995) and some worked examples. By doubling the water use there is a safety factor built in. Nevertheless, it is important to note that the scheme is aimed at UK conditions but might be relevant to many other places with temperate oceanic climates with frequent summer rainfall. It would not be adequate for hot, dry continental climates, eg the South West US, southern Europe or the Mediterranean. The protocol provides a good starting point and for the present, there are no better alternatives. We should, however, seek to develop and improve this type of methodology. A number of areas can be identified where improvements are possible but any sophistication should not add disproportionately to the ease with which such an approach may be used:

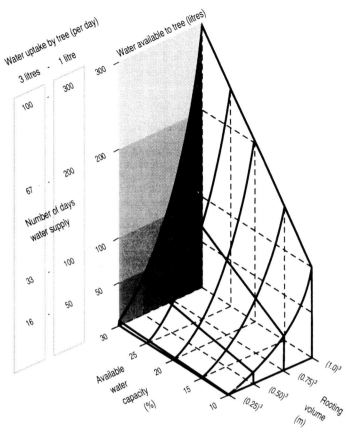

Figure 5.9 A diagram illustrating the model of Gilbertson *et al* (1987). The potential number of days that a volume of soil can supply water at either 1 or 3 l day-1. The influence of reductions in soil volume or available water storage is shown.

- There is a real need for measurements of actual water use by a range of commonly used species over a range of size classes in a range of planting situations (close to buildings or shaded). This call for fundamental data about water use of young trees would probably use some of the approaches advocated for use with established trees.

- There should be enhancement of irrigation when dealing with high water demand species eg poplars and willows.

- Allowance needs to be made for increased demand because of proximity to reflecting buildings or for when the tree is planted within asphalt (see Chapter 6).

- The scheme assumes irrigation only in the area of the root pit. Ideally, this area should include the area below which new roots are establishing.

Watson and Himelick (1997) advise that irrigation should be concentrated where the root-ball of the young tree is. Some evidence to support the strategy

Box 5.2 An example of using Fig 5.9 to determine irrigation requirements for a set of standard trees.

1 Assess tree size and therefore its likely water uptake.
2 Assess likely soil volume containing root system.
3 Assess likely soil water-holding capacity.
4 Read off from Fig 5.9 the number of days water supply (if trees are medium standards using 2 litres of water per day assume the value is half the 1 litre value).
5 If rain has fallen allow 1 day extra for each 10mm of rain.

The minimum amount of water to be applied to the trees is the amount used (equivalent to the water available given on the vertical axis of the graphs); as a safety margin, to ensure soil is properly saturated, apply double this amount to each tree.

6 Repeat for any further drought period, allowing for the likely increase in size of the root systems (it can be assumed that there is no increase in size if necessary watering has not been given).

Example 1: Light standards with roots occupying 50 × 50 × 50 cm pits, backfill ameliorated with 50% peat so water-holding capacity is 25%; no rain since leafing out.
Water uptake 1 litre day^{-1}; water available 31 litres.
Water sufficient for 31 days.
Water each tree by the end of fourth week with about 60 litres.

Example 2: Heavy standards with roots occupying 75 × 75 × 75 cm pits, backfill not amended but poor topsoil with water-holding capacity of 15%; 75 mm of rain during month after leafing out.
Water uptake 3 litres day^{-1}; water available 63 litres.
Water sufficient for 21 days + 8 days contribution from rain.
Water each tree by the end of fourth week with about 120 litres.

of preferentially irrigating the root-ball in the first season comes from a study of drying in the root-ball of green ash (*Fraxinus pennsylvanica*) trees and the adjacent soil by Watson and Kupkowski (1991). They showed that only 14 weeks after planting did the roots begin to remove water from the backfill soil, but even then, the root-ball was drying out more quickly (Fig 5.10). Other authors, eg Bradshaw *et al* (1995), advocate that some irrigation should be allocated outside of the root-ball at the outset. If the soil external to the root-ball remains dry, new roots are less likely to extend outwards and establish a wide root distribution needed to provide the tree with adequate soil resources and wind stability for the future. Watson and Himelick (1997) assume that in north

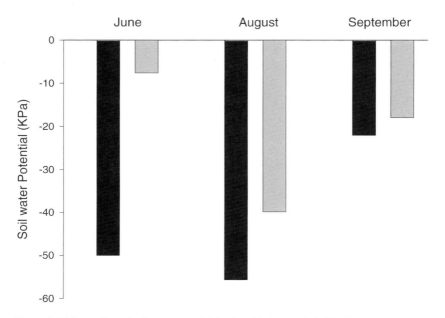

Figure 5.10 Comparison of soil water potential developed in the root-ball (■) of young ash trees and in the backfill (▨). Trees were planted in April. (After Watson and Kupkowski, 1991.)

temperate regions roots extend at approximately 0.5 m yr^{-1}. Based on this value and the rule of thumb that irrigation should be maintained at least until the spread of roots is three times the root-ball diameter, it is clear that irrigation will be required for one to a few years following transplanting depending on the tree size and its root-ball.

Establishment of trees grown in the field with root-balls has been compared to container-grown trees and also trees grown in in-ground fabric bags. Based on water stress evidence, Watson and Himelick (1997) indicate that better establishment occurs with field-grown trees, with container-grown trees establishing more slowly. This result is surprising because the container plants would be expected to have a better root:shoot ratio and to lose fewer roots during transplanting. The information from forestry literature on whether container-grown plants establish better than bare-root plants is quite conflicting (Aldhous and Mason, 1994; Grossnickle, 2000). While there are good examples (Fig 5.11) that the stresses are lower for container-grown plants (Grossnickle and Blake, 1987) in the UK, poorer survival of container plants was found compared to bare-rooted plants (Mason and Biggin, 1988). Given that a high proportion of amenity trees are established from container-grown plants there is a clear need to understand why growth in containers seems to confer little or no advantage in terms of reducing post-planting stress, or can in fact be a handicap.

5.5.2 The influence of weeds or surrounding vegetation

The small amount of text dedicated to competition by weeds and surrounding grass in amenity plantings by American publications such as Hartman *et al*

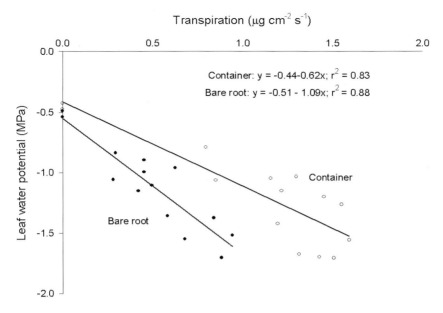

Figure 5.11 The change in leaf water potential with transpiration rate in bare-root and container-grown seedlings of black spruce (*Picea mariana*). (After Grossnickle and Blake, 1987.)

(2000), Harris *et al* (1999) and Watson and Himelick (1997) contrasts sharply with the importance ascribed to weeds and surrounding grassed areas in the UK by Bradshaw *et al* (1995), for example.

The vegetation often found competing with young planted trees will be weeds, but it is misleading to think that weeds alone compete with the young trees. There can be large and important negative impacts because of lawn grass or other amenity plantings close to young trees. Vegetation surrounding trees has two main competitive effects: those that occur above ground as competition for light, and below-ground competition for water and nutrients. Compared to the distribution of radiation by competing canopies, much less is known about the allocation of below-ground resources between tree root systems and the roots of grasses and weeds growing nearby. This understanding is important not only for amenity trees but also in all other circumstances where trees and other vegetation grow together, eg various forms of agroforestry. Equally the practical measures needed to alleviate above-ground competition are fairly well known and the use of mowing, strimming, **tree shelters** and herbicides are well-used practices. What seems to be poorly appreciated by those responsible for caring for trees, is the large impact of below-ground competition from surrounding vegetation, and that lawns and amenity grassland can have the biggest effects.

The rooting of grasses is particularly dense, fibrous and concentrated in the surface layers of the soil (Fig 3.5b). The competition for resources in the layers of soil just below the surface will be particularly intense and critical for a newly planted tree if grass is present. Studies by Davies (1987b) showed that there

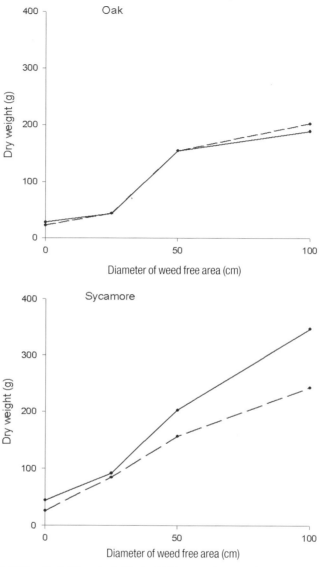

Figure 5.12 The effect of the extent of the herbicide-treated area on the root and stem growth of oak (*Quercus petraea*) and sycamore (*Acer pseudoplatanus*) transplants. (Root growth, ●———●; shoot growth, ● – – ●). (After Davies, 1987b.)

was an increasing benefit of a weed-free area around the tree on both above- and below-ground growth up to and probably beyond a diameter of 1 m for both oak and sycamore (Fig 5.12). Davies (1987b) showed that merely mowing grass did not relieve the competitive effects on young trees, and in fact vigorous regrowth of grass after mowing might make matters worse. Fig 5.13 shows a comparison of the soil water potential developed under different covers and shows that the driest soils are found under mown grass. This is not surprising – mowing maintains the grass cover as a predominantly young population of

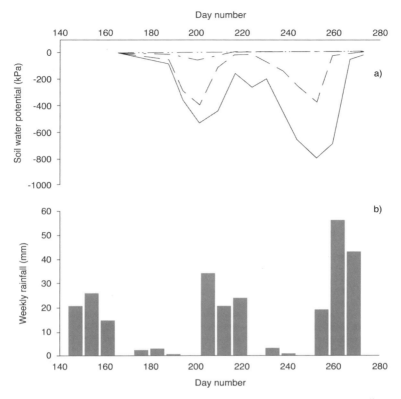

Figure 5.13 (a) Soil water potential developed in an area planted with trees and given different ground surface treatments. (Grass mown, ——; grass unmown, — —; bare soil, — • —; bark and felt — • • —.)**(b)** Weekly rainfall. (After Davies, 1987a.)

leaves. The situation can also be made worse by increasing the levels of fertiliser. Gilbertson *et al* (1987) showed that addition of nitrogen to the soil where grass and trees were growing together increased the competition between the two vegetations (Fig 5.14). Watson and Himelick (1997) imply that the competitive effects of surrounding grass can be overcome with sufficient irrigation and heavy fertilisation, but this seems to be a costly and less assured way of dealing with grass competition compared to herbicides or mulching.

Studies by Dawson *et al* (2001) showed that, in competition with a ryegrass sward, young cherry trees had far fewer roots in the upper 5–10 cm of soil than when the grass was eliminated with herbicide (Fig 5.15). However, even though a 1 m diameter circle of bare ground around each tree was maintained in this way, there was still a substantial amount of grass root around the trees. Clearly, a herbicide area with a diameter of a metre may still be too conservative. Eason *et al* (1992) examined root quantities and distributions below ash adjacent to either ryegrass or clover. They found that clover had far less of an impact on the root density of ash compared to ryegrass. The root length density of pasture grasses will be very high and it is expected that the results observed are likely to be the most extreme. Nevertheless, it is likely that

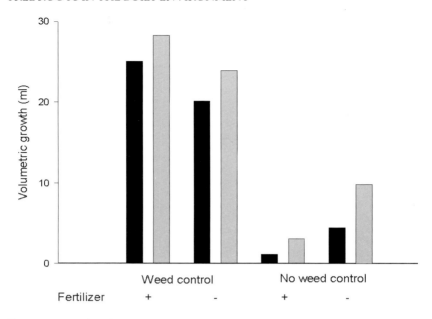

Figure 5.14 The effect of weed growth and fertiliser on the growth of ash and oak transplants under field conditions (■ shoot growth; ▦ root growth). (After Gilbertson *et al*, 1987.)

unless their roots are completely separated spatially there could be an impact of other short vegetation of various ornamental types with which trees are grown on the water uptake of trees. The weeds, grass or other short vegetation will have their biggest competitive influence while the trees are becoming established and only casting a small amount of shade. When the trees overtop the lower vegetation they will alter the microclimate around the vegetation below them and reduce the potential demand that the short plants can then make on the soil water resources they share with the young tree.

In addition to competition for water and nutrients, some lawn grasses, and probably other plants as well, may be able to reduce the growth of trees close to them, through chemicals they produce. The chemicals may be formed in the leaves and leached into the soil or produced by the roots directly. This chemical inhibition is called **allelopathy**. With respect to amenity trees, these effects have only been reported from studies in North America but it is likely that the same effects do occur elsewhere. However, allelopathic effects have not been distinguished from the effects of competition for water or nutrients. In the American literature reviewed by Watson and Himelick (1997), fescue grasses (*Festuca* spp) have been shown to stunt the growth of southern magnolia (*Magnolia grandiflora*), black walnut (*Juglans nigra*) and sweet gum (*Liquidambar styraciflua*). Other combinations of trees and grasses have not been studied. Allelopathic chemicals from grass are likely to persist in the soil even when the grass has been mulched over or killed with herbicide, and may still inhibit tree growth until the chemicals are leached from the soil by rainfall or degraded.

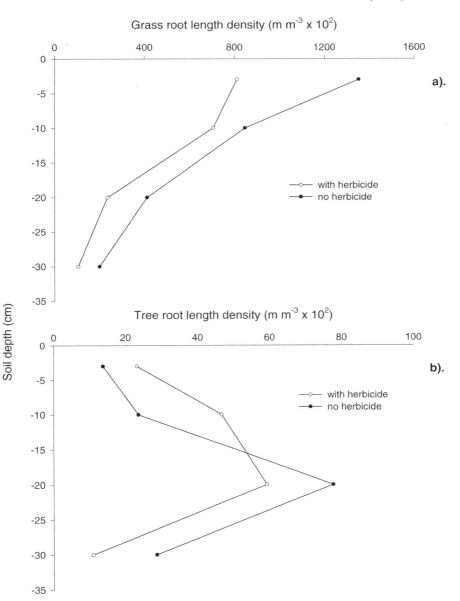

Figure 5.15 Influence of soil depth on root length density of **(a)** grass (*Lolium perenne*) roots and **(b)** white roots of cherry (*Prunus avium*) trees, with herbicide and without herbicide. (After Dawson *et al*, 2001.)

5.5.3 Mulching

Mulching is the application of a cover to the surface of the soil (Fig 5.16). The most often used mulches are organic materials such as shredded bark, leaf-mould, wood chips, organic compost or well rotted manure. Other types of mulching materials include sand, gravel, synthetic and natural mats, plastic

Figure 5.16 Organic mulch around a newly established tree at Milton Park, Didcot.

sheeting and landscape fabrics. Fabric and plastic materials are usually covered over with one of the other mulch materials to hold them down and camouflage them. Applying a mulch is another way to suppress weeds and other competing vegetation but there are several other benefits to be gained from mulching. Mulching can be used to retain soil moisture, to buffer soil temperatures against extremes and to replenish organic matter and nutrients in the soil. All of these effects lead to improved growth in the soil beneath the mulch as well as in the well-established organic mulch layer itself. The roots in the mulch will not be at any greater risk of desiccation, since a well-established layer of mulch can hold as much or more water than the soil itself, without decreasing aeration to the soil beneath it (Himelick and Watson, 1990). An important function of a mulch will be to protect soil around the tree from splash erosion from rainfall or sprinkler irrigation. Erosion of soil can occur by rain splashing as well as the caking and crusting of the soil surface. A mulch will also reduce surface runoff of water after rainfall or irrigation, so that more of the water infiltrates into the soil near the tree. In addition, moisture can accumulate under a mulch because water vapour in the soil condenses on the cold mulch at night. It is important to recognise that most of the positive properties of mulches are provided just as well by inorganic materials as by organic ones. Some mats are made of fibre and are biodegradable. Mulching using either organic or inorganic materials offers many opportunities to exploit recycled materials.

There is substantial evidence for the effectiveness of mulches in increasing root development and improving tree growth. In newly planted trees, mulching at the time of planting resulted in a 400% increase in fine root development in the top 15 cm of soil partially because grass competition is eliminated (Green and Watson, 1989). Above-ground growth is also increased by mulching (Fraedrich and Ham, 1982; Green and Watson, 1989; Neely, 1984; Welker and Glenn, 1985 and Whitcomb, 1981). Harris *et al* (1999) do not support the view that mulched trees develop more shallow root systems overall compared to unmulched trees.

The size of the mulched area needed will depend somewhat on the size of the plant. Watson and Himelick (1997) suggest that for a tree with a stem diameter of 8 cm a mulching area with a diameter of 2–3 m would be best. This will cover the area into which roots will grow during the early part of the establishment period of the tree. Trees will benefit longer from larger areas of mulch but even a small circle of mulch around the trunk will reduce lawn mower injury. Mulch applied directly over grass will usually smother it. At the time of planting deep tilling of the soil around the outside of the planting hole under the entire mulched area would be recommended to create a larger planting hole for better root growth. In very cold winter climates it may be best not to apply mulch to plants installed in the early spring until after the soil has warmed up.

Organic material should be completely composted before it is applied around the base of a tree. There are risks that the decomposition ie composting of fresh organic mulch, eg sawdust, will tie up available nitrogen as it is degraded and this will reduce the availability of nitrogen to the tree. There may also be a change in pH. Some sources of hardwood bark may increase soil pH, and pine needles may decrease soil pH. Depending on the source, mulches can be modified with the addition of nitrogen, lime, or sulphur to avoid some of the soil-related problems.

Composting before use will eliminate potential nutrient imbalances, and should kill plant pathogens and increase micro-organisms that suppress disease (Hoitink et al, 1997). There is no evidence that vascular diseases are transmitted in the mulch. The mulch layer should be 5–10 cm deep after settling. A thinner layer will require replenishment and a deeper layer would not give additional benefits and may be harmful. Roots may be damaged from excess mulch due to insufficient oxygen where soils beneath the mulch are poorly drained. Davies (1987b) found that mulch over heavy loam soils caused poor growth conditions for young cherry trees and some deaths followed. The mulch layer should not be heaped up around the tree stem because of the risk to the bark from fungal attack. This risk is similar to that involved in increasing the soil level around trees, which is discussed in Chapter 9.

Sheets of plastic or **geotextile** fabric are sometimes used under mulch to control weeds. Plastic can cause roots to grow at, or near, the soil surface, presumably because of reduced aeration in deeper soils (Whitcomb, 1980). Weed shoots and roots can penetrate many of the fabrics. Decomposing mulch on top of the fabric or plastic creates an excellent environment for weeds to establish, though the fabric can reduce the time required for weeding the mulch (Derr and Appleton, 1989). Geotextile fabrics under mulch can sometimes become so clogged with gravel and debris that water and air cannot pass through. The fabric will also prevent the humus from the decomposing mulch from being incorporated into the soil.

5.5.4 Shelter and protection for young trees

The establishment of broadleaved tree species is significantly helped by the use of individual tree shelters (Savill et al, 1997). These are semi-translucent plastic tubes with a cross-sectional area of about 80 cm^2 that enclose recently planted trees. Tree shelters are most commonly about 1.2 m tall but need to be taller if fallow or red deer are present, but can be less than 1.2 m if no deer are present and are therefore only suitable for young trees up to feathered size. During the critical first three years in shelters, height growth can be accelerated by three times in *Quercus* and several other broadleaved species; conifers are less responsive. This rapid growth reduced the period of susceptibility to weed competition and frost damage. The shelters also give protection from small mammals such as roe deer and rabbits, and enable chemical herbicides to be used more safely. On very weedy sites it is possible to see clearly where the planted trees are.

Air temperature and relative humidity are higher inside the shelter and result in more rapid height growth and survival (Watson and Himelick, 1997) compared to unsheltered trees. These authors also claim that CO_2 concentrations

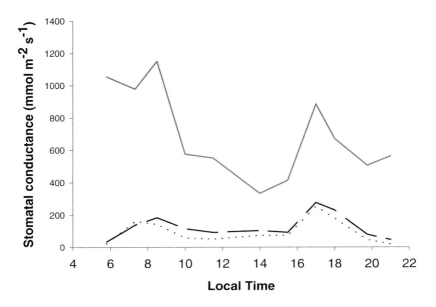

Figure 5.17 Stomatal conductance of cherry (*Prunus avium*) seedlings grown in unventilated tree shelters (——), ventilated tree shelters (·········) or with no tree shelters (— —). (After Bergez and Dupraz, 2000.)

which would increase photosynthesis and growth are higher within tree shelters, but more recent work referred to below questions this. A number of studies have shown that tree shelters can limit diameter increase at the expense of height growth, and the tree trunk may be incapable of supporting the weight of the top when the shelter has been removed. Watson and Himelick (1997) believe that in landscape applications removal of the shelter often occurs prematurely. In their original role as tree shelters in forestry and roadside planting it is normal for the tree shelter to degrade *in situ*. In this circumstance the tree adjusts gradually to a non-shelter situation, but this will not occur if the shelter is removed prematurely. Such premature removal may put the tree under stress. Bergez and Dupraz (1997) examined the leaf stomatal conductance of wild cherry (*Prunus avium*) trees growing in tree shelters. They found that stomatal conductance was high and unresponsive to climatic conditions (Fig 5.17). They predicted that removal of tree shelters prematurely while the leaves were still on the tree would be very damaging, as the leaves have little control of water loss.

Tree shelters can reduce root development but the reasons for this are not clear (Potter, 1991). Light levels inside the shelter will be approximately half that outside the tree shelter, but this alone should not reduce the size of the root system relative to the top. The balance of the radiation spectrum ie the red:far red ratio will be different inside and can produce a reduction in root:shoot ratio. However, this can only be a plausible explanation while the tree and its foliage are totally enclosed within the shelter. Svihra *et al* (1996) found that tree shelters inhibited root development of coastal redwood (*Sequoia*

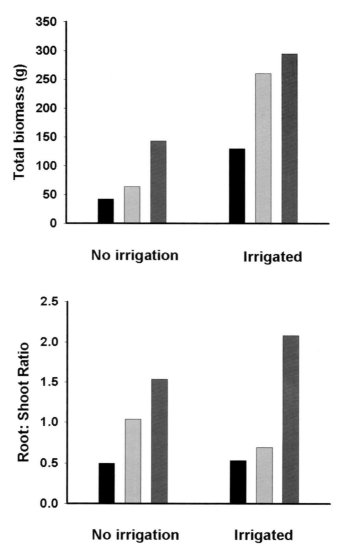

Figure 5.18 Total dry biomass and root:shoot ratio of cherry (*Prunus avium*) seedlings grown in unventilated tree shelters (■), ventilated tree shelters (▨) or with no tree shelters (▨) in two irrigation regimes. (After Bergez and Dupraz, 2000.)

sempervirens) seedlings and did not recommend tree shelters for use with this species for this reason. Unprotected trees growing without tree shelters gained more root fresh weight and dry weight. Trees grown in shelters produced roots with small diameters. If the shelter is removed and tree transpiration is enhanced, the limited root system may leave the tree with difficulties in acquiring sufficient water. Burger (1998) found that six out of the seven species in the trial showed a reduction in biomass, total root length and total root area.

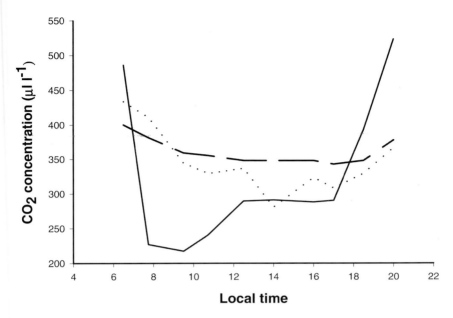

Figure 5.19 Diurnal variations in CO_2 concentration in unventilated tree shelters (———), ventilated tree shelters (·········) or in the open (— —). (After Bergez and Dupraz, 2000.)

The reduced biomass found in most of the tree species in this study is most likely due to a combination of environmental factors associated with the tree shelters. Bergez and Dupraz (2000) also found that tree shelters reduced the proportion of root to shoot in wild cherry trees and this occurred in irrigated or non-irrigated conditions (Fig 5.18). The reduction in the root:shoot ratio compared to trees growing without shelters was less severe in shelters with ventilation holes drilled in them. Bergez and Dupraz (2000) believe the improvement in root–shoot balance is because of higher photosynthetic rates in the ventilated shelters. They examined the carbon dioxide concentrations inside the shelters and calculated that in simple shelters without any additional ventilation there is a significant lowering of carbon dioxide that reduces the photosynthesis of the tree to very low levels (Fig 5.19). These authors questioned the interpretations of earlier work by Kjelgren *et al* (1997) who made instantaneous measurements of photosynthesis of trees in shelters and found high rates. Bergez and Dupraz (2000) contend that their alternative approach that monitored CO_2 concentrations and air exchange within the shelter, indicated that the trees will be suffering CO_2 starvation, and photosynthesis will be limited. A tree shelter equipped with ventilation holes would go some way to prevent the drawdown of CO_2 concentrations in the shelter. Nevertheless, even with ventilation of the tree shelter the balance between roots and shoots is less than trees growing in the open (Fig 5.17). Bergez and Dupraz (2000) believe this may be due to either a lower amount of radiation, a different spectrum, or a lack of wind stimulation of root growth in the shelter.

5.5.5 Support for trees

Unless the transplanted trees are small, they will almost invariably need some form of support when they are transplanted into a site. In public areas very small trees may benefit from having stakes nearby as guards, or a warning to walkers or vehicle users, including grass-cutting operatives, that the tree is present. The scope for variation and ingenuity in tree staking is very wide and the reader is referred to several texts which cover the merits of different configurations for staking, eg Harris *et al* (1999), Littlewood (1988), Hartman *et al* (2000) and Watson and Himelick (1997). As well as the advantages of staking there are some potential problems. Table 5.6 (Bradshaw *et al*, 1995) summarises the

Table 5.6 The potential benefits and problems of supporting newly transplanted trees.

Potential benefits	Potential problems
1. Stabilises transplanted trees, which have truncated root systems 2. Provides anchorage for protection devices	1. Alters tissue distribution in stem and roots 2. Weakens stem at attachment point 3. Requires careful regular maintenance 4. When removed, the tree may be less able to stand upright than a tree which was unsupported from planting 5. Expensive

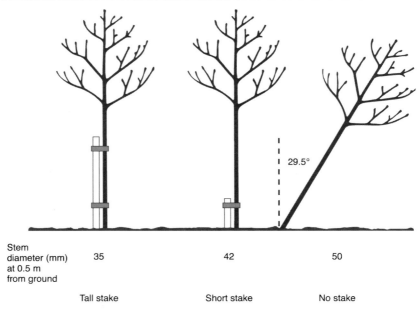

Stem diameter (mm) at 0.5 m from ground

Tall stake	Short stake	No stake
35	42	50

29.5°

Figure 5.20 Influence of high, low and no staking on stem diameter at 0.5 m from the ground. (After Bradshaw *et al*, 1995.)

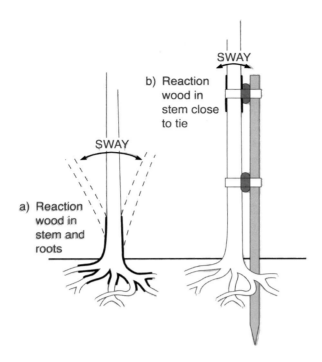

Figure 5.21 Diagram illustrating the influence of **(a)** no staking or **(b)** high staking on the location of reaction wood formation. (After Bradshaw *et al*, 1995.)

benefits and problems associated with supports of newly planted trees. At least two of these problems (1 and 4) are related to root development of the trees. There is plenty of evidence that staking of trees increases height growth relative to unstaked controls eg Harris *et al*, 1999; Svihra *et al*, 1999. This has significant implications for the capacity of the tree root system to support the tree when the tree support is no longer functional or is removed. Bradshaw *et al* (1995) report a study of the variation in stem diameter of plane trees (*Platanus* sp.) growing at a very windy site (Fig 5.20). Stem diameter at 0.5 m from the ground was largest in the unstaked trees and smallest in those with tall stakes. Fig 5.21a shows that in trees with no stakes, any sway occurs at the base and this is the stimulus for reaction wood in the stem base and the large lateral roots (see Chapter 3). There is, for example, evidence from recent work with *Pinus radiata* that the bending moments at the tree base are transmitted as stresses to large lateral roots (Watson, 2000) and these stresses lead to differential production of reaction wood in large surface lateral roots. In trees with tall stakes (Fig 5.21b) the reaction wood is distributed just above the point where tree ties are attached. The failure to develop reaction wood and thickening in the larger lateral roots will seriously compromise the development of strong support roots while the stake is in position and the stability of the tree in strong winds after the stake is removed. If a stake is attached to the tree at a low point on the trunk, it is possible that at least some reaction wood will be created at the stem base and in the large lateral roots. The recommendation is that if

Figure 5.22 A young oak tree stabilised using a wooden frame across the top of the root-ball attached to below-ground anchors with adjustable cables, Droitwich, UK.

staking of trees has to occur then the tying of the tree to the stake should be made at the lowest point on the tree stem that is consistent with the stake having a significant role.

There are alternatives to staking to provide support for young trees. Where the trees are too large to be staked they may be guyed to ground anchors located at suitable distances from the tree. The guy wires will be attached to the tree with plastic- or rubber-covered yokes and are usually located above the lowermost branches. Various options are illustrated in Littlewood (1988). As with staking and tying there is a need for vigilance that the yoke system does not constrain the tree as it develops. The guying system offers some hazard to pedestrians and needs to be made obvious.

Trees can also be stabilised by a frame spread over the root system and attached by adjustable cables to ground anchors located in the base of the planting hole (Fig 5.22). The anchors can be metal spikes driven into the base of the tree pit or they can be heavy stones (eg kerbstones). The steel cables can be adjusted to accommodate volume growth of the root system and can subsequently be detached and removed without disturbing the root system. Details can be found in Littlewood (1988). Because root anchoring systems are partly hidden from view there may be a danger that maintenance is neglected and the root system becomes seriously constricted. Consideration should also be given to the issue that root anchoring systems might present a significant trip hazard in some circumstances.

5.6 Summary

- A wide variety of planting stock is available, ranging from seeds to large trees. For small material the likelihood is that the root system will establish relatively quickly to be able to support the tree. However, small trees are at risk from weeds and make little visual impact. The larger the tree the greater is the proportion of the root system that will be lost at transplanting. The time for a large tree to become fully established will be substantially longer than for smaller trees.

- Although a large proportion of the stock used for amenity plantings is grown in containers there are still problems for container-grown plants. Most of these problems are to do with the root system but others are to do with the incompatibility between container soil and planting site soil.

- There are intrinsic differences in transplantability between tree species that seem to be broadly related to morphological characteristics. Generally, fast-growing trees or those with fibrous root systems tend to be easier to transplant than slow growing trees or those with coarse, fleshy roots.

- Important preparations can be made to the root systems of trees prior to transplanting which will improve their capacity to establish successfully. The major strategy is to increase the density of roots in the soil volume around the roots that will be available after transplanting.

- Studies in natural forest ecosystems have provided overwhelming evidence of the benefits of the mycorrhizal association of fungi with tree roots. A major challenge in the planting of trees in the built environment is the replication of such mycorrhizal associations. Certain controlling factors are recognised and understood, including the need for optimal soil nutrients and pH conditions for colonisation. Fertile soils with a high pH are less likely to encourage prolific mycorrhizal associations of fungi with tree roots but equally these might be the conditions in which mycorrhizal infection would be of least benefit. A major uncertainty for the development of the technique of inoculating the roots of young trees in the built environment is the success or otherwise of competition of fungal species in the inoculum in competition with resident rhizosphere fungi. There is little information about the mycorrhizal species typically resident on roots of long-established amenity trees in built environments.

- A number of soil amendments are available to be incorporated into backfill soils of newly planted trees. Water absorbent gels are one of these but the evidence that they offer a substantial advantage to young trees is conflicting. It is not advisable to rely on such items such as polygels as soil amendments.

- Without any doubt, a major problem for the establishment of young trees in soft landscapes will be competition from weeds, but the most intense competition is likely to be from grasses because of their dense surface rooting. Application of additional fertilisers will only exacerbate the problem. Studies with herbicided areas around young trees showed that areas less than 1 m in diameter would still be influenced by the surrounding grass. Mulching around young trees can be equally beneficial in suppressing weeds and conserving moisture and is more acceptable environmentally than the use of herbicide.

- Unless rainfall is frequent and adequate, irrigation should be provided for young trees until they are fully established. There are, however, areas of uncertainty about irrigation. The amount of irrigation water required by young trees is not known precisely and also the most effective location of the water, ie whether at or outside the root-ball area, is not fully resolved.

- Tree shelters offer protection to young trees against browsing animals, being overgrown by weeds, direct contact with herbicides and mower/strimmer damage. Although height growth of trees in shelters is promoted there are negative impacts: dry matter increase is reduced and the root:shoot ratio is reduced. The tree shelters used should be as short as are required for the site.

There are distinct risks to the tree if the shelter is removed prematurely and the shelter should not be removed from a young tree in full leaf which is fully enclosed in the shelter.

- Small trees may not need support from a stake but there is still a need to warn operatives spraying and mowing and the general public that a small tree is present. A tree shelter will provide this visual warning indication. Stakes will be essential to support large trees up to large standards until their root systems provide that stability. The position at which the stake is tied to the tree is important to root development. Tying the tree to the stake unnecessarily high up the trunk will mean that stimulation of reaction wood in the larger surface roots of the tree will be limited.

REFERENCES

Abod, S.A. & Webster, A.D. 1991. Carbohydrates and their effects on growth and establishment of Tilia and Betula 1. Seasonal changes in soluble and insoluble carbohydrates. *Journal of Horticultural Science*, 66, 235–246.

Aldhous, J.R. & Mason, W.L. 1994. *Forest Nursery Practice*. Forestry Commission Bulletin 111. HMSO, London, UK. 268 pp.

American Association of Nurserymen. 1997. *American Standard for Nursery Stock*. ANSI Z60.1. American National Standards Institute, Washington, DC., USA. 57 pp.

Azcón-Aguilar, C. & Barea, J.M. 1997. Applying mycorrhiza biotechnology to horticulture: significance and potential. *Scientia Horticulturae*, 68, 1–24.

Bassuk, N. 2001. *Structural soil – growing trees in concrete*. Presentation at Arboricultural Association Annual Conference, Lancaster, UK.

Bergez, J.-E. & Dupraz, C. 1997. Transpiration rate of *Prunus avium* L. seedlings inside an unventilated treeshelter. *Forest Ecology and Management*, 97, 255–264.

Bergez, J.-E. & Dupraz, C. 2000. Effect of ventilation on growth of *Prunus avium* seedlings grown in treeshelters. *Agricultural and Forest Meteorology*, 104, 199–214.

Bowman, D.C., Evans, R.Y. & Paul, J.L. 1990. Fertilizer salts reduce hydration of polyacrylamide gels and affect properties of gel-amended container media. *Journal of the American Society of Horticultural Science*, 115, 382–386.

Bradshaw, A.D., Hunt, B. & Walmsley, T. 1995. *Trees in the urban landscape: Principles and practice*. E & FN Spon, London, UK. 272 pp.

Brough, D.W., Jones, H.G. & Grace, J. 1982. Diurnal changes in water content of the stems of apple trees as influenced by irrigation. *Plant, Cell and Environment*, 9, 1–7.

BSI. 1989. BS 4043. *Recommendations for transplanting root-balled trees*. British Standards Institution, London, UK. 12 pp.

BSI. 1992. BS 3936. Part 1. *Nursery Stock. Specification for trees and shrubs*. British Standards Institution, London, UK. 21 pp.

Burch, P.L., Wells, R.H. & Kline, W.N. 1996. Red maple and silver maple growth evaluated 10 years after application of paclobutrazol tree growth regulator. *Journal of Arboriculture*, 22, 61–66.

Burdett, A.N. 1990. Physiological processes in plantation establishment and the development of specifications for forest planting stock. *Canadian Journal of Forest Research*, 20, 415–427.

Burger, D.W. 1998. Physiological and horticultural aspects of the use of tree shelters in the California Landscape. In: *The Landscape below ground II*. Proceedings of an International Workshop on Tree Root Development in

Urban Soils (Ed. by D. Neely and G.W. Watson), pp. 36–45. International Society of Arboriculture, Champaign, IL., USA.

CA. 2006. Compost on trial. *Gardening Which?* January 2006, pp.16-21. Consumers' Association, London, UK.

Cannell, M.G.R., Tabbush, P.M., Deans, J.D., Hollingsworth, M.K., Sheppard, L.J., Philipson, J.J. & Murray, M.B. 1990. Sitka spruce and Douglas fir seedlings in the nursery and in cold storage: root growth potential, carbohydrate content, dormancy, frost hardiness and mitotic index. *Forestry*, 63, 9–27.

Cappiello, P.E. & Kling, G.J. 1987. Increasing root regeneration and shoot growth in two oak species with spray applications of IBA. *HortScience*, 22, 663.

Castle, W.S. 1983. Antitranspirant and root and canopy pruning effects on mechanically transplanted eight-year-old 'Murcott' citrus trees. *Journal of the American Society of Horticultural Science*, 108, 981–985.

Cool, R.A. 1976. Tree spade vs. bare root planting. *Journal of Arboriculture*, 2, 92–95.

Davies, M.J., Hipps, N.A. & Kingswell, G. 2002. The effects of Indole-3-butyric acid root dips on the root development and shoot growth of transplanted *Fagus sylvatica* L. and *Quercus robur* L. seedlings. *Journal of Horticultural Science & Biotechnology*, 77, 209–216.

Davies, R.J. 1987a. Tree establishment: soil amelioration, plant handling and shoot pruning. In: *Advances in Practical Arboriculture* (Ed. by D. Patch), pp. 52–58. Forestry Commission Bulletin 65. HMSO, London, UK.

Davies, R.J. 1987b. *Trees and Weeds: weed control for successful establishment.* Forestry Commission Handbook 2. HMSO, London, UK.

Davies, W.J. & Koslowski, T.T. 1974. Short- and long-term effects of antitranspirants on water relations and photosynthesis of woody plants. *Journal of the American Society for Horticultural Science*, 99, 297–304.

Dawson, L.A., Duff, E.I., Campbell, C.D. & Hirst, D.J. 2001. Depth distribution of cherry (*Prunus avium* L.) tree roots as influenced by grass root competition. *Plant and Soil*, 231, 11–19.

Derr, J.F. & Appleton, B.A. 1989. Weed control with landscape fabrics. *Journal of Environmental Horticulture*, 7, 129–133.

Dobson, M.C. & Moffat, A.J. 1993. *The potential for woodland establishment on landfill sites.* Department of the Environment. HMSO, London, UK. 88 pp.

Dumais, D., Coursolle, C., Bigras, F.J. & Margolis, H.A. 2002. Simulated root freezing in the nursery: effects on the growth and physiology of containerized boreal conifer seedlings after outplanting. *Canadian Journal of Forest Research*, 32, 605–615.

Dutton, R.A. & Bradshaw, A.D. 1982. *Land reclamation in cities.* HMSO, London, UK.

Eason, W.R., Tomlinson, H.F. & Hainsworth, C. 1992. Effect of ground vegetation on root distribution of ash trees. *Aspects of Applied Biology*, 29, 225–231.

Englert, J.M., Warren, K., Fuchigami, L.H. & Chen, T.H.H. 1993. Antidesiccant compounds improve the survival of bare-root deciduous nursery trees. *Journal of the American Society for Horticultural Science*, 118, 228–235.

Findlay, C. & Kendle, A.D. 2001. Towards a mycorrhizal application decision model for landscape management. *Landscape and Urban Planning*, 56, 149–160.

Fraedrich, S.W. & Ham, D.L. 1982. Woodchip mulching around maples: Effect on tree growth and soil characteristics. *Journal of Arboriculture*, 8, 85–89.

Garbaye, J. & Churin, J.L. 1996. Effect of ectomycorrhizal inoculation at planting on growth and foliage quality of *Tilia tomentosa*. *Journal of Arboriculture*, 22, 29–34.

Geisler, D. & Ferree, D.C. 1984. Responses of plants to root pruning. *Horticultural Reviews*, 6, 155–188.

Gilbertson, P. & Bradshaw, A.D. 1985. Tree survival in cities: The extent and nature of the problem. *Arboricultural Journal*, 9, 131–142.

Gilbertson, P., Kendle, A.D. & Bradshaw, A.D. 1987. Root growth and the problems of trees in urban and industrial areas. In: *Advances in Practical Arboriculture* (Ed. by D. Patch), pp. 59–66. Forestry Commission Bulletin 65. HMSO, London, UK.

Green, T.L & Watson, G.W. 1989. Effects of turfgrass and mulch on the establishment and growth of bare-root sugar maples. *Journal of Arboriculture*, 15, 268–272.

Grossnickle, S.C., 2000. *Ecophysiology of northern spruce species: performance of planted seedlings*. National Research Council of Canada, Ottawa. 407 pp.

Grossnickle, S.C & Blake, T.J., 1987. Comparison of water relation patterns for newly-planted bare-root and container jack pine and black spruce seedlings in boreal cut-over sites. *New Forests*, 1, 101–116.

Harris, R.W., Clark, J.R. & Matheny, N.P. 1999. *Arboriculture: Integrated Management of Landscape Trees, Shrubs and Vines*, 3rd Edition. Prentice Hall, Upper Saddle River, NJ., USA. 687 pp.

Hartman, J.R., Pirone, T.P. & Sall, M.A. 2000. *Pirone's Tree Maintenance*, 7th Edition. Oxford University Press, New York, USA. 545 pp.

Himelick, E.B. & Watson, G.W. 1990. Reduction of oak chlorosis with wood chip mulch treatments. *Journal of Arboriculture*, 16, 275–278.

Hipps, N.A., Higgs, K.H. & Collard, L.G. 1997. Effects of root wrenching and irrigation rate on the growth and water relations of *Castanea sativa* and *Quercus robur* seedlings in the nursery and after transplanting. *Canadian Journal of Forest Research*, 27, 180–188.

Hipps, N.A., Higgs, K.H. & Collard, L.G. 1999. Effects of root wrenching on the growth and water relations of *Prunus avium* and *Castanea sativa* seedlings in nursery beds and after transplanting. *Canadian Journal of Forest Research*, 29, 696–704.

Hipps, N.A., Samuelson, T.J. & Farman, L.G. 2000. Effects of root wrenching on leaf mineral content of *Prunus avium* and *Castanea sativa* seedlings. *Canadian Journal of Forest Research*, 30, 958–963.

Hodge, S.J. 1991. Amenity tree planting with bare-root stock. *Arboriculture Research Note* 97/91/ARB. Arboricultural Advisory and Information Service, Farnham, UK. 4 pp.

Hodge, S.J. 1995. The effect of seven organic amendments on planting pit soil and tree performance. *Journal of Arboriculture*, 19, 245–266.

Hoitink, H.A.J., Stone, A.G. & Han, D.Y. 1997. Suppression of plant diseases by composts. *HortScience*, 32, 184–187.

Hummel, R.L. 1990. Water relations of container grown woody and herbaceous plants following antitranspirant sprays. *HortScience*, 25, 772–775.

Insley, H. 1979. Damage to broad-leaved trees by desiccation. *Arboriculture Research Note* 8/79. Arboricultural Advisory and Information Service, Farnham, UK. 4pp.

JCLI. 2002. *Handling and establishing landscape plants*. Joint Council for Landscape Industries, London, UK. 45pp. www.jcli.org.uk/publications.htm

Johnson, M.S. 1984a. Effect of soluble salts on water absorption by gel-forming soil conditioners. *Journal of Science of Food and Agriculture*, 35, 1063–1066.

Johnson, M.S. 1984b. The effects of gel-forming polyacrylamides on moisture storage in sandy soils. *Journal of Science of Food and Agriculture*, 35, 1196–1200.

Kerr, G. & Harper, C. 1994. Assessing the quality of broadleaved nursery stock. *Arboriculture Research and Information Note* 126/94/ARB. Arboricultural Advisory and Information Service, Farnham, UK. 5 pp.

Kjelgren, R., Montague, D.T. & Rupp, L.A. 1997. Establishment in treeshelters. II. Effect of shelter colour on gas exchange and hardiness. *Hortscience*, 32, 1284–1287.

Kling, G.J. 1985. Root regeneration techniques. *Proceedings International Plant Propagators Society*, 34, 618–627.

Koslowski, T.T. & Davies, W.J. 1975. Control of water balance in transplanted trees. *Journal of Arboriculture*, 1, 1–10.

Kropp, B.R. & Langlois, C.-G. 1990. Ectomycorrhizae in reforestation. *Canadian Journal of Forest Research*, 20, 438–451.

Lamont, G.P. & O'Connell, M.A. 1987. Shelf-life of bedding plants as influenced by potting media and hydrogels. *Scientia Horticulturae*, 31, 141–149.

Lauderdale, D.M., Gillam, C.H., Eakes, D.J., Keever, G.J. & Chappelka, A.H. 1995. Tree transplant size influences post-transplant growth, gas exchange, and leaf water potential of 'October Glory' red maple. *Journal of Environmental Horticulture*, 13, 178–181.

Littlewood, M. 1988. *Tree Detailing*. Butterworths, Sevenoaks, UK. 213 pp.

Mason, W.L. & Biggin, P. 1988. Comparative performance of containerised and bare-root Sitka spruce and lodgepole pine seedlings in upland Britain. *Forestry*, 61, 149–163.

McEvoy, C. & McKay, H. 1997. Sensitivity of broadleaved trees to desiccation and rough handling between lifting and transplanting. *Arboriculture Research and Information Note*, 139/97/SILN. Arboricultural Advisory and Information Service, Farnham, UK. 7 pp.

McKay, H. 1992. Electrolyte leakage from the fine roots of conifer seedlings: a rapid index of plant vitality following cold storage. *Canadian Journal of Forest Research*, 22, 1371–1377.

McKay, H. 1997. A review of the effect of stresses between lifting and planting on nursery stock quality and performance. *New Forests*, 13, 369–399.

Mityga, H.G. & Lanphear, F.O. 1971. Factors influencing the cold hardiness of *Taxus cuspidata* roots. *Journal of the American Society of Horticultural Science*, 96, 83–87.

Neely, D. 1984. Grass competition for nitrogen around landscape trees. *Journal of Environmental Horticulture*, 2, 86–87.

NUFU. 1998. *Trees or Turf? Best value in managing urban greenspace. Options compared*. National Urban Forestry Unit, Wolverhampton, UK. 17 pp.

Percival, G. & Galloway, A. 2000. Transplanting shock: getting to the root of the problem. *The Horticulturalist*, Winter 2000, 8–10.

Percival, G. & Gerritsen, J. 1998. The influence of plant growth regulators on root and shoot growth of containerised trees following root removal. *Journal of Horticultural Science & Technology*, 73, 353–359.

Potter, M.J. 1991. *Tree shelters*. Forestry Commission Handbook 7. HMSO, London, UK.

Ranney, T.G., Bassuk, N.L. & Whitlow, T.H. 1989. Effects of transplanting practices on growth and water relations of 'Colt' Cherry trees during reestablishment. *Journal of Environmental Horticulture*, 7, 41–45.

Richards, Moorehead & Laing Ltd. 2002. *Trees in Streets*. Final report for Transport for London, Ruthin, UK. 43pp.
www.rmlconsult.com/acatalog/reports.html

Rook, D.A. 1971. Effect of undercutting and wrenching on growth of *Pinus radiata* D. Don seedlings. *Journal of Applied Ecology*, 8, 477–480.

Sakai, A. & Larcher, W. 1987. *Frost survival of plants. Responses and adaptation to freezing stress.* Ecological Studies, 62. Springer-Verlag, Berlin, Germany.

Savill, P.S., Evans, J., Auclair, D. & Falck, J. 1997. *Plantation silviculture in Europe.* Oxford University Press, Oxford, UK. 297 pp.

Seaby, D.A. & Selby, C. 1990. Enhanced seedling root development in eight conifer species induced by naphthalene acetic acid. *Forestry*, 63, 197–207.

Seddon, E. 2001. Putting down roots. *Horticulture Week*, September 13, 2001, 29–32.

Smith, S.E. & Read, D.J. 1997. *Mycorrhizal Symbiosis*, 2nd Edition. Academic Press, London, UK. 605 pp.

Struve, D.K. 1990. Root regeneration in transplanted deciduous planting stock. *HortScience*, 25, 266–270.

Struve, D.K. & Arnold, M.A. 1986. Aryl esters of indolebutyric acid increase root regeneration in 3-0 red oak seedlings. *Canadian Journal of Forest Research*, 16, 673–675.

Struve, D.K. & Moser, B.C. 1984. Auxin effects on root regeneration of scarlet oak seedlings. *Journal of the American Society for Horticultural Science*, 109, 91–95.

Struve, D.K. & Rhodus, W.T. 1988. Phenyl indole 3-thiolbutyrate increases growth of transplanted 1-0 red oak. *Canadian Journal of Forest Research*, 18, 131–134.

Svihra, P., Burger, D. & Ellis, D. 1999. Effects of 3 trunk support systems on growth of young *Pyrus calleryana* trees. *Journal of Arboriculture*, 25, 319–324.

Svihra, P., Burger, D. & Harris, R. 1996. Tree shelter effect on root development of redwood trees. *Journal of Arboriculture*, 22, 174–179.

Tabbush, P.M. 1986. Rough handling, soil temperature and root development in outplanted Sitka spruce and Douglas fir. *Canadian Journal of Forest Research*, 16, 1385–1388.

Thomas, P. 2000. *Trees: their natural history.* Cambridge University Press, Cambridge, UK. 296 pp.

Thorpe, M.R., Saugier, B., Auger, S., Berger, A. & Methy, M. 1978. Photosynthesis and transpiration of an isolated tree: model and validation. *Plant Cell and Environment*, 1, 269–277.

Travers, D.M. & Ireland, C.R. 1993. A comparative study of the responses of three amenity tree species to differing water supply during establishment. *Acta Horticulturae*, 335, 277–285.

Van den Driessche, R. 1983. Growth, survival and physiology of Douglas-fir seedlings following root wrenching and fertilization. *Canadian Journal of Forest Research*, 13, 270–278.

Van den Driessche, R. 1996. Drought resistance and water use efficiency of conifer seedlings treated with paclobutrazol. *New Forests*, 11, 65–83.

Walmsley, T.J., Hunt, B. & Bradshaw, A.D. 1991. Root growth, water stress and tree establishment. In: *Research for Practical Arboriculture* (Ed. by S.J. Hodge), pp. 38–43. Forestry Commission Bulletin 97. HMSO, London, UK.

Watson, A. 2000. Wind-induced forces in the near-surface lateral roots of radiata pine. *Forest Ecology and Management*, 135, 133–142.

Watson, A. & Tombleson, J.D. 2002. Toppling in juvenile pines: A comparison of the root system characteristics of direct-sown seedlings, and bare root seedlings and cuttings. *Plant and Soil, 239*, 187–196.

Watson, G.W. 2001. Tree size affects root regeneration and top growth after transplanting. *Journal of Environmental Horticulture*, 19, 119–122.

Watson, G.W. & Clark, S. 2001. Girdling root formation in landscape trees. *Arborist News* February 2001, 50–53.

Watson, G.W. & Himelick, E.B. 1997. *Principles and practice of planting trees and shrubs*. International Society of Arboriculture, Champaign, IL., USA. 199 pp.

Watson, G.W. & Kupkowski, G. 1991. Soil moisture uptake by green ash trees after transplanting. *Journal of Environmental Horticulture*, 9, 226–227.

Welker, W.V. & Glenn, D.M. 1985. The relationship of sod proximity to the growth and nutrient composition of newly planted peach trees. *HortScience*, 20, 417–418.

Whitcomb, C.E. 1980. Effects of black plastic and mulches on growth and survival of landscape plants. *Journal of Arboriculture*, 6, 10–12.

Whitcomb, C.E. 1981. Response of woody landscape plants to Bermuda grass competition and fertility. *Journal of Arboriculture*, 7, 191–194.

White, J.J. 1990. *Nursery Stock Root Systems and Tree Establishment – a Literature Review*. Occasional Paper 20. Forestry Commission, Edinburgh, UK.

Winkelmann, M. & Kendle, A.D. 1996. The effect of hydrophilic polyacrylamide gels on establishment of woody plants under droughted and saline conditions. *Arboricultural Journal*, 20, 387–404.

Woodhouse, J.M. 1989. *Water-storing polymers as aids to vegetation establishment in arid soils*. Unpublished Ph.D. thesis, University of Liverpool, UK.

Woodhouse, J.M. & Johnson, M.S. 1991. Water storing soil polymers and the growth of trees. *Arboricultural Journal*, 15, 27–35.

CHAPTER 6

Water Supply and Drought Amelioration for Amenity Trees

6.1 Introduction

In the last chapter we saw that some of the major problems for a young tree during its establishment are to do with acquiring adequate amounts of water to survive and grow. Firstly, there is the need for the root system to develop satisfactorily and exploit sufficient soil resources to supply the tree with nutrients, but also especially water. When a tree is young and does not fully shade the ground, there is the added threat of competition from other plants eg lawns and weeds. The rooting density of competing vegetation in the surface soils, particularly in the case of grasses, can be high. This poses a particular problem for a young tree attempting to acquire adequate supplies of water and nutrients.

Once established, for trees growing in parks and alongside roads the problem of acquiring sufficient water will be reduced unless severe drought occurs or the extent and function of their root systems are limited eg by excavation or soil compaction. For other trees, particularly those growing in town and city centres, there are still problems to be faced. Additional atmospheric demands are placed on trees growing in urban environments because of higher temperatures, greater atmospheric humidity deficits and increased **radiation load** imposed by the proximity of the many built surfaces. A second major problem for trees in towns and cities is the restricted volume of soil allocated to the root system. Particularly in modern landscaping, the planting pit offers only a limited volume of soil for the tree and this can severely restrict the supply of water to the tree and compromise its potential for growth. In this chapter we examine the evaporative demands made on trees in built environments and also the requirements of trees so that they are adequately supplied with water.

6.2 Water demand by amenity trees

6.2.1 The mechanism of tree transpiration

Transpiration is water taken up from the soil and lost through the stomata in the leaves. It is one part of the total evaporation that may occur from vegetation (Box 6.1). In transpiration, water flow through the tree is a passive process, in the sense that water moves in response to physical forces. There are no 'metabolic pumps' that push water from one place to another (Taiz and Zeiger, 1991). From the soil (relatively wet) to the tree roots, up through the trunk and leaves, and out into the atmosphere (relatively dry), there is a consistent decrease in water potential (see also Section 2.2.1.2). Therefore a potential gradient is established, pulling water from regions of high water potential towards areas of lower water potential.

The bulk of the water taken up by a tree is used for transpiration (Kopinga, 1998). Figure 6.1 is a schematic diagram representing the movement of water through the soil – plant – atmosphere continuum. Columns of water confined in very narrow tubes (ie the xylem vessels or tracheids of trees) have high cohesive strength. This means that adjacent molecules are strongly linked to each other. Water molecules lost from a leaf in transpiration will be strongly linked to molecules in the sap stream below, and so on further down the tree, and ultimately to water being taken up by the roots from the soil. The rope in the schematic (Fig. 6.1) reflects the strength and the connection between water in the leaves down through to water entering the roots from the soil. The atmosphere, even with only modest humidity deficits, is a large sink for water vapour and draws water away from the tree through the stomata (pores) in the leaves (Fig. 6.1, upper panel), cooling the leaf surface in the process. The drier the air, the larger the evaporation deficit, or potential for evaporation to occur. This driving force is determined by factors such as solar radiation, temperature and humidity of the ambient air. In much the same way as a burning lamp draws oil through the wick, evaporation from the leaves draws water up through the xylem within the trunk of the tree (Fig 6.1, middle section). The rope in the schematic signifies that in the

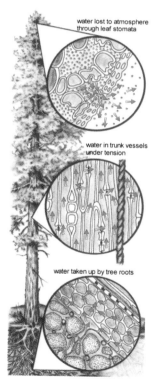

water lost to atmosphere through leaf stomata

water in trunk vessels under tension

water taken up by tree roots

Figure 6.1 The transpiration stream through the soil – plant – atmosphere continuum. (After Salisbury and Ross, 1992.)

Box 6.1 The different forms of evaporation

- **Evaporation** is the process by which water is lost from a surface as vapour

- **Transpiration** is the movement of water up through a plant (ie leaving via the stomata)

- **Interception** is rainfall held on leaves and stems and re-evaporated into the atmosphere

- **Evapotranspiration** refers to the combination of transpired water, intercepted rainfall or dew evaporating from the plant canopy, and water vapour lost from the surrounding soil

- **Units**: Because rainfall is expressed in terms of 'depth' (ie mm or inches), the amount of water lost through evapotranspiration is usually referred to in the same units for purposes of comparison

---

liquid phase, water in the leaf is connected as columns of water to water taken up from the soil by the root system (Fig 6.1, lower section). When water is lost rapidly from the foliage, resistances in the liquid flow pathway will mean that the water columns are under substantial tension – the 'rope' is stretched and taut. Different mechanisms of transport are involved at various stages within the soil – plant – atmosphere continuum. In both the soil and the tree's vascular system, water moves by bulk flow in response to potential gradients. In the air spaces within the leaf, the water becomes vapour. If the stomata in the leaf surfaces are open, water vapour will usually diffuse into the atmosphere because of the relative dryness of the atmosphere compared to the near saturation conditions inside the leaf.

The flow of water through the transpiration stream can be thought of in terms of 'supply and demand'. In many cases, water lost through transpiration is adequately replaced by water abstracted from the soil by the roots. This is determined by the available soil moisture, and thus by the rooting volume of soil afforded to each tree. However, short-term water deficits can occur in trees even when there is adequate soil water available, if the atmospheric demand (ie the evaporation deficit) outstrips the capacity of the roots to meet that demand (Hinckley *et al*, 1978). These deficits can be partly alleviated by the tree closing the stomata, but this closure has other consequences. When the stomata are closed the entry of carbon dioxide into the leaf, a crucial first step in the photosynthesis process and subsequently growth, is prevented.

Stomatal closure will occur in circumstances of severe shortage of water in the soil, damage to the root system or infection of the vascular system with fungal

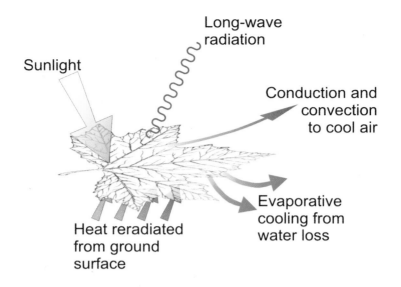

Figure 6.2 A simplified representation of the energy budget of an urban tree leaf. The heat load resulting from absorbed sunlight and re-radiated heat from nearby surfaces is dissipated by various means. (After Taiz and Zeiger, 1991.)

wilt diseases. Closure of the stomata will normally prevent the columns of water in the xylem system of the tree from breaking and air entering the xylem elements – the process of cavitation. It is a natural course of events for a small amount of xylem to be cavitated during the summer period. The cavitated xylem elements are usually refilled in the subsequent winter. In cases when a substantial amount of the xylem is cavitated, the hydraulic system of the tree is severely disrupted and foliage desiccation and tree death may be a consequence.

6.2.2 Potential evaporation and water use

Leaves have to dissipate enormous quantities of heat – as the heat load on a single leaf in bright sunlight is extremely high. Heat is removed from the leaf in several ways (Fig 6.2):

- leaves **re-radiate** energy in the infrared (long-wave)

- if the leaf temperature is higher than the surrounding air temperature, heat will move from one to the other via **convection** and **conduction**

- **evaporation** requires energy and will remove heat from the leaf. Rain that occasionally coats the leaf accounts for a small percentage of this heat loss, but by far the greatest evaporative cooling occurs via transpiration.

Therefore the leaf has an 'energy budget':

$$R_{net} = H + C + \lambda E$$

Figure 6.3 Evaporation pan used to calculate potential evaporation, shown with shelter containing instruments measuring temperature and humidity.

- R_{net} is the net balance between the energy absorbed, reflected and emitted leaf surface

- H is the energy lost from the leaf through convection

- C is the energy lost from the leaf through conduction

- E is the mass of water lost through evapotranspiration

- λ is what is known as the latent heat of vaporisation of water – the amount of energy required to convert 1 kg of liquid water into water vapour.

The principal weather parameters affecting the rate at which water is evaporated from a leaf surface are radiation, air temperature, humidity and wind speed. In much the same way that laundry will dry more quickly if the air surrounding it is dry, a larger vapour pressure deficit will permit greater rates of evapotranspiration. Similarly, if the sun is shining, more energy is available to 'fuel' the evaporative process. As water evaporates from a surface surrounded by still air, it will tend to form a humid layer just above the surface. Therefore the vapour pressure deficit immediately above the evaporating surface is much lower (as the air is wetter) and begins to limit evaporation. If a wind is blowing, this humid layer will be whisked away, replacing the air above the surface with drier air, allowing evaporation to continue. Several procedures have been developed to assess the evaporation rate from these parameters.

Estimates of potential evaporation are sometimes derived from daily direct measurements of water lost from evaporation pans (large tanks of water) common to most weather stations (Fig 6.3). Penman (1948) originally

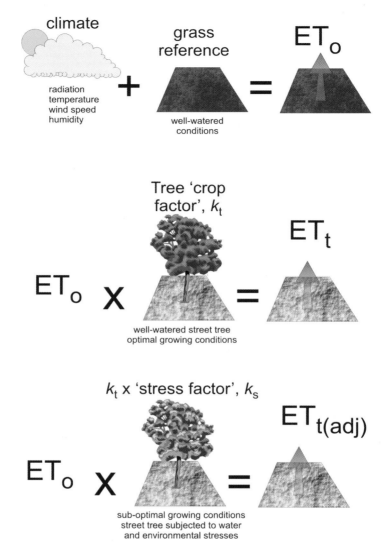

Figure 6.4 Simplified illustration of the steps taken to estimate the water demand of street trees under stress, by adjusting reference evapotranspiration using 'tree' and 'stress' factors. (After Allen *et al*, 1998.)

developed the concept of potential evaporation as the volume of water that can be lost as vapour from the surface of a large expanse of water, and is still the simplest physically based method (Strangeways, 2000). However, this approach implies no surface resistance to water vapour transfer, ie it is considerably 'easier' for water to evaporate from open water than from a plant system. Later on, when it became apparent that vegetation had an effect on evaporation, the concept of reference evapotranspiration (ET_o) was introduced, to study the evaporative demand of the atmosphere independently

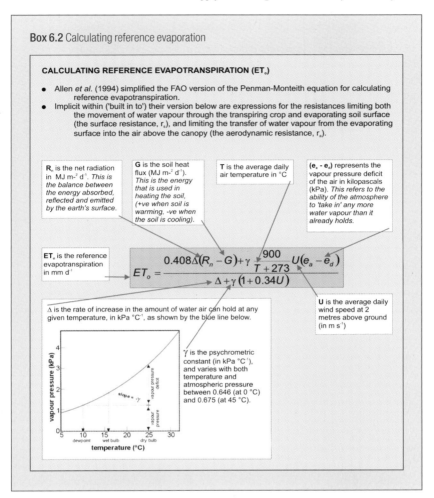

Box 6.2 Calculating reference evaporation

CALCULATING REFERENCE EVAPOTRANSPIRATION (ET_o)

- Allen *et al.* (1994) simplified the FAO version of the Penman-Monteith equation for calculating reference evapotranspiration.
- Implicit within ('built in to') their version below are expressions for the resistances limiting both the movement of water vapour through the transpiring crop and evaporating soil surface (the surface resistance, r_s), and limiting the transfer of water vapour from the evaporating surface into the air above the canopy (the aerodynamic resistance, r_a).

R_n is the net radiation in MJ m^{-2} d^{-1}. *This is the balance between the energy absorbed, reflected and emitted by the earth's surface.*

G is the soil heat flux (MJ m^{-2} d^{-1}). *This is the energy that is used in heating the soil, (+ve when soil is warming, -ve when the soil is cooling).*

T is the average daily air temperature in °C

$(e_a - e_d)$ represents the vapour pressure deficit of the air in kilopascals (kPa). *This refers to the ability of the atmosphere to 'take in' any more water vapour than it already holds.*

ET_o is the reference evapotranspiration in mm d^{-1}

$$ET_o = \frac{0.408\Delta(R_n - G) + \gamma \frac{900}{T + 273} U(e_a - e_d)}{\Delta + \gamma(1 + 0.34U)}$$

U is the average daily wind speed at 2 metres above ground (in m s^{-1})

Δ is the rate of increase in the amount of water air can hold at any given temperature, in kPa °C^{-1}, as shown by the blue line below.

γ is the psychrometric constant (in kPa °C^{-1}), and varies with both temperature and atmospheric pressure between 0.646 (at 0 °C) and 0.675 (at 45 °C).

of crop type, crop development and management practices. Reference evapotranspiration is defined as the evapotranspiration rate from a reference surface (a hypothetical grass reference crop with specific characteristics) that is not short of water (Allen *et al*, 1994, 1998; see upper panel of Fig 6.4). Box 6.2 indicates the data requirements and interrelationships in the calculation of reference evaporation.

However, we are interested in the potential evapotranspiration in the context of the urban forest. It is worth noting that in addition to the obvious physical and physiological differences between a uniform grass surface and isolated tree canopies, many micrometeorological evaporation values are obtained from weather station data recorded from airports or research stations, places often outside the city limits (Lindsey and Bassuk, 1992). As such, they may not accurately represent the micro-site conditions determining the potential evaporation typical of a street tree.

6.2.3 Characteristics of the urban microclimate

The urban forest is characterised by a lack of surface homogeneity (Vrecenak, 1988), containing both areas with typically few, discrete tree canopies, such as lines of trees along streets, as well as more densely planted gardens and suburban areas. These areas will have very different microclimates. In natural landscapes, the partitioning of energy can be into different forms eg into latent heat flux (evaporation) or sensible heat flux (heating of the air). The distribution of energy depends on a number of things, including the canopy biomass, leaf area index, and the availability of moisture. However, in urban areas, the distribution of artificial surfaces substantially modifies the surface energy budget (Quattrochi and Ridd, 1994).

The built environment has been described as a 'harsh montage' of reflective and absorptive surfaces, including roads, buildings, pavement and cars (Lindsey and Bassuk, 1992). Johnson *et al* (1975) found that in comparison with a forest environment, city microclimates were characterised by significantly higher temperatures, wind speeds and net rainfall inputs. The micro-scale horizontal energy exchanges that occur between vegetation and adjacent structures cannot be easily categorised or generalised (Miller, 1980).

Urban centres typically experience higher temperatures than surrounding areas (Bornstein, 1968). This so-called 'heat island' effect results from the storage and re-radiation of heat by building materials, and from the burning of fuel for heating and transportation (Federer, 1976). Lower tree cover in some urban areas can lead to less transpirational cooling and shading than may occur in rural areas with more extensive vegetation. Asphalt and concrete paving create a hot environment with high surface temperatures (Doll *et al*, 1985), and act to reduce soil evaporation that might normally help to cool the soil surface. However, higher potential evaporation rates over paved areas have been reported (Miller, 1980) and have been attributed to heat stored, then re-radiated and advected from the hard surfaces (Kjelgren and Clark, 1992).

One study comparing urban tree transpiration over asphalt and turf surfaces showed that tree species behaved differently in terms of water demand (Kjelgren and Montague, 1998). Flowering pear trees (*Pyrus calleryana*) transpired >30% more water when growing in asphalt than when surrounded by turf. Green ash (*Fraxinus pennsylvanica*) and Norway maple (*Acer platanoides*), however, showed lower transpiration rates when growing over asphalt, and this was attributed to a greater degree of stomatal control over transpiration in these two species, in response to greatly elevated asphalt surface temperature.

By shading the ground, trees can often reduce the amount of radiation reaching, absorbed by, and re-radiated by paved surfaces. Fig 6.5 shows how trees can affect the adjacent asphalt surface of a car park. During the day the area shaded by the tree remains cooler than the surrounding paving, whereas at night the 'shadow' of the tree is still visible as this area takes longer to cool

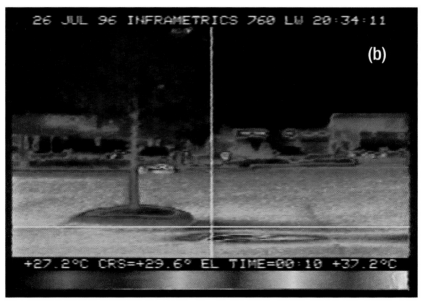

Figure 6.5 Images of a tree surrounded by asphalt near to the Walmart store, Athens, Georgia, USA. Images taken using a thermal infrared camera, during the day **(a)** and at night **(b)**.

down. This will affect the soil heat flux term, G, in the Penman-Monteith equation (see Box 6.2).

As well as increasing potential evaporation rates, paving-induced temperature increases can also affect the tree by other means. In one study, tree root zone

Table 6.1 Infiltration rates of rainfall through a number of different urban surfaces. (After Bakker, 1992).

Type of surface	Infiltration rate (mm hr^{-1})
Loamy soil, wet and compacted	<0.5
Loamy soil, open, not compacted	>200
Sand	>500
Asphalt (tarmac)	0
Open asphalt (semi-permeable)	>100
Paving stones (30 x 30 x 5 cm)	2–5
Paving stones (60 x 60 x 7 cm)	1–2
Paving bricks (20 x 10 x 10 cm)	10–20

temperatures were shown to be significantly higher in urban sites associated with asphalt and concrete than in suburban and woodland sites (Graves and Dana, 1987).

Some of the hottest objects in the city landscape, in terms of radiating heat, are cars. Whitlow and Bassuk (1987) noted that the combination of high temperatures and their proximity to the bottom of the tree canopies makes car roofs potentially damaging to canopy leaf function. At a very local level, a city tree canopy may experience not just a greater radiation 'load' than in a forest setting, due to reflection and re-radiation from adjacent structures, but the daily variation in energy input will vary. Metallic structures like cars both heat up and cool off quickly, whereas concrete and masonry will go on re-radiating heat long into the evening, unlike features in more rural locations. Potential evapotranspiration, and therefore tree water demand, can also be increased by lower air humidity, and by greater wind speeds caused by wind tunnelling around buildings. Wind speeds between tall buildings can frequently match those observed on raised exposed ground (Bradshaw *et al*, 1995).

Compared to rural areas, cities have an unusual hydrological cycle. It has been noted that solitary trees intercept more rainfall than similarly sized trees in a forest situation (Hiege, 1985). However, the typical situation of a small number of widely spaced trees along a roadside will result in lower rates of canopy rainfall interception per unit ground area, as demonstrated by Johnson *et al* (1975). Rainfall that is not intercepted usually falls on paved surfaces that are largely impermeable, leading to lower rates of infiltration and higher rates of runoff.

Bakker (1992) measured infiltration rates through a number of surfaces of different permeabilities all common to the urban environment (Table 6.1).

Figure 6.6 Infiltration of water into porous paving is mainly through the gaps, even when porous concrete paviours are used. Infiltration will be limited by dust and moss growth which needs to be removed by vacuum sweeping. M40 Motorway Service Area, Oxford.

The results showed that rates were slow to non-existent through a number of surfaces ranging from compacted soil through to asphalt and paving slabs, although the behaviour of semi-permeable pavement was closer to that of open, freely draining loam soil. Porous paving allows water to infiltrate through the gaps between the paviours and, where made of porous concrete, through the blocks themselves. Nevertheless, infiltration is about 50 times faster through the gaps than through the blocks (Abbott *et al*, 2000). Any accumulation of dirt or moss growth will seriously reduce infiltration (Fig 6.6) and regular cleaning is required. Regular (twice-yearly) vacuum cleaning of porous paving is recommended to maintain the porosity of the paving (CIRIA, 2002). Cleaning should be done in spring, probably as a part of tidying up after winter and after leaf fall in the autumn. It is very likely that the spillage of soil from nearby landscaping will make a significant contribution to the debris that reduces the effectiveness of **pervious** surfaces, and designs for the edge of the landscaping should make allowance for this.

Using standard rainfall data, the runoff-generating ability can be determined for the sorts of relatively impermeable surfaces typical of towns and cities and will show that only small amounts of runoff would occur from a surface composed of paving bricks, whereas compacted soil would allow little water to soak in, generating large volumes of runoff. Urban runoff is often directed away from areas of soil where water recharge may be needed (ie below a tree canopy), via gutters and storm drains (Bernatzky, 1983). At the same time, access to groundwater or subsurface drainage is usually eliminated, due to the choice of location and planting methods employed (Whitlow and Bassuk, 1988).

From a comparison of the microclimatological and hydrological characteristics of the urban environment as presented above, Whitlow and Bassuk (1987) have suggested urban street trees should be assessed in terms of water supply and demand. In the city, water supply to the tree is usually decreased because of low infiltration rates and high runoff losses, low water-holding capacities of compacted urban soil, and limited access to groundwater. At the same time, water demand by urban trees is higher due to higher radiative energy loading, lower humidities, increased wind speeds and therefore higher evaporative potential. With limited supply and increased demand, urban trees will experience more extreme and more frequent water deficits.

6.2.4 Estimating and predicting amenity tree water use

Methods of estimating tree water use range in their complexity from simple, empirically derived correction factors applied to pan evaporation measurements, through to sophisticated, 'data-intensive' models of the energy and water balance of tree canopies.

Commonly, pan evaporation measurements are adjusted using crop indices (eg Harris, 1998) or forestry correction factors adjusted for the urban setting (Kopinga, 1998). Studies in the Netherlands have derived such correction factors for urban use ranging between 1.5 and 2 (Bakker, 1992), and report that these are in general agreement with factors determined elsewhere (Halverson and Potts, 1981). Lindsey and Bassuk (1992) illustrated a simple method of predicting water use, combining factors that included the projected canopy area (m^2), the estimated leaf area index, and open water estimates of evaporation (mm) from a Symons tank (similar to an evaporation pan but with a larger reservoir). The estimated daily evaporation was then adjusted using a correction factor, to account for the fact that similar areas of open water and leaf surface do not evaporate at the same rate, to give a daily tree water use in litres. Their study showed that for a range of amenity tree species studied, 85% of the variability in tree water use (measured directly by weighing), could be accounted for if one had both the total tree canopy area and pan evaporation data. Knox (1989) found that combining pan evaporation estimates with derived growth indices gave a reasonable prediction of tree water use. Kopinga (1998) has reviewed results of similar studies from the Netherlands, attempting to predict potential tree transpiration rates [ET_t] from micrometeorological data. Initial attempts involved multiplying pan evaporation by the leaf area index (LAI), and adjusting the result by 0.3. Again, this accounted for between 86–90% of the variability in ET_t observed.

Additional research concentrated on determining ET_t using reference evapotranspiration [ET_o] calculated using a form of the Penman-Monteith equation, and adjusting it with a tree crop factor k_t, (Fig 6.4, middle panel). A similar process is described by Allen et al (1998) for estimating crop evapotranspiration [ET_c] under a range of conditions. When a tree is growing in a typical urban environment, the real evapotranspiration will normally deviate from ET_t due to sub-optimal conditions. These will include water shortage (or waterlogging) especially, but other factors such as the presence of pests and diseases, road salt, low soil fertility also contribute. The actual (or adjusted) tree evapotranspiration under non-standard conditions is calculated by using a (water) stress coefficient k_s, and/or by adjusting k_t for other stresses and environmental constraints on evapotranspiration (Fig 6.4, lower panel).

In the case of a street tree, an interesting question is what is the value of k_s at which the tree can still develop and grow well enough to match our expectations. Kopinga (1998) reports that the adjustment factors used in the Netherlands are still largely derived from forestry situations. Few water balance studies on street tree species have been attempted, and those that have usually involved container-grown trees of relatively small size. Another difficulty arises due to the fact that regulation of tree water use is known to vary at the level of species, cultivar and even the individual tree. Additional problems occur from the use of reference evapotranspiration itself. Little is known about how ET_0 varies in an urban setting. All the variables used as inputs to the Penman-Monteith equation are conventionally measured at 2 m above the ground, whereas the evaporative area in question, the tree canopy, is usually higher than that.

6.2.5 Complex transpiration models

Historically, attempts to model transpiration often concentrated on the development of models that simulate water use by simple uniform, often closed, plant canopies (de Wit, 1965; Goudriaan, 1977). As mentioned earlier, the considerable surface heterogeneity of the urban landscape means that it is not possible to model water use by the 'urban forest' as a whole. Instead, one must consider the system at the level of the individual element, the isolated tree crown.

The '**homogeneous** canopy' assumption also appeared in earlier models of water canopy use by tree canopies (Friend *et al* 1997), but subsequent efforts have allowed the modeller to 'dis-aggregate' the canopy to the point of predicting water use by individual tree crowns (Mobbs *et al*, 1997). Some models have been developed to solve the energy budget (described earlier) for individual tree crowns (eg Vrecenak and Herrington, 1984; Wang and Jarvis, 1990; Kjelgren and Montague, 1998). The advantage to this approach is that it is based on the radiation balance of the tree crown itself and is therefore more representative of the field situation. However, it requires accurate measurements of net radiation balance in three dimensions, and this has lead to some innovative approaches (Green, 1993), as shown in Fig 6.7.

The relative complexity, together with the amount of data required to run such models, limits their practicality at present. Nevertheless, estimations of tree water demand based on this type of approach where water use is determined on the basis of energy exchange are the most robust and reliable. As with most complex models, a greater amount of detailed information is needed early in the developmental stage, in order to enable it to simulate the transpirational

Figure 6.7 A 'whirligig' device shown measuring the radiation balance of the crown of an individual olive tree in a plantation in New Zealand.

process as accurately as possible. Once such a complex model is functioning correctly, then we can attempt to generalise and simplify the functions for application to a broader range of tree species and growth classes. Building in 'libraries' or 'look-up tables', which specify the particular value a parameter should have under certain conditions, can also make complex models more accessible. Such libraries would contain, say, stomatal response functions or leaf optical properties for a range of commonly used amenity tree species, or the sort of energy absorbed and re-radiated by different paving materials at different times of the year.

Modelling the water use by single tree canopies in mechanistic terms may often meet the requirement of assessing problems of water supply and demand, and the subsequent effects on health and survival of individual trees. At the same time, combining model estimates of whole tree water use may provide other necessary information, eg in devising irrigation strategies for landscape plantings (Vrecenak and Herrington, 1984), or groups of trees planted in a common 'tree vault', or where the presence of shade trees makes a significant impact on the local urban microclimate, or the effect of trees on shrinkable clay soils.

6.3 Water management for amenity trees

6.3.1 Water budgets for trees

A water budget is a means of accounting for the movement of all water into and out of any entity, whether at the scale of a river basin, a field or a small plot. A water budget can be written for the root zone of an amenity tree by considering all sources of water supply and all outlets for water loss. In the absence of supplemental irrigation or access to groundwater, the sole source of water for a tree is precipitation (P). Water is lost by evaporation, drainage (D) out of the root zone and runoff (R) over the ground surface. There are three sub-components for evaporation. These are transpiration by the tree (E_t), evapotranspiration from the soil (and any understorey vegetation) (E_s) and evaporation of rainfall intercepted by the tree crown (E_i). On an annual basis, the water budget for an amenity tree is then

$$P = E_t + E_s + E_i + D + R$$

If any net addition of water to the root zone of the tree occurs because of flow over the surface (run on), as might occur for a tree occupying low ground, R is given a negative value. Water supply to the tree would then be P+R. Changes in the quantity of water stored in the soil (ΔS) do not appear in the annual water budget because, on average, variation in soil water storage sums to zero from year to year.

A water budget provides a means of assessing whether water management for amenity trees is adequate. From the water budget above, annual tree water use must be met by

$$E_t = P - E_s - E_i - D - R$$

which is suggestive of a number of options for improving water supply to trees where necessary. To increase the availability of water for transpiration, steps can be taken to reduce E_s, the evaporation from the soil and water use by understorey vegetation. For example, rather than a lawn or other vegetative ground cover, which strongly compete for water with trees, soil beneath trees in parks or gardens can be covered with a coarse textured mulch to reduce evaporation (Lindsey and Bassuk, 1991). For trees surrounded by paving, water availability to the tree can be enhanced by focusing on reduction of R, the runoff term in the water budget. Use of more permeable paving materials (Table 6.1) reduces runoff and increases infiltration of water to the root zone.

Reduction of drainage, D, may be a concern on very sandy soils with low water holding capacity. Use of a loam backfill when planting and addition of organic matter to soils, at planting or as a surface mulch, improves the water-holding capacity of soil (Kopinga, 1998; Brady and Weil, 1999). However, it is also critical that drainage from the root zones of trees is sufficient to prevent waterlogging of the root system.

6.3.2 Prevention of water shortages

Over daily, weekly or seasonal intervals, the water budget has a storage term (ΔS) that accounts for changes in the amount of water held by the soil. During periods without precipitation, the soil is drying and ΔS must fulfil the water requirements of the tree. Thus, soil in the root zone must store sufficient water to maintain the supply of water to trees during dry periods, to ensure that tree health and growth are not impaired by drought stress.

A critical issue in the management of water for amenity trees is, therefore, how much water needs to be stored in the root zone? This depends on water use by the tree and the length of dry periods. Trees which use more water – because of leaf area, species or climate – need access to a larger store of soil water, as do trees growing in drier climates where dry periods are longer. A related question is how much water can be stored in the root zone? This depends on soil type and structure and the volume of soil accessible to tree roots. In urban environments, the latter may be severely restricted by waterlogging, poor soil aeration and soil compaction, which create unsuitable conditions for root growth.

6.3.2.1 Adequate soil volumes for amenity trees

The volume of soil required to supply a large amenity tree with the soil resources required for growth has been estimated by a variety of means. Helliwell (1986) used an anecdotal rule-of-thumb as the basis for his estimate that a 20 m tall tree with a crown diameter of 12 m in southern England requires a rootable soil volume of 200 m^3. More robust approaches have typically found lower values. Estimates of required rootable volume of soil, from calculations of demand by mature trees for water and nitrogen, vary between 3 and 76 m^3 (Urban, 1989; Kopinga, 1991; Lindsey and Bassuk, 1992; Couenburg, 1998). Variation among these estimates results from differences in soil type, climate and assumptions about tree size and species used in the calculations.

When compared to the volume of the typical pit into which urban trees are planted, the inadequacy of provision for the root systems of urban trees is clear. Soil surrounding tree pits is commonly hostile to root growth because of severe compaction (Chapter 4), resulting in restriction of root growth to the confines of the pit (Kristoffersen, 1999). With dimensions of about 1.2 x 1.2 x 0.6 m, the total rootable soil volume for a typical tree pit is less than 0.9 m^3 (Craul, 1992). This is many times smaller than the estimates of adequate rootable soil volume. Urban trees must therefore survive with access to only a small fraction of the below-ground resources they require to grow to maturity. Thus, they are vulnerable to deficiencies in resources, particularly water (Lindsey and Bassuk, 1992), unless provision is made for alternative soil resources to be accessible.

6.3.3 Estimation of required soil volumes for tree pits

6.3.3.1 Estimation of rootable volume from seasonal water budgets

The first approach to estimation of required rootable volume is based on the water budget for the root zone during the growing season (Couenburg, 1998). The storage capacity of the soil for water (S, mm) is assumed to be full in the spring, prior to the growing season. Rainfall available for uptake by the tree (P_a, mm) is rainfall during the growing season (P_g, mm) less losses by evaporation, drainage and runoff:

$$P_a = P_g - E_s - E_i - D - R$$

Demand for water by the tree over the growing season must be met by $P_a + S$. The quantity of stored water required can be estimated as $S_{req} = E_t - P_a$, once seasonal transpiration by the tree when mature (E_t, mm) is estimated using one of the modelling approaches outlined in Section 6.2.5. The required rootable soil volume ($V_{s,req}$, m^3) is related to S_{req} by

$$S_{req} A_s = V_{s,req} \theta_a$$

where A_s (m^2) is the ground area enclosing the root zone and θ_a (m^3 m^{-3}) is the plant available water holding capacity of the soil. As shown in Fig 2.6, θ_a is the volume of water stored in the soil above the plant wilting point after drainage under gravity, which is dependant on soil texture (See Chapters 2 and 4). Values of A_s are unknown when planning construction of tree pits, but the maximum depth of soil (d_s, m) is usually specified. The term A_s can be replaced by $1/d_s$, the area of unit soil volume with depth d_s, with units of m^3 m^{-1}, enabling calculation of $V_{s,req}$ from

$$V_{s,req} = \frac{S_{req}}{1000 d_s \theta_a}$$

where the factor of 1000 converts S_{req} from units of millimetres to metres.

Application of this estimation procedure in practice requires data for P_g and θ_a. The former can be determined from mean monthly rainfall over the growing season, available from climatic records, and the latter from an assessment of soil texture using Fig 2.6. To determine P_a from P_g requires estimates of losses by evaporation, drainage and runoff. Where trees are surrounded by paving, soil evaporation, E_s, can be assumed to be negligible. Interception losses, E_i, for broadleaf trees can be approximated as 20% of P_g (Roberts, 1999). In climates with high winter rainfall, such as in Britain, most drainage occurs during the winter months and thus drainage losses, D, in the growing season can also be assumed to be negligible. Runoff losses, R, can be estimated from published data on runoff from different urban surfaces, such as Table 6.1 and Fig 6.8.

Couenburg (1998) used this estimation procedure to determine $V_{s,req}$ for new tree plantings. The volume of soil calculated was too large and could not be accommodated with plans for other amenities such as a market square and

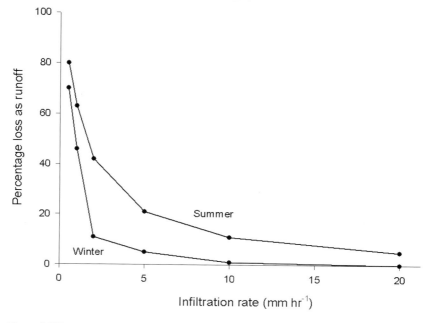

Figure 6.8 The percentage of rain falling on a paved area that is likely to be lost as surface runoff in summer (1 May to 1 October) or winter (1 October to 1 May), as a function of different possible infiltration rates. (After Bakker, 1992.)

parking area. Such restrictions on available space are encountered commonly when designing tree pits. Where this occurs, the tree pit should be made as large as possible and actual storage of water calculated from $V_s\theta_a$. The difference between actual and required S can be supplied by irrigation. The quantity of irrigation water required (I_{req}, mm) over the growing season is $I_{req} = E_t - P_a - S$. The volume of irrigation water required, in m^3 if A_s has units of m^2, is $I_{req}A_s/1000$.

6.3.3.2 Estimation of rootable volume from rainfree duration

Lindsey and Bassuk (1991, 1992) used an alternative approach to estimating the required rootable soil volume, $V_{s,req}$. From climatic records, they determined the 90th percentile for the interval between 'critical' rainfall events (t_{dry}, days), which they defined as rainfall of 2.5 mm or more. This is the interval which is equal to or longer than 90% of dry periods. The volume of the tree pit required was then estimated as the soil volume necessary to store sufficient water to meet demand for water by the tree for the duration of t_{dry}. Demand for water was estimated using an empirical model of daily transpiration $E_{t,d}$ (mm day^{-1}) based on measurements of open water evaporation and leaf area (Section 6.2.4). Values of $V_{s,req}$ were then calculated using

$$V_{s,req} = \frac{E_{t,d}t_{dry}}{1000\theta_a}$$

Table 6.2 Highest mean monthly pan evaporation and predicted rootable soil volumes required to meet demand for water by trees with a crown projection of 28.3 m² at locations in the UK and USA. Soil type is silt loam. (After Lindsey and Bassuk, 1992.)

British station	Highest mean monthly pan evaporation (mm)	Month	10 day soil volume (m³)
Lake Vyrnwy, Powys	80	July	2.91
Rosewarne, Cornwall	83	June	3.16
Otterbourne, Hants	96	July	3.52
Ardsley, S. Yorks.	102	June	3.82
Barrow Gurney, Avon	102	July	3.72
Ormesby, Cleveland	107	July	3.92
Wellesbourne, Warks.	105	July	3.87
Kew, London	120	July	4.37
US city			
Ithaca, NY	158	July	5.89
Seattle, WA	178	July	6.74
Philadelphia, PA	181	July	6.80
Los Angeles, CA	199	July	7.48
Minneapolis, MN	200	July	7.56
Miami, FL	204	July	7.73
Wichita, KS	245	July	9.26
Phoenix, AZ	377	June	14.24

This approach assumes that complete recharge of soil water storage occurs at the end of each dry spell. When recharge is insufficient, supplemental irrigation may be required. Irrigation must also be supplied when the duration of dry spells exceeds t_{dry} (Lindsey and Bassuk, 1991). In long periods without rain and in the absence of supplemental irrigation it is possible for a **soil moisture deficit** to develop close to trees that persists through the winter period (Biddle, 1998a and b). These deficits can increase if two or more years follow each other when the water use by the tree exceeds the rainfall reaching the soil. In Chapter 10 we discuss the development of persistent soil moisture deficits in shrinkable clay soils associated with the abstraction of water by tree roots and the impact on buildings.

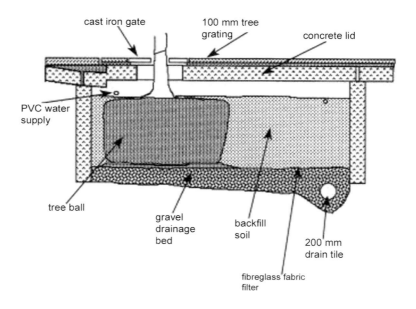

Figure 6.9 A tree pit showing extended soil volume covered by a cantilevered concrete lid and a gravel bed and pipes for adequate drainage. (After Craul, 1992.)

Required rootable volumes tend to be lower than estimates from the seasonal water budget when calculated from rainfree duration. Lindsey and Bassuk (1991, 1992) used a rainfree duration of ten days and found a required rootable volume of 5.8 m^3 for medium-sized broadleaf amenity trees in silt loam soil in Ithaca, NY, USA. The rootable volume required to meet water demand for ten days is lower in more northerly, maritime climates, but higher in more arid locations because of differences in daily water use of trees (Table 6.2).

6.4 Tree pit design

6.4.1 Enhancing rootable soil volume

Provision of adequate soil volumes for trees planted in tree pits can be achieved from a knowledge of tree water use, climate and soil properties. Very often, however, there is not sufficient below-ground space available in urban developments to allocate all of the required soil volume to a tree. Supplemental irrigation can be used to make up the shortfall in water supply that results from restricted soil volume, but this can only be successful where continued irrigation can be assured for the entire life of the tree. As the latter is only rarely possible, other means of increasing rootable soil volume must be considered where the size of tree pits is constrained.

6.4.1.1 Linear planting trenches

Where trees are planted in a row alongside a street or footpath, rootable soil volume can be increased by planting into a continuous trench rather than individual tree pits (Craul, 1992). This enables roots to spread into the space between trees. Once installed, however, soil in the planting trench must be protected from compaction while meeting load-bearing requirements. Planting trenches can be retained as grass boulevards or covered with an iron grate (Craul, 1992). Engineering requirements for the soils may be accommodated by utilising load-bearing soil mixes for trees, such as Amsterdam Tree Soil or structural soils (See Chapter 4). Alternatively, the surrounding paved surface could be suspended over the planting trench using cantilevered supports (see Fig 6.9).

6.4.1.2 Tree root break-out zones

Amenity trees planted along streets are often in close proximity, though not adjacent, to areas of grass or other vegetation. The soil volume accessible to the tree can be vastly increased if provision is made for growth of roots out of the tree pit and into the soil beneath the vegetation. One idea involves the use of break-out zones for roots. It is possible to improve soil conditions in specific areas to direct tree roots to grow away from the kerbs and pavements. Roots growing in a resource-poor situation will seek out adequate resources, and proliferate where those resources are present in large quantities. Knowledge of root extension processes can be used to direct roots away from kerbs and pavements. Two principal methods are baiting and channelling (Coder, 1998).

Baiting involves providing ideal essential resources in some other area, rather than next to infrastructures. The net result is a much higher survival and growth rate in that part of the root system compared to roots near pavements and kerbs. If the volumes of soil worth 'baiting' are too distant from the tree, roots can be guided to find them, along trenches or channels that are filled with rich, well-aerated, growth medium and surrounded by root control obstacles or barriers (McPherson and Peper, 1996). If the growth medium used is suitably uncompacted (with a low bulk density) then it can deform sufficiently to compensate for any increases in root diameter. This will ensure that root diameter growth does not affect the compacted layers of soil or the structures one is seeking to protect. Under pavements, the use of compacted layers above and below a moist, oxygenated coarse layer (sand) can lead roots under infrastructures and out into open soil surface areas (Coder, 1998). A means of ensuring adequate levels of O_2 in the sand, such as buried perforated pipes, must be incorporated into the design.

6.4.1.3 Structural soils

As detailed in Chapter 4, structural soils provide a means of satisfying the requirement that urban soils provide both a load-bearing medium and a medium suitable for root growth. Thus tree pits can be built to accommodate root growth beneath paved surfaces if constructed using structural soils. The required volume of a tree pit depends on water use by the tree, recharge of stored soil water by rainfall and the water-holding properties of the soil, in just the same way as any other soil. Thus, the required volume of structural soil can be calculated using the approaches outlined in Section 6.3.3, provided the water-holding properties (and therefore θa) of structural soils are known.

6.4.2 Drainage from tree pits

In addition to ensuring that trees have access to sufficient water to meet demand for transpiration, it is also imperative that their roots are protected from waterlogging. Saturation and waterlogging is a common feature of urban tree planting pits (Craul, 1985) because of impediments to water movement created by textural discontinuities (Chapter 4) at the interfaces between backfill in the pit and surrounding soil. Seepage of water from pits into compacted clay surrounding a tree pit is very slow and, similarly, water drains into very coarse soils and gravel only when loamy backfill approaches saturation. These phenomena in tree pits are known as 'the teacup effect' (Craul, 1985). Thus, during wet periods, and especially in winter in the British climate, tree pits are easily waterlogged. Many species of amenity tree have very low tolerance of waterlogging because their root systems cannot withstand poor soil aeration (Chapter 4). Consequently, it is important that provision is made in tree pit designs for adequate drainage (Couenburg, 1998).

A simple test of drainage from tree pits can be made by digging a test pit and filling it with water. If most water remains in the pit after 24 hours, drainage is poor because of low hydraulic conductivity in surrounding soil. Drainage should be installed in tree pits constructed at such sites (Craul, 1992). Installation of drainage should also be considered for tree pits in very gravelly soils if loam backfill is used. Designs of tree pits are available which can incorporate a number of features which aim to overcome the problems of simple root pits, namely inadequate soil volumes and poor drainage. Fig 6.9 (Craul, 1992) shows a sophisticated root pit with a suspended surface covering an extended volume of soil and features to deal with drainage problems. Drainage from tree pits can be facilitated by installing drains, eg perforated drainage pipe, at the bottom of the pit. A thin layer of gravel covering the base of the pit serves as a drainage bed, channelling water into the drain pipe. A single pipe can run beneath neighbouring tree pits and empty into a nearby storm sewer.

6.4.3 Avoiding compaction

It is particularly important that the soil on top of the tree pit is not compacted, as this zone may be the only place where water may enter the root pit. Compaction will reduce or stop infiltration completely (Fig 6.10). Where access by pedestrians is likely a tree grille or porous paving placed around the tree base is advisable. The central aperture in the grille/paving will need to be enlarged as time progresses to accommodate the growth of the tree. There are some drawbacks with tree grilles and pavings. They can be dislodged by large surface roots and then may become a hazard or in any case unsightly. It is not

Figure 6.10 With no protection of the soil surface, eg by tree grilles, there can be serious soil compaction by foot traffic. A recent rainstorm shows ponding of water on the soil surface near a beech tree in Didcot, Oxfordshire – clear evidence of poor infiltration.

Figure 6.11 Where pedestrian traffic is slight there is less need to use tree grilles and mulching can be easily applied, as at Banbury, Oxfordshire.

easy to accommodate occasional mulching below tree grilles and definitely not below pavings. Space is often a limitation but the labour involved in dismantling and reassembling the grille or paving can be prohibitive. Where pedestrian traffic is infrequent, robust protection of the soil surface may not be necessary and the trees may benefit from judicious mulching (Fig 6.11).

6.5 Summary

- The controls that the climate has on transpiration from trees are through solar radiation, air temperature, humidity and wind. This climatic influence can be calculated as an estimate of potential evaporation.

- There is an increase in the potential evaporative demand in an urban setting, particularly because of higher temperatures and air humidity deficits.

- For many agricultural crops, and even forests, adjustment factors for reference potential evaporation are available for estimating actual water use. For a number of reasons equivalent factors for trees in urban settings are not available. The influence of additional stress factors particularly associated with trees growing in tree pits, such as limited rooting volumes and waterlogging, will need to be included as well as the influence of pests and diseases on transpiration.

- In built environments, an important consideration for the recharge of soil water by rainfall is the nature of any artificial surface covering the soil. Asphalt is relatively impermeable but modern block paviours have much greater permeability to water.

- There is often a substantial shortfall between estimates of the water requirements of street trees and the available water that can be provided from the soil volume in a tree pit.

- Because of the discontinuities between the soil in tree pits and that surrounding there is often poor drainage. There is often the serious consequence of water-logging and root death. The design and implementation of the tree pits should ensure that water can easily drain between the soil in the root pit and the surrounding soil, or adequate facilities for drainage should be provided.

REFERENCES

Abbott, C.L., Comingo, L. & Angood, C. 2000. *Monitoring performance of infiltration drainage systems.* Report SR 569. HR Wallingford, Wallingford, UK. 22 pp.

Allen, R.G., Pereira, L.S., Raes, D. & Smith, M. 1998. *Crop evapotranspiration – Guidelines for computing crop water requirements – FAO Irrigation and drainage paper 56.* FAO – Food and Agriculture Organization of the United Nations, Rome, Italy. www.fao.org/docrep/X0490E/x0490e00.htm

Allen, R.G., Smith, M., Pereira, L.S. & Pereira, A. 1994. An update for the calculation of reference evapotranspiration. *ICID Bulletin*, 43, 35–92.

Bakker, J.W. 1992. Techniques to promote plant growth applied to urban sites. In: *Water saving techniques for plant growth* (Ed. by H.J.W. Verplancke, E.B.A. de Strooper and M.F.L. de Boodt), pp. 223–228. NATO ASI. Series E: Applied Sciences. Kluwer Academic Publ., The Netherlands.

Bernatzky, A. 1983. The effect of trees on the urban climate. In: *Trees in the 21st Century*, pp. 59–76. AB Academic Publ., UK.

Biddle, P.G. 1998a. *Tree root damage to buildings.* Volume 1: causes, diagnosis and remedy. Willowmead Publ., Wantage, UK. 376 pp.

Biddle, P.G. 1998b. *Tree root damage to buildings.* Volume 2: patterns of soil drying in proximity to trees on clay soils. Willowmead Publ., Wantage, UK. 299 pp.

Bornstein, R.D. 1968. Observations of the urban heat island effect in New York City. *Journal of Applied Meteorology*, 7, 575–582.

Bradshaw, A.D., Hunt, B. & Walmsley, T. 1995. *Trees in the urban landscape: Principles and practice.* E & FN Spon, London, UK. 272 pp.

Brady, N.C. & Weil, R.R., 1999. *The Nature and Properties of Soils*, 12th Edition. Prentice-Hall Inc., Upper Saddle River, NJ., USA. 881 pp.

CIRIA. 2002. *Source control using constructed pervious surfaces: Hydraulic, structural and water quality issues.* Construction Industry Research and Information Association, Publication C582, London, UK. 156 pp.

Coder, K.D. 1998. *Root Control Barriers.* Tree root growth control series, University of Georgia cooperative extension service forest resources publication FOR98-12. www.forestry.uga.edu/warnell/service/library/index

Couenberg, E. 1998. Urban tree soil and tree-pit design. In: *The Landscape Below Ground II: Proceedings of an International Workshop on Tree Root Development in Urban Soils* (Ed. by D. Neely and G.W. Watson), pp. 189–202. International Society of Arboriculture, Champaign, IL., USA.

Craul, P.J. 1985. A description of urban soils and their desired characteristics. *Journal of Arboriculture*, 11, 330–331.

Craul, P.J. 1992. *Urban Soil in Landscape Design*. John Wiley & Sons, Inc., New York, NY., USA. 396 pp.

De Wit, C.T. 1965. *Photosynthesis of leaf canopies*. Agricultural Research Reports, No. 663. Centre for Agricultural Publishing and Documentation, Wageningen, The Netherlands.

Doll, D., Ching, J. & Kaneshiro, J. 1985. Parameterization of subsurface heating for soil and concrete using net radiation data. *Boundary Layer Meteorology*, 32, 351–372.

Federer, C.M. 1976. Trees modify the urban microclimate. *Journal of Arboriculture*, 2, 121–127.

Friend, A.D., Stevens, A.K., Knox, R.G. & Cannell, M.G.R. 1997. A process-based terrestrial biosphere model of ecosystem dynamics (Hybrid v3.0). *Ecological Modelling*, 95, 249–287.

Goudriaan, J. 1977. *Crop micrometeorology: a simulation study*. Centre for Agricultural Publishing and Documentation, Wageningen, The Netherlands.

Graves, W.R. & Dana, M.N. 1987. Root-zone temperature monitored at urban sites. *HortScience*, 22, 613–614.

Green, S.R. 1993. Radiation balance, transpiration and photosynthesis of an isolated tree. *Agricultural and Forest Meteorology*, 64, 201–221.

Halverson, H.G. & Potts, D.F. 1981. *Water requirements of honeylocust (Gleditsia triacanthos f. inermis) in the urban forest*. USDA Forest Research Paper NE-487. 4 pp.

Harris, R. 1998. Irrigation of newly planted street trees. In: *The Landscape Below Ground II. Proceedings of a Second International Workshop on Tree Root Development in Urban Soils* (Ed. by D. Neely and G.W. Watson), pp. 225–232. International Society of Arboriculture, Champaign, IL., USA.

Helliwell, D.R. 1986. The extent of tree roots. *Arboricultural Journal*, 10, 341–347.

Hiege, W. 1985. *Wasserhaushalt von Forsten und Walder und der Einfluss des Wassers auf Wachstum und Gesundheit von Forsten und Walder*. Eine Literaturstudie. Rapport 7a, Studiecommissie Waterbeheer, Natuur, Bos en Landschap (SWNBL), Utrecht, The Netherlands. 190 pp.

Hinckley, T.M., Lassoie, J.P. & Running, S.W. 1978. Temporal and spatial variation in water status of forest trees. *Forest Science Monographs*, 20, 72 pp.

Johnson, F.L., Bell, D.T. & Stanley, S.K. 1975. A comparison of urban and forest microclimates in the Midwestern United States. *Agricultural Meteorology*, 14, 335–345.

Kjelgren, R.K. & Clark, J.R. 1992. Microclimates and tree growth in the urban species. *HortScience*, 10, 139–145.

Kjelgren, R. & Montague, T. 1998. Urban tree transpiration over turf and asphalt surfaces. *Atmospheric Environment*, 32, 35–41.

Knox, G.W. 1989. Water use and average growth index of five species of container grown woody landscape plants. *Journal of Environmental Horticulture*, 7, 136–139.

Kopinga, J. 1991. The effects of restricted volumes of soil on the growth and development of street trees. *Journal of Arboriculture*, 17, 57–63.

Kopinga, J. 1998. Evaporation and water requirements of amenity trees with regard to the construction of a planting site. In: *The Landscape Below Ground II. Proceedings of a Second International Workshop on Tree Root Development in Urban Soils* (Ed. by D. Neely and G.W. Watson), pp. 233–245. International Society of Arboriculture, Champaign, IL., USA.

Kristoffersen, P. 1999. Growing trees in road foundation materials. *Arboricultural Journal*, 23, 57–76.

Lindsey, P. & Bassuk, N.L. 1991. Specifying soil volumes to meet the water requirements of mature urban street trees and trees in containers. *Journal of Arboriculture*, 17, 141–149.

Lindsey, P. & Bassuk, N.L. 1992. Redesigning the urban forest from the ground below: a new approach to specifying adequate soil volumes for street trees. *Arboricultural Journal*, 16, 25–39.

McPherson, E.G. & Peper, P.J. 1996. Costs of street tree damage to infrastructure. *Arboricultural Journal*, 20, 143–160.

Miller, D. 1980. The two-dimensional energy budget of a forest edge with field measurements at a forest-parking lot interface. *Agricultural Meteorology*, 22, 53–78.

Mobbs, D.C., Crout, N.M.J., Lawson, G.J. & Cannell, M.G.R. 1997. Structure and applications of the HyPAR model. *Agroforestry Forum*, 8(2), 10–13.

Penman, H. L. 1948. Natural evaporation from open water, bare soil and grass. *Proceedings of the Royal Society of London*, Series A, 193, 120–146.

Quattrochi, D.A. & Ridd, M.K. 1994. Measurement and analysis of thermal energy responses from discrete urban surfaces using remote sensing data. *International Journal of Remote Sensing*, 15, 1991–2022.

Roberts, J. 1999. Plants and water in forests and woodlands. *Eco-Hydrology: Plants and Water in Terrestrial and Aquatic Environments* (Ed. by A.J. Baird and R.L. Wilby), pp. 181–236. Routledge, London, UK.

Salisbury, F.B. & Ross, C.W. 1992. *Plant Physiology*, 4th Edition. Wadsworth Publishing Company, Belmont, California, USA. 682 pp.

Strangeways, I. 2000. *Measuring the natural environment.* Cambridge University Press, Cambridge, UK. 365 pp.

Taiz, L. & Zeiger, E. 1991. *Plant Physiology*. Benjamin/Cummings Publishing Company, Inc., Redwood City, California, USA. 565 pp.

Urban, J. 1989. New techniques in urban tree planting. *Journal of Arboriculture*, 15, 281–284.

Vrecenak, A.J. 1988. Shade tree transpiration and water use. *Arboricultural Journal*, 12, 77–81.

Vrecenak, A.J. & Herrington, L.P. 1984. Modelling transpiration from selected urban shade tree species. *Journal of Horticulture*, 2, 130–135.

Wang, Y.P. & Jarvis, P.G. 1990. Description and validation of an array model – MAESTRO. *Agricultural and Forest Meteorology*, 51, 257–280.

Whitlow, T.H. & Bassuk, N. 1987. Trees in difficult sites. *Journal of Arboriculture*, 13, 10–17.

Whitlow, T.H. & Bassuk, N. 1988. Ecophysiology of urban trees and their management – the North American experience. *HortScience*, 23, 542–546.

CHAPTER 7

Coping with Soil Contamination

7.1 Introduction

It is important to clarify a number of terms used in relation to land that has received some degree of contamination. Craul (1992) defines soil contamination as the condition when the content of a natural or synthetic substance is above that of the background, natural content. Alloway (1999) points out that various authors distinguish 'pollution' and 'contamination' to indicate the relative severity of adverse effects. Contamination is sometimes used for situations where a substance resulting from human activity is present in the environment but not causing any harmful effects. In contrast, the term pollution is often used when a substance is present and is having a harmful effect. This distinction might be convenient but it often does not remain true when more detailed studies are made of contamination in soils or other components of the environment. Therefore it is appropriate, as Alloway (1999) states, to refer to all cases of pollution or contamination of soil/land as contamination. In this case, 'contaminated' land covers a wide spectrum from the presence of low concentrations of a chemical from an external source up to cases of severe toxicity for plants and/or hazards to animals or humans.

It is also necessary to distinguish between contaminated land and **derelict land**. Urban soil may be one or other or both (Craul, 1992). Natural soils can be contaminated by some substances while the soil of derelict land may be highly disturbed or manipulated but not necessarily contaminated. However, there is a high probability that derelict land contains at least some contaminated soil. A survey of the amount of derelict land in England in 1993 was made (DOE, 1995) with derelict land defined as 'land so damaged by industrial or other development that it is incapable of beneficial use without treatment' and excludes any mention of contamination. Although much of the land surveyed would be likely to be contaminated, not all would necessarily be so.

The effects of contamination may have repercussions on the health and welfare of a wide range of plant and animal life both *in situ* as well as *ex situ* because of the impact on receiving waters and the migration of pollutants from the site. The remit of this chapter is restricted to the impacts of contamination on trees. The text is therefore restricted to categories of contamination impacting trees and shrubs directly or indirectly but does not extend to associated aspects such as the accumulation of contaminants in the fruits and leaves and the consumption of these by animals, birds and humans. Consideration of the impact of soil contamination on humans and animals is made, for example, by Alloway (1999).

7.2 Abiotic stresses

There are several abiotic stresses which trees experience in the built environment and a number of these impacts occur predominantly below ground. The impacts might be divided into those which are recurring at the present time and those which are a legacy of previous land use on the site where trees are expected to be grown. Examples of recurring impacts are applications of salt for de-icing purposes in winter, acid deposition from the atmosphere and alkaline washings from buildings. Soil residues which might have an influence on trees growing in built environments or on derelict land will be heavy metals, industrial waste or various plastics, and there might be miscellaneous rubble and plaster from demolished buildings also. Soil residues might well be imported to a site as backfill or landfill.

There is probably no other abiotic stress factor that is so consistently unique to the urban ecosystem as that of chemical stress. The increasing use of chemicals for pest and weed control, fertilisation, growth regulation and snow and ice removal, makes this stress factor of particular significance in the built environment. A characteristic feature of most organic molecules is that they exert significant physiological effects at very low chemical concentrations. These physiological effects might include alterations in nucleic acid synthesis, direct enzyme activation or the regulation of permeability of cells. Many organic chemicals have a stimulatory effect on respiration, which results from many of the above biochemical changes.

Inorganic chemical stress refers to an excess of inorganic salts or ions and the accompanying changes in pH associated with these imbalances. Large-scale applications of de-icing salts (primarily $NaCl$ and $CaCl_2$) make this stress factor a potentially serious problem in the urban landscape and along all roads receiving substantial de-icing salts during the winter months. The accumulation of inorganic salts alters the osmotic potential of the soil solution making it more difficult for plant roots to acquire water. In addition, excess salt in the plant may interfere with water absorption and have a toxic effect on photosynthesis, respiration, protein synthesis and carbohydrate metabolism and also leaf expansion. Another important consideration for trees growing in urban areas or in close proximity to roads are the levels of heavy metals (eg copper, lead, mercury, nickel or zinc) associated either with mining or previous industrial land uses before the current urban land use or associated with fuels or transport in various ways.

Indiscriminate use of chemical compounds can significantly alter soil pH. Most tree roots grow over a substantial range of pH, but reduced growth is often observed at pH values below 4.0. Changes in soil pH may indirectly influence tree growth as a result of differences in the solubility of inorganic nutrients as well as alterations in the activity of soil organisms responsible for **nitrification**. At the other end of the pH scale there may be problems related to products washed from buildings into the soils rooted by trees. These compounds will be highly alkaline and may cause problems for tree roots.

7.3 De-icing salt

Even in the most inland areas of the UK, sodium (Na^+) and chloride (Cl^-) ions of maritime origin are present in the atmosphere. These chemicals can be deposited on vegetation under dry conditions or washed onto vegetation canopies and soil in rainfall. The amounts of salt deposited inland are very small and offer no threats to plants or soils. However, in exposed coastal locations where sea spray is prevalent the risk to trees can be considerable.

In contrast to the natural delivery of sodium and chloride to vegetation and soil, the amounts of these chemicals received as a consequence of the use of salt as a winter de-icing agent for roads, pavements and pedestrian precincts are considerable and can have severely damaging or lethal effects on vegetation growing close by. The careless spreading of salt and the fate of both runoff water and spray from roads means that vegetation can be injured or killed and important soil properties can be modified.

Many aspects of the damage caused to trees and shrubs by de-icing salt were reviewed for the Department of the Environment by Dobson (1991) and in the same year in the USA a report which also discussed the effects of road salt on trees appeared (TRB, 1991). Blomqvist (1998) reviewed the impact of de-icing salt on vegetation with reference to conditions in Sweden. Dobson (1991) showed that the amount of de-icing salt used in the UK had increased steadily between 1960–1990 and was doubtless responsible for serious damage to roadside trees and shrubs.

7.3.1 Symptoms of damage

7.3.1.1 Direct damage

It is possible to recognise the symptoms of salt damage to trees or shrubs using visual evidence without recourse to detailed chemical analysis of tissues. But it is important to realise that some visual damage symptoms that might be assumed to be caused by salt could well be caused by other factors, such as pathogens, herbicides or cats' urine (Strouts and Winter, 2000). Additionally, drought or desiccation by winds can produce visual symptoms similar to those exhibited by plants suffering salt damage. Small-scale damage appears as

necrosis on the margins of leaves but more serious damage ranges through whole defoliation of branches to complete death of trees.

A conclusion that injury to trees or shrubs is a consequence of salty runoff water or salt spray might involve evidence from one or several sources. It would be valuable to obtain this information as it helps to accumulate knowledge about the relative tolerance of different species to exposure to salt either in the soil or on the foliage. Currently, however, there is no central repository for such information. The visual symptoms of damage to foliage and branches will of course be the most obvious and easy to acquire. Key evidence that de-icing salt is responsible for tree damage will come from the position of the tree relative to the road and other site conditions:

- Trees close to roads are generally the worst affected and damage is most severe within 5 m of the road, injury being minimal around 30 m from the road. If damage occurs at distances substantially greater than these it might be suspected that tree roots have penetrated drains carrying saline runoff water.

- Trees on the downslope side of a road are more likely to suffer damage than those on the uphill slope.

- Trees planted in depressions or with depressions immediately around their bases (eg due to settling) suffer more damage than trees on raised planting sites.

- On high-speed roads (eg motorways) salt spray, more so than runoff, is the major cause of injury to the roadside vegetation.

Other information will help to substantiate that salt is the most likely cause of the injury. A measure of electrical conductivity of a soil sample will give a very good indication of salinity problems but it is important to recognise that salt damage could have occurred, the salt leached from the soil, with no evidence remaining in the soil that can be detected by conductivity determinations. However, when appropriate, soil conductivity can be measured simply and quickly in the field with a portable conductivity meter. A few cubic centimetres of soil are mixed with double that volume of distilled water. The conductivity can be measured after 30 minutes. The conductivity is expressed in units of millisiemens per centimetre ($mS\,cm^{-1}$).

Soil is considered to be saline when the electrical conductivity exceeds 4 mS cm^{-1}. Sensitive crops will show symptoms of excess salinity at levels in the soil of 1 mS cm^{-1} but more tolerant crops can withstand up to 7 mS cm^{-1} (Calow, 1998). Rainwater has a conductivity of around 0.1 mS cm^{-1}. Excess sodium in the soil is also a problem for plants. Its measurement will require laboratory analysis that relates the amount of sodium to other cations that are important for plant growth, calcium and magnesium. Chemical analysis of plant tissues for chloride will be definitive but will also require laboratory analysis. Foliar chloride concentrations are better correlated with damage than sodium

(Sucoff, 1975; Dobson, 1991). In general, injury symptoms are associated with leaf chloride concentrations above 1% by weight in broadleaves and 0.5% in conifers. There seems to be little correlation between the concentration of sodium and chloride in leaves associated with damage of different species and the susceptibility of those species to salt injury. When the salt has been delivered as runoff to the soil, other important evidence of salt injury will be death or complete absence of roots in the surface soil horizons. This symptom might be more obvious in species in which shallow rooting is regarded as particularly characteristic eg sugar maple (Guttay, 1976). Guttay's study concluded that damage to the trees was caused by the downward destruction of the surface root system and its associated mycorrhizae by frequent salt application. An interaction has also been shown between soil salinity and *Phytophthora* diseases. Salinity increases the seriousness of the effects of the disease on the tree.

Gibbs and Palmer (1994) surveyed trees in London for damage by de-icing salt applied in the winter of 1990/1991. Surveys were conducted in the early summer of 1991, again in September of that year, and the following year. Gibbs and Palmer expressed concern, particularly in the case of London plane, that assessment in the early summer following damage may have lead to a decision to condemn certain trees because of post-flushing dieback. Surveys carried out later in the year following winter damage by de-icing salts eg September, are less likely to confuse salt damage with injury caused by a pathogen (anthracnose blight, *Apiognomonia veneta*) and it would be easier to asses the degree to which the tree canopy has recovered.

A major impact for trees of increased salt in the soil is through lowering of the soil water potential through the reduction in osmotic potential because of the presence of salt. The reduction in soil water potential has similar effects to a deficit of water in the soil. The tree will need to generate a larger potential in the foliage to acquire water from the soil. The lowered water potential in the leaves may cause stomata to close and photosynthesis to be limited. The problems for the plant water relations of the tree caused by increased salt in the soil may not be apparent until tree transpiration is substantial, which may be some months after salt has been applied. It is important that any ameliorative measures (eg watering – see Section 7.3.4) are undertaken before transpiration and water uptake commences in the spring.

7.3.1.2 Indirect damage

Salinity is the extent of dissolved salts in soil. Salinisation is the process whereby soils accumulate salts over time. Associated with soil salinisation is alkanisation, in which the clay fraction becomes saturated with sodium, causing soil crumb structure to collapse, which restricts water penetration and aeration. Soils in which more than 15% of the locations on soil particles where cations can be attached and detached (cation exchange sites) that are occupied by sodium are termed sodic. Indirect salt damage to plants can occur when the soil structure is altered and also there is loss of mineral nutrients.

Table 7.1 Tolerance to soil salt of a range of the species relative to a tolerant (*Robinia pseudoacacia*), intermediate (*Fraxinus excelsior*) and an intolerant species (*Acer pseudoplatanus*). The first named species is therefore the most tolerant and the last named is the least tolerant. Differences in ranking of one or two places should not be regarded as significant. (After Dobson, 1991.)

Tolerance	Species
Tolerant	*Ulmus glabra*
	Robinia pseudoacacia
	Quercus robur
	Salix alba
	Gleditsia triacanthos
	Alnus glutinosa
	Elaeagnus angustifolia
	Picea pungens
Intermediate	*Fraxinus excelsior*
	Crataegus monogyna
	Acer campestre
	Picea abies
	Pseudotsuga menziesii
	Aesculus hippocastanum
	Alnus incana
	Sorbus aucuparia
	Fagus sylvatica
	Carpinus betulus
Sensitive	*Acer pseudoplatanus*

Sodium replaces other ions, which have important roles in the nutrition of the tree, on the soil cation exchange sites. This replacement reduces the availability of these ions to the roots of the tree. The presence of sodium also causes **deflocculation**, that is, disintegration of the soil particles and the production of a fine material which enters soil pores. This reduces soil aeration and promotes soil compaction. The influence of salinity on soil biota is not widely reported, but most earthworm species are thought to be quite sensitive to excess salinity (Brady and Weil, 1999). A further impact of excess salinity may be in soils which have a significant content of heavy metals. Excess salinity will mean that sodium can replace heavy metal ions on the cation exchange sites in the soil, thereby releasing the heavy metal ions into soil solution, with the risk that they will be leached to streams and groundwater.

7.3.2 Tolerance of tree species to de-icing salt

Given exposure to salt in sufficient concentrations it is unlikely any trees will prove tolerant. Dobson (1991) reviewed the literature on the tolerance to salt of 332 woody species. Because of the many ways of evaluating tolerance and also because several other factors which might influence the conditions under which the salt is delivered to the tree, Dobson has advocated considerable caution in using the data from these 332 species to assess tolerance in the form of a ranking. As an alternative, Dobson selected a small number of species which emerge consistently as tolerant, intermediate or sensitive to salt in a number of studies, and is reproduced here as Table 7.1. This table contains an assessment of the tolerance of a small number of species relative to three 'marker' species, which, from the list assembled by Dobson, appear to be consistently tolerant (*Robinia pseudoacacia*), moderately tolerant (*Fraxinus excelsior*), or intolerant (*Acer pseudoplatanus*). Other species are placed in relation to these marker species by examining reports which contain these marker species and are concerned only with contamination of the soil by salt (ie not studies reporting spray damage). The other species are then classified as either more or less tolerant than the marker species.

Thompson and Rutter (1986) examined the impact of different ways of applying salt to a number of trees and shrubs occurring commonly in the UK. They found that, in general, salt solutions added to soil had more effect than the same solutions sprayed onto the foliage of plants. There were considerable differences in the tolerance of species to concentrations of salt in the soil. The authors did not find a strong relationship between the susceptibility to spray injury and the damage caused by addition of salt solutions to the soil. In their survey of trees in main roads and side roads in London, Gibbs and Palmer (1994) found that older trees of London plane were less likely to suffer de-icing damage than young trees and suggested that the more extensive root system of the older trees was the explanation.

7.3.3 Options for reducing salt damage

7.3.3.1 Reducing the use of salt

There are a number of ways in which the use or loss of salt can be reduced:

- Salt storage

- Salt spreading

- Wet-salt spreading

- Ice prediction systems.

More salt is used than is necessary to clear roadways of ice and frost. Currently in the UK more than £140 million is spent on winter road maintenance each year. In addition, salt corrosion causes a further £100 million of damage each year to vehicles and structures (Chapman *et al*, 2001). Some of the waste in annual salt use is due to unsatisfactory storage of bulk salt without protection from the rain at the storage depots or at the roadside. There may be considerable loss of salt by rainfall leaching. This will only have local impact on any trees adjacent to unprotected salt piles but watercourses in the immediate vicinity of where the salt is stored are also at risk.

Figure 7.1 This mature horse chestnut is at a central point in the village of Crowmarsh, Oxfordshire and is facing a number of threats. Should this salt vault leak there is risk for the tree. There is already compaction from foot traffic.

Salt bins on the roadside can help to protect the salt from the elements and reduce the amount of leaching. It is important that the siting of salt stores in places such as shopping precincts, railway stations and village centres should avoid places where tree roots are likely to be ie 1 to 1.5 times the height of the tree away from the tree trunk (Fig 7.1). Another major problem for trees in such situations as shopping precincts is the concentration of runoff into the tree pit (Fig 7.2), and one of the means to overcome this is to plant trees on mounds or raised beds that will facilitate discharge of saline material away from the tree roots. Here there may be a conflict with the need to direct runoff water to where it can be most readily available to the tree's root system.

Other losses are due to inefficient spreading. Dry salt might be blown away by winds while wetted salt may be lumpy and be spread in a patchy manner requiring greater amounts to be applied. Spreading salt in a liquid form may be more efficient but the costs of converting vehicles to spray liquids may not be warranted.

The principal means taken to optimise the amount of salt spread on roads in the UK uses the Meteorological Office 'Open Road' ice prediction system. The National Ice Prediction Network (NIPN) is the overall framework within which 'Open Road' operates (Thornes, 1991). Central to the operation of 'Open Road' is an ice prediction model (Thornes, 1992; Thornes and Shao, 1992) which combines traditional synoptic weather forecasts (wind speed, cloud cover, air temperature, dewpoint and rainfall) and data from roadside automatic weather stations located at various points on the road network (Fig 7.3) that monitor air temperature, road temperature, subsurface temperature,

Figure 7.2 Tree pits can fill with water containing dissolved de-icing salt when the soil is below the road level.

humidity, and surface moisture. Ideally these roadside weather stations should be located at least one every 256 km^2 (100 sq miles). There are now more than 750 road weather stations across the UK (1 per 325 km^2). Thermal mapping of the road surface is used to identify representative locations for the weather stations. The mapping is also used to provide thermal 'fingerprints' of the roads. From this information it is possible to identify particular road sections most likely to require de-icing during cold conditions. Some of these roadside weather stations have road salinity sensors that detect residual salt on the road. Information from these sensors

Figure 7.3 Roadside weather station used to provide local weather variables used in ice prediction.

would enable the highway engineer to command a lower application of salt where a salt residue still remains. The detailed information about likely conditions for particular road sections that 'Open Road' provides also enables an optimum de-icing route to be planned for the gritting lorries. The information provided by thermal mapping of road sections most likely to

217

receive salt applications would be valuable to assist decisions about choice of tree species in these locations.

Although it is widely recognised that urban centres will be significantly warmer at night than surrounding rural areas, this is not taken into account in the decision to salt roads, and subsequently city centre roads are salted just as frequently as suburban or rural routes. A recent research initiative in the UK – Natural Environment Research Council (NERC) Urban Regeneration and the Environment (URGENT) thematic programme by a group lead by Dr Thornes of Birmingham University – produced a new road ice prediction system for urban areas (Bradley *et al*, 2002). Clearly, if such a model leads to a significant reduction of salting close to street trees this will be a big advantage.

Considerable damage to trees will occur because of salt applications made to pavements and in pedestrian precincts. This conclusion was supported by the survey for salt damage of 1500 trees in London following the winter of 1990/1991 (Gibbs and Palmer, 1994). They found that damage to trees on main roads was greater than on side roads but an important fraction of the damaged trees on main roads occurred near shops or public buildings. Both Dobson (1991) and Gibbs and Palmer (1994) believe that much more careful applications of salt in these situations will reduce the numbers of damaged trees considerably. Dobson (1991) believes the use of mechanised applicators that control salt dispersion more evenly will lead to improvements. A key problem referred to by Gibbs (1993) is that on local footpaths and shopping precincts the spreading of de-icing salt may be done by direct labour or contract staff who have little experience of administering salt to pathways, etc and probably have little understanding of the implications of excess salt to the welfare of trees. For the case of shopping precincts, for example, it is not known to what extent local retailers, who might have little appreciation of the impacts of salt on trees, might participate in salt spreading. A useful role for tree wardens would be to advise and educate persons likely to be involved with gritting near trees in precincts about the hazards for trees of careless and excessive applications.

7.3.3.2 *Alternatives to salt*

There are a number of alternatives to using salt for road de-icing:

- Roadway heating systems
- Salt/abrasive mixtures
- Chemical de-icing agents
    - Inorganic de-icing agents
        - Chlorides
        - Sulphates
        - Urea

◆ Organic de-icing agents

    ✳ Alcohols and glycols

    ✳ Methanol

    ✳ Calcium magnesium acetate.

Roadway heating systems have been used in a few locations eg entrances to alpine tunnels but the annual running costs are regarded as too high for widespread use.

Mixtures of salts and abrasives, or abrasives alone, are not regarded as being as effective as salt, requiring substantially greater amounts to be applied than salt to achieve the same skid resistance. There is also concern about damage to vehicles from stone particles and the safety implications of larger stones thrown onto windscreens. A further problem with abrasive materials spread on the roads is that they will find their way into gullies which may require more frequent clearing of accumulated grit (Gibbs, 1993). Some authorities may need to use a large fraction of grit in mixtures with salt when the salt is running short.

Dobson (1991) provides a summary of the advantages and disadvantages of the various inorganic and organic alternatives to common salt. The compounds which might have significant advantages over salt are calcium chloride and calcium magnesium acetate. Calcium chloride is two to three times more expensive than salt but is more efficient than salt for reducing the freezing point of water. Therefore less is required to produce the same effect. Unlike sodium chloride in which both the sodium and chloride ions are potentially damaging to plants, in calcium chloride it is only the chloride which poses a problem. Calcium magnesium acetate (CMA) seems to have no harmful effects on plants but is about six times more expensive than salt. Unlike salt it has no corrosive effects on vehicles or buildings. CMA degrades readily in groundwater under aerobic conditions, so there is a potential for O_2 depletion if an appreciable amount of acetate reaches an unconfined aquifer beneath the road. The level of O_2 in the groundwater is an important indicator of its quality, since anaerobic processes can cause odours and other aesthetic problems to water. An active microbial biomass in the unsaturated zone of the soil would mitigate groundwater O_2 demand if the microbial population mineralised the acetate before it reached the aquifer. Ostendorf *et al* (1995) found that the rate of snow melt might exceed the capacity of the microbial biomass to metabolise the acetate before it could reach the aquifer.

7.3.4 Amelioration

A number of studies (eg Constantini and Rich, 1973) have been conducted to evaluate whether anti-transpirants, which coat leaf surfaces with wax, might prevent chloride from salt spray entering the leaves. None of the studies reviewed by Dobson (1991) have given an indication that anti-transpirants offer an effective way of limiting salt spray damage to plants.

7.3.4.1 Watering

Removal of sodium and chloride ions from soils can be achieved by leaching with water. This should be done before growth starts in the spring to be most effective and care should be taken to avoid waterlogging, which could be just as damaging to the tree's health as any salt effects. There does not seem to be a set of simple guidelines, for example, based on the amount of salt applied and the subsequent rainfall, to calculate the amount of watering that should done to leach any applied salt away from tree roots in the spring time.

7.3.4.2 Soil additives

The most commonly used soil additive to counteract salt effects is gypsum ($CaSO_4$). Dirr and Biedermann (1980) showed that *Cotoneaster* plants treated with salt and gypsum showed less than 40% necrosis, while plants treated with NaCl alone had 70–80% necrosis. Gypsum can be applied to the soil around trees but can be more effective if it is mixed with the backfill in new plantings (Dirr and Biedermann, 1980). Rubens (1978) suggested that because gypsum is relatively insoluble one application to a tree may be effective in counteracting the influences of salt for several years. Gypsum can attack concrete, so some care needs to be taken not to apply gypsum close to vulnerable structures. Simple guidelines for the amount of gypsum to be applied to salt-affected soils would be valuable.

7.3.4.3 Engineering solutions

There is a need to balance the requirements of the opposing needs of providing trees with adequate water in a tree pit or plot towards which runoff water is directed, against the dangers that saline runoff would concentrate around the tree root system. One approach to the prevention of salt damage to trees from salty water being splashed onto the soil close to the trees in winter is to provide a simple, cheap barrier that is easily placed in position. Hvass (1986) refers to guards made of straw and plastic which are placed at the base of the tree before the winter. There is always a risk that such guards may become unsightly or be vandalised. In many cases, the need is to prevent runoff from pavements entering the root zone close to the tree. Kerbs to the tree-planting site might prevent this, but equally there may be a risk of salty water accumulating close to the tree (Fig 7.2). A suitable alternative would be to create a slight, permeable paved mound around the tree (Fig 7.4).

7.4 Metals in soils

There are a number of commonly occurring heavy metals that are likely to be toxic to trees and shrubs and are found in the built environment. These heavy metals will occur in the soil as a consequence of mining nearby, or previous industrial activity on or close to the site (Palmer, 1996) (see Table 7.2). The toxic materials may have arrived at the site as waste material or are associated

Figure 7.4 Creating a low mound around the base of a tree can prevent polluted runoff entering the tree pit.

in some way with transport or motor vehicles. Copper, zinc and nickel are commonly associated with industrial processes and will remain in the soil if derelict industrial sites are exploited in newer developments. Although lead-free fuels became widely available in 1986 and the deposition of lead to soils fell sharply as a consequence, lead is persistent in soils and will remain for decades to centuries. Vehicle tyres that contain 1–2% of zinc are a significant source of the metal deposited near busy roads (Royal Commission on Environmental Pollution, 1996). Platinum (from catalytic converters) has been found in soils near busy roads in London but knowledge of the levels that are **phytotoxic** is not available (Royal Commission on Environmental Pollution, 1996). In addition to the heavy metals, aluminium occurs universally in soils and becomes soluble and toxic under strongly acidic soil conditions.

Some metals eg copper, nickel, molybdenum, manganese and zinc are required by plants, but only at very low concentrations. The same applies to the non-

Table 7.2 Sources of selected inorganic soil pollutants harmful to plants.[1]

Cadmium	Electroplating, pigments for plastics and paints, plastic stabilisers, batteries and phosphate fertilisers.
Copper	Mine wastes, fly ash, fertilisers, wind-blown copper-containing dust, and water pipes.
Lead	Combustion of oil, fuel oils, and coal; iron and steel production; and solder on pipes.
Nickel	Combustion of coal, fuel oils, alloy manufacture, electroplating, batteries and mining.
Zinc	Galvanised iron and steel, alloys, batteries, brass, rubber manufacture, mining and tyres.

[1] The list above excludes other inorganic compounds (eg arsenic, chromium, and selenium) which are regarded as being harmful to humans, animals, fish or birds but less so to plants.

metallic element, boron. Other non-essential elements such as cadmium, chromium, mercury and nickel are also harmless in very low concentrations. However, any of these elements, whether essential or non-essential, can prove toxic at concentrations above the physiological requirement. At the appropriate concentration the essential elements are required for a number of physiological processes and are often associated with enzyme functions. However, at excessive concentrations they can cause a reduction in growth and death of the plant.

These elements are needed in only trace quantities and above that level toxicity occurs. A common response of heavy metal toxicity in trees is a reduction in root growth but there are also direct inhibitory influences on mineral nutrition, water uptake and mycorrhizal associations with roots (Kahle, 1993; Lepp, 1996). Most studies have involved measurements on young trees that have been exposed to high concentrations of toxic substances on seriously contaminated sites during attempts to establish trees or in experimental situations. Unfortunately, no clear picture emerges from the literature of the effects of more modest levels of pollution, eg lead coming from car exhausts deposited in roadside soils, on root growth of adult trees.

Determining the concentrations of heavy metals in soils to evaluate whether the level is toxic for trees is not straightforward. Applying strong acids to a sample of soil will extract all the heavy metal and might imply a potentially very toxic concentration. On the other hand, simple leaching with water will yield a much lower concentration of the metal. The level that is experienced by the tree root system will be somewhere in between the two determined values but there is still no knowledge if that concentration is toxic. The major effects of heavy metal accumulation in leaves includes decreased transpiration

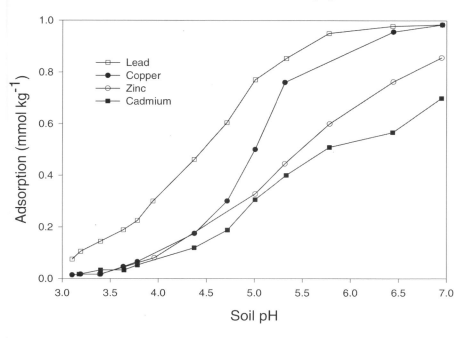

Figure 7.5 The effect of soil pH on the adsorption of four heavy metals. (After Elliot *et al*, 1986.)

and photosynthesis, and therefore reduced growth, frequently leading to mortality of seedlings (Broadmeadow and Freer-Smith, 1996). In fact, there seems to be a lack of information about the effects of heavy metals on the physiology of mature trees.

A number of factors can contribute to the toxicity of heavy metals. Heavy metals are more soluble and therefore toxic at low pH. Fig 7.5 (Elliot *et al*, 1986) shows the strong adsorption of four heavy metals as pH approaches neutrality. The problem of mobility of heavy metals at low pH may be made worse by the increased solubility of aluminium (and its toxicity) at low pH as well. Calcium may be deficient in some soils. This deficiency may cause cell membranes to be more permeable allowing more liberal entry of heavy metals. Organic matter can absorb metals and render them unavailable. One of the effects of sodium in de-icing salts is to occupy exchange sites in the soil to which heavy metal ions may have been held. This means that heavy metals may be leached from the soil (Amrhein *et al*, 1994) and offer a threat to the quality of receiving waters.

7.4.1 Planting trees in toxic soils

It has been recognised that planting trees on sites contaminated with heavy metals has substantial potential, both to remove the heavy metal component (**phytoremediation**) or to stabilise the contamination (**phytostabilisation**). Phytostabilisation can mean, for instance, that woodland might use more

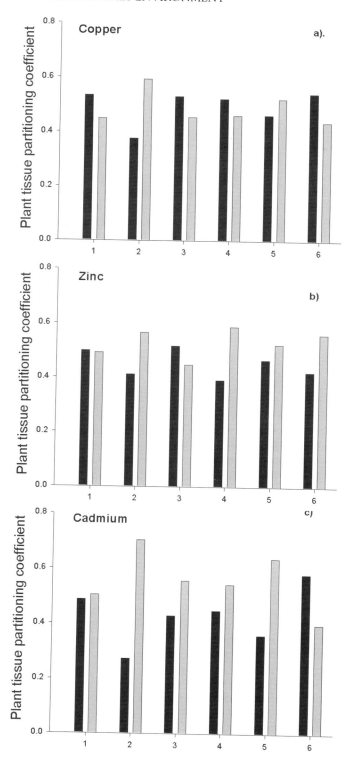

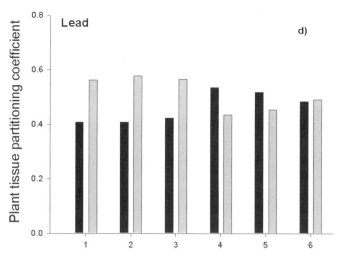

Figure 7.6 Fraction of metal stored in leaves and fine roots ■ and stem, bark and large roots ▦ of six tree species. (1 = sycamore, 2 = poplar, 3 = oak, 4 = birch, 5 = willow and 6 = alder.) (After Hutchings *et al*, 2001.)

water than other vegetation so any soil contamination remains in the soil and is not leached away. Alternatively, trees might reduce the loss of dust containing metals from the soil surface by wind during dry periods. Recent work by the UK Forestry Commission (Hutchings *et al*, 2001) showed that of a range of species tested, ash, birch, poplar and sycamore seemed more likely to survive and grow successfully in contaminated sites. An important consideration in terms of remediation and stabilisation of the heavy metals on contaminated soils is the partitioning of any metals taken up within the trees. It will be less useful if the main storage components are the leaves and fine roots because there will be a high turnover in these fractions and the metal will be returned to the soil or, worse still in the case of leaves, they may be blown off the site to contaminate elsewhere.

Hutchings *et al* (2001) showed that there were substantial variations between species in the partitioning of the different metals into separate fractions of the tree. Fig 7.6 shows the proportion of the metal that is distributed to the fractions of the tree that turn over rapidly (leaves and fine roots) and the long-lived fraction (the large roots, stem and bark). It is unfortunate that oak, a species that stores a large fraction of heavy metals in the larger roots where the metal is not likely to recycle quickly, was one of the species found to be least tolerant of heavy metals. The research suggests that different species might be used for phytoremediation depending on the particular metal contaminant. Poplar is tolerant of metal-contaminated sites and Fig 7.6 shows that it is capable of retaining a large fraction of cadmium in the long-lived parts of the tree. Of the heavy metals, cadmium and zinc are most readily taken up and translocated in the tree and are concentrated in the above-ground parts. Lead, arsenic, cobalt, chromium, mercury and tin show low uptake while copper, nickel and selenium have intermediate uptake.

Populations of heavy-metal-tolerant plants, especially grasses, have been found to occur on soils contaminated by specific heavy metals, distributed as mine spoil. Populations of birch and sycamore have been found growing on land contaminated by heavy metals that are more tolerant of the metal than populations growing at uncontaminated sites (Wilkins, 1997). A number of important practical points have emerged from the research into the metal-tolerance of plant populations:

- Tolerance is almost always specific to the metal in the soil that is being colonised; therefore a copper tolerant plant will not necessarily be zinc tolerant.

- There are many mechanisms by which plants acquire tolerance.

- Tolerance is not a characteristic which is totally present or absent in a population of plants. There is likely to be a spectrum from completely intolerant to highly tolerant.

The importance of mycorrhizae in conferring metal-tolerance to plants including trees has to be recognised. Using birch, Brown and Wilkins (1985) examined growth at three levels of zinc with or without mycorrhizae in three tolerance groups. In all cases the mycorrhizal infection improved growth, even in tolerant plants. Wilkins (1997) emphasises that most results showing the value of mycorrhizae have all been done with young trees and wondered if the more extensive root system of an older tree enables it to explore a larger volume of soil. The main development of the root system would then perhaps be able to avoid the worst areas of toxicity. Meharg and Cairney (2000) question if mycorrhizae bestow metal-resistance to their host plants but instead suggest that the role of ectomycorrhizal and vesicular-arbuscular mycorrhizal infection is much the same as in uncontaminated soils, that is to improve the efficiency of the root system in water and nutrient uptake, and to provide defence against pathogens.

A number of suggestions for improving conditions for tree growth on contaminated soils have been made by Wilkins (1997):

- The surface layers of contaminated soils could be removed and replaced with good soil. This will be an expensive but effective way to provide a good soil environment. There is, however, a requirement for the new soil depth to be adequate to enable sufficient rooting depth and hence ensure the stability of the trees.

- Acid soils could have lime added which will raise the pH and lower the solubility of heavy metals.

- There are tree species that have shown tolerance to metal contaminated soils for example birch, sycamore and willow. Seeds should be obtained from plants growing on sites with a long history of contamination. In a seed lot from a contaminated site only a few seedling will be tolerant therefore direct sowing of a large number of seeds at the new site or into representative soil will be necessary to ensure survival of sufficient individuals.

7.5 Atmospheric deposition

In this section we consider the deposition from the atmosphere of a range of gaseous pollutants that may be directly injurious to trees, or alternatively there may be impacts on the soil that affect the growth of trees. There is little evidence that atmospheric deposition has a direct effect on roots. However, any negative impacts on key canopy processes, eg photosynthesis, can reduce resources available to the root system The gases concerned are a number of those produced by a variety of industrial processes and as a consequence of the combustion of fuels by motor vehicles. Other polluting gases are linked to industrial processes, sewage processing or agriculture.

7.5.1 Polluting gases and particles

7.5.1.1 Sulphur dioxide

Sulphur dioxide (SO_2) is a by-product of the combustion of fuels containing sulphur. SO_2 dissolves in atmospheric water and contributes to acid deposition. However, because of reduction in coal burning and declines in heavy industry, atmospheric concentrations have fallen sharply in Europe in the last 20 years (Bell, 1994).

7.5.1.2 Oxides of nitrogen and nitrate

Oxides of nitrogen (NO_x ie NO, NO_2) are produced in most combustion processes. Concentrations as high as 1000 ppb have been measured close to roads in central London (Broadmeadow and Freer-Smith, 1996). Additionally, NO_2 dissolves in water to form H^+ and NO_3^-, nitrate ions reaching the ground as **acid rain**. If nitrogen supply is limited, inputs of atmospheric nitrogen can actually prove beneficial to trees. On the other hand, if the tree has abundant supplies of nitrogen the additional nitrogen coming from atmospheric sources may prove to be toxic.

7.5.1.3 Ammonia and ammonium

Ammonia (NH_3) is produced in many biological processes. High accumulation can occur in the atmosphere close to intensive animal husbandry enterprises. Ammonia is also in vehicle emissions, as a by-product of incineration, coal combustion, sewage treatment and the production and application of agricultural fertilisers. Even though ammonia itself is not acidic, the main impact of ammonium (NH_4^+) and ammonia is their contribution to the acidification of soils through the leaching of base cations, which is likely to reduce the buffering capacity of the soil. Other ways in which ammonia promotes **acidification** are by increasing the efficiency of SO_2 deposition. Sulphuric and nitric acids react with ammonia to produce ammonium sulphate and nitrate particles which are deposited more slowly than the original acids and are distributed more widely.

7.5.1.4 Particulates and volatile organic compounds

In urban areas, the major source of particulate materials (PM_{10}s, ultra-fine particles smaller than 10 μm in diameter) and volatile organic compounds (VOCs) are vehicle exhaust emissions. The emission of petrol engines is estimated at around 0.015 g km^{-1} but diesel engines produce particulates at about ten times that rate. VOCs are also involved in the production of ozone at ground level.

7.5.1.5 Carbon monoxide

Carbon monoxide (CO) is produced during inefficient combustion of fuels which results in incomplete oxidation of the fuel. CO will also contribute to the production of ozone.

7.5.1.6 Ozone

Ozone (O_3) is a secondary pollutant, produced by the action of sunlight with other pollutants such as volatile organic compounds (VOCs) and nitrogen dioxide (NO_2). It is produced principally during periods in summer in which sunny, calm, anti-cyclonic conditions predominate.

7.5.2 The deposition processes

The deposition of pollutants can occur through one of three pathways:

- Dry deposition – the deposition of gases and particles directly onto terrestrial surfaces. In many parts of the UK dry deposition is greater than wet deposition, and arguably will be the dominant process of deposition to tree canopies of cities and towns of lowland UK. Figure 7.7 shows equipment used to monitor fluctuations in urban air quality and the associated microclimate.

- Wet deposition – the deposition of pollutants in rain and snow, commonly termed 'acid rain' because of early understanding of the deposition of SO_2 and NO_x from the atmosphere as weak acids in rainfall. This is the principal pathway for most upland areas.

- Cloud deposition – the capture of cloud droplets by terrestrial surfaces. Usually pollutants are more concentrated in cloud than in rain. Therefore, over high ground this pathway can provide a significant input of acidic pollutants. This pathway of pollutant deposition has far less relevance to trees in towns and cities but is very important in upland forested catchments.

7.5.3 Sensitivity of trees to pollutants

Trees differ in their sensitivity to polluting gases. Table 7.3 (Bhattacharya, 1994; Last, 1982) indicates that there is no particularly sensitive group (eg conifers or

Figure 7.7 The climate and atmospheric chemical load in a busy town centre (Banbury, Oxfordshire) can be continuously monitored. The air sampling unit is on the container roof.

broadleaves) or even species. Recent studies in the Natural Environment Research Council's URGENT Thematic programme has examined the balance of benefits of trees in absorbing pollution and the amount they emit as volatile organic compounds. The study showed that some species: ash, alder, maple, larch, pine and birch, would be beneficial in the balance of absorbing

Table 7.3 Species grouped according to tolerance of air pollutants.
(Bhattacharya, 1994; Last, 1982.)

Pollutant	Sensitive species	Intermediate species	Resistant species
Sulphur	Acer pseudoplatanus Alnus incana Betula papyrifera B. pendula Corylus avellana Fagus sylvatica Fraxinus americana Larix decidua L. kaempferi L. occidentalis Picea abies P. sitchensis Pinus ponderosa P. strobus P. sylvestris Populus nigra Sorbus aucuparia Ulmus americana U. parvifolia	Acer negundo A. platanoides A. specatum Abies balsamea Pinus monticola P. nigra Populus deltoides Prunus virginiana Pseudotsuga taxifolia Quercus palustris	Acer saccharinum Abies grandis Picea engelmanni Populus angulata P. balsamifera Quercus alba Q. robur Q. rubra Salix caprea Sambucus nigra Taxus baccata
Ozone	Acer saccharinum Pinus ponderosa Populus tremuloides Quercus gumbelli Salix babylonica		
Chlorine	Acer saccharum Pinus strobus Quercus palustris	Pinus taeda	Quercus rubra
Hydrochloric acid	Corylus avellana Larix decidua Picea abies Pinus strobus	Acer platanoides Fagus sylvatica Pinus sylvestris	Acer campestre Quercus rubra

pollution as against producing VOCs. On the other hand some trees were considered to make air quality worse. These included willow, oak and poplar. A brochure describing the results can be obtained at:

www.es.lancs.ac.uk/people/cnh/UrbantreesBrochure.pdf

7.5.4 Deposition and forest decline

The phrase 'acid rain' has come to be used very loosely to mean everything to do with acidification, although rain may not actually be involved. As well as the problems of acidification of lakes and streams in Scandinavia, for example, and the damage to stonework of historic buildings constructed from limestone (both wet and dry deposition of sulphur dioxide is regarded as being responsible) there is the damage caused by acid deposition to trees and forests. The impact of acid deposition on forests became particularly noticeable in Germany in the early 1980s, the worst effects being observed in the Black Forest in the south-east and on the border with former Czechoslovakia in the east. Since those early observations, many other countries have reported similar phenomena.

The consensus now is that the cause of forest decline is a combination of factors. Although some forests in the former Eastern European countries suffer from the effects of very high SO_2 levels, this is not always the case elsewhere. Clarke and Tomlin (1999) list possible mechanisms that contribute to a suite of stresses impacting on trees directly or through soil and root processes:

- The effect of ozone initiating an attack on cell walls, with subsequent further deterioration due to acid rain, mist and fogs. This will leach nutrients from leaves and breakdown of **chlorophyll** will result. Reduced root growth and nutrient uptake follows.

- Acidification of the ground with consequent effects on soil chemistry. A principal response is an increase in the levels of mobile aluminium that will be deleterious to roots.

- Excess deposition of nitrogen (as nitrate and ammonium) that can have a variety of effects. In the soil NH_4^+ can release H^+ during the process of being oxidised to NO_3^- by bacteria. The H^+ can then be leached out of the soil.

- Given the complexity of the range of biological and chemical processes it is clear that control of the effects of acid rain on biological systems should focus on all the potential pollutants – SO_2, NO_x, NH_3 and hydrocarbons (which can be precursors of ozone).

An important consequence of the deposition of gases from the atmosphere is the acidification of soils and streams. A number of long-term studies have shown a decline in the amounts of important cations and lowering of pH below forest cover eg Knoepp and Swank (1994) (Fig 7.8). In addition to the increase in acidity of soils because of inputs from the atmosphere, there are a number of ways in which the acidity of soils can increase:

- uptake by plant roots of positively charged ions from the soil in excess of the uptake of negatively charged ions

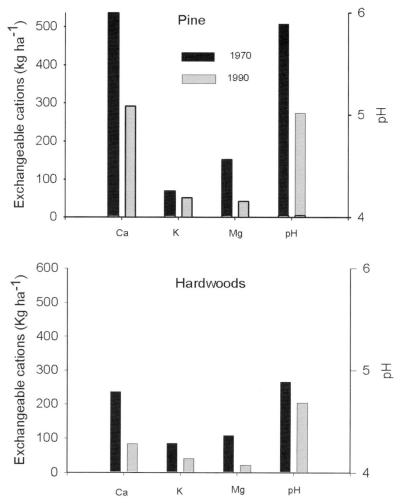

Figure 7.8 Decline of exchangeable Ca^{2+}, Mg^{2+}, K^+ and pH in surface soils of pine and hardwood forests in North Carolina. (After Knoepp and Swank, 1994.)

- the removal of calcium, magnesium, potassium and sodium cations which are semi-permanently locked up in plant material, particularly trees. These cations can also be leached from the soil in rainfall

- oxidation processes, such as nitrification or oxidation of soil organic matter

- the microbial production of organic acids.

The increase in acidity will mean a greater mobility of heavy metals and aluminium in the soil with the possibility of serious consequences for trees growing on the site and for the prospect that the metals will be more readily leached into receiving waters. Long-term studies at Rothamsted Experimental

Station, Hertfordshire, have shown soil pH declining under grass cover over a long duration. Sapling material from an area of regenerated woodland at Rothamsted where soils have become acidified had very much higher concentrations of metals than samples from non-acidified woodland: concentrations of aluminium were seven times, of manganese four times and iron three times as high as in control samples (Royal Commission on Environmental Pollution, 1996).

There are many studies showing a decline in the base status and pH of forests and woodlands in the UK, elsewhere in Europe and also in North America. However, no similar information has been acquired for the soils below urban trees and therefore we have no guide to the nutrient status and levels of pH. We do not know therefore how critical these factors are for adequate tree growth and other aspects which are influenced by soil pH eg heavy metal mobility. In natural and plantation forests and woodlands there is a substantial return of minerals back to the soil in the form of leaf, bark, twig and branch litter. In the case of the majority of street trees this recycling is precluded, but there is no information on the long-term consequences of this to soil fertility and tree health.

Although the deposition of gases such as the oxides of nitrogen is still increasing because of the continuing rise of pollution from vehicles, pollution from power stations has been reduced and much less sulphur dioxide is deposited now than in the 1970s, for example. In 1971 sulphur dioxide emissions were over 6 million tonnes but had fallen to below 2 million tonnes by 1997 (DETR, 1999). In the past, sulphur dioxide deposition served to provide vegetation with all their sulphate requirements and additional fertilisation was not necessary. It is interesting to note that in a recent survey of fertiliser use in UK agriculture, Chalmers (2001) found that some crops are now requiring sulphate fertilisers. There seems to be no information to indicate how adequately trees growing in urban soils are provided with their sulphur requirements.

7.6 Organic chemicals in soil

7.6.1 Pesticides in soils

The general term pesticide covers a range of products that will have been used to control weeds, insects and fungal pests (herbicides, insecticides and fungicides). There is a wide range in the persistence of pesticides and also therefore of the threat they pose if contaminated land is planted with trees. Table 7.4 shows that while some pesticides persist in the soil for as little as a few days, others are very persistent. These persistent forms pose a long-term threat to plants and other organisms in the soil that might be susceptible.

Table 7.4 Range of persistence of a number of organic compounds.

Organic chemical	Persistence
Chlorinated hydrocarbon insecticides (eg dieldrin)	3–20 years
Triazine herbicides (eg atrazine and simazine)	1–2 years
Benzoic acid herbicides (eg amiben and dicamba)	2–12 months
Urea herbicides (eg monuron and diuron)	2–10 months
Vinyl chloride	1–5 months
Phenoxy herbicides (2,4-D and 2,4,5-T)	1–5 months
Organophosphate insecticides (eg malathion and diazinon)	1–12 weeks
Carbamate insecticides	1–8 weeks
Carbamate herbicides (eg barban and CIPC)	2–8 weeks

7.6.1.1 Retention of pesticides in soils

The retention of pesticides in soils is determined largely by soil texture and the pH of the soil. The different nature of soils has a fundamental influence on the capacity of the soil to retain pesticides. Fig 7.9 shows that compared to sand and clay, organic matter is particularly efficient in retaining polychlorinated biphenyl (PCB) (here used as a substitute for pesticide data) in the soil. The diagram shows that not only does organic matter have a high efficiency for adsorption of a contaminant but carries out this adsorption with smaller amounts of material than does clay or sand.

Unlike heavy metals and aluminium the retention of pesticides in soil is promoted by lowering of pH, rather than raising it towards neutrality. It is an important general issue that the soil pH can strongly influence the mobility of heavy metals, aluminium and pesticides. Liming of soils has been used as an ameliorative measure to raise soil pH. In the case of acidified catchments this liming has been done at very large scales.

7.6.2 Polycyclic aromatic hydrocarbons

These compounds are very persistent in soils, lasting for up to 20 or 30 years. The range of materials comprising this group is large. They can be produced by materials being burnt on the soil, or more commonly, fuels and oils that have been spilt. The risks to tree roots of spillages of fuels and lubricants, for example during construction activities, are very real. Considerable caution should be taken when refilling plant and machinery as these sorts of compounds are poisonous to roots and are therefore potentially fatal. Young trees with a

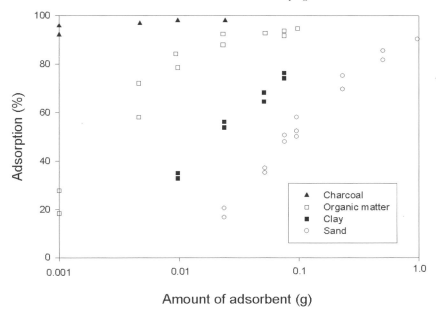

Figure 7.9 Adsorption of polychlorinated biphenyl (PCB) by different soil materials. (After Strek and Weber, 1982.)

localised root system will be especially vulnerable to spillages near their roots. Any practical measures for dealing with spillages of fuels and lubricating oils near to trees are not widely published and evidence of success is difficult to come by. Some of the measures require drastic action. For young trees, one recommendation is to remove the tree as carefully as possible and transplant back with healthy soil. For larger trees, the commercial literature in the USA offers the option of soil vacuuming, which can remove contaminated soil from around the root system for it to be replaced with uncontaminated soil (see Section 4.6.4). It is probable that soil vacuuming is more likely to be successful if the tree is not transpiring actively and relying upon good root-to-soil contact.

7.6.3 Landfill gases

The breakdown of decomposable rubbish in landfills generates significant volumes of a number of gases such as methane, carbon dioxide, carbon monoxide, ethylene, ethane, hydrogen sulphide and propylene. Methane and carbon dioxide dominate the composition, usually accounting for over 90% of the total. Some gases, eg carbon dioxide, are poisonous for roots, whereas methane is not. However, the major effect of the important landfill gases is to displace oxygen and to create anaerobic conditions that are not suitable for root growth and functioning. The impact on roots is very similar to those encountered in waterlogged soils. Arthur *et al* (1981) did find that the flooding-tolerant red maple (*Acer rubrum*) grew better in a gas treatment compared with the less tolerant sugar maple (*Acer saccharum*) but neither grew as well as when no gas was present. Leone *et al* (1982) evaluated a range of species for tolerance of gas and suggested that the least tolerant were honey locust (*Gleditsia triacanthos*) and green ash (*Fraxinus pennsylvanica*). Interestingly, green ash is regarded as tolerant of poor soil aeration. Consideration of this set of results by Gilman *et al* (1981) suggested that the most tolerant species (Japanese black pine (*Pinus thunbergiana*) and Norway spruce (*Picea abies*)) were able to tolerate the landfill gas because of their shallow rooting (<10 cm).

Analysing the same data, Flower *et al* (1981) showed that the most tolerant species had physically smaller root systems at the start of the experiment. They suggested that small trees may adapt to gas concentrations better than older, larger trees. Dobson and Moffat (1993) consider that the ability to grow on sites where landfill gas is a problem is more to do with avoiding the high gas concentrations rather than tolerating them. This avoidance is usually by virtue of shallow root systems but this characteristic disposes the trees with shallow roots to drought. Dobson and Moffat regard planting trees with shallow roots as a means to overcome the problem of landfill gases as a risky option. They believe that other ways should be sought to avoid the accumulation of gas, probably using engineering approaches to vent the gas or ensure an effective capping. The evidence that anaerobic conditions exist can be obtained by using steel rods that do not rust under anaerobic conditions (Hodge, 1993). A pit will reveal blackening of the soil and unpleasant smells. Many of the problems of landfill gases are associated with older landfills that do not have an impermeable clay cap or synthetic barrier above the rubbish, or if there is a cap, it has been damaged in some way.

7.7 Summary

- De-icing salt applied to roads and pavements in winter can be injurious to trees either because of direct action on leaves or roots, enhanced soil water stresses or indirectly because of modification of soil properties, eg ion balance or soil structure.

- Major salt impacts occur away from major roads, eg shopping precincts, because salt is applied excessively by untrained personnel.

- It would benefit future planting schemes to distinguish salt damage unequivocally from other causes of tree damage. A valuable knowledge base of the tolerance of different tree species should be built up.

- Alternatives to salt are less effective or are considerably more costly. Methods to ameliorate salt damage by, for example, watering or applying gypsum require sound guidelines to be drafted.

- Although lead from the combustion of vehicle fuels has been reduced substantially in the last decade or so the heavy metal is very persistent in soils. Zinc from car tyres is a major contaminant associated with vehicle traffic. Other heavy metals will be present where industrial activities previously occupied the site, but dust bearing heavy metal compounds can still reach previously uncontaminated sites.

- Heavy metals and aluminium are relatively immobile in soils if the pH is not too acidic. Lowering of pH will render heavy metals and aluminium more mobile and toxic.

- There seem to be good prospects that metal-tolerant strains of some tree species may be encountered on contaminated sites. Tolerance of one particular metal does not appear to confer a universal tolerance to other metals.

- Although sulphur dioxide emissions have been reduced substantially in the last two to three decades, acidic atmospheric depositions have not been reduced proportionately because NO_x from traffic and industrial combustion has increased. Ammonia produced principally from agricultural activities has also contributed to soil acidification.

- Ozone produced by the photochemical decomposition of volatile organic compounds and oxides of nitrogen is highly toxic to trees. The major sites of action of ozone are in the leaf structure and in the photosynthetic tissues.

- It is probable that acidification effects are not operating singly to produce stresses for trees. Ozone damage to leaves associated with poor root functioning because of acidic conditions below ground are causes of water stress to trees. When these difficulties are combined with limited soil water supplies and high atmospheric demand of hot dry summers the impact on trees can be considerable. Trees in towns, especially those growing in limited soil volumes, will be particularly stressed.

- There is substantial evidence from studies in forests and woodlands that the base status and pH of many forest soils have declined significantly in recent decades. The causes of these changes are considered to be soil acidification from atmospheric depositions and, where new forests have been established, acidification caused by accumulation of base cations in the forest biomass. There is no equivalent knowledge about these important aspects for the soils in which urban trees are growing.

REFERENCES

Alloway, B.J. 1999. Land contamination and reclamation. In: *Understanding our environment: An Introduction to Environmental Chemistry and Pollution*, 3rd Edition (Ed. by R.M. Harrison), pp. 199–236. Royal Society of Chemistry, Cambridge, UK.

Amrhein, C., Mosher, P.A., Strong, J.E. & Pacheco, P.G. 1994. Heavy metals in the environment: Trace metal solubility in soils and waters receiving de-icing salts. *Journal of Environmental Quality*, 23, 219–227.

Arthur, J.J., Leone, I.A. & Flower, F.B. 1981. Flooding and landfill gas effects on red and sugar maples. *Journal of Environmental Quality*, 10, 431–433.

Bell, J.N.B. 1994. (Ed.) *The ecological effects of increased aerial deposition of nitrogen*. Ecological Issues No. 5, Field Studies Council, Shrewsbury, UK. 36 pp.

Bhattacharya, A.K. 1994. Efficacy of tree species towards gaseous pollutants and its significance in air pollution control by plantations of pollutant resistant trees. *Indian Forester*, 658–669.

Blomqvist, G. 1998. *Impact of de-icing salt on roadside vegetation – a literature review*. Swedish National and Transport Research Institute, Report 427A. 36 pp.

Bradley, A.V., Thornes, J.E., Chapman, L., Unwin, D. & Roy, M. 2002. Modelling spatial and temporal road thermal climatology in rural and urban areas using a GIS. *Climate Research*, 22, 41–55.

Brady, N.C. & Weil, R.R. 1999. *The Nature and Properties of Soils*. Prentice-Hall, New Jersey, USA. 881 pp.

Broadmeadow, M.S.L. & Freer-Smith, P. 1996. *Urban woodland and the benefits for local air quality*. Research for Amenity Trees, No. 5. TSO, London, UK. 89 pp.

Brown, M.T. & Wilkins, D.A. 1985. Zinc tolerance of mycorrhizal *Betula*. *New Phytologist*, 99, 101–106.

Calow, P. 1998. *The Encyclopaedia of Ecology and Environmental Management*. Blackwell Science Ltd., Oxford, UK. 805 pp.

Chalmers, A.G. 2001. A review of fertiliser, lime and organic manure use on farm crops in Great Britain from 1983–1997. *Soil Use and Management*, 17, 254–262.

Chapman, L., Thornes, J.E. & Bradley, A.V. 2001. Modelling of road surface temperature from a geographical parameter database. Part 2: Numerical. *Meteorological Applications*, 8, 421–436.

Clarke, A.G. & Tomlin, A.S. 1999. The Atmosphere. In: *Understanding our environment: An Introduction to Environmental Chemistry and Pollution*, 3rd Edition (Ed. by R.M. Harrison), pp. 9–70. Royal Society of Chemistry, Cambridge, UK.

Constantini, A. & Rich, A.E. 1973. Comparison of salt injury to four species of coniferous tree seedlings when salt was applied to the potting medium and to the needles with or without antitranspirant. *Phytopathology*, 63, 200.

Craul, P.J. 1992. *Urban soil in landscape design.* John Wiley, Chichester, UK. 396 pp.

DETR. 1999. *A better quality of life: A strategy for sustainable development for the UK.* Cm 4345. Department of the Environment, Transport and the Regions, London, UK. 96 pp.

Dirr, M.A. & Biedermann, J. 1980. Amelioration of salt damage to Cotoneaster by gypsum. *Journal of Arboriculture*, 6, 108–110.

Dobson, M.C. 1991. *De-icing salt damage to trees and shrubs.* Forestry Commission Bulletin 101. HMSO, London, UK. 64 pp.

Dobson, M.C. & Moffat, A.J. 1993. *The potential for woodland establishment on landfill sites.* Department of the Environment. HMSO, London, UK. 88 pp.

DOE. 1995. *Survey of derelict land in England 1993.* 2 Volumes. Department of the Environment. HMSO, London, UK.

Elliot, H.A., Liberati, M.R. & Huang, C.P. 1986. Competitive adsorption of heavy metals in soils. *Journal of Environmental Quality*, 15, 214–219.

Flower, F.B., Gilman, E.F. & Leone, I.A. 1981. Landfill gas, what it does to trees and how its injurious effects can be prevented. *Journal of Arboriculture*, 7, 43–52.

Gibbs, J.N. 1993. Saving salt and the earth. *The Surveyor*, Part 5262, 7 October 1993, pp. 14–15.

Gibbs, J.N. & Palmer, C.A. 1994. A survey of damage to roadside trees in London by the application of de-icing salt during the 1990/1991 winter. *Arboricultural Journal*, 18, 321–343.

Gilman, E.F., Leone, I.A. & Flower, F.B. 1981. The adaptability of 19 woody species in vegetating a former sanitary landfill. *Forest Science*, 27, 13–18.

Guttay, A.J.R. 1976. Impact of deicing salts upon the endomycorrhizae of roadside sugar maples. *Soil Science Society of America Journal*, 40, 952–954.

Hodge, S.J. 1993. *Using steel rods to assess aeration in urban soils.* Arboriculture Research and Information Note 115. Arboricultural Advisory and Information Service, Farnham, UK. 5 pp.

Hutchings, T.R., Moffat, A.J. & Stubbs, I. 2001. Woodland restoration on contaminated land. In: *Forest Research. Annual Report and Accounts 1999–2000*, pp. 30–37. Forestry Commission. TSO, London, UK.

Hvass, N. 1986. Defending street trees against road salt in Denmark. *Arboricultural Journal*, 10, 89–94.

Kahle, H. 1993. Response of roots of trees to heavy metals. *Environmental and Experimental Botany*, 33, 99–119.

Knoepp, J.D. & Swank, W.T. 1994. Long term soil chemistry changes for aggrading forest systems. *Soil Science Society of America Journal*, 58, 325–331.

Last, F.T. 1982. Effects of atmospheric sulfur-compounds on natural man-made terrestrial and aquatic ecosystems. *Agriculture and Environment*, 7, 299–387.

Leone, I.A., Gilman, E.F. & Flower, F.B. 1982. Growing trees on completed sanitary landfills. *Arboricultural Journal*, 7, 247–252.

Lepp, N.W. 1996. Uptake, mobility and loci of concentration of heavy metals in trees. In: *Heavy Metals and Trees* (Ed. by I. Glimmerveen), pp. 68–84. Institute of Chartered Foresters, Edinburgh, UK.

Meharg, A. & Cairney, J.W.G. 2000. Co-evolution of mycorrhizal symbionts and their hosts to metal-contaminated environments. *Advances in Ecological Research*, 30, 69–112.

Ostendorf, D.W., DeGroot, D.J., Pollock, S.J. & Gagnon, P.J. 1995. Aerobic acetate degradation near the capillary fringe of roadside soil: Field simulations from soil microcosms. *Journal of Environmental Quality*, 24, 334–342.

Palmer, J.P. 1996. Heavy metals in derelict and contaminated land. In: *Heavy Metals and Trees* (Ed. by I. Glimmerveen), pp. 10–17. Institute of Chartered Foresters, Edinburgh, UK.

Royal Commission on Environmental Pollution. 1996. Nineteenth Report, *Sustainable Use of Soil*. Cmd 3165. HMSO, London, UK.

Rubens, J.M. 1978. Soil desalination to counteract maple decline. *Journal of Arboriculture*, 4, 33–43.

Strek, H.J. & Weber, J.B. 1982. Adsorption and reduction of bioactivity of polychlorinated biphenyl (Arochlor 1254) to redroot pigweed by soil organic matter and montmorillonite clay. *Soil Science of America Journal*, 46, 318–322.

Strouts, R.G. & Winter, T.G. 2000. *Diagnosis of ill-health in trees*. Research for Amenity Trees No. 2. DETR. TSO, London, UK. 311 pp.

Sucoff, E. 1975. *Effects of de-icing salts on woody plants along Minnesota roads*. Minnesota Agricultural Experimental Station, Technical Bulletin 303.

Thompson, J.R. & Rutter, A.J. 1986. The salinity of motorway soils. IV. Effects of sodium chloride on some native British shrub species and the possibility of establishing shrubs on the central reserves of motorways. *Journal of Applied Ecology*, 23, 299–315.

Thornes, J.E. 1991. Thermal mapping and road-weather information systems for highway engineers. In: *Highways Meteorology* (Ed. by A. Perry and L. Symons), pp. 38–67. E & FN Spon, London, UK.

Thornes, J.E. 1992. The impact of weather and climate on transport in the UK. *Progress in Physical Geography*, 16, 187–208.

Thornes, J.E. & Shao, J. 1992. Objective method for improving the operational performance of a road ice prediction model using interpolated mesoscale output and a templet for correcting systematic error. *Meteorological Magazine*, 121, 197–204.

TRB. 1991. *Highway Deicing: Comparing salt and calcium magnesium acetate.* Special Report 235. Transportation Research Board, National Research Council, Washington, DC., USA.

Wilkins, D.A. 1997. Potential for tree growth on sites contaminated with heavy metals. In: *Arboricultural Practice: Present and Future* (Ed. by J. Claridge), pp. 125–129. Research for Amenity Trees No. 6. TSO, London, UK.

CHAPTER 8

Protecting Trees During Excavation

8.1 Below-ground infrastructure in the built environment

The impact of excavation on tree roots is dealt with in this chapter; the following chapter focuses on tree root damage during construction. However, although the likely causes of damage, ie excavation (this chapter) and soil compaction or changes in soil level (Chapter 9) differ, the net effects can be similar. It is therefore important to appreciate that activities such as excavation and soil compaction can occur side by side, and efforts to avoid damage to tree roots should assume and account for this.

Underground space in towns and cities, particularly in the UK, is commonly crowded with the infrastructure needed to connect homes, offices, factories

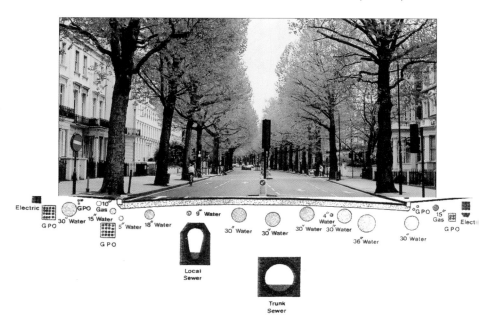

Figure 8.1 Underground services (minus any more recent cable installations) in Holland Park Avenue, London as depicted in *The Surveyor* of January 1982. Above – the same street in summer 2001.

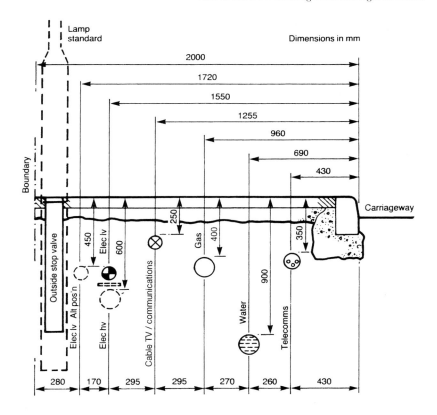

Figure 8.2 Recommended arrangement of mains in a 2 m footway including cable TV / communications duct showing the centre line. (After NJUG, 1997.)

and other buildings to utility networks (Fig 8.1). Numerous pipes and cables for the supply of water, gas, electricity and telecommunications may be buried beneath roads, footways, and sometimes gardens and areas of landscaping. There may still be coal cellars under the pavement on both sides of the road in older urban areas. The space occupied by these installations may severely reduce the space available for trees (O'Callaghan, 1998). Where space is particularly limited, for example beneath a narrow footway alongside a road, utility infrastructure may occupy all available below-ground space, preventing any tree planting. The recommended arrangement of underground pipes and cables shown in Fig 8.2 for a 2 m wide footway, for example, illustrates the problem.

Installation, maintenance or renewal of underground services in existing streets usually necessitates the digging of a trench. If trees are planted along the street, or if there are large trees in adjacent parks or gardens, this leaves root systems vulnerable to damage. Digging near trees also occurs during highway maintenance and on construction sites. Regardless of the reasons for digging a trench, loss of considerable proportions of a tree's root system may result if care is not taken during excavation.

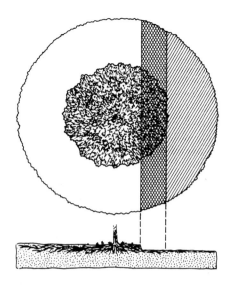

Figure 8.3 Plan view of a tree showing the outline of the canopy edge and the outermost extent of the roots. Lowering the soil level back to the canopy edge, or digging a trench, on one side would cut off 20% of the roots; lowering the soil level halfway between the canopy edge to the trunk on one side would eliminate about 30% of the shallow roots. (After Harris *et al*, 1999.)

8.2 Loss of roots during excavation

8.2.1 Distribution of lateral roots

In Chapter 3 (3.2.2) the key features of the lateral spread and horizontal distribution of tree roots have already been covered. The important conclusions from Chapter 3 are that a very large fraction of the root system occurs within 1.0 m of the ground surface and that substantial amounts of the tree's root system can occur well beyond the perimeter of the leaf canopy – the dripline. These features of the root system mean that the root systems of trees are vulnerable to any form of excavation within the zone where the majority of roots occur. Because of the concentration of tree roots in surface soils, even minor digging without due care can cause significant damage to the root system of a tree.

8.2.2 Damage to root systems by excavation

The digging of a trench through the root zone of a tree can entail severing of roots, unless care is taken to protect roots exposed during digging. Trenching near trees by conventional means, using a mechanical excavator, inevitably causes root loss, as the bucket easily rips through roots. An example of root system loss when a trench is dug is given in Figs 8.3 and 8.4. If roots are symmetrically distributed around the tree, trenching or lowering the soil level along one edge of the crown perimeter severs lateral roots and causes the loss of about 20% of the root system. This proportion increases if a trench is dug under the branches, reaching roughly 50% adjacent to the trunk.

Figure 8.4 Many large roots of English elm (*Ulmus procera*) trees were cut during unauthorised trenching in Parkville, Melbourne, Australia.

If root spread from the tree is restricted, for example by a compacted road base surrounding the tree, proportional loss of roots may not be as severe at a given distance from the tree. However, if root spread around the tree is asymmetrical, which might be the expected distribution in many urban settings, root loss when a trench is dug can be very severe. A tree growing next to a road or building is likely to have virtually all of its roots growing on the opposing side of the tree, as observed by Cermak *et al* (2000) using ground penetrating radar to map coarse roots. Trenching close to such a tree could cause loss of almost the entire root system and would almost certainly have a severe impact on the viability and stability of the tree (Figs 8.3 and 8.4).

8.3 Effects of root severance on tree growth and survival

8.3.1 Functional equilibrium of roots and shoots

Growing plants maintain a balance between the size of the shoot and the root system. This ensures a functional equilibrium between the demand for resources by above- and below-ground plant organs and the capacity for supply (Brouwer, 1983). Shoots supply energy and organic compounds to the plant, and in return the roots supply water and mineral nutrients from the soil. Balance between the shoot and root systems ensures that resources supplied by each can meet demand by the other. The ratio of root and shoot biomass is consequently a conservative property of plants, with characteristic values for different species that, in a stable environment, decline gradually with plant size and age (Kramer and Kozlowski, 1979).

A key feature of the functional equilibrium between roots and shoots is that disturbance of the root:shoot ratio, by root cutting or crown pruning for example, causes changes in patterns of growth that restore the original balance (Brouwer, 1983; Geisler and Ferree, 1984a). This results from changes in the availability and demand for the resources required for growth, as well as the effects of growth regulators or plant hormones.

8.3.1.1 Growth responses to root and shoot pruning

In the case of crown pruning, removal of shoot biomass raises the root:shoot ratio. Carbohydrate synthesis is severely reduced, but the root system is undisturbed and the availability of water and nutrients to the shoot is therefore unaffected. Carbohydrates available from reserves, or carbon fixation by remnant leaves, are utilised for vigorous growth of new leaves. Water and nutrients are amply available for new shoot growth, but root growth is limited by the reduced supply of carbohydrate. Thus, after crown pruning, changes in the allocation of carbohydrate result in crown regrowth and reduced root growth, causing the root:shoot ratio to gradually return to its former state (Brouwer, 1983). An example of this behaviour in plants was provided by Randolph and Wiest (1981) for holly (*Ilex crenata*). Shoot pruning increased the root:shoot ratio from 0.64 to 0.99, but the significant reduction in root growth after shoot pruning resulted in re-establishment of the root–shoot balance within 3–4 months (Fig 8.5).

Removal of roots lowers the root:shoot ratio and impairs the supply of water and mineral nutrients, rather than carbohydrates. If the supply of nitrate, for example, becomes limiting after root severance, growth of stems and leaves is reduced. Carbohydrates not utilised for shoot growth are then used for root growth, leading to restoration of the root–shoot balance. If the supply of water is limiting after root severance, the water potential in shoot tissues required to maintain transpiration is more negative, as movement of water through the diminished root system requires stronger suction. Expansion of growing cells in

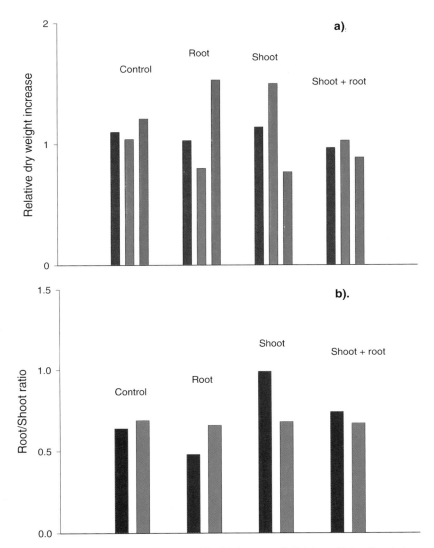

Figure 8.5 (a) Relative dry weight increment (absolute increment/initial dry weight) on the whole plant ■, the shoot ■ and the root ■ of *Ilex crenata* as influenced by pruning treatments. **(b)** Root/shoot ratios of *Ilex crenata* influenced by pruning at the time of transplanting. Initial values ■ and final values ■. (After Randolph and Wiest, 1981.)

leaves and stems is reduced, and therefore carbohydrate becomes available for root growth, again resulting in gradual restoration of the root:shoot ratio which existed previously.

Further data for holly from Randolph and Wiest (1981) illustrate plant response to root cutting. Root pruning reduced the root:shoot ratio from 0.64 to 0.48 (Fig 8.5). Shoot growth over the following 3–4 months was significantly suppressed, while root growth matched the unpruned control plants (Fig 8.5), resulting in restoration of the root–shoot balance. Water potentials in the

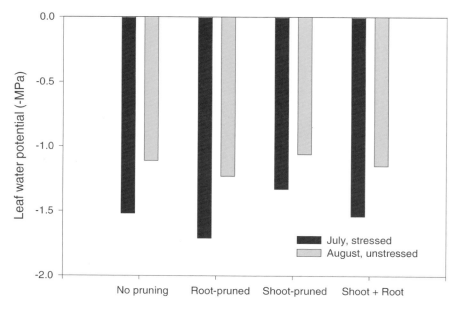

Figure 8.6 Xylem water potential of *Ilex crenata* under stressed and unstressed conditions following pruning treatments. (After Randolph and Wiest, 1981.)

crowns of root-pruned plants were more negative than in either controls or shoot-pruned plants (Fig 8.6), suggesting that the mechanism responsible for changes in growth patterns after root pruning was related to water uptake in this case. Low water potentials would have reduced cell expansion in the shoots and potentially impaired carbon assimilation, as photosynthesis declines when stomatal openings are reduced in leaves with low water potential (Poni *et al*, 1992).

8.3.1.2 Effects of root cutting on hormonal control of growth

Changes in hormone synthesis and transport are also thought to have a role in the maintenance of the root–shoot equilibrium (Richards and Rowe, 1977). Cytokinins are chemicals produced at the tips of growing roots. They are known to stimulate cell division and are therefore an important means by which plants regulate growth (Salisbury and Ross, 1992). Sugars and nutrients are also preferentially transported to tissues rich in cytokinins (Taiz and Zeiger, 1991). Cytokinins produced by roots are thought to be transported to the shoot in the transpiration stream, where they accumulate in growing tissues such as young leaves, fruits and seeds. Removal of roots reduces the quantity of cytokinins supplied to the shoot, resulting in less cell division and reduced transport of sugars to shoot tissues. Growth is consequently reduced in the shoot, which makes more carbohydrate available for root growth and restoration of the root–shoot equilibrium. Changes in both the supply of resources for growth and hormones are therefore implicated in the maintenance of the functional equilibrium between roots and shoots in plants.

8.3.2 Impacts of root cutting on tree growth

Cutting of roots affects growth for three possible reasons: these are impaired uptake of water, reduced absorption of mineral nutrients and reduced synthesis of growth-regulating hormones (Geisler and Ferree, 1984b). The theory of functional equilibrium between roots and shoots indicates that, given sufficient time, the resulting changes in growth should be self-correcting. Deficiencies in nutrient or water uptake caused by root severance, and changes in the hormone balance between roots and shoots, result in reallocation of carbohydrates and regrowth of the root system. Allocation of carbohydrate to the root system occurs, however, at the expense of shoot growth (Brouwer, 1983). For this reason, a commonly observed effect of root severance after trenching near trees is loss of vigour in above-ground growth (Hamilton, 1989; Watson, 1998). If carbohydrate availability within the plant is limited for some reason, however, re-establishment of the root–shoot equilibrium may not be possible and trenching can threaten the survival of the tree. A number of possibilities exist, for example the root system may be inadequate to supply the canopy with sufficient water and desiccation occurs. Alternatively, or in addition, the stability of the tree may be compromised and it may blow over in high winds.

8.3.2.1 Root pruning of fruit trees to control crown size

Data illustrating the effects of root severance on tree growth are available from research into root pruning of fruit trees. This practice is intended to take advantage of the functional equilibrium between root and shoot by restricting the size of the root system and thereby preventing excessive vegetative growth in the crown. Reduced vegetative vigour is desirable in commercial orchard systems because it helps to improve fruit yield and quality (Geisler and Ferree, 1984b).

An experiment with potted one-year-old apple (*Malus domestica*) and pear (*Pyrus communis*) trees compared growth of control plants and root-pruned or droughted trees (Poni *et al*, 1992). All trees were irrigated with the same quantity of water, but this was added to only half the root system of droughted trees, and half of the root system was removed from root-pruned trees. Shoot growth was significantly reduced only in root-pruned trees (Fig 8.7), because of increased allocation of carbohydrate to the roots. Root growth was sufficient to re-establish the root:shoot ratio of pear after 64 days of growth. In apple, restriction of shoot growth was severe and the final root:shoot ratio was higher than the control (Fig 8.8).

Similar suppression of above-ground growth occurs in older, field-grown trees. Schupp and Ferree (1988) used a mechanical subsoiler to prune roots in four consecutive years on two sides of 15 year-old apple trees, at distances of 60 or 80 cm from the trunk and depths up to 50 cm. Annual shoot extension and girth increment of the trunk was significantly reduced by root pruning (Fig 8.9). Growth reductions were largest for the more severe root pruning treatment, at 60 cm from the trunk, which removed more of the root system.

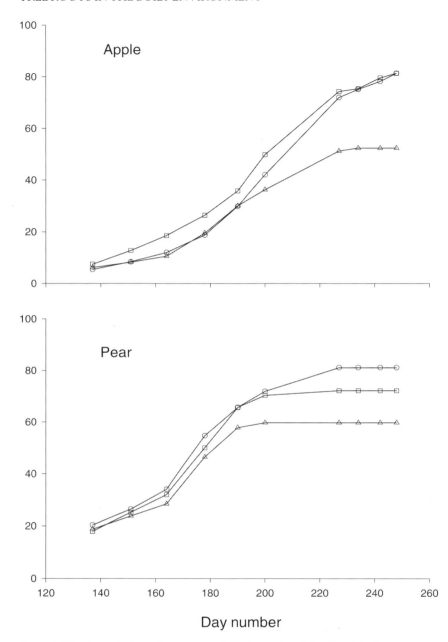

Figure 8.7 Shoot growth of pear (*Pyrus communis* 'Conference' on Quince C rootstock) and apple (*Malus domestica* 'Granny Smith' on MM106 rootstock) in untreated control ○, pruned □ and stressed ▲ treatments. Root treatment applied in the first week of July, – Day 186. (After Poni *et al*, 1992.)

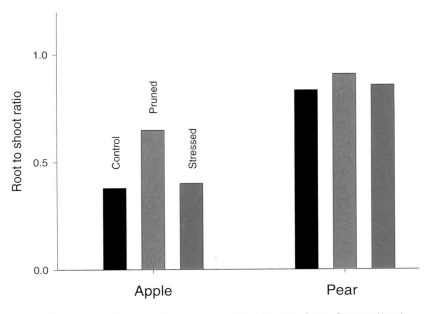

Figure 8.8 Root/shoot ratios of pear (*Pyrus communis* 'Conference' on Quince C rootstock) and apple (*Malus domestica* 'Granny Smith' on MM106 rootstock) as affected by pruning and stress shown with control untreated values. (After Poni *et al*, 1992.)

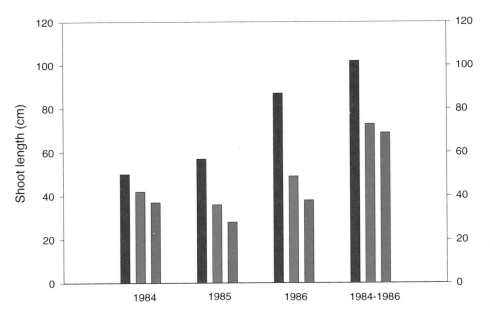

Figure 8.9 Shoot length of untreated controls ▪ and root pruned at 80 cm ▪ and 60 cm ▪ from the trunk in 1984, 1985 and 1986. Fourth set of columns to the right with the right-hand axis shows girth increment from 1984–1986. (After Schupp and Ferree, 1988.)

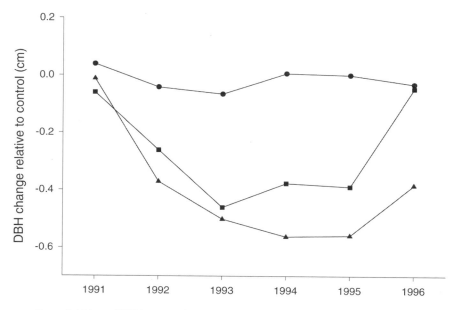

Figure 8.10 Annual DBH increase of pin oaks (*Quercus palustris*) relative to control after root injury from different degrees of trenching. 1 trench ●, 2 trenches ■ or 3 trenches ▲. (After Watson, 1998.)

8.3.2.2 Injury to landscape trees by root severance

Experimental evidence for the impacts of trenching and root severance on large landscape trees is rare. However, Watson (1998) tested the effects of trenching on pin oaks (*Quercus palustris*) with an average diameter at breast height (DBH) of 29 cm. Trenches were dug in late spring approximately 90 cm from the trunk, on either one, two or three sides of the tree. Injury to the trees was assessed by comparing growth and branch dieback for trenched and control trees, over a period of six growing seasons after treatment. Annual increment in trunk diameter was not significantly reduced in any year if trenching was on only one side of a tree (Fig 8.10). Trenching on three sides reduced the diameter increment in every year but the first (as growth was mostly complete when the trenches were dug) and sixth, suggesting that recovery had begun. Trenching on only two sides had similar, but less severe, effects as trenching on three sides, with recovery initiated earlier. Patterns of twig growth were similar, with cumulative twig growth over six years significantly reduced by trenching on three sides. Dieback of branches was also most severe after trenching on three sides, although this was only apparent two to six years after trenching. Trenching on three sides caused the death of lateral branches, as well as the central leader in some cases. Dieback was minor after trenching on one side, but intermediate after trenching on two sides.

Resilience to damage by trenching thus depends on the severity of root losses, as trenching on three sides removed the highest proportion of the root system and had the most damaging impacts. While his results demonstrated tolerance of trees to moderate root loss by trenching, Watson cautioned that other tree species might be less able to withstand root removal. The trees used in the experiment had good vigour prior to the experiment and were growing in high quality soil without impediments to root growth on any side. Less healthy, or older trees, or those impaired or stressed by growing in an urban environment may be less resilient to injury from trenching. For example, 12 years after a single trench was dug within the perimeters of the crowns of older street trees in Illinois, USA, 44% of 135 trees had been removed and a further 10% were showing severe dieback (Morell, 1984).

8.3.3 Trees with low resilience to excavation damage

Research and anecdotal evidence suggest that there is considerable variation in the impact of trenching on trees. In urban situations especially, the rooting system may be asymmetrical due to restrictions caused by building foundations, basements or other underground structures. Previous service or engineering work may have resulted in root loss and an imbalanced root system. So, part of the variation in root distribution is attributable to differences in the proportion of the root system removed by trenching operations. The quantity of roots severed during excavation depends on the proximity of the digging, the extent of root spread and asymmetry in root distribution relative to the location of the trench (Fig 8.3). In general, as suggested by the results of Watson (1998), if a higher proportion of roots are removed, more severe injury should be expected. However, the severity of injury caused by trenching also varies because some trees are more resilient to root removal than others (Hamilton, 1989).

Resilience to root severance requires the ability for regrowth of roots, to enable re-establishment of the root–shoot balance. Without regrowth of roots, the tree remains susceptible to deficiencies in water and nutrient uptake, and therefore reduced carbon assimilation and growth. Regrowth of roots requires energy, in the form of sugars synthesised by the foliage or supplied from reserves of carbohydrate stored in the trunk or major structural roots. Energy from reserves is especially important for rapid regrowth after injury. Consequently, if carbohydrate reserves are depleted at the time of damage, the resilience of trees to root severance, or other stress, is reduced (Waring, 1987).

8.3.3.1 Replenishment of carbohydrate reserves in trees

Stored carbohydrates in trees are depleted during rapid growth of leaves and shoots in the early spring (see Section 3.2.6 and Fig 3.12). Subsequently, carbon assimilated by photosynthesis over the growing season is allocated to growth and storage. However, there is a hierarchy which generally results in allocation of carbon for growth before storage.

Waring (1987) provides a hierarchy for normal carbon allocation (Fig 8.11). Buds, new foliage and new roots have the highest priority for new assimilates, with reserves replenished only if additional carbohydrate is available. Diameter growth of the trunk and major roots or branches also has a lower priority for assimilates than new roots and foliage. Production of defensive compounds,

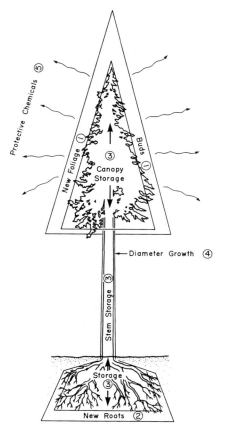

Figure 8.11 A postulated hierarchy for normal carbon allocation in a tree. Photosynthetic tissue represented by buds and new foliage **(1)** and new roots **(2)** have high priority. If additional carbohydrates are available, they are likely to go into storage reserves **(3)**, diameter growth **(4)**, and defensive compounds **(5)**. Under stress, allocation patterns can be expected to deviate from this pattern. (After Waring, 1987.)

which provide protection against disease, insect attack and other agents of defoliation, has the lowest priority. Stresses which reduce carbohydrate synthesis over the growing season thus cause reduced vigour, as increases in tree size are limited, and increased vulnerability to pathogens and insects. Critically, they also reduce replenishment of carbohydrate reserves, which compromises future growth, particularly if the tree is injured (Waring, 1987).

The full extent of damage to a tree caused by root severance is unlikely to be immediately apparent, as the crown is intact and the foliage may appear healthy. Allocation of energy to the regrowth of roots causes depletion of carbohydrate reserves and reduces replenishment over the growing season. Without adequate reserves of energy, the tree is less resilient to other stresses. Equally, if carbon assimilation by the tree has been impaired in the years prior to trenching, for example by drought or disease, reserves of energy may have already been depleted, leaving the tree less able to recover. Thus, resilience of a tree to trenching depends on the state of its carbohydrate reserves prior to trenching and during recovery.

8.3.3.2 Seasonal loss of resilience to excavation

The severance of roots during trenching raises the risk to trees of long-term injury or mortality. This risk can be eliminated by re-routeing trenches away from trees or by using trenching methods that do not require root cutting (see Section 8.6). If trenching is unavoidable and roots must be cut, the risk of damage to the tree can be minimised by (i) ensuring the minimum necessary proportion of the root system is removed and (ii) not allowing root cutting at times of the year when reserves of energy in the tree are low. The latter stipulation is derived from reasoning based on the principles of growth and carbon allocation in trees.

Reserves of carbohydrate are lowest in mid to late spring, after leaf emergence and rapid shoot growth (Wargo, 1979; Waring, 1987). Consequently, regrowth of roots after damage (cutting/loss) is likely to be most limited during this period and in the weeks afterwards. It therefore seems prudent to avoid any root cutting during the period of active shoot growth and in the weeks afterwards, when reserves are being refilled (Hamilton, 1989). On the basis of the same principle, roots should not be cut during other periods when carbohydrate reserves should be expected to be in a depleted state. Thus, trenching should not be permitted near trees under stress or recovering from stress caused by, for example, prolonged drought, flooding, disease or defoliation by insects, or in the urban context, vandalism.

8.3.3.3 Resilience to root removal in mature trees

Despite a lack of research into the effects of ageing on the health of urban trees, it is commonly observed that resilience to root severance declines as trees become more mature. Young, vigorously growing trees are more able to withstand damage to their roots than older trees, because growth slows as trees age (Hamilton, 1989; Ryan *et al*, 1997). This characteristic of trees results in a decline in productivity as forest stands age. Ecologists have made progress in recent years in understanding the reasons why trees become less vigorous with age.

It was thought previously that growth declined as trees aged because photosynthetic surface (leaf area) in the crown remains relatively constant as the volume of wood in trunks, branches and roots increases. As a result, it was reasoned that an increasing proportion of photosynthate is used for maintenance respiration as tree size increases, leaving diminishing quantities for new growth (Kramer and Kozlowski, 1979). More recent evidence has shown, however, that maintenance respiration in woody tissue consumes much less carbon than previously thought (Ryan and Waring, 1992).

Instead, reduced photosynthesis appears to be responsible for slower rates of growth in older trees. For forests, this is explained in part by a decline in leaf area index with age, resulting in less interception of solar radiation and thus less carbon assimilation (Ryan *et al*, 1997). It is unclear whether a similar pattern exists for landscape trees growing away from neighbours or in small groups. Carbon assimilation in older trees is reduced further, however, by a loss of photosynthetic capacity and performance. Nitrogen content is often lower in foliage from older trees, which is an indicator of lower photosynthetic efficiency, or the amount of carbon fixed per unit of light absorbed (Ryan *et al*, 1997). Additionally, resistances to water movement between the soil and leaves increase as trees age, because the trees grow taller and branches lengthen (Mencuccini and Grace, 1996). As a consequence, closure of stomata occurs earlier in the day for older trees, with the result that total daily carbon assimilation is reduced (Yoder *et al*, 1994; Ryan *et al*, 1997) (Fig 8.12).

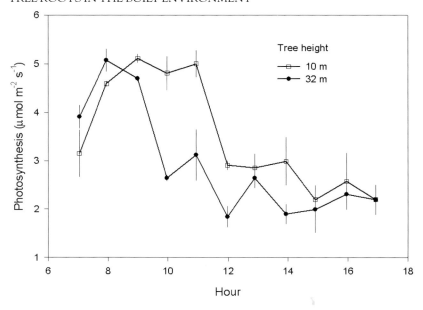

Figure 8.12 Diurnal pattern of photosynthesis of 1-year old foliage from 55-year old (10 m tall) and 229-year old (32 m tall) *Pinus ponderosa* foliage from the upper one-third of the canopy. (After Yoder *et al*, 1994.)

Reduced photosynthesis in more mature trees is likely to result in less accumulation of carbohydrate reserves during the growing season, because of the hierarchy of carbon allocation (Fig 8.11). Ageing trees are thus more prone to depletion of reserves, leaving them more vulnerable to stress and injury (Waring, 1987). Mature trees subjected to damage by excavation are consequently less able to regrow roots after severance than younger trees growing more vigorously. There is also some evidence that there are genetic limitations on growth as the sites of cell division, the meristems, age (Ryan *et al*, 1997). This could further impair regrowth of roots from mature trees. From the evidence available, therefore, it is especially important to protect mature trees from injury caused by excavations in the root zone.

8.3.3.4 Root damage and tree mortality

The death of a tree is a complex event, usually resulting from the cumulative effects of multiple stresses over a prolonged period. Unless tree death is obviously the result of some catastrophic event such as fire or severe winds, attributing death to a single cause or event is not usually possible (Franklin *et al*, 1987). In general, however, trees die when they are unable to acquire or mobilise sufficient resources to occlude injuries[1] or otherwise sustain life (Waring, 1987). Thus, death depends on carbon assimilation and allocation to

---

[1] The term 'heal' is not used here. Shigo (1991), for example, believes that tree wounds do not heal but are occluded by bark. The wound may still be present as well as decay affecting the wood behind the wound area/pruning cut.

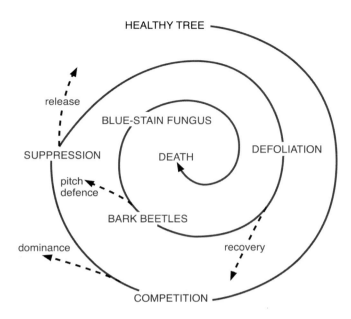

Figure 8.13 Mortality spiral for a Douglas fir tree (*Pseudotsuga menziesii*) illustrates the series of events leading to its death. The sequence of the spiral begins with the tree being suppressed by larger trees. If not released from competition the tree is predisposed to attack by defoliators. Once partially defoliated, the weakened tree is attractive to bark beetles that also carry the blue-stain fungus. The fungus disrupts the transpiration stream causing severe water stress. As the tree moves along the spiral the likelihood of its death become greater. (After Franklin *et al*, 1987.)

reserves and defensive strategies over preceding years. If energy reserves have been depleted, a tree faced with stress from disease, drought, or perhaps damage to its roots, may be unable to recover.

The effects of multiple stresses on a tree over periods of years, eventually leading to death, has been conceptualised as a *mortality spiral* (Franklin *et al*, 1987). An example from forest ecology in the US, is shown in Fig 8.13. Although the particular circumstances may be specific to certain forests in the US the general principles are common to the demise of trees either growing alone or as a group. In the example, a healthy tree in a forest stand is suppressed by larger trees, reducing its ability to synthesise defensive compounds because of limited carbon assimilation. The tree is predisposed to defoliation by insect attack as a result, which further weakens the tree, leaving it vulnerable to infestation by bark beetles (Wickman, 1978), which transmit the blue-stain fungus (Berryman, 1982). The fungus blocks the transpiration stream, causing desiccation in the crown and eventual death of the tree. The dashed lines on the spiral represent escape routes from the spiral which would enable the tree to return to a healthy state.

It is possible to construct hypothetical mortality spirals for urban trees which include damage to their root systems by excavation. An example might be where the initial stress on a tree results from replacement of turf below a portion of the crown with pavement. Runoff is diverted away from the root zone and the tree suffers from drought in summer, which reduces its ability to accumulate reserves of energy. Ozone damage to foliage during a subsequent growing season because of a severe air pollution event would cause further depletion of reserves. If at this stage a trench was dug along one side of the tree, removing a significant proportion of roots, regrowth of roots would be impaired by the reduced availability of carbohydrates from reserves. The resulting imbalance between root and shoot would exacerbate the effects of drought and perhaps cause nutrient deficiencies, because of the diminished size of the root system. Desiccation of portions of the crown and branch dieback might follow in subsequent years, further impairing carbon assimilation and increasing vulnerability of the tree to insects or disease. Death of the tree could follow and might be attributed to a particular pathogen. However, infection probably resulted from increased vulnerability to disease caused by the series of stresses encountered by the tree over preceding years.

In an example such as this, several years may pass between damage to the root system and death of the tree. At the time of death, root damage could not be said to have killed the tree outright, but death of the tree might have been avoided if root cutting had not occurred during excavation near the tree. Resilience to root damage thus depends on the life history of the tree before this damage occurred, as well as growing conditions in subsequent years. When determining the likely resilience of a tree to root damage, therefore, the state of the tree in previous years and its exposure to prolonged stresses should be incorporated into an overall assessment of vigour.

In recent years a number of examples have emerged which illustrate that stresses on trees in roadside or urban trees have increased their vulnerability to attack by pests. The dieback of roadside ash trees is more likely when there has been ditching nearby. Studies by Foggo and Speight (1993) showed that root damaged seedlings suffered a higher amount of attack by the ash bud moth (Fig 8.14). A further example of the impact of stress in the built environment on susceptibility to pest attack comes from a detailed study of horse chestnut trees at sites in Oxford, UK, varying in degree of urbanisation and impermeability of the surface beneath the trees (Speight *et al*, 1998). There was a significantly higher incidence of the horse chestnut scale on trees in more heavily paved and asphalt-covered areas.

8.3.3.5 Increased resilience to root removal by shoot pruning

As a principal effect of root removal is disruption of the functional equilibrium between roots and shoots, pruning of shoots after root severance may be a means of rebalancing growth within the plant. Shoot pruning in compensation for root loss may reduce nutrient requirements and water deficits in the crown, and thereby lessen physiological stress and dieback. However, it has been advocated that compensatory shoot pruning may be undesirable because regrowth of roots requires photosynthate, and reduction of leaf area impairs

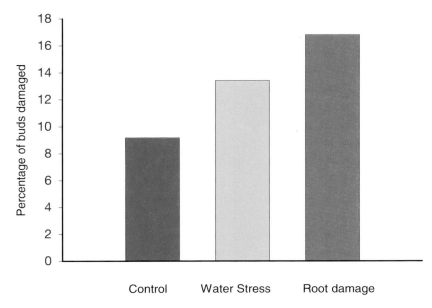

Figure 8.14 Mean proportion of buds attacked by the ash bud moth (*Prays fraxinella*) in control, water stressed and root damaged ash seedlings. (After Foggo and Speight, 1993.)

photosynthesis (Hamilton, 1989). Carbohydrates are also stored in branches; therefore, major reduction in the amount of branches is inappropriate.

Watson (1998) tested whether shoot pruning after root severance was beneficial, as part of his experiment investigating the impacts of trenching on growth (see Section 8.3.2). Within a day of cutting roots of the trees, the crowns were pruned using normal commercial practices. The crowns were moderately thinned and lateral branches cut back 1 to 2 m, removing about 30% of total leaf area. Shoot extension was significantly higher after root pruning if tree crowns were pruned, regardless of the severity of root damage (Fig 8.15). Furthermore, dieback in the most severely root-damaged trees (Watson, 1998), which were trenched on three sides of the trunk, was reduced by shoot pruning. Without shoot pruning, dieback in these trees continued through the sixth year after treatment; if pruned, however, dieback ceased from the fourth year onwards. Thus, compensatory shoot pruning appears to aid recovery of trees from root loss (Watson, 1998).

8.3.4 Effects of cutting of roots on tree stability

In addition to their role in taking up essential resources for growth from soil, roots provide anchorage for trees, ensuring that they remain upright. There is a danger that root cutting can compromise the support function of roots and increase the risk from trees falling during periods of strong wind. Particularly in an urban environment, this would pose an unacceptable danger to life and property.

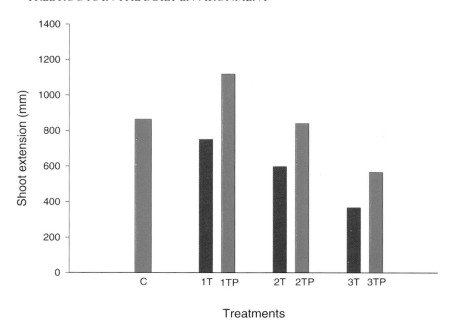

Figure 8.15 Total shoot extension of pin oaks (*Quercus palustris*) after root injury from trenching with and without compensatory crown pruning. 1T, 2T, or 3T indicates the number of trenches, P indicates crown pruning also. (After Watson, 1998.)

The mechanisms of structural failure of tree root systems under loading from wind were reviewed by Mattheck and Breloer (1994). They distinguished between the anchorage properties of the three principal forms of tree root system architecture: the surface, heart root and tap-root systems (Fig 3.4). Failure of tap-root, surface and heart root systems under wind loading has been discussed in Section 3.5 and shown in Figs 3.17, 3.18 and 3.19 respectively. Tree failure after root severance or root pruning does occur, according to tree maintenance professionals surveyed by Hamilton (1989). In the London Borough of Havering, major structural roots of several windthrown street trees were found to have been severed by trenching two years previously. Examination of other trees resulted in felling of 6% of over 1000 trees because of an unacceptable risk of windthrow caused by severance of large structural roots during trenching (Crane, 1997). A further 17% of the trees required pruning to reduce the risk of windthrow.

There has been no direct research on the effects of root severance on the stability of urban trees, but understanding of the mechanisms of failure indicates how the danger from anchorage failure after trenching can be reduced. Anchorage provided by roots on the windward side of trees appears to be particularly important in surface and heart root systems, as these roots must be pulled out of the soil for failure to occur. Indeed, Crook and Ennos (1996) showed by mechanical analysis of anchorage in a heart-rooted larch (*Larix* spp) that 75% of anchorage strength is provided by lateral and sinker roots on the windward side of the tree. Similarly, O'Sullivan and Ritchie (1993) showed that cutting of roots on the windward side of trees dramatically reduced anchorage strength of surface-rooted Sitka spruce (*Picea sitchensis*). As a means of manipulating anchorage mechanics, trenches were dug 1 m from the stem on the windward side of trees. The force required to pull the tree over was then reduced by 66%. Cutting of major structural roots on the side of the tree facing the direction of prevailing storm winds should therefore be considered as dangerous.

There is thus evidence that root severance by trenching is liable to compromise tree stability. The danger posed by trenching is likely to be highest if severe winds load the tree on the same side as the trench was cut in the period following digging, before any regrowth has occurred. The duration of this period of risk is not known, but it is likely to be longer for trees under stress and with depleted reserves of the energy required for regrowth. The size (area and density) of the crown will also have an effect. Pruning may be necessary to provide temporary respite by reducing the '**sail area**' of the canopy by thinning or reduction. This would reduce the wind resistance of the crown and the leverage exerted on the root system.

8.4 Control of root damage during excavation

8.4.1 Root protection zones

Prevention of damage to roots requires careful control of activities within a protected area surrounding the tree. Recommendations on the required size of this zone vary, but all are based on some measure of the size of the trunk or crown. Quite reasonably, larger trees are assumed to have root systems which spread further from the trunk and therefore require a larger protected area. However, little information is provided on how the different estimates of the size of the protected area were developed. None appear to be derived from actual observations of root spread; instead, they are approximations of the extent of crown spread, either directly or from relations between crown size and trunk diameter.

As tree roots spread further from the trunk than do branches, even in trees with broad spherical crowns (Gilman, 1997 and Chapter 3), recommended protection areas are unlikely to completely protect trees from root loss during excavations. If digging occurs within a radius of the trunk that is less than two to three times the branch spread, some loss of roots can be expected. However, the proportion of roots lost by excavation outside this protected area (ie two to three times the branch spread) is likely to be small. However, this will not apply to tree species having narrow, upright branching (fastigiate) patterns, eg Lombardy poplar (*Populus nigra* var. *italica* or Italian cypress (*Cupressus macrocarpa*). Trees in good health and showing good vigour are likely to recover easily from such disturbance, but stressed or older trees with low energy reserves may require better protection.

The methods used to estimate the size of tree protection zones also assume that roots are distributed equally on all sides of a tree. For isolated trees in parks or gardens, this is likely to be a reasonable assumption. In many urban settings in which trees must grow, however, an even distribution of lateral roots is probably very rare. Restrictions on root growth created by buildings and compacted subgrades beneath roads and footways, as well as residual soil compaction on former construction sites, can cause root distributions to be heavily biased towards one side of a tree. Root protection zones estimated using the conventional methods might not adequately protect such trees from damage during excavation.

8.4.2 Guidelines on root protection

In the UK, two sets of guidelines are used for determining the size of the protected area and the activities permitted within this zone. These are the British Standard, BS 5837: *Trees in relation to construction – Recommendations* (BSI, 2005), and NJUG 10: *Guidelines for the Planning, Installation and Maintenance of Utility Services in Proximity to Trees*, published by the National Joint Utilities Group (NJUG, 1995). NJUG 10 is the principal set of guidelines on working near trees for the utilities sector.

8.4.2.1 BS 5837(2005)

BS 5837 (2005) specifies that a root protection area (RPA) should be provided for individual trees or groups of trees and that this area would be a simple function of the tree size as determined from the stem diameter at 1.5 m. The means to calculate the RPA from BS 5837 is given in Table 8.1. The size of the protection area increases as trees grow in size and age. The calculated RPA should be capped to 707 m² which is equivalent to a circle with a radius of 15 m or a square with approximately 26 m sides. BS 5837 specifies that for individual open-grown trees it may be acceptable to offset the distance by up to 20% in any one direction.

To comply with BS 5837[2], any excavations near a tree should not pass through the protection zone. Underground services which cannot be routed outside the protection zone should be installed using trenchless techniques to bore a tunnel along the section of the route within the protected zone or dug by hand. An alternative would be to hand dig a trench and minimise the cutting of roots. Pipes or ducted cables can then be fed through the borehole, enabling installation with very little damage to the root system, provided that the borehole is small and deeper than the main lateral roots.

BS 5837 also provides an alternative to the conventional protection zone that it is claimed causes only minimal root severance. A narrow trench is excavated with machinery or by hand along a trajectory leading to the trunk. At 1 m from the trunk, excavation is stopped and a tunnel is bored directly beneath the tree,

---

[2] BS 5837 is not mandatory. It only becomes enforceable when referred to in other legal documents, eg contract or planning conditions.

Table 8.1 Calculating the Root Protection Area (RPA) (after BSI, 2005)

Number of stems	Calculation
Single stem tree	$RPA\ (m^2) = \left(\dfrac{\textit{stem diameter (mm) @ 1.5 m x 12}}{1000} \right)^2 x\,3.142$
Tree with more than one stem arising below 1.5 m above ground level	$RPA\ (m^2) = \left(\dfrac{\begin{array}{c}\textit{Basal diameter (measured immediately}\\\textit{above root flare) (mm) x 10}\end{array}}{1000} \right)^2 x\,3.142$

NOTE: The 12x multiplier is based on NJUG 10 (NJUG, 1995) and published work by Matheny and Clark (1998

at a depth greater than 0.75 m. Boring stops at a distance no closer than 1 m from the opposite side of the tree, from where excavation is resumed (Fig 8.16). The logic underlying this strategy is that, as lateral roots radiate from the trunk, few are severed by a trench dug along a line of radius. The borehole is also sufficiently deep to avoid damage to lateral roots, though any tap-root is liable to be cut if present. In reality, some roots are likely to be severed using this strategy because lateral roots do not radiate from the tree in straight lines and they will have sizeable roots growing out of them which grow across the radii. No assessment of the extent of root damage liable to result from use of this strategy for trenching is available. Harris et al (1999) describe a similar strategy, but recommend manual excavation within the root protection zone, to prevent severance of major roots.

8.4.2.2 NJUG 10

The root protection zone specified in NJUG 10, termed the '**precautionary area**', is shown in Fig 8.17. The radius of the protection zone is simply four times the circumference of the tree at breast height. The simplicity of this relationship makes implementation of the guidelines fast and easy for operators on site. NJUG 10 sets out how work within the protection zone should be carried out and what precautions should be taken. These precautions are listed in Box 8.1. Perhaps the most important recommendation is that machinery must not be used for excavation within the protection zone. Only manual excavation or trenchless techniques should be used. When excavating manually, roots larger than 25 mm in diameter should not be cut. NJUG 10 is available to be downloaded at www.njug.org.uk/publications.html. NJUG 10 is now referred to in 'Best Practice for Street Works and Highway Works' (DETR, 2001) (www.street-works.dft.gov.uk/bestpractice/) which includes the text 'All undertakers and highway authorities have a duty to protect the environment. Examples of best practice include .... avoidance of damage to trees and shrubs, particularly to the roots, and verge damage by material storage'. The current specification for the reinstatement of openings in

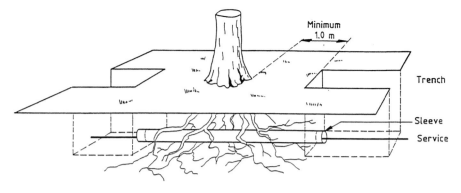

Figure 8.16 Trenching along radii to minimise damage. (After BSI, 2005.)

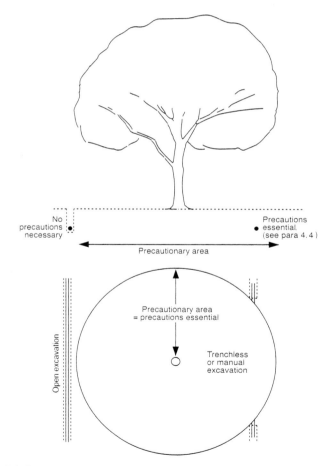

Figure 8.17 Precautionary area (= 4 x trunk circumference) recommended by NJUG (1995).

Box 8.1 Precautions within the root protection zone under NJUG 10

NJUG 10 advises that the following precautions are taken with the root protection zone:

- Don't excavate with machinery. Use trenchless techniques where possible. Otherwise, dig only by hand.

- When hand digging, carefully work around roots, retaining as many as possible.

- Don't cut roots over 25 mm in diameter, unless the council's Tree Officer agrees beforehand.

- Prune roots which have to be removed using a sharp tool (eg secateurs or handsaw). Make a clean cut and leave as small a wound as possible.

- Backfill the trench with an inert granular material and topsoil mix. Compact the backfill with care around the retained roots. On non-highway sites backfill only the excavated soil.

- Don't repeatedly move/use heavy mechanical plant except on hard standing.

- Don't store spoil or building material, including chemicals and fuels.

- Protect roots with dry sacking if they are to be left exposed overnight when there is a risk of frost. Sacking must be removed before backfilling.

(After NJUG, 1995)

Highways (DfT, 2002) recommends that NJUG 10 should be followed (www.street-works.dft.gov.uk/specification/index.htm). Specific information about the excavation and reinstatement of openings in the vicinity of trees is given in NJUG 10.

8.4.2.3 Comparison of protection strategies

Protection of roots during excavation requires that activities within the protection area surrounding the tree are restricted to ensure that root severance is minimised. The recent revision of BS 5837 (BSI, 2005) means that the size of the protection zone now specified compares far more closely (Fig 8.18) to that specified by the National Joint Utilities Group in NJUG 10 (NJUG, 1995). The presentation of the means to calculate the root protection area (RPA) in BS 5837 is somewhat involved but the radius of the RPA is calculated, for a single tree, as the diameter of the tree at 1.5 m multiplied by 12. The specification of NJUG 10 derives the radius of the root protection zone as simply 4 x the circumference at 1.5 m and yields a protection zone around

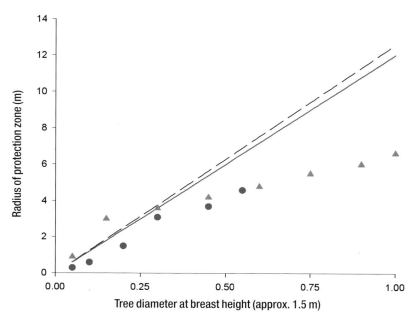

Figure 8.18 Radius of tree protection zone related to diameter at breast height from recommendations in NJUG 10 (— — —) and BS 5837 (———). Also shown are recommendations from work done in Illinois by Morell (1984) (●) and by Harris *et al.*, 1999 (▲) in Toronto.

9% greater than BS 5837. BS 5837 specifies for multi-stemmed trees that the radius of the root protection area should be 10 times the basal diameter. The latest version of BS 5837 (BSI, 2005) does not specify, as did the previous version, a greater protection zone for trees of low vigour. From the radius it is then possible to calculate the area for the RPA using the formula πr^2. The resulting area is the minimum which should be left undisturbed. Its shape may be changed but the protected area must not be reduced and adequate protection of the root system must still be provided. BS 5837 also specifies that the RPA should be capped at 707 m² which is equivalent to a circle with a radius of 15 m.

Both the BS 5837 and the NJUG 10 specifications offer more protection than at least two other specifications used elsewhere. Also included in Fig 8.18 are specifications drawn up by Morell (1984) for Illinois and another used in Toronto, Canada (Harris *et al.*, 1999).

8.5 Good trenching practice

8.5.1 Planning ahead for trenching

When construction work or the installation or maintenance of underground services requires trenching near trees, it is essential that plans on how to protect the trees from damage are established in advance. All parties, including contractors, utility companies and local authorities must co-operate to ensure that vulnerable trees are identified before digging commences, to ensure steps are taken to reduce the risk of damage. This requires assessment of trees along proposed trenching routes for their resilience to root disturbance.

A procedure for assessing the risk of damage to trees by trenching was described by Browell (1996). It was developed in the 1990s in the UK for use during the nationwide programme for installation of fibre-optic telecommunications cable, which entailed digging more than 100,000 km of trenches, mostly along residential streets (Baines, 1994). The assessment is undertaken by arboriculturists, who classify all trees along proposed trenching routes into three categories:

- high risk, as root disturbance will seriously affect the tree
- medium risk, as root disturbance will moderately affect the tree
- low risk, as root disturbance will not affect the tree.

The criteria used to assess vulnerability to damage are:

- tree species, age, vigour, size and condition
- past tree management
- ground levels and water table
- adjacent surface cover (paved or soft)
- exposure and slope
- other recent construction work
- height of crown base
- number of ducts to be installed.

The assessment is intended to be rapid, with only the risk level recorded, as judged by the surveying arboriculturist. Thus, while the assessment is superficial and subjective, it enables rapid identification of the most vulnerable trees. Trees classified as high risk tend to be mature, already under stress, displaying dieback, experiencing restricted rooting or with the potential to become unstable. The ability of high-risk trees to regenerate roots after disturbance is judged to be 'questionable' or 'inhibited' (Browell, 1996). Such trees would likely be approaching the centre of the mortality spiral (Fig 8.13) and therefore liable to enter terminal decline because of root damage during excavation.

Trees classified as low risk are usually young, vigorous and considered able to regenerate any roots lost because of manual trenching within the root protection zone, or mechanical excavation beyond this limit (Browell, 1996). Trees at medium risk are judged to be vulnerable to moderate damage. As such, they are likely to have partially descended the mortality spiral (Fig 8.13), but are not yet approaching terminal decline. In this condition, it is important to recognise that trenching may leave these trees highly vulnerable to other stresses in subsequent years. Thus, although not in the highest risk category, trees classified as medium risk still require careful protection to avert potential impacts in the years after trenching.

When planning the installation of underground services it is essential that a tree risk assessment is completed in advance. There are three main options available to avoid damaging trees (Jones, 1996). These are:

- re-routeing of trenches to avoid trees altogether
- diversion of trenching routes around trees
- stipulation of precautions to be taken near trees.

Re-routeing is possible, for example, where houses may be accessed from a rear lane, or by spurs from a trench on the opposite side of a road, where there may be fewer trees (Browell, 1996). Diversion of trenches into the carriageway may be possible, depending on the locations of other services, if excavation in the footway requires digging through root systems (Jones, 1996). If work near trees is unavoidable, guidelines such as NJUG 10 must be followed within the root protection zone. The advantage of identifying trees as high risk during the planning stage is that supervisors on site can be alerted that work near these trees must be monitored closely to ensure that all precautions stipulated by guidelines such as NJUG 10 are fully implemented by the utilities' own or contractor's operatives.

8.5.2 Training and awareness

A key to preventing damage to trees during excavations for infrastructure development or maintenance is ensuring that contractors and their operatives are aware that tree roots require protection and that they are trained in methods of working near trees. In the UK, leaflets are available to assist with this process. The NJUG 10 guidelines are published with a plastic insert card to provide personnel on site with easy access to a summary of the guidelines, including the procedure for determining the size of the root protection zone (NJUG, 1995). The Black Country Urban Forestry Unit (BCUFU, 1994) produced a short video on how to install underground services near trees, with an emphasis on hand-digging in the protected zone to prevent severance of

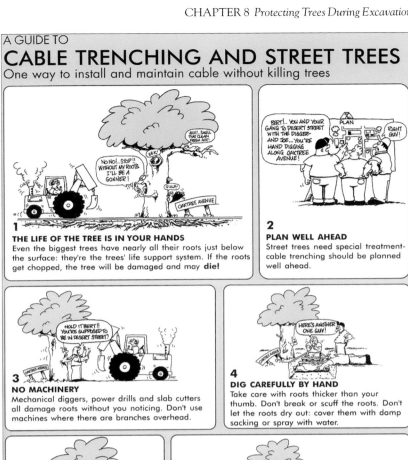

Figure 8.19 A guide to cable trenching and street trees. (After National Urban Forestry Unit.)

roots. The recommended practices are summarised in a six-step guidance sheet (Fig 8.19) for use by contractor's operatives.

Formal training for contractors, supervisors and operatives has been successfully implemented as part of trenching programmes (Box 8.2). Training sessions, which can be led by local authority arboriculturists and need not be long, cover topics including: the role of tree roots and where they grow; the

Box 8.2 Trenching for cable TV: the Cheltenham experience

Cheltenham is a Regency spa town in the south-west of England with a rich horticultural heritage. It contains many large, mature trees in parks and gardens and along streets. In 1994, installation of a fibre-optic network for television and telecommunications was due to begin. Fearing that the large amount of trenching posed a serious threat to the health of amenity trees in the town, the Tree Officers at Cheltenham Borough Council were determined to prevent damage to their trees. To achieve their aims, they employed an interactive team approach which combined careful co-ordination of responsibilities within the Council and close liaison with the cable company and contractors. Provision of training to supervisors and operatives was vital (Eden, 1996).

The Council team

To ensure co-ordination of activities within the Council, a team of officers was established which included all those likely to be dealing with the cable company. Members of the team were:

- the Highways Officer, with formal responsibility for the management and maintenance of street trees

- a Planning Officer, to administer the tree protection provisions in the Town and Country Planning Act

- a Solicitor, to advise on the Council's legal powers and to implement them if necessary

- a Tree Officer, with knowledge of trees and the documented guidance on excavating near them

- Monitors, to inspect trenching operations, provide on-site advice to supervisors and operatives and record breaches of agreed working practices.

Liaison

The first action taken by the team was to begin liaison with the cable company. Building and maintaining a good working relationship with the cable company and contractors was regarded as essential. This relationship enabled the Council team to accomplish five key tasks. These were to:

1. establish an agreed working standard near trees

2. complete a tree risk assessment survey in co-operation with consultants contracted by the cable company

3. offer free training to everyone involved in the cable laying process

4. undertake monitoring of trenching and provide help and advice on site

5. hold bi-monthly liaison meetings with the cable company to discuss specific tree-related issues.

Tree risk assessment

Trees along the proposed trenching routes were classified as having high, medium or low risk of damage from root disturbance, using the procedure outlined by Browell (1996). This exercise was jointly undertaken by Tree Officers from the Council and independent arboricultural consultants engaged by the cable company. Options for avoiding damage to high-risk trees were agreed by both parties.

Training

At the time that cable installation was initiated in Cheltenham, NJUG 10, published in 1995, was not yet available for guidance on trenching near trees. Instead, the Council Tree Officers wrote a guidance leaflet based on BS 5837 (1991). This leaflet provided the basis for the code of practice agreed by the Council and cable company. It was later published by the Arboricultural Association for use nationwide (Eden *et al*, 1997). Use of the leaflet in Cheltenham was promoted during training sessions staged by the Council team for operatives, supervisors and others involved in cable laying, including planners, engineers and consumer affairs personnel at the cable company. Training sessions were short (less than 1 hour) and held at the contractor's base or other suitable location just prior to the end of the working day. Presentations were made by a Tree Officer, a highways engineer and a solicitor using slides and video. Topics covered were: the role of tree roots and where they are found; the effects on trees of damage to roots; measures used to avoid damage; and the potential legal consequences of damage to roots. All trainees received a copy of the guidance leaflet and a certificate of attendance issued by the contractor.

Monitoring

In addition to training of personnel, successful implementation of the agreed code of practice for trenching near trees required monitoring of work on site. The role of monitors was to continue liaison on site, with the people actually doing the digging. Monitors were members of the Council team and were available to advise on specific problems encountered during trenching. Consequently, it was important that supervisors could easily contact monitors by mobile phones. In practice, where there were specific difficulties on site, the agreed working standards were modified. It was the role of the monitor to approve and record these concessions to the code of practice. Monitors also recorded unauthorised breaches of standards, taking notes and photographs.

Legal support

In Cheltenham, legal back-up was used for two purposes. One was to issue Tree Preservation Orders (TPO) where it was felt necessary to ensure that trees had the maximum possible protection. The second was to pursue prosecutions where Tree Preservation Orders were contravened. This was rarely necessary because of the excellent liaison and mutual understanding established between the Council and cable company. Early on, however, there were instances where the agreed code of practice was not followed and major roots were severed on a tree subject to a Tree Preservation Order. Documentary evidence of damage to the trees was collected and used in a successful prosecution of the offenders under the Town and Country Planning Act (1990).

Prosecutions

There were two prosecutions brought against contractors working for United Artists – the local cable TV licence holder, now Telewest. The first was for causing wilful damage to a highway tree on which there was a TPO (several roots greater than 25 mm diameter were cut within the protected area as defined by BS 5837 (1991) – it was a year before NJUG 10 was released – but not likely to lead to death of the tree). A fine of £230 was levied and costs of £300 awarded to the Council, making a total bill of £530 to the operator. The operator admitted doing the damage and the Council insisted it was wilful because its tree officers had personally delivered awareness training to the operator on working near trees several weeks earlier. The second was for causing damage to a tree within a Conservation Area (CA) (the tree did not have a TPO and the damage was similar to the first case) – again the Council was successful but there was no fine (the operator was given a conditional discharge) with costs to the Council of £150.

The operator admitted doing the damage but pleaded ignorance (he had only started the job two weeks earlier and had no training on working near trees). The tree officers fought a continual battle with the cable company to inform them when new people started so that training could be given and suggesting they work in non-treed areas until they had received the tree awareness training.

The Council sought to prosecute a contractor working on behalf of the Midlands Electricity Board for damaging a tree in a Conservation Area but the Council's solicitors advised against it (no one saw the operator do it and he had not admitted it).

The Council also successfully brought an injunction against felling a tree in a Conservation Area alleged to be causing damage to adjacent buildings (thereby being a 'nuisance' and so being exempt from the CA protection). [Information kindly supplied by Nick Eden, formerly Trees and Ranger Services Manager, Cheltenham Borough Council.]

consequences of damaging roots; measures to avoid damage; and the legal ramifications of damaging trees or their roots (Jones, 1996; Smith, 1996). Rules for working near trees are presented as obligatory, not voluntary, to avoid ambiguity and confusion. Short training sessions also serve to build trust and open lines of communication between contractors, operatives and arboriculturists, thus encouraging operatives and their supervisors to seek advice when uncertainties or problems related to tree roots arise on site.

8.5.3 Ensuring tree protection

Prior to the start of trenching, local authority arboricultural staff, utility companies and contractors should agree to a code of practice for trenching near trees. In the UK, the usual guidelines for trenching by utility companies are provided by NJUG 10. By agreeing to the guidelines to be followed during trenching, all parties are assured that problems can be solved using a common set of criteria. Implementation of the agreed rules is then ensured by supervision and monitoring on site (Smith, 1996). Supervisors from the contractor direct operatives to follow the agreed practices, while Tree Officers from the local authority monitor compliance. Monitoring cannot be constant, but regular visits to sites enable supervisors to seek advice and obtain approval for concessions to the agreed rules, based on the professional judgement of the monitor. The monitor also must record breaches to the agreed practices.

8.5.4 Legal back-up and compensation for damage

In the UK, local authorities have statutory powers under the Town and Country Planning Act (1990) to protect trees from damage or felling where they are thought to be under threat. Damaging or carrying out unauthorised work to a tree subject to a tree preservation order can result in prosecution, with substantial fines possible on conviction (DETR, 1999). Offenders have been successfully prosecuted for severing the roots of trees protected by a tree preservation order during trenching for utility installation (Box 8.2) (Aylett, 1996).

Contractors have also been financially liable for costs incurred because of damage to tree roots during trenching. Compensation paid to the owners of trees (including local authorities) can be substantial, including the costs for investigation of damage by arboricultural consultants, remedial pruning and felling, and replacement trees, where necessary (Crane, 1997). In Toronto, Canada, and other jurisdictions, deposits must be paid prior to trenching along city streets. Failure to comply with agreed codes of practice for protection of trees results in forfeiture of the deposit. This has created a valuable incentive for contractors to ensure that their operatives are trained in the use of working practices to protect tree roots (Richard Ubbens, City Forester, Toronto, pers. comm.).

8.6 Alternatives to conventional excavation

Modern technological development has provided a number of new methods to enable installation and maintenance of underground services without the need for open trenching. If used, therefore, these techniques can reduce damage to root systems caused by mechanical diggers, as well as reducing the time and expense devoted to hand digging around roots. It is unfortunate that opportunities offered by alternative approaches to conventional trenching and digging are not well appreciated by tree care professionals, planners or others aiming to protect trees during street and construction works.

8.6.1 Trenchless techniques

There are a number of techniques of trenchless and minimum excavation (TME) available for installing and replacing underground services (Thomson and Rumsey, 1997). The three main types are guided and unguided boring and pipe replacement by lining or bursting. Guided boring systems use a steerable drill head and above-ground detector (used to monitor the alignment of the drilling head) to bore a pathway below ground for ducts or pipes. The borehole need not be straight. The typical diameter of the borehole is 12–15 cm, although **back-reaming** can be used to enlarge this. The surface need only be opened at intervals, as boreholes can have lengths up to approximately 150 m. Shorter distances between access holes would be required, though, where many spurs were required off a main pipe or duct (Fig 8.20). This type of system is not currently in as widespread use in the UK as is traditional excavation. Elsewhere it is used more commonly. For example, in Toronto, Canada, guided boring is used for installing 40–50% of new underground services, including electricity and gas, mainly because it causes less disruption than open trenching and because of economic advantages (Richard Ubbens, City Forester, Toronto, pers. comm.). In unguided boring there is less precise control on the direction of the bore that is made with a cylindrical percussive hammer 'mole' driven through the ground by compressed air.

In the UK trenchless replacement of pipes is more commonly used (Burrows and Gough, 1997; Thomson and Rumsey, 1997). Existing pipes are relined, either by inserting polythene pipe or by spraying the inside walls of the pipe with epoxy resin or cement. Resin-impregnated fabric liners are also used (Thomson and Rumsey, 1997). An alternative to pipe lining is pipe bursting (Fig 8.21). This technique uses a percussive moling tool to break open the existing pipe, while pulling a new length of polythene pipe behind it. Use of

Figure 8.20 A typical self-contained rig for horizontal direct drilling.

Figure 8.21 Installation of new water mains using trenchless techniques. The old pipe is broken by a device operated from an access hole. Excavation near to tree roots will be minimised.

trenchless techniques instead of open trenching can result in economic savings, as well as less damage to tree roots (Burrows and Gough, 1997).

8.6.2 Manual excavation using high-pressure air or water

Systems for dislodging soil from around tree roots using high-pressure air or water and removal of soil using vacuum techniques have been developed in recent years. This aspect has been fully covered in Section 4.6.4. There are excellent prospects of removing soil from around roots close to trees, with far less damage than conventional digging, with these techniques. The excavation of 'tunnels' within the zone occupied by the root system close to trees as advised in NJUG 10 is a realistic prospect using air or water in the excavation. These non-digging approaches have considerable value also, for removing contaminated and compacted soil, as well as investigating the distribution of roots.

8.7 Summary

- Damage to tree root systems can be associated with a wide variety of excavation activities close to trees. Because a large fraction of the root systems of trees is concentrated in the surface soil layers, relatively shallow digging can still cause serious damage.

- Trees will be especially vulnerable to root damage if their vigour is low and their inability to regenerate their roots is prejudiced.

- The features that will make a tree more vulnerable to any excavation damage are numerous. Counted among them are the age of the tree, previous episodes of drought, pest attacks or other mechanical injuries.

- The mortality spiral is a useful concept with which to consider the influence of a wide variety of factors such as tree age, and the impact of previous episodes of stress such as drought or disease, on tree vigour that renders the tree unable to recover from root damage caused by excavation.

- There are alternatives to conventional trenching and excavations that can help to reduce damage to tree roots. Trenchless technologies, pneumatic or hydraulic excavations are all techniques that need to be developed and promoted for use near trees. Where there is a choice and the costs of alternative methods are being compared, the impact of the operation on trees, road users, local community and environment should also be taken into account.

REFERENCES

Aylett, M. 1996. Case study – Cheltenham. Solicitor. In: *Trenching and Street Trees*, National Conference, London, 23 April 1996, pp. 22–24. National Urban Forestry Unit, Great Barr, West Midlands, UK.

Baines, C. 1994. Trenching and street trees. *Arboricultural Journal*, 18, 231–236.

BCUFU. 1994. *Trenching and street trees* (video). 1994. Black Country Urban Forestry Unit, UK.

Berryman, A.A. 1982. Mountain pine beetle outbreaks in Rocky Mountain lodgepole pine forests. *Journal of Forestry*, 80, 410–413.

Brouwer, R. 1983. Functional equilibrium: sense or nonsense? *Netherlands Journal of Agricultural Science*, 31, 335–348.

Browell, M.F. 1996. Tree risk assessment. *Arboricultural Journal*, 20, 3–12.

BSI. 2005. BS 5837: *Trees in relation to construction – Recommendations*. British Standards Institution, London, UK. 32 pp.

Burrows, B. & Gough, T. 1997. Utilising trenchless technology to achieve a high quality, low cost, water mains rehabilitation programme. Wasser Berlin: International Symposium on Construction of Underground Assets.

Čermák, J., Hruška, J., Martinkova, M. & Prax, A. 2000. Urban tree root systems and their survival near houses analysed using ground penetrating radar and sap flow techniques. *Plant and Soil*, 219, 103–116.

Crane, B. 1997. Trenching: a cause of root damage. In: *Arboricultural Practice: Present and Future* (Ed. by J. Claridge), pp. 39–44. HMSO, London, UK.

Crook, M.J. & Ennos, A.R. 1996. The anchorage mechanics of deep rooted larch, *Larix europea* x *L. japonica*. *Journal of Experimental Botany*, 47, 1509–1517.

Cutler, D.F. & Richardson, I.B.K. 1989. *Tree Roots and Buildings*. Longman, Harlow, UK. 71 pp.

DETR. 1999. *Protected trees: a guide to tree preservation procedures*. Department of the Environment, Transport and the Regions, London, UK.

DETR. 2001. *Best practice in street works and highway works*. Department of the Environment, Transport and the Regions. TSO, London, UK, 25 pp.

DfT. 2002. *Specification for the reinstatement of openings in highways: a code of practice*, 2nd Edition. Department for Transport, TSO, London, UK, 159 pp.

Eden, N. 1996. Case study – Cheltenham. Trees and Ranger Services Manager. In: *Trenching and Street Trees*, National Conference, London, 23 April 1996, pp. 18–19. National Urban Forestry Unit, Great Barr, West Midlands, UK.

Eden, N., Smith, P. & Gardiner, J. 1997. *Trees: Excavations and highway maintenance*. Leaflet no. 11. 1997. Arboricultural Association, Romsey, UK.

Foggo, A. & Speight, M.R. 1993. Root damage and water stress: treatments affecting the exploitation of the buds of common ash *Fraxinus excelsior* L., by larvae of the ash bud moth *Prays fraxinella* Bjerk. (Lep., Yponomeutidae). *Oecologia*, 96, 134–138.

Franklin, J.F., Shugart, H.H. & Harmon, M.E., 1987. Tree death as an ecological process. *BioScience*, 37, 550–556.

Geisler, D. & Ferree, D.C. 1984a. The influence of root pruning on water relations, net photosynthesis, and growth of young 'Golden Delicious' apple trees. *Journal of the American Society of Horticultural Science*, 109, 827–831.

Geisler, D. & Ferree, D.C. 1984b. Response of plants to root pruning. *Horticultural Reviews*, 6, 155–188.

Gilman, E.F. 1997. *Trees for Urban and Suburban Landscapes*. Delmar, Albany, NY., USA. 662 pp.

Hamilton, W.D. 1989. Significance of root severence on performance of established trees. *Arboricultural Journal*, 13, 249–257.

Harris, R.W., Clark, J.R. & Matheny, N.P. 1999. *Arboriculture: Integrated Management of Landscape Trees, Shrubs and Vines, third edition*. Prentice Hall, Upper Saddle River, NJ., USA. 687 pp.

Jones, P. 1996. Case study – Cheltenham. Build Manager. In: *Trenching and Street Trees*, National Conference, London, 23 April 1996, pp. 27–32. National Urban Forestry Unit, Great Barr, West Midlands, UK.

Kramer, P.J. & Kozlowski, T.T. 1979. *Physiology of Woody Plants*. Academic Press, New York, NY., USA. 811 pp.

Mattheck, C. & Breloer, H. 1994. *The body language of trees: a handbook for failure analysis*. Research for Amenity Trees No. 4. HMSO, London, UK. 240 pp.

Mencuccini, M. & Grace, J. 1996. Developmental patterns of above-ground hydraulic conductance in a Scots pine (*Pinus sylvestris* L.) age sequence. *Plant, Cell and Environment*, 19, 939–948.

Morell, J.D. 1984. Parkway tree augering specifications. *Journal of Arboriculture*, 10, 129–133.

NJUG. 1995. NJUG 10: Guidelines for the planning, installation and maintenance of utility services in proximity to trees. National Joint Utilities Group, London, UK. 23 pp.

NJUG. 1997. NJUG 7: Recommended positioning of utilities' apparatus for new works on new developments and in existing streets. National Joint Utilities Group, London, UK. 45 pp.

O'Callaghan, D.P. 1998. Planning installation of underground services. In: *The Landscape Below Ground II: Proceedings of an International Workshop on Tree Root Development in Urban Soils* (Ed. by D. Neely and G.W. Watson), pp. 114–124. International Society of Arboriculture, Champaign, IL., USA.

O'Sullivan, M.F. & Ritchie, R.M. 1993. Tree stability in relation to cyclic loading. *Forestry*, 66, 69–82.

Poni, S., Tagliavini, M., Neri, D., Scudellari, D. & Toselli, M. 1992. Influence of root pruning and water stress on growth and physiological factors of potted apple, grape, peach and pear trees. *Scientia Horticulturae*, 52, 223–236.

Randolph, W.S. & Wiest, S.C. 1981. Relative importance of tractable factors affecting the establishment of transplanted holly. *Journal of the American Society of Horticultural Science*, 106, 207–210.

Richards, D. & Rowe, R.N. 1977. Effects of root restriction, root pruning and 6-benzylaminopurine on the growth of peach seedlings. *Annals of Botany, NS*, 41, 729–740.

Ryan, M.G., Binkley, D. & Fownes, J.H. 1997. Age-related decline in forest productivity: pattern and process. *Advances in Ecological Research*, 27, 213–262.

Ryan, M.G. & Waring, R.H. 1992. Maintenance respiration and stand development in a subalpine lodgepole pine forest. *Ecology*, 73, 2100–2108.

Salisbury, F.B. & Ross, C.W. 1992. *Plant Physiology*, 4th Edition. Wadsworth, Belmont, CA., USA. 682 pp.

Schupp, J.R. & Ferree, D.C. 1988. Effects of root pruning at four levels of severity on growth and yield of 'Melrose'/M.26 apple trees. *Journal of the American Society of Horticultural Science*, 113, 194–198.

Shigo, A.L. 1991. *Modern Arboriculture*. Shigo and Trees, Associates, Durham, New Hampshire, USA. 424 pp.

Smith, P. 1996. Case study – Cheltenham. Trees Officer. In: *Trenching and Street Trees*, National Conference, London, 23 April 1996, pp. 20–21. National Urban Forestry Unit, Great Barr, West Midlands, UK.

Speight, M.R., Hails, R.S., Gilbert, M. & Foggo, A. 1998. Horse chestnut scale (*Pulvinaria regalis*) (Homoptera: Coccidae) and urban host environment. *Ecology*, 79, 1503–1513.

Taiz, L. & Zeiger, E. 1991. *Plant Physiology*. The Benjamin/Cummings Publishing Co., Redwood City, CA., USA. 595 pp.

Thomson, J. & Rumsey, P. 1997. Trenchless technology applications for utility installation. *Arboricultural Journal*, 21, 137–143.

Wargo, P.M. 1979. Starch storage and radial growth in woody tissues of sugar maple. *Canadian Journal of Forest Research*, 9, 49–56.

Waring, R.H. 1987. Characteristics of tree predisposed to die. *BioScience*, 37, 569–574.

Watson, G.W. 1998. Tree growth after trenching and compensatory crown pruning. *Journal of Arboriculture*, 24, 47–53.

Wickman, B.E. 1978. Tree mortality and topkill related to defoliation by the Douglas-fir tussock moth in the Blue Mountains outbreak. Research Paper PNW-233. USDA Forest Service, Pacific Northwest Forest and Range Experiment Station, Portland, Oregon, USA.

Yoder, B.J., Ryan, M.G., Waring, R.H., Schoettle, A.W. & Kaufmann, M.R. 1994. Evidence of reduced photosynthetic rates in old trees. *Forest Science*, 40, 513–527.

CHAPTER 9

Causes and Control of Damage to Tree Roots on Construction Sites

9.1 Preserving the amenity value of trees

New construction on existing sites or on development land commonly threatens the health and survival of trees. Trees may have to be removed to make way for new structures and landscaping, but excavation, regrading and other changes to the soil environment can damage the roots of trees that remain, resulting in impaired growth or death. Protection of trees from such damage enables preservation of their amenity value and maintenance of the services they provide in the urban ecosystem. There may also be legal requirements for tree retention and protection during construction, the advantages of which will benefit developers, property owners and the community at large.

The amenity value of trees encompasses all of the benefits they provide to the public (Round and Lawson, 1999). Trees have a broad range of benefits, many of which vary subjectively according to the tastes and preferences of individuals or communities. Benefits from trees in urban settings are summarised in Box 9.1. Trees often improve the aesthetic and cultural appeal of urban landscapes, as well as providing economic benefits. Direct economic benefits of trees include a significant premium on house prices where landscaping surrounding property contains mature trees (NUFU, 2005). In more extreme climates shelter and shade from trees near buildings result in substantial savings from reduced energy usage for heating and cooling of residential and commercial buildings (McPherson and Rowntree, 1993). In the context of the UK the savings from energy conservation from tree shelter are likely to be modest. Patch (1998) cites an estimate of an energy conservation of around 3% from the shelter provided by trees being roughly equivalent to the savings achieved in a residential property by draught exclusion. The amenity value of trees is further enhanced by their ecological importance. Ecosystems, whether urban or rural, provide benefits – or services – to people at scales ranging from local to global. Urban environments featuring trees provide ecosystem services to city and town dwellers including filtration of atmospheric pollutants, amelioration of microclimatic extremes, increased infiltration of rainwater and reduction of noise from traffic and other sources (Bolund and Hunhammar, 1999).

Box 9.1 The amenity value of trees

Retention of trees during construction and land development has many potential benefits for people and the environment. The amenity value of trees is varied and often subjective, but it is an important consideration in planning for new buildings or landscaping. Planners and designers should recognise which amenities are provided by existing trees at a site, and develop plans for tree retention that preserve these benefits in consultation with arboricultural professionals. The amenity values of trees are summarised below (Round and Lawson, 1999):

Type of amenity	Examples
• Visual	attractive shape or form screening
• Cultural	landscape character Conservation Area features historical landmarks
• Social	health recreation privacy
• Economic	tree products property value tourism
• Protection	shelter and shade energy conservation
• Pollution	particulate filtering gaseous deposition noise reduction
• Wildlife	habitat provision species conservation
• Biodiversity	maintenance of genetic resources

Preservation of the amenity value of trees during construction is thus a highly desirable goal of urban development, as it has potential to increase returns for developers; to improve the aesthetic environment of people living and working nearby; and to reduce the impact of development on the local community, the wider public and ecosystems at local, regional and even global scales. Tree preservation must be integrated into the development process, from the planning stages to completion, to ensure that trees with the highest amenity value are identified and protected from damage during construction

(Matheny and Clark, 1998; BSI, 2005). Careful retention of mature trees on development sites can ensure immediate provision of full benefits from trees. Where retention of trees is not possible, however, for engineering reasons or because pre-existing trees are of unsuitable condition, size or species, planning should include consideration of replacement trees and new plantings.

A key to successful preservation of trees on construction sites is protection of their roots and the soil environment. As roots are unseen, their needs are easily overlooked, even when great care is taken to prevent damage to the trunk and crown. Protection of tree roots during construction requires an understanding of the causes of damage.

9.2 Causes of root damage during construction

Multiple threats to the root systems of trees exist on building sites. Construction entails extensive soil workings, including excavation, cutting, filling and compaction. These operations may directly cause injury to roots, or changes in the chemical and physical properties of soils which impair the growth and function of roots.

9.2.1 Root loss during construction

New buildings require level ground, connections to utility networks, foundations and footings[1], drainage, footpaths and, possibly, new access roads and parking areas. Each of these is likely to require excavation or stripping of topsoil. Excavation risks severance of roots and partial destruction of the root system if undertaken too close to a tree. Stripping of soil may be necessary to change the soil level or to expose subsoil prior to compaction. The depth of soil removed during stripping may vary from a few centimetres to many metres, depending on the topography of a site and the design requirements of the new structure. As root densities for trees are typically highest very close to the soil surface (Gale and Grigal, 1987; Gilman, 1990; Schroth, 1995), any soil stripping within the root zone of the tree will result in root loss. Schoeneweiss (1982) suggests that stripping of not more than 5 cm of topsoil within the root zone does not cause severe damage (unless the tree has a very shallow root system), especially if organic mulch is added to the soil surface to stimulate new root growth.

9.2.1.1 Impacts on tree stability

Severance of major structural roots, whether as a result of excavation or soil stripping, increases the risk of windthrow, as anchorage of the tree is reduced (see Section 8.3.4) (Hamilton, 1989, Crane, 1997, Matheny and Clark, 1998). The danger from reduced tree stability is highest if roots are cut on the

---

[1] The terms footings and foundations are loosely used in arboricultural texts. Here the distinction is that footings are the deepest load bearing structures while the foundations are the lowest common support level for the structure.

windward side of the tree (O'Sullivan and Ritchie, 1993; Crook and Ennos, 1996). This hazard will persist until regrowth of roots re-establishes adequate anchorage. There may be severe limits on the extent of regrowth possible in the context of construction, however, because physical barriers to root growth may have been created (Wargo, 1983). For example, concrete structures may replace excavated soil or heavy compaction may follow soil stripping, resulting in restricted regrowth of roots. Thus, if major structural roots of a tree are cut and construction creates very poor conditions for regrowth, the hazard caused by reduced anchorage of the tree could become permanent.

9.2.1.2 Impacts on tree growth and mortality

Another major threat to trees resulting from cutting of roots is loss of functional equilibrium between the roots and shoot (see Section 8.3). Functional equilibrium in plants ensures that supply and demand for resources by roots and shoots are in balance (Brouwer, 1983). To restore equilibrium after severance of roots, trees produce enhanced root growth but shoot growth is reduced. Reductions in above-ground growth and dieback of branches increase with the severity of root loss (Watson, 1998). Functional equilibrium can be successfully restored if carbohydrate reserves are sufficient for regrowth of roots (Waring, 1987). If a tree has depleted reserves, resilience to root severance is reduced. Carbohydrate reserves are low in late spring after rapid shoot growth and leaf emergence (Wargo, 1979; Waring, 1987) and in older trees, because of lower carbon assimilation (Yoder et al, 1994; Ryan et al, 1997). Thus, resilience to root loss is reduced in the spring and declines as trees age.

The consequence of inadequate regrowth after root severance, in addition to reduced above-ground growth, is a reduction in the ability of a tree to recover from attacks by pathogens or other injury. Each additional stress causes further depletion of carbohydrate reserves. As damage accumulates over several years, the tree will decline and may die. Death from cumulative injury and disease is referred to as the **mortality spiral** (Fig 8.13) (Franklin et al, 1987; Manion, 1991). Root loss resulting from excavation or soil stripping during construction may represent a significant step along the spiral.

9.2.2 Degradation of soil properties

Construction has three principal effects on the physical environment of the soil. These are compaction, reduction of soil aeration and changes in soil hydrology. Each causes degradation of the capacity of the soil to serve as a growth medium for trees and is detrimental to root growth and function. Contamination of soil can also occur during construction.

9.2.2.1 Soil compaction

Soils are intentionally compacted on construction sites to ensure stability and prevent subsequent damage to buildings and hard surfaces because of uneven settlement of the soil. Engineering specifications consequently require soils beneath structures or roads to be compacted using heavy machinery to within

Figure 9.1 Poor practice at a construction site. No tree protection zones identified, vehicle movements and storage of building materials and topsoil occurring in the rooting zones of trees.

Figure 9.2 Poor practice at a construction site. No tree protection zones identified, vehicle movements compacting soil in the rooting zones of trees.

95% of the maximum bulk density (see Section 4.2.3). It is common, however, for severe compaction of soil to occur in other areas of construction sites as an unintended impact of other activities (Alberty *et al*, 1984; Randrup and Dralle, 1997). Repeated movement of heavy machinery and construction vehicles across a site and storage of building materials cause compaction beyond those areas where it is needed for engineering purposes (Figs 9.1 and 9.2). Unless

Figure 9.3 Poor practice near to a construction site. No tree protection zones identified. Overnight parking of vehicles associated with connection of utilities to a new development.

carefully controlled, this can include the root zones of existing trees retained on site and areas designated for future tree planting under landscaping plans. Although most compression will occur when vehicles and plant, eg excavators, dumpers and delivery lorries, are moving and turning, parking of vehicles and plant will also cause compaction and should be avoided near trees. Trees on adjacent land may be affected by activities on the site of construction or by the connecting of utilities to the site (Fig 9.3).

The effects of compaction on soil properties are discussed in Section 4.2.3. The major effect of compaction is destruction of soil structure, resulting in reduced macropore space and increased bulk density (Foil and Ralston, 1967). Infiltration, drainage and aeration are consequently restricted (Schoeneweiss, 1982; Craul, 1985). Soil strength is increased, which impedes root elongation and rates of root growth resulting in tree decline in compacted soils (Taylor and Gardner, 1963; Unger and Kaspar, 1994; Kozlowski, 1999).

9.2.2.2 Changes in soil level

When preparing ground for construction, it is commonly necessary to change the soil level. Because of topography, this may entail both soil stripping (to lower the soil level) and the addition of fill (to raise the soil level). The danger from soil stripping is root severance (Section 9.2.1) and removal of nutrient-rich soil layers, resulting in deficiencies, particularly for potassium and phosphorus (Craul, 1992; Harris *et al*, 1999). Filling creates the problem of poor soil aeration. Consequently, if fill is placed over the root zone of an existing tree, the growth and function of the root system may be impaired, depending on the depth of fill and material used.

286

For example, Yelenosky (1963) found that oxygen was severely depleted from soil air beneath 0.3–1.0 m of clay fill. Harris *et al* (1999) suggested, however, that where soil will not be load-bearing (beneath buildings or hard surfaces), and therefore does not require compaction, up to 150 mm of well-aggregated fill soil may be spread over the root zone of a tree without adverse effects on most species. They cautioned that this treatment is only appropriate for young trees capable of vigorous growth. Trees should also be resistant to crown rot, which may afflict trees when the trunk is persistently wet. Some American texts (eg Harris *et al*, 1999; Hartman *et al*, 2000) refer to crown rot as occurring in response to covering of the root system with fill. Crown rot is not defined explicitly and in any case does not seem a good description of the initial symptoms, at least. In UK horticulture, crown rot has been described as an infection at soil level girdling and killing the host (Pollock and Griffiths, 1998). Early symptoms are rotting of the bark and inner tissues at the base of the tree and *Phytophthora* infection is a common occurrence. Reduced soil aeration restricts the supply of oxygen to roots, which is required for aerobic respiration. In poorly aerated soils, consequently, root respiration becomes anaerobic, which is inefficient and causes root growth and essential functions such as mineral uptake to decline or cease (Section 4.2.4). Poor soil aeration can reduce the effectiveness of the root system and therefore threaten the health of the whole tree.

9.2.2.3 Reduction in the availability of water

Reductions in the availability of water to trees result from changes in runoff and infiltration, reduced water-holding capacity, diversion of streams and drainage of the water table. Runoff is increased and infiltration reduced when the surface is paved, compacted or becomes crusted because of loss of soil structure (Fig 9.2). Paving or compaction of soil around a tree may cause the diversion of substantial quantities of precipitation away from the root system if the surface slopes away from the tree. The rooting environment will then be drier than existed previously. This may increase the frequency of stress, especially for mature trees with large crowns adapted to wetter conditions. Reduced water-holding capacity, because of compression of pore space when soil is compacted (Section 4.2.5.3), has a similar impact on trees.

The long-term viability of existing, natural vegetation retained on development sites may be reduced by changes in stream flow and water table depth that accompany construction. Ditches and small streams may be diverted to facilitate construction, leaving trees and shrubs on the former stream banks in drier conditions and without their accustomed source of water. As such **riparian** vegetation normally thrives in wet conditions, irrigation may be required to sustain it during dry periods of the year after stream diversion (Matheny and Clark, 1998). Installation of drainage may be required to facilitate construction on sites with high water tables. Natural vegetation is commonly unable to adapt to the subsequent drop in the level of the water table (Fig 9.4) and declines quickly as a result. Thus, retention of natural vegetation in drained areas or on the banks of diverted streams is unwise and

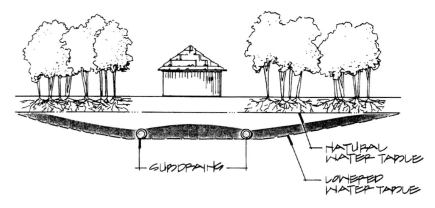

Figure 9.4 Survival and regeneration of retained trees may be compromised if site development requires lowering of the water table. (After Matheny and Clark, 1998.)

should be restricted to areas where water table levels are not affected by site preparation and the stream course is unaltered (Matheny and Clark, 1998).

9.2.2.4 Excess soil water

Modifications to the landscape and changes in soil physical properties during construction can cause inundation and waterlogging of the root systems of trees. In contrast to dry soil conditions created when paving or crusting of slopes channels water away from trees, if the base of the trunk is lower than surrounding soil, water will be diverted towards the tree. The root zone may then be prone to waterlogging. Waterlogging severely reduces aeration of soils (Section 4.2.5.4) and therefore impairs root function, including uptake of water. Contrary to intuition, insufficient uptake of water is a principal effect of excess soil water on trees. The symptoms of waterlogging exhibited by trees – **chlorosis**, leaf drop and dieback of twigs – are consequently very similar to those of drought, which easily leads to misdiagnosis of the cause of tree decline (Berrang *et al*, 1985).

Waterlogging of the surface may occur on construction sites because of compaction. This may cause ponding of water in low-lying areas. If finely textured soil is compacted and then covered with a layer of topsoil, a saturated zone – called a perched water table – may develop at the interface with the compacted layer during wet periods of the year. A perched water table is also possible where coarse fill such as rubble or gravel is covered by fine topsoil (Section 4.2.5.1). Perched water tables may saturate the root zones of trees and cause them to decline.

Changes in drainage caused by construction may reduce the depth of the water table and cause inundation of the root systems of existing trees. The lack of aeration under these conditions is likely to have serious consequences for the health of the roots. Underground structures such as footings, foundations and retaining walls can block drainage below ground. The water table may rise as a

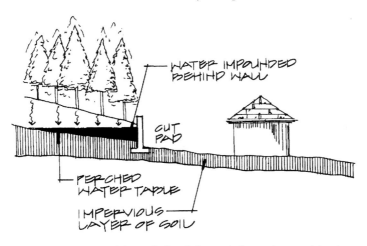

Figure 9.5 Building roads, retaining walls, foundations and other underground structures can intercept underground water flow. Trees may be damaged by rising water tables. (After Matheny and Clark, 1998.)

Figure 9.6 Adequate drainage should be installed where retaining walls are likely to lead to saturated soil conditions. Retaining wall with drainage pipes, Droitwich, UK.

result and saturate the root zones of trees previously growing in well-drained conditions (Fig 9.5) (Matheny and Clark, 1998). To prevent accumulation of excess water behind retaining walls adequate provision for the drainage must be made (Fig 9.6).

9.2.2.5 Soil contamination

Details of contamination of soil are given in general terms in Chapter 7. Chemicals used on construction sites can contaminate soils and damage trees.

Herbicides may be used during land clearance or to suppress weed growth during construction. Although not targeted by spraying, trees designated for retention can be injured because of inappropriate choice of herbicide, or because of spray drift or movement of herbicide in soil water (Harris *et al*, 1999). Important contaminants on construction sites are the fuels and lubricants, either spilt during refuelling of machinery, or leaked from tanks or storage drums. These create serious toxic soil conditions harmful to roots (Cutler, 1993). Many of the pieces of machinery which are used on construction sites will be fuelled by diesel and a number will have hydraulic systems filled with fluid. Both diesel and hydraulic fluids are likely to be injurious if they contact roots so spillages must be avoided if at all possible. There are no quick and effective remedies for spillages of fuel and hydraulic fluids which means that a lot of care is needed in the storage and handling of these materials to avoid spillages. *In situ* remediation is a long-term process but removal of small amounts of contaminated soil without further damage to tree roots might be considered as an option. In Chapter 4, the use of soil vacuuming was discussed. This would seem to be a useful option to remove contaminated soil from around roots. It is feasible to burn small amounts of removed soil, a process that will consume the diesel as well as the organic fraction of the soil. The organic content of the soil may be reconstituted with compost. This burnt and composted soil could be then replaced around the tree. If the spillage is in the vicinity of a small but valuable tree, it might be feasible to excavate the tree, remove the contaminated soil and replant the tree in good soil. Clearly, however, the season has to be right so this is only an option under certain limited circumstances.

Given the difficulties of dealing with spillages of diesel, and other toxic compounds, the emphasis must be on the need for zones to protect existing trees and care in handling fuel anywhere on a site where trees may be planted. Aldous (2000) reports that biodegradable lubricants based on rapeseed oil are now available for hydraulic systems and chainsaw lubrication in forestry. Spillage of cement and disposal of rubble, plaster and masonry on site, perhaps in fills, causes soil pH to increase. This may damage the roots of many common species of shade tree that are intolerant of high pH (Schoeneweiss, 1982). The remedy here would be to carefully remove as much of the cement, plaster and masonry without damaging roots and to mix in peat material to neutralise the pH.

9.3 Protection of trees on building sites

With so many hazards for the root systems of trees on building sites, it is vital for their long-term health and survival that trees are given adequate protection against damage. Successful retention of trees during construction and landscaping requires both careful planning and diligent implementation of protection measures. The benefit of using recommended practices for tree protection were demonstrated by Gilbert (1996) who surveyed tree survival on building sites in northern England between 1979 and 1993. During the 1970s, when the attitude to tree conservation was poor and protection was weak, mortality rates for trees two years after completion of construction varied from 20 to over 60%. In the 1980s, this figure dropped to 20–30%. By the early 1990s, mortality rates were around 10%, because of more widespread use of a professional approach to tree retention and protection by developers, landscapers, contractors and local authorities.

Recommendations for the protection of trees on construction sites are provided in the UK in British Standard 5837 (BSI, 2005). A practical manual on tree preservation during development was published by Matheny and Clark (1998). Both publications stress the importance of careful planning and selection of trees for retention followed by implementation of protection measures.

9.3.1 Planning of tree retention and protection

9.3.1.1 Land and tree surveys

Trees can be protected by law, in the UK by tree preservation orders, conservation areas and by the need to obtain felling licences. Penalties for damage and carrying out work without consent from the local authority or Forestry Commission can lead to financial penalties. Planning conditions imposed on planning consents may specify which trees are to be retained and require physical protection to be installed. Trees should be considered by all parties early in the planning process, assessing the needs of both trees and the development. It is far easier to accept and implement change and compromise during the preplanning stage than after work on the site has started. BS 5837 promotes the inclusion of arboricultural expertise in a multi-disciplinary design and development team from the earliest phases. This will help to ensure that balanced decisions are made regarding tree retention, impact on design considerations and tree protection.

The first step in preparing plans for tree protection is to survey the site and develop an inventory of existing trees and shrubs. This should be undertaken well before any clearance or construction begins and forms part of the background work necessary in making an application for planning consent. By ensuring that tree surveys are completed early in the development process, information on trees can be shared among developers, engineers, architects and landscapers and integrated into the planning of the new development from the outset. This will increase the chances of successfully retaining trees on site and maximise their amenity value to the completed project. The evaluation of trees on a site, including species, condition and suitability for retention, requires expert knowledge of amenity trees and should therefore be undertaken by a professional arboricultural consultant.

The initial land survey should include:

(a) the location of all trees, shrub masses, hedges, etc.;

(b) other relevant features, such as streams, buildings and other structures, boundary features, trenching scars near to trees, and services including drainage runs;

(c) spot heights of ground level throughout the site, as a basis for avoiding changes in soil level around retained trees;

(d) the approximate location of trees on land adjacent to the development site, that might influence the site or might be important as part of the local landscape character (BSI, 2005).

The next step is a survey of the individual attributes of trees at the site. BS 5837 recommends that all trees with a stem diameter (at 1.5 m above ground level) over 75 mm are included in the survey. Also included should be trees over this size growing on land adjacent to the site, which are at or within a distance equal to 12 times their stem diameter from the boundary (or 10 times their base diameter, in the case of multi-stemmed trees), or where their crowns overhang the site boundary. For trees with more than one stem below 1.5 m above ground level, the stem diameter should be measured immediately above the root flare.

The following information should be provided on a schedule which lists all the trees or groups of trees:

(a) reference number (to be recorded on the tree survey plan);

(b) species (common and scientific names, where possible);

(c) height in metres;

(d) stem diameter in millimetres at 1.5 m above adjacent ground level (on sloping ground to be taken on the upslope side of the tree base) or immediately above the root flare for multi-stemmed trees;

(e) branch spread in metres taken at the four cardinal points to derive an accurate representation of the crown (to be recorded on the tree survey plan);

(f) height in metres of crown clearance above adjacent ground level (to inform on ground clearance, crown stem ratio and shading);

(g) age class (young, middle aged, mature, over mature, veteran);

(h) physiological condition (e.g. good, fair, poor, dead);

(i) structural condition, e.g. collapsing, the presence of any decay and physical defect;

(j) preliminary management recommendations, including further investigation of suspected defects that require more detailed assessment and potential for wildlife habitat;

(k) estimated remaining contribution in years (e.g. less than 10, 10–20, 20–40, more than 40;

(l) R or A to C category grading (see Box 9.2) to be recorded in plan on the tree survey plan.

Criteria recommended by Matheny and Clark (1998) for assessing relative conditions of trees are given in Table 9.1.

9.3.1.2 Tree selection

BS 5837 recommends that trees are divided into four categories according to their priority for retention. Criteria for each category are listed in Box 9.2. These assessments of the trees and the constraints they may impose will help to strike a balance between the impact of development proposals and the need to retain and protect trees. Selection of trees for retention should be co-ordinated with other members of the development team. Preference should be given to retention of trees that are able to make a substantial or significant contribution after development. Trees that are of low quality or value are usually retained only if they do not interfere with plans for building and landscaping.

When selecting trees for retention, it is important to recognise that attempts to retain too many trees are often counterproductive. Requirements for tree protection can become too restrictive, which is not forgiving of error and easily leads to tree damage. Further, when selecting trees, it is vital that implementation of protection for each tree is practically feasible and can realistically be achieved by contractors (BSI, 2005; Gilbert, 1996). There may be little point in retaining trees already identified through the prioritising process, which only have a short life expectancy (even though they may be notable trees), or which are unlikely to survive in a good state of health following development. There are occasions when it may be more appropriate to remove such trees and allow new planting to take place. A variation on the selection process for tree retention is the Safe Useful Life Expectancy (SULE) procedure, an assessment scheme developed by Barrell (1993). The philosophy behind SULE is that in a planning context the overriding long-term consideration is the length of time a tree can be expected to be usefully retained. Barrell explains that SULE prioritises individual trees within a defined area and enables value judgements to be made to determine which are the most suitable for retention when there is a shortage of space. SULE summarises information on age, species lifespan, life expectancy, health and structure in a context of management, impacts and sustaining amenity. SULE is a ranking of the effective, safe and useful lifespan of the trees on a site. The

Box 9.2 Cascade chart for tree quality assessment (After BSI, 2005)

TREES FOR REMOVAL

Category and definition	Criteria	Identification on plan
Category R Those in such a condition that any existing value would be lost within 10 years and which should, in the current context, be removed for reasons of sound arboricultural management.	• Trees that have a serious, irremediable, structural defect, such that their early loss is expected due to collapse, including those that will become unviable after removal of other R category trees (i.e. where, for whatever reason, the loss of companion shelter cannot be mitigated by pruning). • Trees that are dead or are showing signs of significant, immediate, and irreversible overall decline. • Trees infected with pathogens of significance to the health and/or safety of other trees nearby (e.g. Dutch elm disease), or very low quality trees suppressing adjacent trees of better quality. NOTE Habitat reinstatement may be appropriate (e.g. R category tree used as a bat roost: installation of bat box in nearby tree).	DARK RED

TREES TO BE CONSIDERED FOR RETENTION

Category and definition	Criteria – Subcategories			Identification on plan
	1 Mainly arboricultural values	**2 Mainly landscape values**	**3 Mainly cultural values, including conservation**	
Category A Those of high quality and value: in such a condition as to be able to make a substantial contribution (a minimum of 40 years is suggested).	Trees that are particularly good examples of their species, especially if prominent, rare or unusual, or essential components of groups, or of formal or semi-formal arboricultural features (e.g. the dominant and/or principal trees within an avenue).	Trees, groups or woodlands which provide a definite screening or softening effect to the locality in relation to views into or out of the site, or those of particular visual importance (e.g. avenues or other arboricultural features assessed as groups).	Trees, groups or woodlands of significant conservation, historical, commemorative or other value (e.g. veteran trees or wood-pasture).	LIGHT GREEN
Category B Those of moderate quality and value: those in such a condition as to make a significant contribution (a minimum of 20 years is suggested).	Trees that might be included in the high category, but are downgraded because of impaired condition (e.g. presence of remediable defects including unsympathetic past management and minor storm damage).	Trees present in numbers, usually as groups or woodlands, such that they form distinct landscape features, thereby attracting a higher collective rating than they might as individuals but which are not, individually, essential components of formal or semi formal arboricultural features (e.g. trees of moderate quality within an avenue that includes better, A category specimens), or trees situated mainly internally to the site, therefore individually having little visual impact on the wider locality.	Trees with clearly identifiable conservation or other cultural benefits.	MID BLUE
Category C Those of low quality and value: currently in adequate condition to remain until new planting could be established (a minimum of 10 years is suggested), or young trees with a stem diameter below 150 mm.	Trees not qualifying in higher categories.	Trees present in groups or woodlands, but without this conferring on them significantly greater landscape value, and/or trees offering low or only temporary screening benefit.	Trees with very limited conservation or other cultural benefits.	GREY
NOTE Whilst C Category trees will usually not be retained where they would impose a significant constraint on development, young trees with a stem diameter of less than 150 mm should be considered for relocation.				

visual amenity value of the tree's location is not considered by SULE. The details of SULE as outlined by Barrell (1993) are given in Box 9.3.

9.3.2 Preconstruction treatment of trees

The complete site survey data will allow informed decisions to be made on the siting of buildings and infrastructure to minimise the risk of damage to any tree selected for retention. If there is sufficient time between planning for tree retention and the start of construction, treatments may be applied to increase the tolerance of trees to construction impacts. The applicability of these treatments depends on the condition of the tree and its maintenance history, but the intention is to invigorate the tree. By maximising carbohydrate reserves and the effectiveness of growth regulators, trees will be better able to respond defensively to wounding or stress and to generate new root and shoot growth.

Trees under drought stress should be irrigated. Fertilisation with 10–25 kg ha^{-1} of available nitrogen may be beneficial to slow-growing trees with poor colour, if application is possible in the growth season prior to the start of construction. Pests and diseases should be controlled and dead, weak or diseased branches should be pruned from the crown (Matheny and Clark, 1998).

9.3.3 Implementing tree protection measures

9.3.3.1 Tree protection zones

The key action required for preserving existing trees on construction sites is the establishment of tree protection zones. These are areas surrounding each tree or group of trees designated for retention in which activities are tightly controlled. A variety of means of determining the size of tree protection zones have been suggested (Matheny and Clark, 1998). Each is based on proportionality with some dimension of the tree above ground, whether it is the dripline of the crown, tree height or trunk diameter, on the assumption that larger trees have roots which spread further, requiring a larger protection zone.

In the UK, the standard method of determining the size of the protection zone on development sites is specified in BS 5837 (BSI, 2005). In this revised standard, a root protection area (RPA) is designated as a zone around a tree. The RPA has a radius specified as 12 times the tree diameter measured at 1.5 m above ground level which can then be used to calculate the area of a figurative circle. Once this is calculated the most appropriate shape to protect the roots of the tree can be defined, providing the area is not reduced. The area of protection for the roots now closely matches that recommended by the National Joint Utilities Group in NJUG 10 (NJUG, 1995). The optimum protection zone that is derived can be reduced by up to 20% on one side of the tree only.

An alternative means for setting the boundaries of the RPA is also provided in Matheny and Clark (1998). If the radius calculated for the RPA exceeds 15 m

Box 9.3 Preplanning life surveys: Safe Useful Life Expectancy (SULE) categories

Long SULE: trees that appear to be retainable with an acceptable level of risk for more than 40 years.
(a) Structurally sound trees located in positions that can accommodate future growth.
(b) Storm damaged or defective trees that could be made suitable for retention in the long term by remedial tree surgery.
(c) Trees of special significance for historical, commemorative or rarity reasons that would warrant extraordinary efforts to secure their long-term retention.

Medium SULE: trees that appear to be retainable with an acceptable level of risk for 15 to 40 years.
(a) Trees that may only live between 15 and 40 more years.
(b) Trees that may live for more than 40 years but would be removed to allow the safe development of more suitable individuals.
(c) Trees that may live for more than 40 years but would be removed during the course of normal management for safety or nuisance reasons.
(d) Storm-damaged or defective trees that can be made suitable for retention in the medium term by remedial work.

Short SULE: trees that appear to be retainable with an acceptable level of risk for 5 to 15 years.
(a) Trees that may only live between 5 and 15 more years.
(b) Trees that may live for more than 15 years but would be removed to allow the safe development of more suitable individuals.
(c) Trees that may live for more than 15 years but would be removed during the course of normal management for safety or nuisance reasons.
(d) Storm-damaged or defective trees that require substantial remedial work to make them safe, and are only suitable for retention in the short term.

Remove: Trees with a high level of risk that would need removing within the next 5 years.
(a) Dead trees.
(b) Dying or suppressed and trees declining through disease or inhospitable conditions.
(c) Dangerous trees through instability or recent loss of adjacent trees.
(d) Dangerous trees through structural defects including cavities, decay, including bark wounds or poor form.
(e) Damaged trees that are considered unsafe to retain.
(f) Trees that will become dangerous after removal of other trees for reasons given in (a) to (e).

After Barrell (1993).

then the recommended RPA should be based on 15 m, or the actual crown periphery plus 1 m, whichever is the greater. Care must be taken, however, when using the crown periphery method if a tree is leaning or the crown lopsided, as roots on the opposing side of the tree may be left unprotected.

Table 9.1 Criteria recommended by Matheny and Clark (1998) for assessing the relative condition of trees.

Criterion	Condition rating				
	1	2	3	4	5
Overall vigour	severe decline	declining	low	good	excellent
Canopy density	<20%	20–60%	60–90%	90–100%	100%
Amount of deadwood	major branches	twig and branch dieback	small twigs	little or none	none
History of failure	two or more major branches	one major branch	small branches	none	none
Pests	infested	infestation of significant pests	minor	minor	none
Extent of decay	major fungal brackets and cavities	a few fungal brackets; small cavities	at pruning wounds	at pruning wounds	absent

9.3.3.2 Protective fencing and ground protection

All trees which are being retained on site should be protected by barriers and/or ground protection. Vertical barriers and ground protection should be installed before any materials or machinery is brought onto the site and before any demolition, development or soil stripping begins. Areas identified for new planting should be similarly protected.

To ensure that tree protection zones are not breached during construction works, they should be surrounded by protective fencing. Under BS 5837, fencing should be 2.5 m in height and constitute weldmesh wired to the uprights and horizontals of a well-braced scaffolding framework (see Fig 9.7) There should be uprights at least at 3 m intervals (BSI, 2005).

Where it has been agreed during the design stage and shown on the tree protection plan, that vehicle and pedestrian access may take place within the RPA, there should be barriers to protect trees and ground protection. For pedestrian movement within the RPA ground protection can be a single thickness of scaffold boards above a compressible layer laid onto geotextile or supported by scaffold. For wheeled or tracked construction traffic movements within the RPA the ground protection should be designed by an engineer to accommodate the likely loading. Further information about the importance of limiting compaction of pedestrian and wheeled traffic is given in Section 9.3.3.4. BS 5837 (BSI, 2005) recommends that consideration might be given to installing temporary roadways to minimise damage to soil and roots. An option for such a construction is given in Section 9.4.3.

9.3.3.3 Control of tree protection zones

Tree protection zones must be considered sacrosanct, according to BS 5837, with the protective fencing neither moved, removed or breached during construction operations. To ensure protection against injury to roots or compaction and degradation of the soil, the following rules, which can be enforced through planning conditions and contract documents, must be adhered to within the protected area (Matheny and Clark, 1998):

- no soil disturbance, including compaction;
- no change in the soil level, by stripping or filling;
- no storage of materials;
- no dumping of materials, whether into a skip or onto the ground;
- no vehicles permitted and no parking;
- no temporary buildings, sheds or offices;
- no fires;
- all underground utilities must be routed outside protection zones;
- changes in surface runoff that direct water into or out of the protection zone must be prevented;
- changes in drainage should be designed to maintain the natural water table levels within the protection zone;

Access to tree protection zones should be allowed only in consultation with an arboriculturist and where necessary the local authority. If excavation within the protection zone cannot be avoided, by re-routeing services for example, digging must be done by hand or using trenchless techniques (Section 8.4.2.1). Where diversion of water away from trees occurs, because of changes in drainage or runoff, consideration should be given to installing irrigation systems to replace natural water sources for trees.

Figure 9.7 Good practice in creating a tree protection zone following BS 5837 recommendations using pre-formed mesh panels.

9.3.3.4 Strategies to minimise/localise soil compaction on construction sites

A major cause of degradation of soil conditions and root function on construction sites will be soil compaction caused by vehicle movements and the storage of heavy materials on the ground. Even outside the root protection zones it will be important to minimise compaction, not only because of future landscaping requirements but also because drainage of the site will be influenced by compacted soils. There is a risk that soil structure at locations well outside building zones may be damaged during development and this might prejudice the quality of future landscaping sites available on the development. Nicholson (2001) has proposed that these potential development zones be identified ('Zone 4') and also be protected during development. In this context it should be noted that the latest British Standard BS 5837 (BSI, 2005) recommends that areas designated for future landscaping should be marked on site plans and afforded the same protection as the root protection areas of existing trees. It is very important that all those involved in construction activities near to trees should be aware of the seriousness of soil compaction. Figs 9.8(a) and (b) are examples from a leaflet produced by Lambeth Borough Council to relate the message about the need to avoid damage to soil and roots by building activities. Avoiding compaction figures prominently in this leaflet.

So any vehicle traffic and even pedestrian movement will cause soil compaction with adverse effects on soil conditions important to root growth and function. In Section 4.2.3 it was shown that the major contribution to soil compaction from vehicle movements comes from the first passes of vehicles over the ground. As soil bulk density and soil strength increase with compaction, subsequent passes on the same ground have a decreasing influence on soil bulk density and its mechanical strength measured as the resistance to the entry of a penetrometer. The greater fraction of damage is likely to occur after the first passages of the vehicles on the ground.

There are a number of options for managing traffic on building sites. Construction managers should consider what size of plant and machinery is necessary and safe to complete the tasks. Smaller, lighter construction vehicles, eg excavators and dumpers, will have a smaller influence on soil properties compared to heavier machines. Smaller, lighter machinery is also likely to prove more fuel-efficient.

Temporary roads that should minimise soil compaction can be constructed from materials such as railway sleepers. Temporary access roads can be hired/purchased from suppliers who provide temporary roads for military applications and for large public outdoor functions on soft land where damage would be unacceptable e.g.

www.plantuk.com/trac/index.php or
www.sgb.co.uk/eventstemproadway.php4

The failure of temporary roads is likely to occur more frequently with certain soil/roadway interactions and was the subject of research at Southampton University (Lees, 2000), www.soton.ac.uk/geotech/projects/Lees/Lees.htm.

9.4 Landscape and building design for root health

Integration of tree protection zones into designs for buildings and new landscaping may at times create conflict between the needs of designers and the needs of tree root systems. Approaches to building and landscaping close to trees are available that minimise the impacts of construction on roots and enable the maintenance of healthy, functioning root systems after development of a site is complete. These approaches can be used to enable compromise between design requirements and the rules prohibiting disturbance within the tree protection zone.

9.4.1 Changing the soil level near trees

Changes in soil level are harmful to tree roots (Section 9.2.1 and 9.2.2), because of the filling or soil stripping entailed. Consequently, the original soil level should be maintained within the protection zone around retained trees. Changes in slope and soil level can be implemented close to trees without disturbing soil in the protection zone by incorporating retaining walls into designs for new landscaping. Examples are shown in Fig 9.9. In Fig 9.9(a), use of the retaining wall has enabled cutting of the soil up to the edge of the root

Figure 9.8 (a) Part of a leaflet highlighting the risks to trees from construction activities, and **(b)** *overleaf* how these damages can be avoided. Leaflet provided courtesy of Mr Jim Harrisson, Reigate and Banstead Council (formerly of Lambeth Borough Council) and Lambeth Borough Council.

system. In Fig 9.9(b), a retaining wall has been constructed rather than extending fill over the root system of the tree. If the transition in soil level in either case was created using slopes, much more of the root system would have been damaged (Schoeneweiss, 1982; Craul, 1992; Matheny and Clark, 1998). Root disturbance can be further minimised by using discontinuous footings to construct the retaining walls (Fig 9.10), which avoids the need for digging of a trench at the base of the wall. Where changes in soil levels create a low area

Preventative Action **(b)**

The most effective protection of trees on development sites is obtained by the erection of strong fencing around the tree and its roots before any work begins.

Keep stored materials, site huts and site vehicles (whether working or parked) away from roots under trees.

Protect trunks by wrapping at least two layers of chestnut paling to the tree

Necessary excavations near roots should be done by hand

LAMBETH

around a tree which will collect water, drainage should be provided (see Fig 9.6). To avoid severing roots, the drain should be positioned as far from the tree as possible, near a retaining wall (Harris *et al*, 1999).

9.4.2 Maintaining soil aeration under fill

Although it is widely recommended that root systems of trees are not buried under fill, there may be instances where it is decided that raising soil levels beneath a tree cannot be avoided. In such cases, steps can be taken to try and maintain aeration, watering and fertilisation of the original root system.

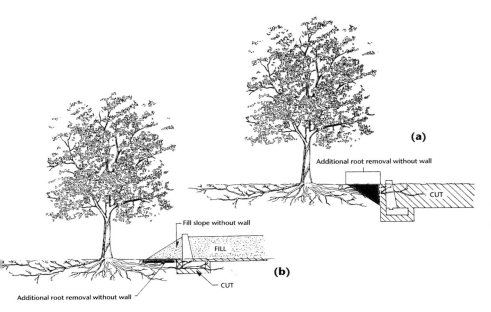

Figure 9.9 How changes in level are handled can significantly affect root disturbance. Retaining walls can be used to reduce the horizontal distance for level changes for **(a)** a cut or **(b)** a fill. (After Matheny and Clark, 1998.)

Details of several aeration systems have been published (eg Schoeneweiss, 1982 and Harris *et al*, 1999) and systems are available commercially. Fig 9.11(a) shows a ventilation system being installed prior to tree planting near a canal in Amsterdam. The system includes 160-mm vertical pipes that have perforations and are capped at the surface by a concrete or plastic tile (Fig 9.11(b)). These ventilators can be used within the root plate area of mature trees. Newly planted trees or trees in soil with a fill applied can be provided with vertical ventilators joined by flexible corrugated piping placed on the soil surface within the region of the root plate and up the dripline of the tree. The essentials of the system shown here for aeration within soil fill are the same as for providing an adequate ventilation for tree root systems below pavements (see 9.4.3, Fig 9.18).

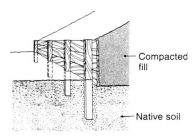

Figure 9.10 Discontinuous footings, such as in this post and retaining barrier may reduce root injury to adjacent trees, depending on the size and spacing of the posts. (After Harris *et al*, 1999.)

Harris *et al* (1999) cautioned that the aeration systems recommended by Schoeneweiss (1982) are costly and that, to date, there is no evidence from research that they are effective in maintaining the health of the root system. In one of the few tests of the 'wagon wheel' aeration system, Smith *et al* (1995) found that soil aeration was not reduced by 15–20 cm of fill, whether or not the aeration system was installed. In their trial, however, soils were not

subjected to compaction and therefore retained excellent bulk density and porosity. It is unclear whether these results would be repeated where soil is subjected to levels of compaction and disturbance typical of construction sites.

As a consequence of the uncertainty over the effectiveness of soil aeration systems, Harris *et al* (1999) recommended avoiding changes in soil levels within tree protection zones, using retaining walls if necessary. They concluded that if a tree protection zone cannot be established and maintained because of engineering and design considerations, removal of the tree should be considered. Preparations can then be made for planting of new trees after completion of the project.

A recent report by Day *et al* (2001) investigated the influence of 20 cm of soil cover over the root systems of young trees of white oak (*Quercus alba*) and sweet gum (*Liquidambar styraciflua*). They found no adverse effects on the trees over a three-year period. The major effect that was observed was that the fill disrupted normal soil water distribution patterns.

Figure 9.11 (a) Installation of below-ground ventilation system in the rooting area for a proposed tree planting close to a canal in Amsterdam. **(b)** Concrete tile used to cap individual vertical ventilation tubes at pavement level.

Under the sweet gum, soil below the fill was drier than the fill itself. The oaks grew roots upwards into the fill and although the sweet gums did not grow roots into the fill there was an upward shift in root distribution in that species. There have already been concerns expressed by Harris *et al* (1999) that the roots covered by fill may preferentially root in the fill and the original roots may die and induce instability for the tree. It is not clear whether the roots grow preferentially in the fill because the layer of additional soil created a stimulus to the root system or because of different soil water distribution caused by the presence of the fill (Day *et al*, 2001).

9.4.3 Maintaining air and water movement under paving

Laying a hard surface (eg concrete, asphalt, paving slabs or paviours) over the root system of trees should be avoided, as far as possible, because of the danger that it may fully or partially seal the surface to air or water entry. Additionally, installation of hard surfaces usually requires some degree of soil cutting and compaction. The thickness of supporting bases for roadways depends on the weight of traffic they will bear. Construction of carriageways for roads requires excavation of as much as 1 m of soil and the installation of heavily compacted layers of fill. Driveways, footpaths and patios require much less disturbance of the soil. Cutting of the soil can be avoided altogether if soil levels allow and geotextile fabrics can be used to reduce compaction of natural soils beneath hard covering (Harris *et al*, 1999; Matheny and Clark, 1998). Thus, hard

---

Box 9.4 No-dig method for constructing access drives and parking near to trees

Construction should ideally be undertaken in dry weather between May and October when the ground is driest and least prone to compaction.

Ground vegetation should be killed using a translocated herbicide such as glyphosate. (Care in the selection of a herbicide that will not affect desirable vegetation is advocated.) To prevent severe oxygen depletion in the soil during the process of decomposition, all dead organic material should be removed.

All major protrusions such as rocks and tree/shrub root stumps should be removed. It is proposed that stumps should be ground out to minimise disturbance.

Fill major hollows with sharp sand.

Lay the geogrid or equivalent onto the soil over the whole of the driveway/ parking area.

Construct an edging with boards attached to pegs driven into the ground through the geogrid. Pegs should be long enough to give adequate support during the construction.

The geogrid should be covered with a minimum of 100 mm of aggregate. This should be tipped at one end of the geogrid so that machinery moves on already spread sub-base not directly on the geogrid or the ground close to the geogrid.

Compact the sub-base to ensure binding with the geogrid and to minimise rutting when in final use.

The final surface may be gravel or tarmacadam placed directly on top of the aggregate. Paving slabs or brick paviours should be dry-bedded on the sub-base and the joints left unsealed.

After Patch and Dobson, 1999.

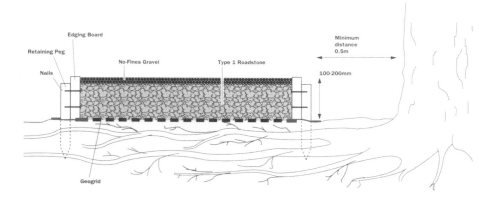

Figure 9.12 Diagram of a no-dig method for constructing drives and parking areas close to trees. (After Patch and Dobson, 1999.) The extension to the geogrid (shown in red) is a recent amendment (D. Patch, *Pers. Comm.*, 2003).

surfaces for heavy loads should be routed well away from trees, while footpaths and patios may be more readily accommodated closer to trees.

If any hard surfaces are added within the tree protection zone, they should cover as small an area as possible and be built without soil compaction. For example, footpaths or patio areas may be installed close to trees as a part of new landscaping. It is preferable that pervious rather than **impervious** paving is used under trees. Pervious paving enables water and air to penetrate to the soil beneath. Examples include brick, interlocking paviours, granite setts and concrete blocks or slabs. The joints between paving units in these materials allow air and water exchange with the underlying soil, provided that permeable jointing materials are used (Evans *et al*, 1990; Harris *et al*, 1999).

To avoid compaction of soil in the root zone, paving under trees should be laid using a sand base and geotextile over soil subjected only to smoothing and hand tamping. Construction of pavements using this approach offers protection to the roots of existing trees, though frost heave may occur in cold areas. However, repair of heaved paving is easier if block paviours are used, as small sections are readily removed and re-laid (Matheny and Clark, 1998).

Patch and Dobson (1999) describe a technique of drive or path construction requiring no digging which is intended to have only a limited impact on roots close to trees. It is, however, difficult to see how this can be guaranteed given that some construction operations are required. The sequence of construction is given in Box 9.4 and Figs 9.12 and 9.13. The interlock between the aggregate and the **geogrid** (eg Tensar SS30, Netlon Ltd, Blackburn, UK) provides a reinforced platform and efficient spreading of load into the ground below. This Arboricultural Practice Note is currently being revised and will show the geogrid extending beyond the drive edging (as shown in red in Fig 9.12). This will allow the grid to be secured by a suitably designed edging. Pressure applied to the surface by vehicles will then tend to force the edging outwards thus

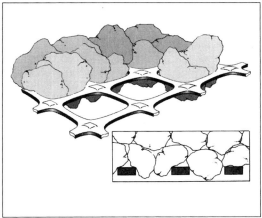

Figure 9.13 Interlock between the aggregate and the geogrid. (After Patch and Dobson, 1999.)

Figure 9.14 Filling the 'Geoweb' with aggregate (upper photograph). Detail of the 'Geoweb' (lower photograph).

increasing the tension in the grid. An alternative to the geogrid could be the use of 'Geoweb' (Cooper Clarke Ltd, Bolton, UK). Fig 9.14 shows details of Geoweb laid on permeable matting and filled with aggregate. It seems likely that the 'Geoweb' system will better resist the tendency for aggregate to move sideways below the paving. The impact of paving construction on tree roots has considerable relevance at present and is likely to increase in importance in the future. It is estimated that currently in the UK 2 million m^2 of block paving is laid annually and this is on the increase (NCE, 2001).

Severe flooding in the UK in the winter of 2000 focused thinking on the influence of hard urban surfaces in controlling infiltration into the soil. The permeability of open joint paving is greater than sealed surfaces such as asphalt (Table 6.1), a feature of particular importance to the recharging of soil water around tree roots and the

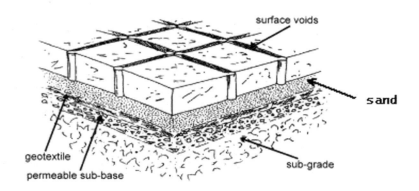

Figure 9.15 Brick or interlocking paviours on sand serve as pervious paving. Use of geotextile under the sand and manually firmed subgrade can minimise impacts to roots.

Figure 9.16 Extensive porous paving around a tree in a pedestrian precinct, Droitwich, UK.

reduction of surface runoff which contributes to flooding. The detailed construction of the paving is important in this respect and the water entry points between paviours are crucial (Figs 9.15 and 9.16). The provision of pervious coverings and uncompacted soils to maintain infiltration and water supply to tree roots is wholly compatible with the aims of SUDS (Sustainable Urban Drainage Systems). This is discussed further in Chapter 13.

Concrete and asphalt paving is sometimes used under trees, for example where they are retained close to new residential parking areas or driveways. It is not a good idea to depend on the gradual development of porosity in concrete and asphalt through breaks and cracks to provide aeration to the covered tree roots. However, simple aeration systems can be installed. Regularly spaced holes,

Figure 9.17 Perforated bollards as used in streets in the Netherlands. The uninstalled bollard on the left illustrates the perforated length of bollard that is located below ground.

20–50 mm in diameter, can be cut through the paving once it has set. Alternatively, short sections of PVC pipe can be stood on end in a base of gravel before concrete paving is poured. Once the concrete is set, the pipe is cut flush with the surface, filled with gravel and capped with a grate (Matheny and Clark, 1998; Harris *et al*, 1999). An alternative soil/root aeration system employed in the Netherlands incorporates aerators within pavement bollards (Fig 9.17).

A possible drawback with individual tube ventilation systems is that they cannot exploit the 'chimney effect' in which air is drawn through them from another vent. Installations are available which have numerous vertical tubes connected together below ground. In the UK, systems are available commercially (eg the Scott-Heidemy system) which comprise up to 1 m of 30% perforated plastic pipe inserted vertically in the soil, surrounded by a column of baked clay granules and capped by a plastic or concrete top that is also perforated (Fig 9.18). The vertical tubes can be connected together below ground with either flexible or rigid tube (see Fig 9.11). However, Harris *et al* (1999) cautioned that, like those for fill, aeration systems for pavement have not been tested and shown to improve conditions for tree growth. It would be reassuring to be able to cite a substantial body of robust research literature confirming the value of such systems.

9.4.4 Constructing walls and buildings over tree roots

Innovative designs for footings and foundations have been used effectively to suspend walls and buildings over tree root zones. Harris *et al* (1999) cite an example from Maryland where a three-storey residential building was built at a wooded location, with trees preserved within 1.5 m of the structure. This was accomplished by using pilings to construct the foundation and by spanning the distance between pilings with beams suspended above soil level. The potential for injury to roots from this approach depends on the required diameter and spacing of the pilings, as well as on the size and weight of the equipment used for installation. Great care and skill must be used in minimising soil compaction if roots are to be successfully protected.

Discontinuous footings have also been used to bridge root systems in the construction of garden walls. The bricks or other materials are laid on a lintel between piers supported on discrete footings, as illustrated in Fig 9.19. Roots growing between the footings are left undisturbed, provided that the soil is adequately protected during construction (Matheny and Clark, 1998). It is unlikely that the costs of constructing a wall with a lintel bridging roots

Figure 9.18 Aeration pipes (top) and cover plate for aeration below hard surfaces (below).

Figure 9.19 Major roots of a large sycamore tree bridged by a lintel in a section of wall constructed from local stone (Chipping Norton, UK).

will be significantly greater than a conventional wall. The costs of the lintel will be offset by the savings in material and labour costs of not having footings running the full length of the wall.

9.5 Remedial treatment of construction damage to tree roots

The care of trees after completion of a project is an important phase in the process of successfully retaining trees during construction. Consequently, aftercare should be included in plans for tree retention from project initiation onwards. The first step, once building and landscaping are finished, is a reassessment of the condition of retained trees and, if possible, comparison with the preconstruction tree survey (Section 9.3.1). Trees found to have declined in health may then be targeted for remedial treatment. Trees found to be a hazard because of reduced structural stability, as a result of root damage or increased exposure after site clearing, should be removed (Matheny and Clark, 1998).

The goal of remedial treatment of trees after construction is the maintenance of tree health and structural stability. The duration of treatment may have to be several years, as construction impacts can manifest themselves over extended periods. The most common elements of tree maintenance programmes after construction are described below.

9.5.1 Irrigation/drainage

Trees that have suffered root loss may have to survive with access to a reduced soil volume or changes in soil hydrology may have diverted water away from trees. Consequently, trees retained on construction sites may benefit from supplemental irrigation.

9.5.2 Tree pruning

Where dieback of the crown has occurred as a result of injury to roots or for other reasons, dead, dying or diseased branches should be removed. Pruning of the crown was shown by Watson (1998) to increase the speed of recovery from root severance, at least under the experimental conditions imposed (Section 8.3.3.5), although some controversy exists over the efficacy of this practice (Matheny and Clark, 1998).

9.5.3 Fertilisation

Supplemental fertilisation of trees after construction activities have occurred is recommended by Matheny and Clark (1998) where changes to the site have resulted in modification of historical patterns of nutrient cycling, or where root system size or function has been reduced by injury or soil compaction. Harris *et al* (1999) recommended application of 50 kg ha^{-1} of available nitrogen where trees have suffered root injury or changes in the availability of nutrients. Schoeneweiss (1982) contended that surface application of 300 kg ha^{-1} of nitrogen was needed to stimulate weakened trees on development sites. Where phosphorus or potassium fertilisation is warranted, Schoeneweiss (1982) recommended that fertilisers should be injected at depths of 30–60 cm in the tree root zone.

9.5.4 Pest management

Pest management is an important part of post-construction maintenance for trees, because injury to root systems or degradation of the soil environment can cause trees to descend further into the mortality spiral (see Section 8.3.3.4). As a result, trees can be more susceptible to attack by pests and diseases after construction. Thus, plans for tree maintenance should include monitoring for the presence of pests and application of control treatments when required. Treatments used to improve general tree health and condition, such as irrigation, pruning and fertilisation, also serve to enhance resilience to pests and diseases (Schoeneweiss, 1982; Matheny and Clark, 1998).

9.5.5 Alleviation of soil compaction

Soil compaction is common on construction sites, whether intentional or inadvertent (see Section 4.2.3). Where compaction of the root zones of retained trees occurs, efforts should be made to rebuild soil structure and improve soil physical properties. Reference should be made to Section 4.6.5 where the various means of dealing with soil compaction are discussed.

9.6 Summary

- Trees add value to landscapes in both economic and amenity terms. Preservation of trees on construction sites is consequently a highly desirable goal of urban development. A key to successful preservation of trees on construction sites is protection of their roots and the soil environment.

- Construction entails extensive soil workings, including excavation and stripping of topsoil. If undertaken in the root zones of trees, these activities cause severance of roots. Loss of roots may reduce the structural stability of trees, as well as breakdown of the functional equilibrium between roots and shoots. If trees are in a weakened state, restoration of functional equilibrium may not be possible and they may enter terminal decline because of increased susceptibility to additional stresses.

- Soil disturbance on construction sites, because of excavation, cutting, filling or compaction, causes degradation of the soil environment and impaired root growth and function:

  - Soil compaction during construction is necessary for structural stability, but severe compaction is also commonly an unintended impact of activities elsewhere on site. Compaction destroys soil structure, causing impaired infiltration, drainage and aeration, as well as reduced rates of root growth.

  - Lowering of the soil level in the root zone of a tree, by stripping topsoil, results in root severance and the removal of nutrient-rich soil layers.

  - Raising the soil level by the addition of fill creates the problem of poor soil aeration, which impairs root growth and function.

  - Disturbance of soil, modification of the surface by compaction or covering with impervious surfaces causes reduced water availability to trees, because of changes in runoff, infiltration and water holding capacity. Diversion of streams and drainage of the water table can also deprive trees of water.

  - If hard surfaces or crusting channel water towards trees, waterlogging of root systems may result, causing severely reduced aeration. Perched water tables created by restricted drainage during wet periods of the year may cause inundation of root systems. Blockage of drainage pathways by the installation of underground structures can raise the water table and cause waterlogging of root systems.

  - Construction activities can cause chemical contamination of soils. Injudicious use of herbicides, spillage or leakage of fuel and lubricants from tanks and storage drums, and dumping of rubble, plaster and masonry all create conditions harmful to roots.

- Protection of trees on building sites requires careful assessment of the stock of trees available and planning for retention. Assessment should include a survey of the tree species on site, their condition and suitability for retention. Under BS 5837, trees over 75 mm in diameter at 1.5 m above the ground should be assessed for: species and positive contribution; health and condition; size and form; and location relative to landscaping features. On the basis of these criteria, trees should be categorised for their retention and potential contribution to the development and the environment. Plans for retention of trees should include those with high and moderate priority. Attempts to retain too many or inappropriate trees may be not feasible and be counterproductive. If sufficient time is available, preconstruction treatment of trees, including irrigation and fertilisation for example, may increase their tolerance to construction impacts.

- The key action required for preserving trees on construction sites is formation of tree protection zones. A variety of means of determining the size of the protection zone have been suggested, but in the UK, the specification in NJUG 10 (NJUG, 1995) and adopted in the revised BS 5837 (BSI, 2005) is widely recommended. Protection zones must be surrounded by protective fencing sturdy enough to withstand impacts from vehicles and machinery. Within tree protection zones, access and activities must be strictly controlled to prevent injury to roots or soil degradation.

- If conflicts occur between designs for buildings or new landscaping and the needs of tree roots systems, specialised techniques can be used close to trees to minimise the impacts of construction on roots. Arboriculturists should be able to offer a range of possible solutions:

  - Changes in soil level can be made up to the edge of tree protection zones by incorporating retaining walls in designs for landscaping. Alternatives, such as the creation of slopes, may damage more of the root system.

  - If burial of root systems beneath fill cannot be avoided, aeration systems can be constructed around trees. These are designed to facilitate the movement of air, water and nutrients to the root system, although their efficacy in sustaining the viability of root systems and tree health has not been adequately tested.

  - If any surfaces are paved below trees, they should cover as small an area as possible and utilise pervious paving materials. Cutting of the soil and compaction must be avoided. Paving should be constructed using a sand base with geotextile membrane placed over smoothed and hand-tamped soil. Therefore, only paving for footpaths and patios should be installed near tree root systems, with roads routed well away from trees.

  - Walls and buildings have been effectively suspended over root systems by building foundations built on pilings, with beams above soil level. However, great care and skill must be used in minimising soil compaction during installation if this approach is to be used successfully.

- After completion of construction, the condition of retained trees should be reassessed and compared to records from the preconstruction survey. Trees found to be a hazard should be removed. Trees found to have declined should be targeted for remedial treatment. Post-construction care of trees commonly includes irrigation, crown pruning, fertilisation, pest management and alleviation of soil compaction.

REFERENCES

Alberty, C.A., Pellet, H.M. & Taylor, D.H. 1984. Characterization of soil compaction at construction sites and woody plant response. *Journal of Environmental Horticulture*, 2, 48–53.

Aldous, J.R. 2000. (Ed.) *Pesticides, pollutants, fertilizers and trees; their role in forestry and amenity woodlands*. Research Studies Press, Baldock, UK. 588 pp.

Barrell, J.D. 1993. Pre-planning tree surveys: Safe useful life expectancy (SULE) is the natural progression. *Arboricultural Journal*, 17, 33–46.

Berrang, P., Karnosky, D.F. & Stanton, B.J. 1985. Environmental factors affecting tree health in New York City. *Journal of Arboriculture*, 11, 185–189.

Bolund, P. & Hunhammar, S. 1999. Ecosystem services in urban areas. *Ecological Economics*, 29, 293–301.

Brouwer, R. 1983. Functional equilibrium: sense or nonsense? *Netherlands Journal of Agricultural Science*, 31, 335–348.

BSI. 2005. BS 5837: *Trees in relation to construction – Recommendations*. British Standards Institution, London, UK. 32 pp.

Coder, K.D. 1995. Tree quality BMPs for developing wooded areas and protecting residual trees. In: *Trees & Building Sites* (ED. by G.W. Watson & D. Neely), pp. 111–124. International Society of Arboriculture, Champaign, IL., USA.

Crane, B. 1997. Trenching: a cause of root damage. In: *Arboricultural Practice: Present and Future* (Ed. by J. Claridge), pp. 39–44. HMSO, London.

Craul, P.J. 1985. A description of urban soils and their desired characteristics. *Journal of Arboriculture*, 11, 330–331.

Craul, P.J. 1992. *Urban Soil in Landscape Design*. John Wiley & Sons, Inc., New York, NY. 396 pp.

Crook, M.J. & Ennos, A.R. 1996. The anchorage mechanics of deep rooted larch, *Larix europea* x *L. japonica*. *Journal of Experimental Botany*, 47, 1509–1517.

Cutler, D.F. 1993. Interactions between tree roots and construction work. *Arboricultural Journal*, 17, 47–55.

Day, S.D., Seiler, J.R., Kreh, R. & Smith, D.W. 2001. Overlaying compacted or uncompacted construction fill has no negative impact on white oak and sweetgum growth and physiology. *Canadian Journal of Forest Research*, 31, 100–109.

Evans, M., Bassuk, N.L. & Trowbridge, P. 1990. Sidewalk design. *Landscape Architecture* (March), 102–103.

Foil, R.R. & Ralston, C.W. 1967. The establishment and growth of loblolly pine seedlings on compacted soils. *Soil Science Society of America Proceedings*, 31, 565–568.

Franklin, J.F., Shugart, H.H. & Harmon, M.E. 1987. Tree death as an ecological process. *BioScience*, 37, 550–556.

Gale, M.R. & Grigal, D.F. 1987. Vertical root distributions of northern tree species in relation to successional status. *Canadian Journal of Forest Research*, 17, 829–834.

Gilbert, O.L. 1996. Retaining trees on construction sites. *Arboricultural Journal*, 20, 39–45.

Gilman, E.F. 1990. Tree root growth and development. I. Form, spread, depth and periodicity. *Journal of Environmental Horticulture*, 8, 215–220.

Hamilton, W.D. 1989. Significance of root severance on performance of established trees. *Arboricultural Journal*, 13, 249–257.

Harris, R.W., Clark, J.R. & Matheny, N.P. 1999. *Arboriculture: Integrated Management of Landscape Trees, Shrubs and Vines*. Prentice Hall, Upper Saddle River, New Jersey. 687 pp.

Hartman, J.R., Pirone, T.P. & Sall, M.A. 2000. *Pirone's Tree Maintenance*, 7th Edition. Oxford University Press, New York. 545 pp.

Kozlowski, T.T. 1999. Soil compaction and growth of woody plants. *Scandinavian Journal of Forest Research*, 14, 596–619.

Lees, A.S. 2000. *Soil/Structure Interaction of Temporary Roadways*, unpublished PhD thesis. Department of Civil and Environmental Engineering, University of Southampton, UK. 226pp.

Manion, P.D. 1991. *Tree Disease Concepts*. Prentice Hall, Englewood Cliffs, New Jersey. 416 pp.

Matheny, N.P. & Clark, J.R. 1998. *Trees and Development*. International Society of Arboriculture, Champaign, IL., USA. 183 pp.

McPherson, E.G. & Rowntree, R.A. 1993. Energy conservation potential of urban tree planting. *Journal of Arboriculture*, 19, 321–331.

NCE. 2001. New kids on the block. *New Civil Engineer*, 29 March 2001.

Nicholson, R. 2001. APN1, BS: 5837 and PPG3 – Guidance for trees: Conflict or complement? *Arboricultural Journal*, 25, 361-376.

NUFU. 2005. *Trees matter! Bringing lasting benefits to people in towns*. National Urban Forestry Unit, Wolverhampton, UK. 22 pp.

O'Sullivan, M.F. & Ritchie, R.M. 1993. Tree stability in relation to cyclic loading. *Forestry*, 66, 69–82.

Patch, D. 1998. *Trees, shelter and energy conservation*. Arboriculture Research and Information Note 145. Arboricultural Advisory and Information Service, Farnham, UK. 10 pp.

Patch, D. & Dobson, M. 1999. *Driveways close to trees*. Arboricultural Practice Note, APN 1. Arboricultural Advisory and Information Service, Farnham, UK. 10 pp.

Pollock, M. & Griffiths, M. 1998. *Shorter Dictionary of Gardening*. The Royal Horticultural Society. Macmillan, London, UK. 836 pp.

Randrup, T.B. & Dralle, K. 1997. Influence of planning and design on soil compaction in construction sites. *Landscape and Urban Planning* 38, 87–92.

Round, L. & Lawson, M. 1999. *Amenity Trees & Insurance Issues – The Local Authority Perspective*. Sustainability of Resources Programme (SORP), International Society of Arboriculture UK/I Chapter, 119 pp.

Ryan, M.G., Binkley, D. & Fownes, J.H. 1997. Age-related decline in forest productivity: pattern and process. *Advances in Ecological Research*, 27, 213–262.

Schoeneweiss, D.F. 1982. Prevention and treatment of construction damage to shade trees. *Journal of Arboriculture*, 8, 169–175.

Schroth, G. 1995. Tree root characteristics as criteria for species selection and systems design in agroforestry. *Agroforestry Systems*, 30, 125–143.

Smith, K., Ham, D., Miller, A. & Chesnut, T. 1995. Soil aeration systems: do they work? In: *Trees & Building Sites* (Ed. by G.W. Watson and D. Neely), pp. 17–21. International Society of Arboriculture, Champaign, IL., USA.

Taylor, H.M. & Gardner, W.R. 1963. Penetration of cotton seedling taproots as influenced by bulk density, moisture content, and strength of soil. *Soil Science*, 96, 153–156.

Unger, P.W. & Kaspar, T.C. 1994. Soil compaction and root growth: a review. *Agronomy Journal*, 86, 759–766.

Wargo, P.M. 1979. Starch storage and radial growth in woody tissues of sugar maple. *Canadian Journal of Forest Research*, 9, 49–56.

Wargo, P.M. 1983. Effects and consequences of stress on root physiology. *Journal of Arboriculture*, 9, 173–176.

Waring, R.H. 1987. Characteristics of trees predisposed to die. *BioScience*, 37, 569–574.

Watson, G.W. 1998. Tree growth after trenching and compensatory crown pruning. *Journal of Arboriculture*, 24, 47–53.

Yelenosky, G. 1963. Soil aeration and tree growth. *International Shade Tree Conference*, 39, 16–25.

Yoder, B.J., Ryan, M.G., Waring, R.H., Schoettle, A.W. & Kaufmann, M.R. 1994. Evidence of reduced photosynthetic rates in old trees. *Forest Science*, 40, 513–527.

CHAPTER 10
Tree Root Damage to Buildings

10.1 Introduction

Trees can damage buildings and other forms of infrastructure both directly and indirectly. Direct action includes damage as a result of the pressures exerted by radial growth of roots, and most often occurs close to the tree from the growth of the main trunk and roots, and diminishes rapidly with distance (MacLeod and Cram, 1996; Biddle, 1998a). Both longitudinal and radial pressures exerted by root growth are comparatively weak (see Chapter 3), and therefore roots will tend to distort around a significant obstruction rather than displace it. Soil conditions common to the built environment, including soil compaction, will further reduce root growth pressure. Large roots can exert great enough pressures to damage pavements or low walls. This type of direct damage can be extended to cover instances where the trunk lifts or distorts structures or services, or occasionally when the tree or branches fall. This topic is covered in Chapter 11.

Indirect action means, in particular, the problems associated with shrinking and swelling subsoils (BRE, 1999). Over the last 25 years concern over subsidence risk on the part of householders and insurers alike, has lead to increased anxiety about trees in close proximity to building structures (Biddle, 1998b). This in turn has lead to substantial pruning or even removal of many trees in areas prone to subsidence. Much of the recent housing in the UK is built on shallow concrete strip foundations (Lawson and O'Callaghan, 1995). In contrast, much housing in North America, where ground frosts are common, incorporates a basement that reduces the likelihood of subsidence damage. Timber-framed construction is also more common in the USA and is more able to cope with ground movement due to its flexibility. Whereas indirect, subsidence-related damage is generally restricted to expansive clay soils, direct damage due to root growth pressures can occur in any soil type.

10.2 History of the problem

Up to around 1970, subsidence and settlement were terms often used interchangeably (Pryke, 1993), with the former generally used to refer to the very large, and often rapid surface movements resulting from mining activity. The latter term covered the slower and less catastrophic field of downward movement of foundations. Structural failure of buildings is not a recent phenomenon. Pryke (1979) mentions discussions with a homeowner who

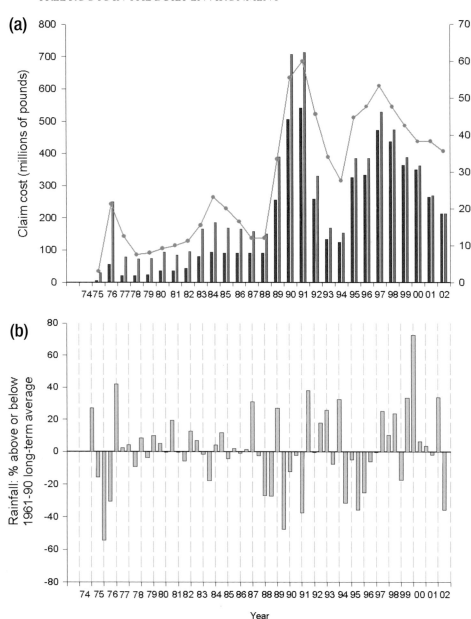

Figure 10.1 (a) Annual value of domestic insurance claims for subsidence and heave damage to housing in the UK (■) with figures adjusted for inflation shown (■) separately. The number of claims is indicated by the line (— ● —). **(b)** Seasonal variation in winter and summer rainfall in the Thames valley is shown for purposes of comparison. (After ISE March (1994); ABI Yearbooks (1988–1998); DETR housing statistics; CEH Hydrological yearbooks and personal communication with ABI.)

recalled foundation damage in Essex occurring in 1921, with buildings requiring bracing support for up to two years. There have been several periods during the latter half of the 20th century when subsidence problems have come to the fore, especially during and after stretches of prolonged dry weather. In 1947, when repair to war damaged London was in full swing, an extremely dry summer lead to difficulties in distinguishing foundation failures due to bomb damage from failures from other causes such as subsidence (Ward, 1948).

Following wetter weather in the 1950s, the dry summer in 1959 lead to a sharp rise in structural failures (Pryke, 1979). The 1960s again showed average rainfall, but following the drought of 1975/76, there was another large increase in reports of subsidence (Radevsky, 2000). Fig 10.1 provides a comparison of the annual cost of subsidence claims against above- and below-average seasonal rainfall. Inflation over the period masks the large increase in claim cost in 1975/76, and the silhouetted figures have been adjusted to take account of inflation, in this case by using the retail price index (RPI) over the period (Twigger, 1999). In 1989/90 another extremely hot summer was followed by an excessively dry winter and subsidence problems escalated again (Shabha and Kuhwald, 1995). Insurance claims for structural damage rose again from the middle to the late 1990s but in the last four years, in association with a sequence of wet years, claims have fallen.

The reason for the substantial amounts of money paid out annually was the decision in 1971 by the insurance companies to extend household cover to include subsidence (Biddle, 1979). As the number of claims rose sharply after the 1975/76 drought, the insurance companies discontinued offers of cheap subsidence cover (Lawson and O'Callaghan, 1995). In the last couple of years subsidence claims have decreased slightly, with the number of claims down by 8% in 1998 over 1997, and the total cost falling by 5% (ABI, 1999). However, subsidence costs in 1998 were still significantly higher than those at the lowest point in the 1990s.

10.3 Nature of the problem

10.3.1 Expansive clay soils

As insurance claims have mounted, so has the attention diverted towards the interaction between man-made structures and the soils upon which they are built. Clay soils are those in which clay particles predominate. These particles are small with diameters less than 2 μm (0.002 mm) in diameter (see Box 10.1). Firm, shrinkable clay soils occur throughout the UK, but predominate in the south-east of England (Fig 10.2), an area south-east of a line drawn between Exeter and Hull (NHBC, 2003). They are produced by organic and chemical weathering, they have complex chemistries, and are highly variable in their abilities to absorb and retain water (Round and Lawson, 1999). These soils are generally considered capable of supporting low-rise buildings (Atkins *et al* 1994)

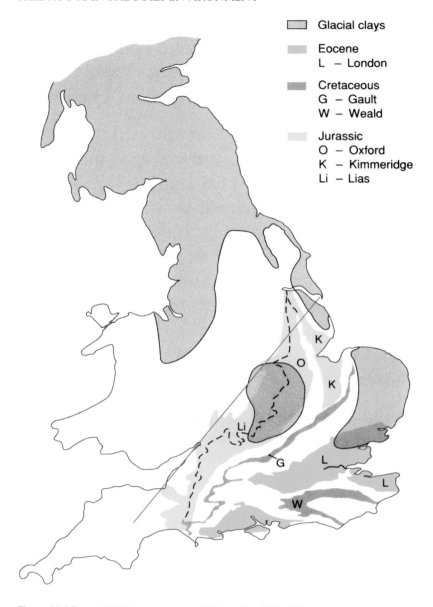

Figure 10.2 Firm shrinkable clay deposits in Britain. (After BRE, 1993.)

of up to four stories on fairly shallow foundations. Some shrinkable clays occur further north, eg around Sunderland, and north of Shrewsbury, but these soils generally have a higher sand fraction and lower shrinkage potential (BRE, 1993). The presence of silt, sand, and other non-clay materials are effectively dilutants that reduce the clay-mineral content per unit soil volume and therefore reduce swelling potential (Komornik and David, 1969). The term clay is variously used in soil physics and mechanics (Box 10.1).

Box10.1 Clay

In engineering, the word *clay* can have three distinct meanings and it is sometimes used ambiguously. It is important to be clear about which use is intended.

- The most common use of the term *clay* is to describe a soil that contains enough clay-sized material or clay minerals to exhibit cohesive properties. The fraction of clay-sized material required varies, but can be as low as 15%.

- The term can be used to denote the *clay minerals*. These are specific, naturally occurring chemical compounds, predominately silicates.

- The term is often used as a particle size descriptor. Soil particles which have a nominal diameter of less than 2 μm are normally considered to be of clay size, but they are not neccessarily clay minerals. Some clay minerals are larger than 2 μm and some particles, 'rock flour' for example, can be finer than 2 μm but are not clay minerals.

Source: *BRE Digest 240* (1993).

Silicate clay minerals are the dominant inorganic colloidal particles found in most soils (Brady and Weil, 1999). The inherent swelling potential of aggregates of clay minerals is closely related to the total external and internal surface areas of clay mineral particles. Clay minerals are capable of adsorbing water on their outer surfaces, and this water will cause a small amount of swelling related to enlargement of the capillary films. Each clay particle is formed from a series of layers, rather like the pages of a book, and some types of clays, particularly smectites (eg montmorillonite), can also absorb appreciable amounts of water between these layers of the clay lattice. It is this adsorption of water that results in a high swelling potential. On a microscopic scale, water molecules are attracted into the spaces between the clay layers. This movement of water forces the layers apart, causing the mass of soil to swell in volume. The reverse of these processes occurs when the soil dries and water is withdrawn from between the clay layers, causing shrinkage and cracking. Expansive soils are rich in these types of clay, such as smectites. Large changes in volume were reported from laboratory tests on rehydrated montmorillonite clays (Mielenz and King, 1955). However, it should be noted that the volume changes observed in swelling clays under laboratory conditions are usually considerably greater than those generated by the same clay in the field under natural conditions.

Fig 10.3 shows the volume changes of a clay soil with changes in water content. Dry swelling clays absorb much larger quantities of water before becoming plastic than do dry, non-swelling clays, and as they wet up, demonstrate distinct changes in behaviour and consistency. Hard and rigid when dry, they

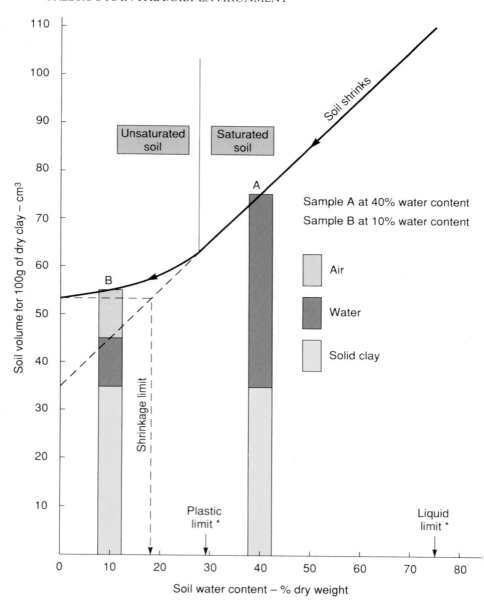

Figure 10.3 Clay soil shrinkage. *Typical values for clay with high volume change potential. (After BRE, 1993.)

become crumbly after a certain amount of water is added (defined as the *shrinkage limit*). They also remain plastic over a wider range of moisture contents.

The liquid limit is the moisture content (%) at which a clay loses its plastic properties and begins to behave more like a liquid. The greater the liquid limit the more 'clayey' the soil (BRE, 1993). The **plastic limit** is the moisture content (%) at which the soil can no longer be moulded without it breaking apart. The range in moisture content between these two limits is referred to by engineers as the **plasticity index** (PI) and is expressed as the numerical difference between the liquid limit and the plastic limit.

The plasticity index depends on both the amount and type of clay minerals present in the soil, and on the orientation and size of these clay particles. In general, the PI *increases* with:

- an increase in the amount of expandable clay minerals
- a decrease in the degree to which the clay minerals are aligned
- a decrease in the size of the clay particles.

Plasticity indices range from as low as 1 for some kaolinites to higher than 600 in some montmorillonites (Grim, 1962), and are generally thought to be good indicators of swelling potential. Sowers and Kennedy (1967) found the PI to be '*the most reliable working tool*' in identifying potentially troublesome clays in the humid coastal plains of the south-eastern United States. Soils with a high plasticity index (more than 25%) are generally expansive clays that make for poorer foundations (Brady & Weil, 1999). Typically, Oxford clays have a plasticity index of around 44% and London clays values of between 46 to 63%, corresponding to a high to very high volume change potential (BRE, 1993; NHBC, 1999).

Time is an important factor affecting the change in volume occurring in response to localised changes in the environment and moisture status of a clay. Expansive clays have low permeabilities to water. When they are wetted, and the clay mineral fraction expands, this further reduces the permeability. Due to the slow rate of water movement through expansive clay soils, it may take several years for soil moisture levels to reach an equilibrium beneath paved or built-on areas (Means, 1959; Blight, 1965). The length of time required will depend on the soil type itself (Carothers, 1965), including soil structure and gross features such as bands of sand *etc*. In addition, the local climatic variation and the initial soil moisture status during construction will also play a part.

10.3.2 Techniques for assessing the desiccation of clay soils

Desiccation can be defined as the drying of the soil resulting from an increase in suction (or decrease in pore water pressure) over the normal, 'equilibrium' values (BRE, 1996). When investigating soil subsidence claims on a clay site it is often useful to know by how much, if at all, the soil has desiccated. An accurate estimate of the lateral and vertical extent of any such desiccation may give an indication, for example, of the potential for heave if the source of desiccation (eg a large nearby tree) is removed.

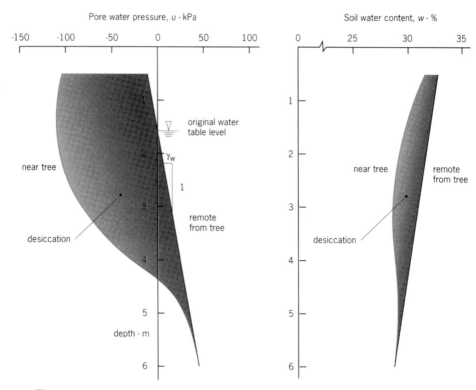

Figure 10.4 Profiles near and remote from trees at the end of summer in a high volume change potential clay soil. (After BRE, 1996.)

In the UK, comparing depth profiles of soil water content is one method used to identify desiccation. However, there are several intrinsic problems associated with this technique (Chandler et al, 1992). In general, differences in soil profile water content between desiccated and non-desiccated situations are not very large, in comparison with parameters such as the **soil suction** (or soil water potential). Fig 10.4 shows this for a typical example of soil profiles in a clay soil with high expansive potential. It is often difficult, especially in confined garden situations, to find a suitable location far enough away from the cause of suspected desiccation to drill a 'control' borehole for comparison (BRE, 1996).

While it is assumed that the soil will achieve an 'equilibrated' moisture profile at some point during the spring, there is no means of accurately determining what this is from measurements of water content alone. Finally, clay soils can exhibit hysteresis (a 'lagging behind') in the relationship between soil suction and water content. This may have the effect of two samples with the same soil suction having different water contents, depending on whether the soil is in the process of wetting-up or drying.

The comparison of suction in soil samples provides an alternative measure of desiccation, and a simple method is described in some detail in Chandler and

Gutierrez (1986). In short, a piece of filter paper is placed in co____il
sample, which is then wrapped to prevent evaporation, ____o
equilibrate, ie a certain amount of water moves out of the sc____e
paper, and can be measured. This amount is directly related to t____.
Case studies where this technique has been widely used ar____y
Chandler *et al* (1992), and by Plante (1998).

10.3.3 The effect of vegetation

Changes in soil moisture brought about by the demands of adjacent vegetation can lead to volume changes in the soil which, in turn, can lead to structural damage. This problem is not restricted to the UK, with reports of similar foundation damage on expansive clay soils common in Africa, Australia, Burma, China, India and in parts of Canada and the United States (Legget and Crawford, 1965; Radevsky, 2000). The recently revised BRE Digest 298 (BRE, 1999) distinguishes four types of ground or formation movement associated with interactions between vegetation and underlying clay soils:

- *normal seasonal movements*, associated with evaporation and transpiration from, say, a grass-covered area of ground

- *enhanced seasonal movements*, associated with increased transpiration following introduction of trees

- *long-term subsidence*, as a persistent water deficit develops

- *long-term heave*, as a persistent water deficit dissipates.

The interaction between the tree and the soil involves water, and it is the constant movement of water within the system that comprises the water balance. Water enters the system as rainfall (Fig 10.5) and is lost from the system through a manner of processes:

- rainfall intercepted by and re-evaporated from the tree crown

- evaporation of water from the soil surface

- water transpired by the growing vegetation (trees and other underlying vegetation)

- vertical drainage and/or lateral runoff of excess soil water

As Biddle (1998b) noted, the introduction of a building (and accompanying paved areas) will act to influence the water balance by limiting the amount of water able to enter the soil directly beneath, by excluding vegetation and by preventing soil evaporation. However, under current climatic conditions in the UK, these effects are minor in comparison with the effects of trees and other vegetation on the water balance. In comparison with the largely static effects that an introduced building or paved area would have on the water balance, a tree is a highly dynamic 'structure'.

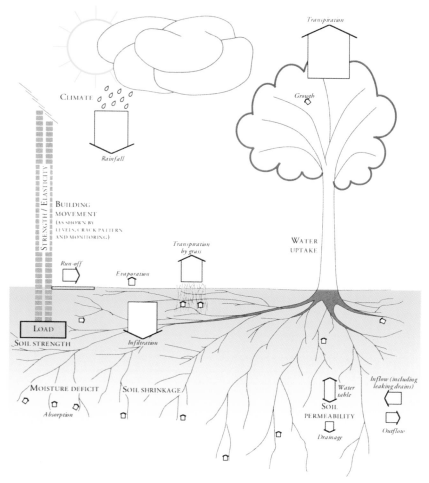

Figure 10.5 The water balance in the tree-soil-building system, and factors determining tree root damage to buildings. (After Biddle, 1998a.)

It is possible to make reasonable estimates of what the water use of large trees is (Box 10.2) but there is really a need for a robust set of actual measurements. In the late spring and throughout the summer months, when the tree crown is at maximum expansion, transpired water losses can be enormous; a single large tree can transpire the equivalent of 380 litres of water on a sunny day (Perpich *et al*, 1965). At the same time, interception losses from the large crown can be significant, especially during light showers. In many species crown interception does not simply reduce the amount of rainfall reaching the ground below the tree, but significantly redistributes it via stemflow and crown drip (Prebble and Stirk, 1980). In some cases, rainfall input by the base of the tree is similar to, and can sometimes exceed, rainfall input to the soil out in the open as the tree 'funnels' water to the soil around its roots (Jackson and Wallace, 1999). The presence of the tree roots can lead to increased infiltration rates as reported by Zinke (1961) and Eschner (1967). Compaction of the soil around the bases of trees can substantially reduce infiltration, however.

Box 10.2 Water use by large amenity trees

Rainfall and evaporation, including different forms of evaporation from trees, transpiration and rainfall interception loss are normally expressed as a depth of water (mm).

There are abundant statistics for rainfall for most of the British Isles. There is a large range in annual rainfall from west to east across the country. One of the wettest towns in the British Isles is Fort William in western Scotland. Average annual rainfall there is 2010 mm. At 540 mm, the average rainfall in Felixstowe in the east of the British Isles is only a little more than a quarter of the rainfall at Fort William (Eden, 1995).

Because on average places like Fort William have more cloud, low solar radiation, lower temperatures and higher humidity, potential evaporation will also be lower than at places with greater duration of sunshine, such as Felixstowe. Penman's potential evaporation (Section 6.2.2) is used to estimate the evaporation from well watered short grass. This concept can provide estimates for individual days. It would not be exceptional for an estimate of potential evaporation for short, well watered grass to reach 5–6 mm day^{-1} on a bright, warm day in southern England. One millimetre lost (gained by the plant/soil system) from 1 m^2 of ground will be a loss (gain) of 1 l or 1 kg of water. Therefore the potential evaporation loss (5 mm day^{-1}) will mean that from 1 ha (10,000 m^2) of well watered pasture the total water lost would be expected to be 50,000 l. In contrast to the large amount of data on rainfall, direct measurements of evaporation from different types of vegetation are few and far between. There are techniques available to measure evaporation directly hour by hour and daily loss rates of 5–6 mm from grassland without water stress on hot summer days have been observed, confirming potential evaporation estimates made using the Penman Equation.

There are far fewer studies in which forest evaporation has been measured directly. Maximum daily transpiration rates are usually somewhat less than those from well watered grass but can still reach 4.5–5.0 mm day^{-1}. Transpiration of these rates has typically been measured over managed forests, with around 800 trees ha^{-1}. This means that on average if transpiration from a hectare is 45,000 to 50,000 l (4.5–5.0 mm day^{-1}) then between 56 and 62 l will be transpired by each tree per day. The same transpiration rates for a more mature forest, with perhaps far fewer trees per hectare, 100, for example, the loss rate per tree will be as much as 500 l per day.

This last example suggests that daily water use by large individual trees in parks or streets will be very substantial. However, there are a number of circumstances that are likely to mean that water use of an isolated large tree in a park or street is greater than that of a similar tree (species and age) growing in a forest. A particular reason for this is because isolated trees are likely to have a greater crown depth, the canopy sometimes extending almost to ground level. In an open situation, at least all the foliage on the outside of the crown will be well exposed to sunlight and be well ventilated by the wind. Research in forests has shown greater soil drying occurs at the edges of the forest. This situation arises because both transpiration and interception loss are greater at forest edges than inside the forest. There is foliage down to ground level in edge trees and the edge experiences more total solar radiation and is better ventilated by the wind than foliage at the base of the canopy of trees within the forest. Isolated amenity trees could be conceived as trees having edge-tree characteristics around the complete crown. In addition, for the amenity tree there may be additional factors that will enhance evaporation. These factors are the direction of additional radiation onto the tree's canopy from the surfaces of buildings and pavements and the higher temperatures and lower humidity occurring in built areas.

Although it is useful to speculate about the water use of individual trees, there is no substitute for robust measurements. Unfortunately we still lack a body of data about water use of large specimens of the tree species used most commonly in urban plantings and how water use varies with both weather conditions and surroundings. With such information we can plan adequate provision of soil volumes (and therefore water supply) for large trees and realise more clearly the need for effective water recharge below urban surfaces to the root zones of trees. Knowledge of the water use of large trees and the controlling factors also enables a better assessment of the risks to buildings and structures built on shrinking clay soils from water use by trees.

Several studies have shown that stemflow is proportionately greater in younger, smaller tress than in mature, taller individuals. This is due to a number of factors, especially the 'funnel' shape of young canopies, in contrast to older canopies, where the tree crown tends to comprise a greater number of longer, heavier branches that are not angled upwards (Fig 10.6). As the fraction of the crown angled closer to the vertical decreases, the proportion of rainfall diverted to stemflow is reduced, and the patterns of soil water content surrounding the tree will be altered. Hutchinson and Roberts (1981) found that for a Douglas fir 9 m tall, 69% of the stemflow came from the top 50% of the crown, and they attributed this difference to the more vertically oriented branching geometry in this part of the crown. Differences such as these will obviously be of interest to those choosing trees of particular 'shapes' for city landscaping. Trees chosen for predominantly columnar 'form', eg where available space for trees is restricted, will most likely exhibit greater stemflow than would more spherical canopies.

In addition to interception, some rainfall will run off and some will be used by surrounding vegetation. Balanced against this, the tree crown will reduce soil evaporation around it, as the leaves shade the soil surface. It happens to be the case that the parts of the UK where evaporation usually exceeds rainfall for the part of the year that trees are most active, ie from late spring to early autumn, also happen to be areas where expansive clays soils are prevalent (CEH, 2000). During this period of high evaporative demand, the water requirements of large trees exceed the net inputs from rainfall after interception and soil evaporation, with the result that a soil moisture deficit develops during the summer (Fig 10.7). This is defined as the amount of water that would be required to return the soil to field capacity and freely draining.

From late autumn onwards, deciduous trees shed their leaves and the water balance shifts significantly. At this point transpiration has ceased, and movement of water into the tree

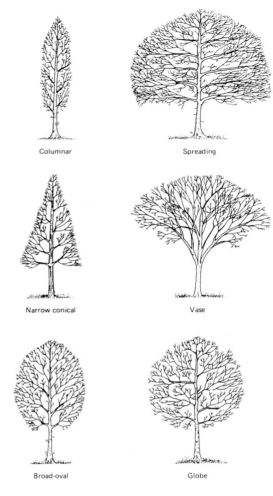

Figure 10.6 Typical amenity tree crown shapes that will result in different patterns of rainfall interception and redistribution. (After NJFSTC, 2000.)

via the roots is effectively nil. With no leaf crown to speak of, it would be expected that interception rates would be drastically reduced, with only the trunk and branches offering any obstruction to rainfall. However, the expected winter reduction in interception loss due to leaf fall from deciduous broadleaved species has on occasions been found to be surprisingly small (Reynolds and Henderson, 1967; Hall and Roberts, 1990). Evergreen trees, whose canopies will continue to intercept rainfall during the winter, will have higher interception loss than deciduous trees. Interception loss is greater from needle-leaved trees than from broadleaved trees (Zinke, 1967). In one study over the length of a year, beech was shown to intercept 93 mm of precipitation, whereas spruce intercepted 314 mm over the same period (Eidmann, 1959). Conifers, in particular, will also maintain modest transpiration rates for part of this period, especially during mild weather.

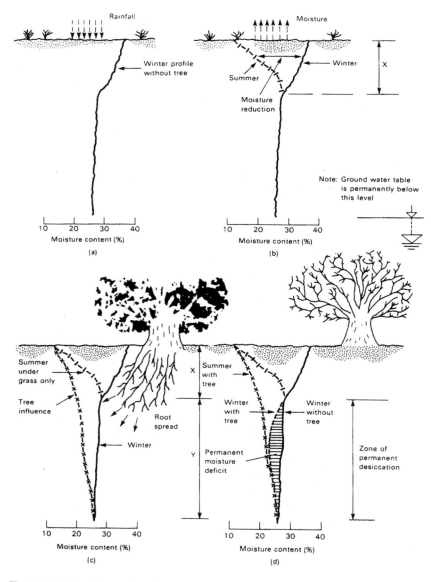

Figure 10.7 Soil moisture content changes: **(a)** winter; **(b)** summer; **(c)** tree influence (summer); **(d)** tree influence (winter). (After Boden and Driscoll, 1987.)

As the days shorten, sunshine becomes weaker and overcast days are more frequent, soil evaporation rates, and transpiration from understorey vegetation (eg grasses) also decline. During this period, rainfall inputs to the soil significantly exceed losses from the system and under normal conditions the soil recovers completely from the moisture deficit that had built up during the summer.

332

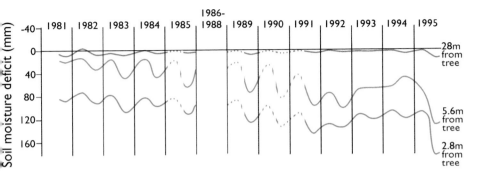

Figure 10.8 Seasonal fluctuations in moisture deficit at 1 m below the soil surface measured at three distances from a 14–15 m tall horse chestnut (*Aesculus hippocastanum*) growing in London clay. (After Biddle, 1998a.)

In some exceptional circumstances, it is impossible for a soil that has dehydrated over the summer months to recover to normal moisture content over a single winter (Fig 10.8), and there is still a measurable soil moisture deficit by the time the next drying cycle begins in the spring. Reasons for this include below average winter rainfall (see Fig 10.1), and the permeability of the clay, which limits the amount of water entering the soil during the winter months, although even low-permeability soils will show seasonal patterns of desiccation and recovery. A deficit of this sort is referred to as a **persistent moisture deficit** (Biddle, 1998b), and may occur gradually over a period of a few years where seasonal recovery is less than the drying, particularly while the tree is growing rapidly before reaching maturity. For a persistent deficit to develop, it is also necessary for the tree to cause soil drying to a deep enough extent that complete recovery cannot occur over a single winter.

Biddle (1998b) states that once a persistent deficit has developed, it can often be maintained for many decades during which the tree is at maturity, but once it becomes 'overmature' and its water uptake starts to reduce, the persistent deficit can gradually diminish. If the tree is removed or its water uptake is reduced in some way, the soil will rehydrate and swell, and can lead to heave of foundations. The time it takes for the soil to recover, in the same way as the time taken for a moisture deficit to develop, depends on both how permeable the clay is, and the extent and intensity of soil drying.

10.3.4 Water demand of trees

When trees are implicated in cases of subsidence damage, it is often on the basis of their requirements for water. This requirement is often referred to as the tree water demand in various publications drawn up for arboriculturists, insurers, building contractors etc, although an explicit definition of the term has seldom been provided. Biddle (1998b) notes that the term was originally used for the NHBC Practice Note 3 (1986) which was a precursor to their Chapter 4.2 guidance.

Lawson and O'Callaghan (1995) suggested the following definition for tree water demand: '*The amount of water required by a tree in order to keep its metabolism functioning at optimum levels to meet its physiological requirements*'. However, when trying to provide a physiological basis for tree water demand, it must be noted in comparison with the overall amount of water taken up by a tree, the percentage that is used for metabolic processes is tiny.

In the context of subsidence on expansive clay, Biddle (1998b) has suggested that it should be defined as '*the ability of vegetation to cause drying of a clay subsoil*'. This takes account of several factors that affect soil drying, including the relative ability of roots of different tree species to exploit such soils, but '*should not be taken as indicating any specific physiological distinction between species.*' However, the potential exists for the same tree to cause different rates of subsoil drying in different environments, eg on shaded or exposed sides of a building, and hence different water demands using this latter definition.

10.3.5 Relative water demand by different tree species

Advice to the construction industry from arborists often relies heavily on the ranking of relative tree water demand given in the NHBC Chapter 4.2 'Building near trees'. The table summarising this information is reproduced here, in part (Table 10.1), and illustrates the distinction made in terms of high, moderate and low water demand. Trees were assigned to a particular class partly on the basis of research, but more on NHBC experience and identified cases of tree-related damage up to 1985 (Biddle, 1985). The majority of species fall into the 'moderate' water demand category; with only a few trees (beech, birch, holly etc) recognised as posing significantly lower risk than others.

NHBC Chapter 4.2 does not rank the water demand of individual species within the low, moderate or high categories. However, several other researchers have attempted to do this, and Table 10.2 illustrates the similarities and differences noted by various observers. In particular, the low rank of oak and high ranking of alder in Ward's (1947) classification is inconsistent with other surveys. Ash and plane came bottom of the ranking of McCombie (1993b), and higher up the ranking from Biddle (1998b). Biddle also noted that some *Sorbus* species, eg Whitebeam, may often be grafted onto aggressive hawthorn rootstock, and cited personal experience of this combination producing severe soil drying.

The ranking by Biddle (1998b), only part of which is included in Table 10.2 is based on personal experience, and is a revision of his earlier ranking (Biddle, 1979) in the light of further soil moisture measurements around trees. He has produced a classification of six groups of broadleaved species (and six other coniferous species) ranked from highest to lowest water demand. McCombie's ranking used previously unpublished data on tree height from the Kew root survey (Cutler and Richardson, 1989, and Cutler, 1993 in McCombie, 1993b), based on the premise that the tallest trees will have the greatest lateral spread of roots and, most likely, the highest water demand. Comparisons between species were achieved by weighting the heights of trees involved in cases of damage, by the maximum reported heights for that species. Much of the available data on water demand of trees in the scientific literature comes from forestry research. Rutter (1968) reviewed studies covering more than 40 tree species including pine, spruce, oak and poplar and found that there was generally little difference in water demand.

The recently revised BRE Digest 298 (BRE, 1999) cites research experience that water abstraction by oak trees can be significantly greater than that by other species, concurring with anecdotal evidence provided by a number of local authority tree officers in the UK (pers. comm.). However, Table 10.3 shows that there is little difference between oak and beech transpiration rates in closed forestry stands of various ages. This difference between forest and urban response suggests that, when grown in the open, oak seems to have a greater capacity to exploit resources made available to it, than does beech. The resources in question may lie in the soil or in the radiation reaching the tree crown.

Lawson and O'Callaghan (1995) have suggested that the differences in water demand in such species under urban conditions might be related to differential urban fitness, reflecting a variable ability to tolerate poor soils, low water availability and poor air and still remain able to perform at optimum capacity. This could be further expanded to deal with other differences in the urban environment such as soil compaction, soil pollution, and altered microclimate. Urban fitness may reflect tolerance that relates to above-ground or below-ground physiology, or most likely a combination of both. Lawson and O'Callaghan (1995) proposed that tree species in the built environment could best be classified according to their rooting habit, as opposed to their water demand. Under their definition, oak falls under the heading of 'deep rooted species', as it is apparently able to take advantage of more hospitable rooting conditions following fissuring of a clay soil (when soil moisture and oxygen at depth levels are temporarily higher). It is suggested that intermediate rooting trees (such as lime), and shallow rooting trees (such as beech) are increasingly limited in their potential to exploit fissuring in clay soils. Many more data on the rooting patterns of tree species in urban soils are needed in order to substantiate this hypothesis, as other factors are undoubtedly at work when forest tree species are grown in isolated conditions.

In almost all tree species grown under forest conditions, observable vertical gradients exist in terms of leaf physiological capacity and water use, due largely to reduced light levels lower in the forest. It may be that this vertical stratification in crown response, ie the ability of different parts of the crown to adapt to deal with higher light levels, is, to a greater or lesser extent, genetically determined. If so, it may be that in species such as oak, the crown response is more versatile, and the tree is therefore able to make the most of higher light levels when grown as an individual tree. In other species, such as beech, the tree might exhibit a more rigid response and be unable to utilise this increased illumination. A simple experiment comparing transpiration profiles vertically

Table 10.1 The relative water demands and mature heights of trees. Broad leaved orchard species present in the original NHBC table have been omitted for clarity in this instance. (Source: NHBC, 2003.)

| | BROAD LEAVED TREES | | | CONIFERS | |
Water demand	Species	Mature height (m)	Water demand	Species	Mature height (m)
High	*Elm:*		High	*Cypress:*	
	English	24		Lawson's	18
	Wheatley	22		Leyland	20
	Wych	18		Monterey	20
	Eucalyptus	18			
	Hawthorn	10			
	Oak:				
	English	20			
	Holm	16			
	Red	24			
	Turkey	24			
	Poplar:				
	Hybrid black	28			
	Lombardy	25			
	White	15			
	Willow:				
	Crack	24			
	Weeping	16			
	White	24			
Moderate	Acacia (False)	18	Moderate	Cedar	20
	Alder	18		Douglas fir	20
	Apple	10		Larch	20
	Ash	23		Monkey Puzzle	18
	Bay laurel	10		Pine	20
	Blackthorn	8		Spruce	18
	Beech	20		Wellingtonia	30
	Cherry:			Yew	12
	Japanese	9			
	Laurel	8			
	Orchard	12			
	Wild	17			
	Chestnut:				
	Horse	20			
	Sweet	24			

BROAD LEAVED TREES			CONIFERS		
Water demand	Species	Mature height (m)	Water demand	Species	Mature height (m)
	Lime	22			
	Maple:				
	Japanese	8			
	Norway	18			
	Mountain ash	11			
	Pear	12			
	Plane	26			
	Plum	10			
	Sycamore	22			
	Tree of heaven	20			
	Walnut	18			
	Whitebeam	12			
Low	Birch	14			
	Elder	10			
	Fig	8			
	Hazel	8			
	Holly	12			
	Honey locust	14			
	Hornbeam	17			
	Laburnum	12			
	Magnolia	9			
	Mulberry	9			
	Tulip tree	20			

Notes:

1. Where hedgerows contain trees, their effects should be assessed separately. In hedgerows, the height of the species likely to have the greatest effect should be used.

2. Within the classes of water demand, species are listed alphabetically; the order does not signify any gradation in water demand.

3. When the precise species is unknown the greatest height and highest water demand should be assumed.

4. Further information regarding trees may be obtained from the Arboricultural Association or the Arboricultural Advisory and Information Service (see appendix 4.2-G).

downwards through isolated canopies from various species with values for similar age classes from forestry situations would substantiate this. Having established to what degree, if any, water demand is related to differences in crown response, the need for the urban rooting studies mentioned previously, can be reassessed.

Any differences in upper and lower crown water use would have implications for crown pruning as a strategy to reduce whole tree water demand. If significant differences between species do exist, then removal of the lowest, most accessible, parts of the crown might have significantly greater effects in some species than in others. It is likely that more data linking pruning with tree water demand will result from a project led by Horticulture Research International (HRI) that is currently underway. The project, *Controlling tree water use and subsidence risk*, aims to improve the understanding of water use by large isolated amenity trees, and to determine the value of both crown thinning and reduction techniques in reducing tree water demand. Studies are being made on wild cherry and London plane at East Malling in Kent.

Table 10.2 Comparison of ranking order of water demand of different tree species found in the built environment, derived by various different methods. (Redrawn and expanded from Biddle, 1998a.)

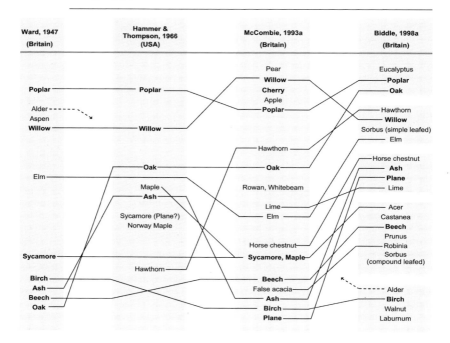

Ward, 1947 (Britain)	Hammer & Thompson, 1966 (USA)	McCombie, 1993a (Britain)	Biddle, 1998a (Britain)

10.3.6 Direct measurements of water demand

There is to date little published scientific data where direct measurements of the water use of mature, established, isolated trees have been made, and which could definitively assign species to low, moderate or high water demand. However, the HRI project is likely to provide some such direct measurements of water use.

Up until recently, the water demand of individual urban trees has been difficult to measure. Such data as does exist is based either on using a combination of leaf area index and pan evaporation rate (Lindsey and Bassuk, 1991), or on the patterns of soil drying and developing soil moisture deficits near trees as measured using neutron probes (Messenger and Ware, 1981; Biddle, 1983, 1998c). Empirical evidence of soil drying in the vicinity of a tree is, however, not the same thing as measuring the amount of water taken up by that same tree. Such datasets do not take account of water taken up by other, understorey vegetation, or lost through soil evaporation. In studies such as these, it is important that the water abstracted from the soil by the tree is examined and quantified separately from the other mechanisms (ie other parts of the water balance) by which moisture is lost from the soil (Lawson and O'Callaghan, 1995). In addition, without any comprehensive (albeit costly) study of rooting patterns of the tree, it is impossible to state with certainty, what proportion of the soil drying is attributable to the tree.

Table 10.3 Comparison of annual transpiration of mature, established beech and/or oak forest cover. (Source: Roberts, 1999.)

Species	Country	Transpiration (mm yr^{-1})	Forest age (years)	Reference
Beech	Belgium	344	30-90	Schnock (1971)
Beech	UK	393	64	Roberts and Rosier (1994)
Beech	France	288	—	Chassagneux and Choisnel (1987)
Beech	Germany	283	100	Kiese (1972)
Oak, sessile	Germany	342	18	Brechtel (1976)
		298	54	Brechtel (1976)
		342	165	Brechtel (1976)
Oak	Denmark	293	70	Rasmussen and Rasmussen (1984)
Oak	France	301	32	Bréda *et al.* (1993)
Oak	France	340	120	Nizinski and Saugier (1989)
Oak/Beech	Netherlands	267	100	Bouten *et al.* (1992)
"	"	362	100	"
"	"	239	100	"

Technological developments in the last few years have lead to instruments becoming available that can measure water use by individual trees, even on an hourly basis. Using 'sap flow' techniques, transpiration rates can be measured for entire trees or for selected parts of a tree, eg a root found to be growing in the direction of building foundations. Two main sap flow methods are available: stem (or trunk sector) heat-balance, and the heat-pulse method (Smith and Allen, 1996). The amount of heat taken up by the moving sap stream is used to calculate the flow of water though the trunk. Fig 10.9 shows typical daily fluctuations in the amount of water moving through the trunks of beech trees of different sizes growing over chalk in southern England. These methods provide a concrete way of measuring water demand in absolute terms. It is certain that stem heat-pulse techniques on large, isolated urban trees could significantly augment and improve upon the current ranking of species in terms of water demand. A combination of trunk heat-pulse measurements, coupled with heat-balance gauges on specific roots could provide an extremely powerful investigative tool that would tell you exactly what fraction of the tree water demand, say, came from a root suspected of taking water from soil beneath a building foundation. A recent study (Čermák *et al*, 2000) has used sap flow gauges together with ground-penetrating radar to compare water abstraction by field maple from an urban clay soil, with the root distribution of the trees in close proximity to buildings.

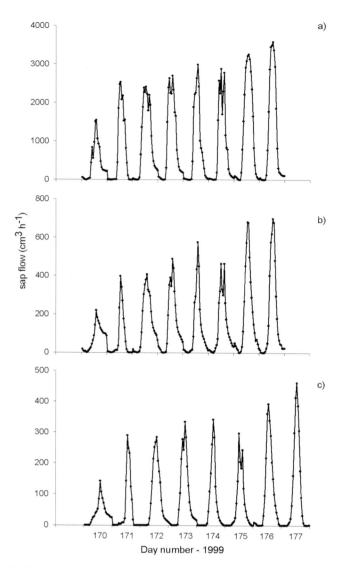

Figure 10.9 Daily fluctuations in sap flow in beech trees growing on chalk in the south of England, as measured using the heat-pulse method. Tree size: **(a)** diameter at breast height (dbh) of 20–27.5 cm; **(b)** dbh 12.5–20 cm; c) dbh < 12.5 cm. (After Roberts *et al.*, 2001.)

10.3.7 Risk of damage by different tree species

As stated in the BRE Digest 298, one way to avoid tree root problems is by ensuring a safe distance between tree and building, large enough to avoid any influence of the tree on the soil beneath the structure. This raises the question of the relationship between the size of the tree and the radial spread of the roots. It is necessary to be able to distinguish between the effects of a semi-mature tree growing close to a house and a fully grown tree of another species growing further away. Often the height of the tree is used as a convenient measure or index of the size, although it is arguable that other criteria such as crown size or leaf area index (McCombie, 1993b) are of greater use. However, methodologies based on leaf area indices are complex due to difficulties in definition and measurement of leaf area (Lindsey and Bassuk, 1991).

Ward (1953) proposed what has come to be referred to as the '1H' rule, in which it is best to assume that the roots spread out in a circle with a radius roughly equal to the height of the tree. Following an extensive review of the scientific literature on tree rooting patterns, Reynolds (1979) found there were so little data concerning tree root abstraction by mature urban trees on heavy soils in England, that he was unable to disprove the 1H rule. He concluded that root systems in soils which show seasonal variations in moisture content are probably more widespread than those with access to continuous and abundant soil moisture, and that impermeable paving in built-up areas might lead to such wider spread of roots. As mentioned in Chapter 3, results presented by Coile (1937) suggest that maximum tree root spread occurs before the crown has completely expanded, implying that the ratio of root spread to crown spread may decrease as trees become older. McCombie (1993b) demonstrated that smaller trees are capable of influencing soil conditions at proportionally greater distances than trees of larger size. Whether this is as a result of subtle changes in leaf distribution within the tree crown, or more obvious changes in root:shoot growth ratio is disputed (Biddle, 1998b).

As with tree water demand, it is possible to rank tree species common to the built environment with regard to their likelihood to cause damage to foundations, and some of these are summarised in Table 10.4. The first four ranking orders were constructed using data from the Kew root dataset (Cutler and Richardson, 1989), which consisted of results from two surveys. The main part of the work comprised information collected from cases where trees had caused damage to buildings and, as such, is a key reference for anyone wanting to explore the area of tree root damage to buildings. However, there are no comparable data from trees of similar sizes and distances from buildings where damage did not occur, ie the scientific control to which the data can be accurately compared. The manual cites the example of oak from the Kew data, where in 50% of damage cases attributable to oak the tree lay within 9.5m of the building, based on a sample size, $n = 293$. There must, as the manual suggests, be thousands of oak trees in similar circumstances that have not caused damage, suggesting that the likely risk may be as low as 1% or so. With no data it is impossible to be certain.

From the Kew data, Driscoll (1983) ranked trees on the basis of relative danger by comparing the incidence of damage with the incidence of planting those types of tree in the built environment. McCombie re-examined the original data and normalised each case by the actual tree height recorded. Conifers were excluded from McCombie's analysis as they are dealt with separately in the NHBC Standards, and elm was not listed, as no planting frequency data was available.

Table 10.4 Selected examples of ranking tree species based on the likelihood of causing damage to buildings. (Sources: Cutler and Richardson, 1981; Driscoll, 1983; McCombie, 1993a; Biddle, 1998a; BRE, 1999.)

	Driscoll (1983)	McCombie (1993a)	Biddle (1998a)	BRE Digest 298 (1999)	Reynolds (in Biddle, 1998a)
1	Oak	Oak	Oak	Oak	Poplar
2	Poplar	Common ash	Plane	Poplar	Willow
3	Lime	Poplar	Poplar	Ash	Elm
4	Common ash	Lime	False acacia	Elm	Plane
5	Plane	Beech	Horse chestnut	False acacia	Sycamore
6	Willow	Hawthorn	Lime	Horse chestnut	Lime
7	Elm	Willow	Elm	Hawthorn	Ash
8	Hawthorn	Horse chestnut	Willow	Lime	Oak
9	Sycamore, Maples	Plane	Ash	Willow	Horse chestnut
10	Cherries (*Prunus*)	Apple, Pear	Apple	Beech	*Prunus*
11	Beech	False acacia	Sycamore	Plane	Maple
12	Birch	Cherries (*Prunus*)	Beech	Apple, Pear	Whitebeam
13	Whitebeam, Rowan	Sycamore, Maples	Hawthorn	Sycamore, Maples	Beech
14	Cypresses (*Cupressus*)	Birch	Cherries (*Prunus*)	Cherries	Birch
15	Horse chestnut	Whitebeam, Rowan	*Sorbus*	Birch	Alder
16	Apple, Pear		Birch	Cypresses (*Cupressus*)	Holly
17	False acacia		Cypresses (*Cupressus*)	Rowan, Service tree	Conifer

Biddle ranked tree species in a similar fashion to Driscoll, using tree-planting records from London boroughs to weight the relative likelihood of damage. However, he correctly states that as 80% of all urban trees are commonly found on private land, local authority planting records may not accurately reflect the relative impacts that each tree species might have. He revised the analysis using tree population data obtained from the 'Trees in Towns' survey (Land Use Consultants, 1993) to weight the damage index instead. It is the latter ranking that is shown in Table 10.4, although it should be noted that this approach also has drawbacks. This survey does not distinguish between species comprising less than 2% of the overall population, which unfortunately includes many of the species towards the top of many rankings, such as oak and poplar, as well as species lower down like beech. In addition, while reflecting private as well as public tree ownership records, this survey includes data on tree populations outside the areas where expansive soils predominate. The ranking presented in the most recent version of BRE Digest 298 also makes use of the Kew root data, although what data were used to provide the 'estimated planting frequency' is not made explicit.

It is interesting that all four of these analyses place oak at the top of the ranking, and most agree that birch, cypresses and assorted *Sorbus* species all seldom contribute to significant damage. An alternative approach to ranking tree species was taken by Reynolds and Alder (1980), where their categorisation was based on the responses to a questionnaire sent out to 50 'professionals' involved in the inspection and assessment of tree root damage to buildings. Biddle (1998b) discusses this approach in some detail, and the ranking achieved by the authors forms the last column in Table 10.4 for purposes of comparison. Only a small subsample of replies listed all 17 of the species common to the other four studies, and as such there is a degree of uncertainty associated with the results. Also, care should be taken when interpreting results achieved from 'polling' individual opinions. It is difficult to be sure if the responses given accurately reflect personal experience, or whether views are coloured by previously published data (Biddle, 1998b), or indeed by a common consensus amongst the wide range of professionals consulted that is, as yet, unsubstantiated by direct measurements of water use.

10.4 Development of guidance, recommendations and standards

The National House-Building Council (NHBC) technical requirements are contained within the NHBC Standards, which are technical requirements backed up with detailed performance standards which must be achieved. Part 4 of the standards covers foundations, and comprises five separate chapters covering the technical requirements and recommendations relating to foundations. Subjects covered include site appraisal, building near trees and foundation types. A synopsis of the development of the various guidelines was provided by Atkins *et al* (1994), and is reproduced in a shorter form here for information purposes.

Following the drought of 1947, and subsequent research by the Building Research Station (now the Building Research Establishment, BRE) on the relationship between the tree height, the distance from the tree and damage to buildings, BRS Digest 3 was produced in 1949. The concept of separating trees and buildings by a distance approximately equal to the maximum tree height has been incorporated in subsequent guidelines and codes. The most recent standards incorporate guidance for the proximity of shrubs to buildings.

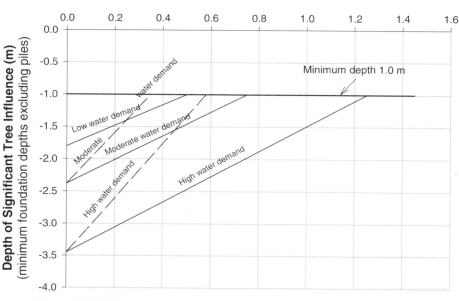

Figure 10.10 NHBC recommended foundation depths for: highly shrinkable soils, and low to high water-demand broadleaved (——) and coniferous trees (– – –). D/H is the ratio of the distance to tree in metres divided by its height in metres. (See NHBC, 2003.)

The National House-Builders Registration Council (now the NHBC) conducted studies on low-rise dwellings built on clay soils that had been affected by trees, in order to provide practical guidance (qualitative, rather than quantitative) to builders for constructing safe foundations on shrinkable clay sites where there still were, or had been, trees. Furthermore it drew attention to the need for caution when building near trees. This guidance was introduced as Practice Note 3 (PN3: Root damage by trees – siting of dwellings and special precautions) in 1969. PN3 was completely rewritten in 1974, to include minimum recommended foundation depths in heavy clay soils, related to the tree species, the distance from the tree and the expected mature height.

Once again, in 1985 PN3 was completely revised under the new title *Building near trees*, (together with a supplement 'A quick way to find the right depth of foundations on clay soils'), and took the following into consideration:

- high-, medium- and low-shrinkage potential of clay soils, based on the plasticity index

- high, moderate and low tree water demand (see Fig 10.10)

- potential tree heights on clay soils

- foundation depth required using the classifications for soils and trees

- variations in the UK climate affecting the recommended foundation depth (Fig 10.11)

0.50m (500mm)

0.45m (450mm)

0.40m (400mm)

0.35m (350mm)

0.30m (300mm)

0.25m (250mm)

0.20m (200mm)

0.15m (150mm)

0.10m (100mm)

0.05m (50mm)

Figure 10.11 Reductions in foundation depths due to UK climate variations. The foundation depth may be reduced by the amounts shown on the map for each climatic zone. Where it is unclear which zone applies, the higher value can be used. (After NHBC, 2003.)

NHBC produce a two-sided plastic ready reckoner to calculate foundation depths. The calculator incorporates the important factors influencing the requirements for different foundation depths recognised in Chapter 4.2 (NHBC, 2003). The calculator can be used in relation to broadleaved or coniferous trees and is shown in Fig 10.12.

Figure 10.12 Foundation depth calculator with scales for broadleaved trees on one side and conifers on the other. (Available from NHBC.)

Practice Note 3 was incorporated into the new NHBC Standards as *NHBC Standards Chapter 4.2 (Building near trees)* in 1992, and additional material was added dealing with precautions for clay heave, recommending that where heave is probable, suspended ground-floor slabs are used with a void appropriate to the soil type to allow for soil expansion.

British Standard 5837 (*Trees in relation to construction*) also deals with the avoidance of damage to structures by trees (BSI, 2005), and touches on both direct (see Table 10.5) and indirect damage caused by tree roots, including guidelines for consideration when building on clay soils. BS 5837 recommends that buildings should be constructed to allow for the future growth of planted and self-sown trees.

10.5 Prevention and mitigation of direct and indirect damage

Preventing damage from occurring in the first place is obviously of great importance. Biddle (1998b) mentions different situations where appropriate action may prevent structural damage.

10.5.1 Effects of 'new build' near existing trees

The guidelines described in the previous section go some way towards informing builders as how best to proceed. That said, as far back as the early 1950s, BRE were strongly recommending the use of short-bored pile foundations for structures on expansive clay soils (Ward and Green, 1952). However, 50 years on, the practice is still uncommon. Even if, in general terms,

Table 10.5 Minimum distances (m) between young trees or new planting and structure to avoid direct damage to a structure from future growth (after BSI, 2005).

Type of structure	Diameter of stem at 1.5 m above ground level at maturity		
	< 30 cm	(30–60) cm	> 60 cm
Buildings and heavily loaded structures	–	0.5	1.2
Lightly loaded structures such as garages, porches, etc	–	0.7	1.5
Drains and underground services			
< 1 m deep	0.5	1.5	3.0
> 1 m deep	–	1.0	2.0
Masonry boundary walls[a]	–	0.5	1.0
	–	(1.0)	(2.0)
In situ concrete paths and drives[a]	–	0.5	1.5
	(0.5)	(1.0)	(2.5)
Paths and drives with flexible surfaces or paving slabs[a]	–	0.5	1.0
	(0.7)	(1.5)	(3.0)

[a] These distances assume that some movement and minor damage might occur. Guidance on distances which will generally avoid all damage is given in brackets.

prevention may be better than cure, it is usually considered more economic to repair the cases where foundations fail than to deepen all foundations (Pryke, 1979). Some of the most important elements of the guidelines are obviously the recommendations for foundation depth for new build in proximity to existing trees. Having contributed significantly to their development, Biddle (1998b) stresses that there is an implicit 'mathematical simplicity' in the guidelines and that, given the unpredictability of tree/clay soil interactions, it would be unreasonable to expect tree behaviour to follow the guidelines in all cases. As in most situations, the recommendations strike a balance between the interests of several parties. '*They seek to provide a compromise between the benefits of increasing the [foundation] depth so as to minimise the risk, against the costs incurred as a result of such an increase*' (Biddle, 1998b). There are examples where innovative engineering solutions have enabled new buildings and established trees to coexist in close proximity (see Fig 1.1).

10.5.2 Effects of existing and/or newly planted trees near established structures

Even if foundation construction was to change to more robust designs, this would not address the problems faced by much of the existing housing in the

UK, the bulk of which is built on relatively shallow trench fill foundations of less than a metre. In cases where trees are planted, consideration must be given to how the tree might affect the structure when it has achieved its mature size if, indeed, it is intended to allow it to reach that size. The recommendations in BS 5837 (Table 10.5) are relevant in the case of direct damage from roots, although our older trees would have been planted before there was a general public awareness of the possible problems, and often substantially closer than is recommended by current guidelines.

10.6 Assessment of risk of damage to buildings

There has recently been an increasing demand from mortgage lenders, insurance companies and others for standardised assessments of the risk of subsidence damage to structures from nearby trees. Attempts have been made to produce subsidence risk assessments formulae but they have not always been successful due to the range of variables for which there is still very little scientific data. Anumba and Scott (1997) have developed a subsidence case management system (SCAMS) that uses a computer knowledge-based tool. It provides graphics-oriented guidance for engineers in assessing tree damage to residential buildings, addressing subsidence diagnosis, choice of an appropriate course of investigation, and the specification of effective remedial measures. The database appears to contain library files for individual tree types, including 'water demand', 'mature height' and 'safe distance', although references as to where these values originate is unclear. The authors mention literature surveys, case studies, interviews with experts and industry surveys. Only one arboricultural reference (Biddle, 1979) is mentioned, and the application to engineering management of subsidence is emphasised.

The Arboricultural Association (AA, 1998) developed a spreadsheet method of subsidence risk but this was withdrawn in 2001. Only a limited number of individuals subscribed to the scheme and this was one of a number of reasons given for its withdrawal (Eden, 2001). There were, however, a number of arboriculturists who were concerned that the scheme was likely to lead to decisions to remove trees based solely on a formula and would not involve their knowledge and experience. Nevertheless, some arboriculturists who used the scheme did find it a useful check-list to prompt their sequence of thinking.

The Royal and Sun Alliance Insurance group developed a tree risk assessment tool (TreeRAT) which is based on a statistical analysis of information about trees and subsidence damage from several thousand insurance claims (Glanville, 2002). TreeRAT was launched in December 2002. Detailed information and evaluations of the performance of TreeRAT are awaited with interest.

In *Amenity Trees and Insurance Issues*, Round and Lawson (1999) deal with subsidence assessment in the context of highway trees under the control of the local authority. The report presents both a technical framework for subsidence assessment, and a series of policies that may be implemented in addition to or in place of existing local authority policies on subsidence claims. Under these policies the local authority would require the provision of expert arboricultural evidence to determine the appropriate course of action in tree-related subsidence cases. One of the relevant pieces of information required would be a tree root survey, obtained by digging test pits, without which patterns of drying in clay soil are more difficult to interpret. Specifically, the course of action might include tree pruning/felling, application of growth suppressants, root barriers or foundation improvement in the vicinity of the trees in question. They stress that when drawing up recommendations for management of the problem, a distinction is made between 'arboricultural' and 'engineering' reasons. On the other hand, in terms of evidence supporting subsidence claims made against the local authority, detailed information from a structural engineer would be required.

Clearly there is much remaining to be done if a completely acceptable subsidence risk assessment scheme is to emerge. It is a concern that we lack important physiological knowledge and this is substituted in risk assessments by empirical factors. A particular worry is the use of tree size as one of the inputs to calculate risk. This step wholly disregards the likely physiological difference between a large, vigorous young tree of a particular species and one of similar size but which is considerably older. The older tree may well appear vigorous and healthy but functioning physiologically at a lower rate. One of the key functions that might be proceeding at a lower level in the older tree is transpiration and this will have major implications to assumptions about the risk of subsidence. Only relatively recently has a better physiological understanding begun to emerge of the various ways in which the physiological capacity of trees can decline with their age. The implication of this decline in capacity with age is that simply assessing risk on size alone is misleading and runs the risk that over mature trees will be managed eg by pruning or removal when this might be completely unnecessary. Equally importantly these older trees will be well down the mortality spiral and any remedial action eg crown reduction will put the tree in a further predicament. Some ways to improve the basis on which subsidence risk assessments are made are discussed in Chapter 13.

10.7 Investigation and mitigation of damage after it has occurred

Correct investigations of incidences of damage are essential both to determine the cause or causes of the damage, and to decide on the most appropriate remedy. Biddle (1998b) provides a detailed approach to the process of investigating subsidence damage to buildings, and suggests that the emphasis within most investigations should be on determining the best remedial action, as the exact cause of the damage usually becomes apparent once the remedial work has begun. Correct investigations would involve considering aspects of the building, the soil and of the tree or trees in question.

Once tree root-related damage has been identified, a number of options are available to the householder to deal with the problem. The first is, somewhat obviously, to tolerate the damage where possible. Biddle (1998b) states that structural damage to buildings on clay soil is not a new phenomenon, and that in the past, such damage was often ignored unless it caused frequent and serious cracking and problems. Modern structures are more rigid than those built using lime mortar etc. These older buildings had the capability to absorb a certain amount of ground movement (ISE, 2000). Occasional damage, occurring once a problem tree has reached its 'mature' size, can often be tolerated. On the other hand, persistent and increasingly serious damage cannot, and remedial action will become necessary.

A report commissioned by the Association of British Insurers (Radevsky, 2000) stated that British insurers spend millions of pounds each year on repairs for minor subsidence cracks that would be ignored in other countries, but can affect the saleability of houses in the UK. The report compared the way subsidence is viewed and dealt with in the UK, with other countries where expansive clay soils are a problem, including Australia, South Africa and the USA. The report concluded that in the UK, subsidence damage causes far more concern than in any other country included in the study, despite the fact that many reported cases involved only minor structural movement. In addition, because subsidence cover is a standard component of household insurance policies in the UK, extensive repairs are more often undertaken. Faced with similar subsidence damage, Australian, South African and American householders will, in general, have to cover the costs of repair themselves, with the result that tolerance of cracks is much higher. In these other countries, when greater remedial work is necessary then options other than underpinning are employed. Consequently, in these countries subsidence rarely affects house saleability. Furthermore, it is suggested that a large part of the remedial work carried out in the UK is not warranted on technical grounds, but is undertaken to repair small cosmetic cracks. This contributes significantly to the overall cost of subsidence claims, resulting in higher insurance premiums. Assuming that, for whatever reason, the damage cannot be tolerated, remedial work will be required to restabilise the soil and/or the foundations. This can be achieved in several ways.

10.7.1 Controlling the water use by the tree

Once foundation damage is diagnosed it is usually considered a top priority to restabilise the building as rapidly as possible. If a substantial soil water deficit has developed over some time, it will take a long period of time for the soil to re-equilibrate. Given the customary reluctance to 'tolerate' minor damage mentioned above, it is unlikely that homeowners would be willing to wait for this to happen. Therefore, reducing the tree water demand should not be relied upon to immediately remedy the situation, and is not advised for cases where persistent moisture deficits have accrued, but can be used where the soil movement is largely seasonal.

It may be necessary to identify and relate tree roots associated with damage with trees growing nearby. It is possible to distinguish roots to at least the genus level using anatomical features and specialist companies offer an identification service (e.g Richardsons Botanical Identifications, Reading UK). Recently, techniques have been developed to use DNA sequencing to enable a sample of root to be linked to nearby trees and a number of companies offer an analysis service (eg EPSL Ltd, Alnwick, UK). However, DNA sequencing will not be able to allocate a root to one of several nearby trees that may have reproduced naturally from the same stock or clonal stock that is growing in close proximity.

Controlling tree water use can be achieved by a number of methods, either by regulating the amount of water transpired by the tree, or by controlling the spread of the roots, and thus the tree's access to soil water. In most cases, controlling the transpiration of the tree is achieved by direct modifications to the tree crown. As water is lost from the tree through the leaves, reducing the number of leaves would be expected to lower the total transpiration, and hence lower the amount of water abstracted from the soil. At it's most drastic, this method might involve felling the tree or removing the crown. However, pruning the tree crown to reduce the degree of soil drying is also an option in some cases.

Felling the tree would obviously halt any transpiration immediately, but there are potential disadvantages to this technique. It is possible that once the tree is felled and the soil begins to rehydrate, damage may occur as a result of the soil heaving. Some arborists have advocated tree felling in 'stages' to offset this possibility, eg sequential and substantial pruning of the tree in the first two years, followed by complete removal. As Biddle (1998b) remarks, although this will slow the rate at which heave may develop, the extent of that heave is predetermined by the size of the soil water deficit and the expansive nature of the soil. The total heave or distortion will be unaffected by the timing and extent of pruning before felling. The cost of tree work will be increased and recovery of soil properties may be delayed by this process, though the final outcome will not be affected.

Pruning the tree crown will also only mitigate the problem if long-term persistent moisture deficits have not developed. Crown pruning is achieved through crown reduction or crown thinning, or, most often, a combination of the two. The first involves the removal of some of the exterior parts of the crown, decreasing the height and width of the crown. Thinning involves the removal of some of the branches within the crown, subsequently decreasing the foliage density throughout the crown. A tree will adjust the mass of roots or shoots to correct any deficiency in photosynthesis rates or nitrogen uptake

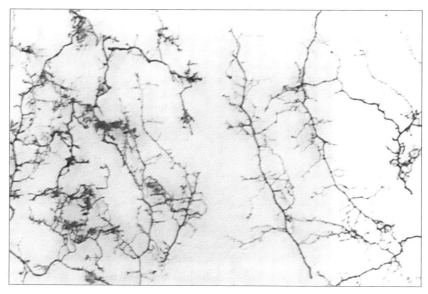

Figure 10.13 Pin oak (*Quercus palustris*) fine roots from a tree treated with paclobutrazol (left) and untreated control (right). (After Watson, 1996.)

(Coder, 1997b). Hipps and his colleagues at HRI have investigated the effect of crown thinning and reduction on water use by trees (Section 10.3.5).

It is tempting to try and 'balance' the water uptake of the tree by pruning, ie to ensure that the tree takes up neither too much water (leading to subsidence) or too little water (leading to heave). While this may sometimes be achievable, Biddle (1998b) states that it is impossible to do so where a persistent deficit exists. The size to which a tree will grow is ultimately limited by the resources to which it has access, water, nutrients, light etc. Pruning the crown, whether by thinning or reducing the size, can slow the immediate growth, but does not alter the potential size of the tree. Therefore, unlike felling, crown pruning is an ongoing strategy, and is often more expensive than felling.

In addition to direct manipulation of the tree crown, techniques exist for controlling water use by indirect means, eg the use of chemicals that affect and regulate tree growth. One of these, paclobutrazol (PBZ), was originally developed as a fungicide, but was later found to have significant growth retardant properties (Sugavanam, 1983), and has been used as an alternative to pruning in apple orchards (Curry and Williams, 1983). The effects of PBZ on shoot and root growth have been investigated in several conifer species, including Douglas fir (*Pseudotsuga menziessii*) (Wheeler, 1987), and several North American *Pinus* sp. (Wheeler, 1987; Rietveld, 1988; Barnes and Kelly, 1992). Reports vary from both increased root growth upon application of PBZ (Ashokan *et al*, 1995), to a decrease in rooting (Early and Martin, 1988). The main effect, however, seems to be an increased root:shoot ratio (Marquard, 1985; Swietlik and Miller, 1983; Ruter, 1994).

The bulk of the research into the effects on the root:shoot ratio appears to have been conducted on nursery stock. However, Watson (1996) investigated the effects of PBZ injected into the soil around the base of large oak trees (20 to 70 cm dbh), and found similar increases in the ratio of root to shoot biomass. PBZ application increased the density of fine roots (Fig 10.13) but it was unclear whether this occurred due to an increase in root branching, elongation, or both. The way in which PBZ affects root growth and morphology needs to be determined if this technique is to be adopted in the context of reducing tree water demand.

Roots may spread out some distance from the trunk to areas of soil where the soil water potential gradient makes it 'easier' to take up water. This is not to say that the roots have abstracted all soil water closer to the tree. It is likely that a significant amount of water may remain in this zone, but that it is far enough away from any tree root that the resulting soil resistances make it difficult to abstract. If the effect of applying PBZ was to increase root branching, more than increasing root elongation rate, root density might increase in this zone, ie close to the tree. With current models of root growth and activity it should be possible to calculate what the optimum density of roots in this zone should be, in order for this water to become as 'easily' abstractable as that found at greater distances from the tree.

At first glance, this idea of increasing rooting density seems at odds with the aim of reducing water demand. However, it might ensure a situation where the tree makes more effective use of the soil water in close proximity, and does not need to scavenge for wetter areas of soil such as those that may occur under buildings. It is possible that PBZ application might be used in conjunction with other methods such as root pruning, to reshape the root system from a sparse, expansive one to a compact dense form, causing less damage to adjacent structures. However, at this point the way in which PBZ works is poorly understood and more research is needed.

10.7.2 Controlling the spread of roots

It is possible to restrict the spread of roots, and hence the volume of soil from which water is abstracted, either by pruning them or by deflecting them using some sort of barrier. Root barriers may be considered where either direct or indirect damage is a potential problem. However, in most cases, the installation of a barrier will most likely entail some degree of root pruning. Root barriers are usually considered as a means of directing roots away from structures and hence avoid either pruning or felling problem trees.

A considerable amount of literature is available on the topic of root control barriers, and a similar amount of disagreement concerning their effectiveness exists. Indeed, some authors have dismissed root barriers as an option for reducing damage (eg Mead, 1994), citing results that show most tree roots have an extraordinary ability to find their way over, under or around installed barriers (Wagar, 1985; Costello *et al*, 1997). Gilman (1996) showed that roots of both oak and sycamore, although deflected downwards by root barriers, returned to the surface within 1.2 m from the barrier, to avoid waterlogging and low soil aeration. However, other authors report successful applications of the technique (eg Coder, 1998). Wilson (1967) found that red maple roots returned to their original direction after being deflected by a shallow barrier, but that their final angle of growth was determined by the original angle of contact with the barrier, and on the distance they were in contact with it. This latter factor seems to be important in root barrier effectiveness, and Coutts (1989) has suggested that the duration of contact between the roots and the barrier may be more important than the length of the barrier. In another study, poplar roots were only slightly deflected by short root barriers, but barriers of 10–12 cm length deflected almost half of the roots surveyed to continue in the same direction as the barrier (Riedacker, 1978).

Consideration should be given as to whether the intention is to entirely isolate a structure from the influence of tree roots, rather than simply reduce the amount of root growth near to a structure (Marshall *et al*, 1997). If the barrier can be bypassed by roots growing through, around, under or over it, then the roots will again proliferate in the soil beyond it. This may lead to further damage, and, even worse, can lead to a sense of 'false security' (Biddle, 1998b). To be effective, a barrier should both extend below the likely rooting depth and protrude above ground level, and hence should be UV-resistant. However, the roots of some species, eg poplar, have been known to grow over a barrier even when it extended well above ground level (Barker, 1994). Nicoll and Coutts (1998) recommend installing barriers with a lip protruding above the soil surface to prevent roots from growing over the top.

Three main barrier types are available. Firstly, there are barriers that comprise permeable materials that allow only moisture to penetrate, and trap or constrict root growth. Roots that do manage to make it through the mesh are constrained and stunted, and do not exhibit sufficient axial pressure to thicken and become damaging, unless present in large numbers (Wagar and Barker, 1993). There are also diversion barriers that form a wall, deflecting roots from their original direction. Improvements on this design include constructing the barrier with vertical ridges to direct roots downwards (Barker and Peper, 1995), in much the same way vertical ridges in some nursery containers force seedling roots to grow downwards (Appleton, 1995). Finally, there are barriers containing chemical inhibitors that prevent root development near a chemically treated fabric. The chemical is usually released as a gas (Phillips, 1999) which kills growing root hairs. The chemical biobarrier can be applied vertically, horizontally, or around the perimeter of the planting pit. A controlled-release chemical is most effective as the correct dosage is released over a long period. The purpose of both the diversion and chemical root barriers is to deflect surface-growing tree roots deeper into the soil where they will likely cause less damage to paved areas.

In situations where the tree rooting habit leads to roots quickly returning to the surface, it may be more effective to use barriers which retard root growth rather

Table 10.6 A selected list of tree root growth control barriers found to be effective for various lengths of time. (Source: adapted from Coder, 1998.)

Barrier type:	Reference
Root trapping/constricting:	
Nylon fabric/screen	Wagar and Barker (1993)
Permeable woven fabric sheets	Kopinga (1994)
Fibre-welded synthetic fabric/mesh	Kopinga (1994)
Root deflecting:	
Fibreglass and plastic panels	Coder (1998)
Copper screen	Wagar and Barker (1993)
Rock impregnated tar paper/felt	Kopinga (1994)
Ground-contact preserved plywood	Coder (1998)
Infrastructure aprons and footings	McPherson and Peper (1995; 1996)
Chemically inhibiting:	
Copper sulphate-soaked, synthetic, non-woven fabric	van der Werken (1982)
Cupric carbonate in latex paint	Arnold and Struve (1989)
Slow-release chemical barriers	McPherson and Peper (1995; 1996); Wagar and Barker (1993)
Thin layer asphalt/herbicide mix	Reynolds (1990)

than just deflecting them (Nicoll and Coutts, 1997). No single type of root barrier will stop all roots under all conditions, as features of the barrier, the site, installation and maintenance are all critical (Coder, 1998). As pointed out by Biddle (2001) there may be a physical problem in sealing root barriers around underground services. In addition soil on the side of the barrier nearer to the tree might be subject to seasonal movement of 100 mm or more while soil on the far side might be much more stable. These soil movements might also make it difficult to seal around underground services. However, several types of barriers have been shown to work for various lengths of time, and a sample of these is shown in Table 10.6. There are other materials such as 'weeding' and mulch fabrics that are not effective when used as root barriers as they lack enough strength to resist root elongation or radial expansion (Kopinga, 1994).

When dealing with situations involving expansive clay soils, a number of factors are worth considering. Following installation, the backfilled soil is likely to be looser than undisturbed soil, and may allow greater root proliferation and a relatively easy route to the bottom of the barrier. To discourage root growth, the barrier should be fitted tightly against the undisturbed soil face on the 'tree side' of the trench. If the barrier material used is impermeable to water as well as to roots, the wetter soil near the building may expand as the drier soil nearer the tree contracts. Even so, an air gap between the barrier and the soil may then develop. As rain collects in this gap, together with adequate aeration, conditions conducive to root growth develop. Roots will tend to grow down the face of the barrier until they eventually pass right beneath. The barrier material used must be capable of withstanding the forces that can be exerted through differential soil movement (Bonshor and Bonshor, 1996), or else be flexible enough to respond to them. Flexible materials include geomembranes and geotextiles, and can be impregnated with herbicides, although Wagar and Barker (1993) caution that in highly organic soils the herbicidal effect may become diluted.

As root barriers are a relatively recent development, it is not known how long the materials will last under soil conditions. The maximum guaranteed performances do not exceed 20–30 years, but both buildings and the trees close to them can have considerably longer life spans. Moffat *et al* (1998) conducted a properly replicated investigation into the effectiveness of various forms of root barriers, and found that polyethylene sheeting and herbicide-impregnated geotextile sheeting performed best. A full discussion of the various materials available is provided by Marshall *et al* (1997), and by Coder (1998a).

Root pruning has several adverse impacts on the tree, including reducing the absorption and conduction of moisture and mineral elements, and slowing growth by eliminating access to energy reserves that were stored in the severed roots. So long as a sufficient number of roots are severed, root pruning should be an effective way of reducing tree water uptake, at least until the roots have regrown. However, when used as a stand-alone treatment, it often leads to similar levels of root infestation, or worse, within a short period of time (Coder, 1998a; McPherson and Peper, 1996). A severed root can regenerate from the callus that forms over the cut end (Fig 10.14). In addition, other roots in the general vicinity (eg below the pruning depth) can also respond to exploit the soil previously accessed by the severed roots. As such, root pruning is unlikely to provide effective long-term control, but may be a temporary expedient in some situations (Biddle, 1998b).

One of the first outwardly visible reactions to root pruning is often shedding leaves. The tree is constantly trying to balance supply with demand of resources (Coder, 1998b) and the reduced capacity to absorb and conduct moisture and minerals leads the tree to reduce the demand, in this case the crown, by abscising some of the foliage. If root pruning is to be considered, care must be taken not to destabilise or kill the tree. Cutting too close to the tree can compromise structural stability (Wagar and Barker, 1993; McPherson and Peper, 1995).

10.7.3 Controlling the water content of the soil

As discussed earlier in this chapter, expansive clay soils can absorb significant amounts of water in the interstices between the clay silicate layers. One method of remedial work common in other parts of the world is clay stabilisation. This works by adjusting the capacity of the soil to hold water by injecting fluids into the soil, such as solutions of potassium or ammonium ions, rendering the clay no longer so expansive. Lime injection is also used, as calcium ions from

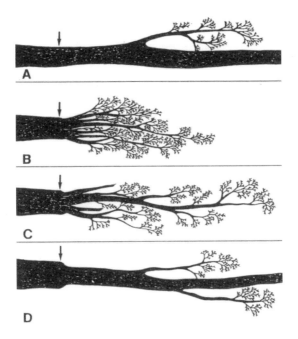

Figure 10.14 Stages in the replacement of a severed root.
(A) The root is cut at the arrow.
(B) Lots of small roots develop from callus formed after cut.
(C) One root becomes dominant and elongates.
(D) Other roots lose out and a single root remains in place of original root. (After Watson, 1996.)

the lime bond to available silica in the clay, to form stabilising compounds such as calcium silica hydrates. Chemical clay stabilisation is generally more effective at reducing expansive properties of clays than other methods (Basma and Al-Sharif, 1994).

10.7.4 Engineering work to underpin and strengthen the foundations

If soil movement is, or is probably going to become excessive, so that the use or safety of the building becomes dangerous, then underpinning may be a solution. Several methods are available for the strengthening of foundations, from traditional block underpinning (which is a technique which has evolved over centuries), to more recent systems using reinforced concrete beams or rafts (thick reinforced concrete slabs) supported by piers or piles.

It is most often done by excavating below the shallow footings, and pouring concrete to extend the foundation depth down to beyond that affected by soil movement (Richardson, 1997). Biddle (1998b) deals with the issues surrounding underpinning in some detail, and should be consulted for details relating to underpinning with a view to allow tree retention.

A compelling consideration in the choice between retaining a tree and underpinning the foundations, or felling it to eliminate proven problems of soil drying and soil movement near to foundations, will be the comparative costs and convenience. Both may be viable courses of remedial action but a balanced decision should be made between the financial cost of the action and any environmental cost in terms of tree removal or pruning (Biddle, 1998b). The cost of underpinning the foundations would be substantially more expensive than tree felling. There is also the additional convenience factor. On the one hand, engineering work to underpin foundations might take weeks to complete. On the other, while professional tree removal might be accomplished within a working day or so, soil recovery will take several months.

10.8 Climate change and subsidence

Recently, the UK has experienced some of the driest periods of weather on record. This has meant that many clay soils have not been able to replenish their seasonal moisture loss during the winter months. If climatologists are correct in their projections of global warming, then subsidence damage has become an endemic hazard of home ownership (Page, 1998). The potential role of global warming to increase the risk of damaging events is well understood by the insurance industry (Palutikof, 1999). Lowered groundwater levels and clay soil shrinkage have already begun to create a problem with building subsidence, which the insurance industry has acknowledged as one of the first tangible effects of climate change (National Trust, 1998). Air and soil temperatures are expected to rise, with the potential for increased evaporation, and a likelihood of increased risk of tree root damage, unless preventative action is taken (Biddle, 1998b). As mentioned earlier, the water demand of a tree is determined, at least in part, by environmental conditions. Therefore tree water demand would be expected to alter if climate change occurs.

The most common response by the insurance industry to climatic extremes has been to modify the terms of policy cover and insurance premiums (CII, 1994). Although these response mechanisms may still be useful in the future, additional measures should be taken to limit exposure to risk (Brignall et al, 1999). In order to accomplish this, it is necessary to gain a better understanding of how subsidence hazard may alter as a result of climate change, and a greater certainty, from predictive models, of how the climate may change.

10.9 Summary

- Direct damage by growth of roots most often occurs close to the tree, and diminishes rapidly with distance.

- Indirect damage includes that associated with shrinking and swelling subsoils, often but not always, involving trees in close proximity to building structures. Changes in soil moisture brought about by the demands of adjacent vegetation can lead to volume changes in the soil which, in turn, can lead to structural damage.

- In the UK, winter rainfall inputs to the soil significantly exceed winter losses from the system, and thus under normal conditions the soil recovers completely from moisture deficits accumulated during the summer.

- Persistent moisture deficits are uncommon, but may occur gradually over a period of a few years where winter recovery is less than summer losses through drying. For a persistent deficit to develop, it is also necessary for the tree to cause soil drying to a sufficient depth so that complete recovery cannot occur over a single winter.

- Our current understanding of tree water demand relies heavily on scientific literature from forestry research, and more work is needed on assessing water demand of isolated amenity trees.

- Mitigating tree-related damage can involve controlling the tree water use, either by regulating the amount of water transpired by the tree, or by controlling the spread of the roots, and thus the tree's access to soil water.

- Climate change scenarios suggest a rise in temperature and potential evaporation, and therefore a likelihood of increased risk of tree root-related damage.

REFERENCES

AA. 1998. *Subsidence Risk Assessment User's Handbook*. Arboricultural Association, Romsey, UK. 52 pp.

Anumba, C.J. & Scott, D. 1997. Intelligent assessment of tree damage to residential buildings. *Structural Survey*, 15, 80–86.

Appleton, B.L. 1995. New nursery production methods lead to tree root circling reduction or elimination. *Arboricultural Journal*, 19, 161–174.

Arnold, M.A. & Struve, D.K. 1989. Growing green ash and red oak in $CuCO_3$-treated containers increases root regeneration and shoot growth following transplant. *Journal of the American Society of Horticultural Science*, 114, 402–406.

Ashokan, P.K., Chaney, W.R. & Premachandra, G.S. 1995. Soil applied paclobutrazol affects leaf water relations and growth of American elm (*Ulmus americana* L.) seedlings. *Plant Growth Regulation Society of America Quarterly*, 23, 1–12.

ABI. 1999. *News release: significant rise in the cost of household claims*. Association of British Insurers, London, UK.
www.abi.org.uk/newsreleases/viewNewsRelease.asp

Atkins, F.J., Johnson, R.W. & Barrett, J.S. 1994. Building near trees – the development of NHBC standards for the foundations of low rise buildings. *The Structural Engineer*, 72(16): August 1994.

Barker, P.A. 1994. Root barriers for controlling damage to sidewalks. In: *The landscape below ground*: I (Ed. by G.W. Watson and D. Neely), pp. 179–185. International Society of Arboriculture, Savoy, IL., USA.

Barker, P.A. & Peper, P.J. 1995. Strategies to prevent damage to sidewalks by tree roots. *Arboricultural Journal*, 19, 295–309.

Barnes, A.D. & Kelly, W.D. 1992. Effects of a triazole, uniconazol on shoot elongation and root growth in loblolly pine. *Canadian Journal of Forest Research*, 22, 1–4.

Basma, A.A. & Al-Sharif, M. 1994. Treatment of expansive soils to control swelling. *Geotechnical Engineering*, June 94, 3–19.

Biddle, P.G. 1979. Tree root damage to buildings – an arboriculturist's experience. *Arboricultural Journal*, 3, 397–412.

Biddle, P.G. 1983. Patterns of soil drying and moisture deficit in the vicinity of trees on clay soils. *Geotechnique*, 83, 107–126.

Biddle, P.G. 1985. Arboricultural implications of revision of National House-Building Council Practice Note 3: building near trees. *Arboricultural Journal*, 9, 243–249.

Biddle, P.G. 1998a. *Tree roots and foundations.* Arboricultural Research and Information Note 142, Arboricultural Advisory and Information Service, Farnham, UK. 6 pp.

Biddle, P.G. 1998b. *Tree root damage to buildings.* Volume 1: causes, diagnosis and remedy. Willowmead Publ., Wantage, UK. 376 pp.

Biddle, P.G. 1998c. *Tree root damage to buildings.* Volume 2: patterns of soil drying in proximity to trees on clay soils. Willowmead Publ., Wantage, UK. 299 pp.

Biddle, G. 2001. Tree root damage to buildings. In: *Expansive clay soils and vegetative influence on shallow foundations* (Ed. by C. Vipulanandan, M.B. Addison and M. Hasen). Geotechnical Special Publication 115, American Society of Civil Engineers, Reston, VA, USA, pp.1–23.

Blight, G. E. 1965. The time-rate of heave of structures on expansive clays. In: *Moisture equilibria and moisture changes in soils beneath covered areas* (Ed. by G.D. Aitchison), pp. 78–88. Butterworths Publ., Sydney, Australia.

Boden, J.B. & Driscoll, R.M.C. 1987. House foundations – review of the effects of clay soil volume change on design and performance. *Municipal Engineering,* August 1987, 181–213.

Bonshor, R.B. & Bonshor, L.L. 1996. *Cracking in buildings.* Construction Communications Ltd/BRE, London, UK.

Bouten, W., Schaap, M.G., Bakker, D.I. & Verstraten, I.M. 1992. Modelling soil water dynamics in a forested ecosystem. A site specific evaluation. *Hydrological Processes,* 6, 435–444.

Brady, N.C. & Weil, R.R. 1999. *The nature and property of soils,* 12th Edition. Prentice Hall, Englewood Cliffs, USA. 881 pp.

Brechtel, H.M. 1976. Influence of species and age of forest stands on evapotranspiration and ground water recharge in the Rhine-Main Valley, Proceedings of XVI IUFRO World Congress, Oslo, Norway.

Bréda, N., Cochard, H., Dreyer, E. & Granier, A. 1993. Water transfer in a mature oak stand (*Quercus petraea*): seasonal evolution and effects of a severe drought, *Canadian Journal of Forest Research,* 23, 1136–1143.

Brignall, M.J., Gawith, M.J., Orr, J.L. & Harrison, P.A. 1999. Assessing the potential effects of climate change on clay induced land subsidence. In: *Climate, Change and Risk* (Ed. by T.E. Downing, A.J. Olsthoorn and R.S.J. Tol). Routledge, London, UK.

BSI. 2005. BS 5837: *Trees in relation to construction – Recommendations.* British Standards Institution, London, UK. 32 pp.

BRE. 1993. BRE Digest 240. *Low-rise buildings on shrinkable clay soil:* Part 1. 4pp. Buildings Research Establishment, Watford, UK.

BRE. 1996. BRE Digest 241. *Desiccation in clay soils.* 12pp. Buildings Research Establishment, Watford, UK.

BRE. 1999. BRE Digest 298. *Low-rise building foundations: the influence of trees in clay soils.* 8 pp. Buildings Research Establishment, Watford, UK.

Carothers, H. P. 1965. Engineered foundations in expansive clay. In: *Engineering effects of moisture changes in soils: International Research and Engineering Conference on Expansive Clay Soils*, pp. 302–323. Texas A&M Press, USA.

CEH. 2000. *Hydrological Yearbook* data. Centre for Ecology & Hydrology, Wallingford, UK.

Čermák, J., Hruška, J., Martinková, M. & Prax, A. 2000. Urban tree root systems and their survival near houses analyzed using ground penetrating radar and sap flow techniques. *Plant and Soil*, 219, 103–116.

Chandler, R.J., Crilly, M.S. & Montgomery-Smith, G. 1992. A low-cost method of assessing clay desiccation for low-rise buildings. *Proceedings of the Institution of Civil Engineers*, 92, 82–89.

Chandler, R.J. & Gutierrez, C.I. 1986. The filter paper method of suction measurement. *Geotechnique*, 36, 265–268.

CII. 1994. *The impact of changing weather patterns on property insurance.* Chartered Insurance Institute, London, UK.

Chassagneux, P. & Choisnel, E. 1987. Modélisation de l'évaporation globale d'un couvert forestier. II. Calibrages et résultats du modèle, *Annales des Sciences Forestières*, 44, 171–188.

Coder, K.D. 1997a. *Control of shoot/root balance in trees.* Tree root growth control series, University of Georgia cooperative extension service forest resources publication FOR98-3. www.forestry.uga.edu/warnell/service/library

Coder, K.D. 1997b. Crown pruning effects on roots. In: *Proceedings of the Third European Congress of Arboriculture*, May 15, 1997.

Coder, K.D. 1998. Root control barriers. Tree root growth control series, University of Georgia cooperative extension service forest resources publication FOR98-12. www.forestry.uga.edu/warnell/service/library

Coile, T.S. 1937. Distribution of forest tree roots in North Carolina Piedmont soils. *Journal of Forestry*, 36, 247–257.

Costello, L.R., Elmore, C.L. & Steinmaus, S. 1997. Tree root response to circling root barriers. *Journal of Arboriculture*, 23, 211–218.

Coutts, M.P. 1989. Factors affecting the direction of growth of tree roots. *Annales des Sciences Forestières* 46 suppl.: *Forest Tree Physiology* (Ed. by E. Dreyer *et al*), pp. 277–287. Elsevier/INRA, Amsterdam.

Curry, E.A. & Williams, M.W. 1983. Promalin or GA3 increase pedicel and fruit length and leaf size of 'Delicious' apples treated with paclobutrazol. *HortScience*, 18, 214–215.

Cutler, D.F. & Richardson, I.B.K. 1989. *Tree Roots and Buildings*, 2nd Edition. Longman, London, UK. 71 pp.

Driscoll, R. 1983. The influence of vegetation on swelling and shrinking of clay soil in Britain. *Geotechnique*, 33, 93–105.

Early, J.D. Jr. & Martin, G.C. 1988. Sensitivity of peach seedling vegetative growth to paclobutrazol. *Journal of the American Society for Horticultural Science*, 113, 23–27.

Eden, N. 2001. Response from the AA Technical Director. Arboricultural Association Newsletter, No. 113, p. 7.

Eden, P. 1995. Weatherwise. *The Sunday Telegraph Companion to the British Weather*, McMillan, London, UK. 323pp.

Eidmann, F.E. 1959. Die interception in Buchen und Fichtenbestandedn; Ergebnis Mehrjahriger Untersuchungen in Rothaargebirge (Saverland). *International Association of Scientific Hydrology*, 48, 5–25.

Eschner, A.R. 1967. Interception and soil moisture distribution. In: *International Symposium on Forest Hydrology* (Ed. by W.E. Sopper and H.W.Lull), pp. 191–200. Pergamon Press, Oxford, UK.

Gilman, E.F. 1996. Root barriers affect root distribution. *Journal of Arboriculture*, 22, 151–154.

Glanville, G. 2002. Subsidence prediction – a return? Royal & Sun Alliance tackle the issue. Presentation at 36th National Arboricultural Conference, Cambridge, UK.

Grim, R. E. 1962. *Applied clay mineralogy*. McGraw-Hill, New York, USA. 422 pp.

Hall, R.L. & Roberts, J.M. 1990. Hydrological aspects of new broadleaf plantations. *SEESOIL*, 6, 2–38.

Hammer, M.J. & Thompson, O.B. 1966. Foundation clay shrinkage caused by large trees. American Society of Civil Engineers, *Journal of Soil Mechanics and Foundations Division*, (92) no. SM6, 1–17.

Hutchinson, I. & Roberts, M.C. 1981. Vertical variation in stemflow generation. *Journal of Applied Ecology*, 18, 521–527.

ISE. 2000. *Subsidence of low rise buildings: A guide for professionals and property owners*, 2nd Edition. Institution of Structural Engineers, London, UK. 176 pp.

Jackson, N.A. & Wallace, J.S. 1999. Rapid changes in surface soil water content in an agroforestry system measured with high spatial resolution using TDR. *Hydrology and Earth Systems Sciences*, 3, 517–527.

Kiese, O. 1972. Bestandmeteorologische untersuchungen sur bestimmung des wärmehaushalts eines buchenwaldes, *Berichte des Instituts fur Meteorologie und Klimatologie der Technischen Universitat*. Hannover, No. 6. 132 pp.

Komornik, A. & David, D. 1969. Prediction of swelling pressure of clays: American Society of Civil Engineers, *Journal of Soil Mechanics and Foundations Division*, (95) no. SM1, 209–225.

Kopinga, J. 1994. Aspects of the damage to asphalt road pavings caused by tree roots. In: *The landscape below ground: I* (Ed. by G.W. Watson and D. Neely), pp. 165–178. International Society of Arboriculture, USA.

Land Use Consultants. 1993. *Trees in towns: a survey of trees in 66 towns and villages around England.* Department of the Environment. Research for Amenity Trees, No. 1. 51 pp.

Lawson, M. & O'Callaghan, D. 1995. A critical analysis of the role of trees in damage to low rise buildings. *Journal of Arboriculture*, 21, 90–97.

Legget, R.F. & Crawford, C.B. 1965. CBD-62. Trees and Buildings. *Canadian Building Digest.* www.nrc.ca/irc/cbd/cbd062e.html

Lindsey, P. & Bassuk, N. 1991. Specifying soil volume to meet water needs of mature urban street trees and trees in containers. *Journal of Arboriculture*, 17, 141–149.

McCombie, P.F. 1993a. Trees and foundations – a reassessment. *Arboricultural Journal*, 17, 341–357.

McCombie, P.F. 1993b. The relative water demand of broad-leaved trees – a new analysis of the Kew root survey. *Arboricultural Journal*, 17, 359–374.

MacLeod, R.D. & Cram, W.J. 1996. *Forces exerted by tree roots.* Arboriculture Research and Information Note 134. Arboricultural Advisory and Information Service, Farnham, UK. 5 pp.

McPherson, E.G. & Peper, P.J. 1995. Infrastructure repair costs associated with street trees in 15 cities. In: *Trees and Building Sites: Proceedings of an International Workshop on Trees and Buildings* (May 31–June 2,1995) (Ed. by G.W. Watson and D. Neely), pp. 49–63. International Society of Arboriculture, Savoy, IL., USA.

McPherson, E.G. & Peper, P.J. 1996. Costs of street tree damage to infrastructure. *Arboricultural Journal*, 20, 143–160.

Marquard, R.D. 1985. Chemical growth regulation of pecan seedlings. *HortScience*, 20, 919–921.

Marshall, D., Patch, D. & Dobson, M. 1997. *Root barriers and building subsidence.* Arboricultural Practice Notes 4, Arboricultural Advisory and Information Service, Farnham, UK. 8 pp.

Mead, J.M. 1994. Tree and buildings: insurance consequences. *Arboricultural Journal*, 18, 149–154.

Means, R. E. 1959. Buildings on expansive clay. In: *Theoretical and practical treatment of expansive soils*: Papers from the First Soil Mechanics Conference, Colorado School of Mines, Golden, April 23, 1959, Colorado School of Mines Quarterly, 54, 1–31.

Messenger, S. & Ware, G. 1981. Damage to buildings foundations: do tree roots play a role? *Morton Arboretum Quarterly*, 17, 1–7.

Mielenz, R. C. & King, M. E. 1955. Physical and chemical properties and engineering performance of clays. In: *Clays and clay technology:* National Conference on Clays and Clay Technology, Berkeley, California, July 21–25, 1952, Proceedings (Ed by J.A. Pask and M.D. Turner). California Division of Mines Bulletin 169, pp. 196–254.

Moffat, A.J., Bending, N.A.D. & Dobson, M.C. 1998. *Barriers against tree roots – an experimental investigation.* Arboriculture Research and Information Note 141. Arboricultural Advisory and Information Service, Farnham, UK. 5 pp.

NHBC. 2003. NHBC Standards. *Chapter 4.2: Building near trees.* National House-Building Council, Amersham, UK.

National Trust. 1998. *Climate Change.* Paper presented by the Head of Nature Conservation and the Environmental Practices Adviser on behalf of the Chief Agent.
www.nationaltrust.org.uk/environment/html/enviss/fspapers/fsenvissu2.htm

Nicoll, B.C. & Coutts, M.P. 1997. Direct damage by urban tree roots: Paving the way for less damaging street trees. In: *Arboriculture Practice – Present and Future*, pp. 77–84. Tree Advice Trust.

Nicoll, B.C. & Coutts, M.P. 1998. *Deflection of tree roots by rigid barriers.* Arboriculture Research and Information Note 143. Arboricultural Advisory and Information Service, Farnham, UK. 5 pp.

Nizinski, J. & Saugier, B. 1989. A model of transpiration and soil-water balance for a mature oak forest. *Agricultural and Forest Meteorology*, 47, 1–17.

NJFSTC. 2000. *Trees for N.J. Streets*, fourth revision. New Jersey Federation of Shade Tree Commissions, 29 pp.

Page, R.C.J. 1998. Reducing the cost of subsidence damage despite global warming. *Structural Survey*, 16, 67–75.

Palutikof, J.P. 1999. Domestic property insurance claims related to damaging weather events. In: *Indicators of Climate Change in the UK* (Ed. by M.G.R. Cannell, T.H. Sparks and J.P. Palutikof). DETR Report 99DPL001. www.nbu.ac.uk/iccuk

Perpich, W. M., Lukas, R. G. & Baker, C. N. 1965. Desiccation of soil by trees related to foundation settlement: *Canadian Geotechnical Journal*, 2, 23–39.

Phillips, L.E. 1999. Tips for the Municipal Arborist: Tree Roots versus Sidewalks. City Trees, 35(5). www.urban-forestry.com/citytrees/v35n5a05.html

Plante, S. 1998. Subsidence case studies: using soil suction techniques. *Structural survey*, 16, 141–145.

Prebble, R.E. & Stirk, G.B. 1980. Throughfall and stemflow on silverleaf ironbark (*Eucalyptus melanophloia*) trees. *Australian Journal of Ecology*, 5, 419–427.

Pryke, J.F.S. 1979. Trees and buildings. *Arboricultural Journal*, 3, 388–396.

Pryke, J.F.S. 1993. Subsidence: the time is ripe for a change. *Structural Survey*, 11, 357–365.

Radevsky, R. 2000. *Subsidence – a global perspective*. General insurance research report 1. Association of British Insurers, London, UK.

Rasmussen, K.R. & Rasmussen, S. 1984. The summer water balance in a Danish oak stand. *Nordic Hydrology*, 15, 213–222.

Reynolds, E.R.C. 1979. *A report on tree roots and built development*. Department of the Environment. HMSO, London, UK. 24 pp.

Reynolds, E.R.C. & Alder, D. 1980. Trees and buildings. 6. A matter of opinion – settlement or heave of houses and the role of tree roots. *Arboricultural Journal*, 4, 24–30.

Reynolds, E.R.C. & Henderson, C.S. 1967. Rainfall interception by beech, larch and Norway spruce. *Forestry*, 40, 165–185.

Reynolds, T.D. 1990. Effectiveness of three natural biobarriers in reducing root intrusion by four semi-arid plant species. *Health Physics*, 59, 849–852.

Richardson, C. 1997. *The philosophy of underpinning*. The Building Conservation Directory 1997. Cathedral Communications Publ., Wilts., UK.
www.buildingconservation.com/articles/underp/underp.htm

Riedacker, A. 1978. Étude de la déviation des racines horizontales ou obliques issues de boutures de peuplier qui rencontre un obstacle: applications pour la conception de conteneurs. *Annales des Sciences Forestières*, 35, 1–18.

Rietveld, W. 1988. Effect of paclobutrazol on conifer seedling morphology and field performance. In: *Proceedings, combined meeting of the western forest nursery associations*. USDA, Forest Service General Technical Report No. RM-167, pp. 19–23.

Roberts, J.M. 1999. Plants and water in forests and woodlands. In: *Eco-hydrology: Plants and water in terrestrial and aquatic environments* (Ed. by A.J. Baird and R.L. Wilby), pp. 181–236. Routledge, London, UK.

Roberts, J.M. & Rosier, P.T.W. 1994. Comparative estimates of transpiration of ash and beech forest at a chalk site in southern Britain. *Journal of Hydrology*, 162, 229–245.

Roberts, J.M., Rosier, P.T.W. & Smith, D.M. 2001. *Effects of afforestation on chalk groundwater resources*. Final Report to the UK Department of the Environment, Transport and Regions. 81 pp.

Round, L. & Lawson, M. 1999. *Amenity trees and insurance issues – the local authority perspective*. ISA Sustainability of resources programme. ISBN 0953702502. 119 pp.

Ruter, J.M. 1994. Growth and landscape establishment of *Pyracantha* and *Juniperus* after application of paclobutrazol. *HortScience*, 29, 1318–1320.

Rutter, A.J. 1968. Water consumption by forests. In: *Water deficits and plant growth Volume II* (Ed. by T.T. Koslowski), pp. 23–76. Academic Press, London.

Schnock, G. 1971. Le bilan d'eau dans l'écosystème d'une forêt – application à une chênaie mélangée de haute Belgique. Conf. UNESCO, Paris, 1969. Productivité des écosystèmes forestieres. *Actes Colloq., Bruxelles*, 41–47.

Shabha, G. & Kuhwald, K. 1995. Subsidence and the associated problems with reference to low-rise housing. *Structural Survey*, 13, 28–35.

Smith, D.M. & Allen, S.J. 1996. Measurement of sap flow in plant stems. *Journal of Experimental Botany*, 47, 1833–1844.

Sowers, G. F. & Kennedy, C. M. 1967. High volume change clays of the southeastern Coastal Plain. In: *Panamerican conference on soil mechanics and foundations engineering*, Caracas, July 1967. Proceedings: Caracas, Socieded Venezolana de Mecanica del Suelo e Ingeneria de Fundaciones, v. 2, pp. 99–120.

Sugavanum, B. 1983. Diastereoismers and enantiomers of paclobutrazol: their preparation and biological activity. *Pesticide Science*, 15, 296–302.

Swietlik, D. & Miller, S.S. 1983. The effect of paclobutrazol on growth and response to water stress of apple seedlings. *Journal of the American Society of Horticultural Science*, 108, 1076–1080.

Twigger, R. 1999. *Inflation: the Value of the Pound 1750–1998*. Economic policy and statistics section, House of Commons Library, Research Paper 99/20. www.parliament.uk/commons/lib/research/rp99/rp99-020.pdf

van der Werken, H. 1982. Effects of physical and chemical root barriers on growth of *Koelreuteria bipinnata*. *27th Annual Report and Proceedings of the Southern Nurserymen's Association Research Conference*, Nashville, TN. 74 pp.

Wagar, J.A. 1985. Reducing surface rooting of trees with control planters and wells. *Journal of Arboriculture*. 11, 165–171.

Wagar, J.A. & Barker, P.A. 1993. Effectiveness of three barrier materials for stopping regenerating roots of established trees. *Journal of Arboriculture* 19, 332–338.

Ward, W.H. 1947. The effect of fast growing trees and shrubs on shallow foundations. *Journal of the Institute of Landscape Architects*, 11, 7–16.

Ward, W.H. 1948. The effect of vegetation on the settlement of structures. *Proceedings of the Conference on Biology and Civil Engineering. Sept 1948*. Institute of Civil Engineers, London, UK.

Ward, W.H. 1953. *Soil movement and weather. Proceedings of the 3rd International conference of soil mechanical and foundations engineers*, Switzerland.

Ward, W.H. and Green, H. 1952. *House foundations. The short bored pile*. Public works and municipal services congress 1952. Institute of Civil Engineers, London, UK.

Watson, G.W. 1996. Tree root system enhancement with paclobutrazol. *Journal of Arboriculture*, 22, 211–217.

Wheeler, N.C. 1987. Effect of paclobutrazol on Douglas fir and loblolly pine. *Journal of Horticultural Science*. 62, 101–106.

Wilson, B.F. 1967. Root growth around barriers. *Botanical Gazette*, 128, 79–82.

Zinke, P.J. 1961. Patterns of soil properties developed under the influence of forest trees. *XI International Botanical Congress*, vol. II, pp. 1641–1646.

Zinke, P.J. 1967. Forest interception studies in the United States. In: International Symposium on Forest Hydrology (Ed. by W.E. Sopper and J.W. Lull), pp. 137–161. Pergamon Press, Oxford, UK.

CHAPTER 11

Tree Root Damage to Pavements and Low-Rise Structures

11.1 Introduction

Damage to pavements and kerbs due to the proximity of tree roots is a common occurrence, especially in the close confines of urban settings. However, there is currently no way of predicting which tree will cause damage, or when, due to the unique nature of each tree and each site. While it is probable that roots from adjacent trees will grow underneath roads, they are very unlikely to have penetrated the road base, due to the severely compacted nature of the medium (DETR, 1999). Trees may damage paved surfaces *indirectly*, by contributing to soil moisture changes in any underlying shrinkable soils, but the degree to which this happens is not known. On the other hand, *direct* damage to pavements caused by the growth of tree roots (Fig 11.1) is a considerable concern for engineers and arboriculturists in cities and towns, who realise that uneven surfaces can be hazardous to public safety and costly to repair and therefore give street trees a bad reputation. It is a universal and costly problem

Figure 11.1 Damage to pavement in Reading, UK caused by roots of a large Norway maple.

Figure 11.2 Damage caused by horse chestnut tree roots growing under the adjacent brick wall (Reading, UK).

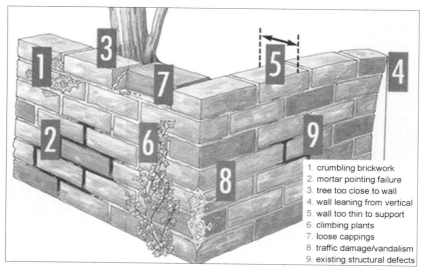

1. crumbling brickwork
2. mortar pointing failure
3. tree too close to wall
4. wall leaning from vertical
5. wall too thin to support
6. climbing plants
7. loose cappings
8. traffic damage/vandalism
9. existing structural defects

Figure 11.3 A nearby tree can damage a low garden wall, especially if it is already compromised by other factors. (After DETR, 2001.)

in the United Sates and in other parts of the world (Hamilton, 1984a). Much research has been done on the damage caused to pavements and kerbs in cities in the Netherlands and the USA but there are few comparable studies on similar damage by street trees in the UK (Wong *et al* 1988; Nicoll and Armstrong, 1997).

Box 11.1 Forces exerted by roots

MacLeod and Cram (1996) present some sample calculations of the forces that can be exerted by tree roots and consider the likely damage to pavements, non-reinforced concrete slabs and walls. Using a point pressure value that was an average of a number of literature values (800 KPa = 8×10^5 N m^2 for the radial pressure of secondary roots), MacLeod and Cram estimate the force (pressure per unit area) exerted by roots against paving slabs and various built structures.

The likelihood that the root will dislodge or fracture a structure depends on the ability of the structure to resist the force exerted by the root. In the worked examples given by MacLeod and Cram (1996), there is an estimate that a root 1 cm in diameter in contact with the full length (30 cm) of a paving slab will have sufficient force to dislodge the slab. The force is calculated as 8×10^5 N m^2 / 0.003m^2 = 2400N. In this particular case the 13 kg paving slab would have a downward force of 140N. Therefore, in the absence of any other forces to overcome (e.g. a frictional force between adjacent slabs would be very likely and would be substantial) the root has 10 times the force necessary to lift the slab.

MacLeod and Cram (1996) use the point pressure value 8×10^5 N m^2 and likely contact areas to estimate that roots are unlikely to force a brick wall apart but could possibly fracture a non-reinforced concrete slab floor. Clearly the calculated force is wholly dependent on the point of pressure assumed from literature values and the surface area of roots that are in contact with a structure. In some circumstances it is not obvious that growth conditions are such as to promote large areas of contact between tree roots and structures.

Damage seems to be less severe for soft or loose soils that can deform as the roots grow, rather than dense or hard soils, often the result of compaction during pavement construction (Day, 1991). Given the magnitude of the forces that growing roots can exert (MacLeod and Cram, 1996), it seems likely that direct damage is usually limited to more lightly loaded structures, such as pavements, roads, and low walls (Fig 11.2). In some cases roots form callus growth which will increase the surface area of the root that is in contact with the paved surface and will lift a structure with no tensile strength (eg a paving brick) relatively easily (D. Patch, pers. com.).

As trees get larger there may be a risk of direct damage to walls from the roots. A number of factors can affect the structural integrity of low-rise structures such as walls (Fig 11.3), with the result that pressure from growing tree roots can damage or topple an already weakened structure (Box 11.1). A wall that is not tied in to or supported by another structure will be toppled more easily than it could be lifted by root pressure. Wind-induced tree movement can also lead to damage of low-rise structures. The rocking movement that occurs as the

Figure 11.4 'Cut-out' in replacement boundary wall to allow for tree expansion and avoid loading.

wind loading changes will be transmitted to the structure if the roots are in direct contact with it, even if above-ground the tree seems not to directly affect the structure. Damaged sections of wall may require rebuilding, at which stage cut-outs can be added to the wall to give the tree more space (Fig11.4) and 'bridges' can be incorporated to lift and support the wall above and away from the roots (Fig 9.19) (DETR, 2001).

11.2 Scope of the problem

Wong *et al* (1988) surveyed over 2000 street trees, 13% of the total population growing in the streets of Manchester, UK. Of those trees surveyed they found that 30% had caused damage to pavements and 13% had damaged kerbs. A similar survey conducted in Oak Park, Illinois found that 5% of street trees had caused pavements to uplift, with elm (*Ulmus americana*) responsible for the majority of incidents. Nearly 60% of cases were caused by immature trees (Stankovich, 1990). A 1974 survey of the San Francisco Bay Area cities indicated that more than 60% of the problem trees were causing severe pavement damage and between 20% and 60% were causing some damage (Hamilton, 1984a). Results from a 1988 survey of city and county tree managers in California indicate that street tree roots are a serious problem in most of the state's cities (Bernhardt and Swiecki, 1988). The current situation regarding the degree of root damage to pavements and kerbs in the UK is unknown.

The resulting repairs to pavements are expensive (McPherson and Peper, 1996). Hamilton *et al* (1975) reported an average annual cost of $27,000 per city in northern California for root-related pavement damage. The estimated repair cost for more than 200,000 m^2 of pavement damage in San Jose was $14.3 million (Sealana and Associates, 1994). A recent survey of 18 Californian cities indicated that approximately $70.7 million was spent annually to deal with conflicts between street tree root growth and infrastructure. The frequency of pavement repair averaged 1 per 99 street trees and the average repair cost was $480 (McPherson, 2000).

In addition to the costs directly associated with repair, city authorities are usually responsible for injuries allegedly resulting from uneven pavement surfaces. Half of the claims against a city can be from root-caused problems (Hamilton, 1984a). As society in the United States becomes increasingly litigious, municipalities are more susceptible to lawsuits that are the result of someone tripping over raised paving (paviours). In 1997 the City of Cincinnati was involved with 21 suits seeking damages from the city as a result of damaged pavements (Sydnor *et al*, 2000). For example, in some Californian cities, for every $1 spent on repairing pavements, more than double this ($2.26) is spent on litigation (McPherson and Peper, 2001). Comments from arboricultural officers at the Trees 2000 conference (held at Keele University, June 2000) suggest an increasing trend in root-related 'trip and slip' claims against UK local authorities.

11.3 Factors influencing root growth below pavement

Where roots are near the surface, distortions of the pavement can be expected irrespective of the soil characteristics beneath the hard surface (Hamilton, 1984a). These distortions result from the secondary thickening of roots growing below the pavement (Nicoll and Armstrong, 1997). Each growth ring increases the root diameter and pushes the roots against the underside of the pavement, often with sufficient force to buckle and crack tarmac or concrete, or to lift paving slabs or brick paviours (see Fig 11.5).

In young trees, increases in root length predominate as they explore and extend into the soil, but as the tree matures the trunk enlarges and is supported by root enlargement. Most trees have some surface roots (Sydnor *et al*, 2000) and the tree roots that develop near the surface respond to several factors that direct their growth (Harris *et al*, 1999). Roots tend to grow downwards (geotropism) and away from light (negative phototropism). However, roots will grow towards optimum conditions of water, nutrients and oxygen levels. The balance between upward and downward growth responses enables these shallow-growing roots to track close below the soil surface (Nicoll and Coutts, 1997), exploiting the soil where conditions of temperature, water and oxygen are often the most favourable. It is uncertain as to which of these factors or

Figure 11.5 Tree roots lifting concrete paving slabs.

tropisms most strongly determines root direction, as data is scarce and what does exist comes mainly from experiments with crop seedlings.

Contrary to popular belief, the soil environment beneath paved areas often favours tree root growth (Day, 1991; Wagar and Franklin, 1994). If the soil is covered with a solid layer like paving, the absence of light, together with other factors, may permit the roots to continue to grow upwards until they make contact with, and may possibly distort, the hard surface. These roots may often experience soil conditions more favourable for growth, such as soil oxygen and water content, than those growing deeper in the soil. Favourable conditions close to the surface can encourage rapid growth of roots below paved surfaces, only to form an extensive root system again once they have reached the other side of the covered area (Kopinga, 1994). However, even if occasional damage occurs beneath the paved area, it is almost always the case that the majority of the damage that the roots cause occurs close to the base of the tree where the expansion of the trunk and adjacent roots is greatest.

11.3.1 Compaction, pore space and aeration

The effects of soil compaction on root growth and extension are dealt with in detail in Chapter 3. To summarise, root growth through the granular soil matrix is affected by a number of different forces. To confidently predict root growth, one must take account of both the axial and radial stresses on the roots as well as the compression and failure characteristics of the soil. However, the physiology of roots growing in impeded conditions, such as those common in paved situations, is still poorly understood (Atwell, 1993).

Paved areas such as roads, footpaths and parking areas must be constructed with a firm, stable base. This is usually achieved by excavating to a depth of about 0.5 m, mechanically compacting the base material where necessary, and backfilling with an inert material, also compacted (Patch and Dobson, 1996). Soil compaction acts to restrict root elongation directly, as the mechanical impedance to root extension is greatly increased (Fig 3.10).

Air and water are held in pores between the soil particles. In uncompacted soil the pores are generally large, and the soil is well aerated, freely draining (soil water potential close to zero), and ideal for root growth. In soils with smaller pores, either as clays or in compacted soils, the pore size is smaller, the soil is less well aerated, and is prone to both waterlogging, and to water deficits (where water potentials are much lower than zero). Lower soil water potentials will act to limit root growth and elongation (see Fig 3.9).

Surface soil almost always possesses the best conditions for root growth, while the number of pore spaces in the soil and the available oxygen decrease with depth below the surface (Perry, 1982). Lack of oxygen reduces root growth almost immediately (Hamilton, 1984a), and root activity has been reported to halt completely below 10% oxygen in the soil air spaces (Kopinga, 1994). Fig 3.11 shows that in relatively uncompacted soil (1.3 Mg m^{-3}), root growth is unimpeded until soil oxygen levels drop to around 5%, whereas the reduction in root growth occurs at higher oxygen levels as the soil compaction or bulk density increases.

Urban trees often have limited rooting space and are similar in this respect to large potted plants (Duryea and Malavasi, 1993). Kopinga (1994) noted that in The Netherlands, street trees are often planted in soil pits surrounded by soil that cannot be penetrated by tree roots because of compaction. He concluded that much of the damage to surrounding asphalt surfaces was caused by the roots searching for more favourable conditions via the underside of the road pavings, and that in paved areas even species not normally considered 'aggressive' can cause root damage to the pavements. However, in a survey of rooting damage the Dutch team were unable to find a distinct correlation between the available rooting volume and the rate at which damage appeared. Gilstrap (2001) reports that in Modesto, California, where severe compaction often limits the available rooting volume, holes are drilled to break through hardened soil layers and allow greater root system development.

11.3.2 Soil temperature and water content

Wagar and Barker (1983) found that root damage to paving generally occurred closer to the tree as the roots formed small buttresses against the trunk. The formation of these buttresses is usually linked to shallow rooting habit and with raised soil temperatures and humidity (Hamilton, 1984a). Such conditions often occur beneath pavements. The soil below impermeable paving loses very little water, if any, to the atmosphere through evaporation. Kopinga (1994) found that over the course of a summer, the soil humidity below a road surface remained constantly high, while the soil beside the road gradually dried out (Fig 11.6). The soil is effectively 'vapour-locked', as happens in many tropical soils that form surface crusts. Water vapour present condenses on the underside of the pavement leading to humid conditions ideal for root growth. On the other hand, impermeable pavement prevents the soil water content from recharging rapidly following rainfall. Such recharge as does occur must take place laterally, at a much reduced rate.

Several studies have shown that during the summer months, average temperatures below paved surfaces (Fig 11.7) are higher than at comparable depths in adjacent soil (Halverson and Heisler, 1981). Any increase in soil temperature below paving is determined by the physical characteristics of the pavement material. The albedo (a measure of how reflective a material is) is obviously different for the grey-white concrete typical of American pavement construction than for the darker asphalt typical of many pavements in the UK. Secondly, the conductivity and depth of the pavement determines how much heat is stored in the pavement, and how much travels through to the soil underneath. In general, the thicker the paving the smaller the diurnal variation in soil temperature.

11.3.3 Plant growth regulators

Severe soil compaction induces changes in the amounts and balances of growth hormones in woody plants, especially increases in abscisic acid and ethylene (Kozlowski, 1999). Several authors have speculated that the production of the plant growth regulator ethylene is implicated in the radial enlargement of impeded roots. Kays et al (1974) showed that bean roots produced around six times the amount of ethylene when they grew against a mechanical barrier, than they did in unimpeded conditions. Moss et al (1988) found that maize responded to mechanical impedance by growing shorter, thicker roots and evolving ethylene faster. There is little information on the degree to which ethylene production occurs in tree roots that are mechanically impeded, but tree root ethylene production in response to other factors common to paved surfaces, such as waterlogging, are available (Coder, 1994). The effects of plant growth regulators on root function are dealt with in detail in Chapter 3.

11.4 Relative effects of different tree species

As in the case of tree root damage to buildings, much attention has focused on the relative amounts of damage caused by different tree species. Perhaps even more so, the question seems to hinge on trees that are 'shallow' or 'deep' rooted by habit. As has been stressed in other chapters, root phenology and development is extremely variable, and a deep rooted forest species may well turn into a shallow rooted problem tree in street conditions. Nevertheless, lists of trees occur in the literature. Maples, ash, *Liquidambar*, oak, poplars, willows and American elm are cited as examples of shallow rooted trees (Rindels,

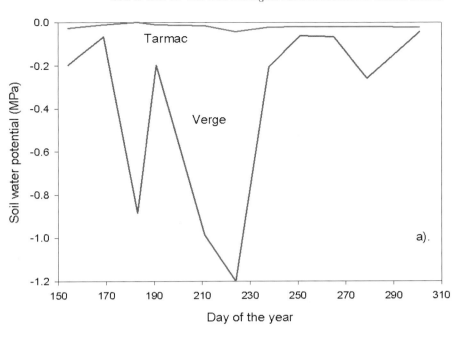

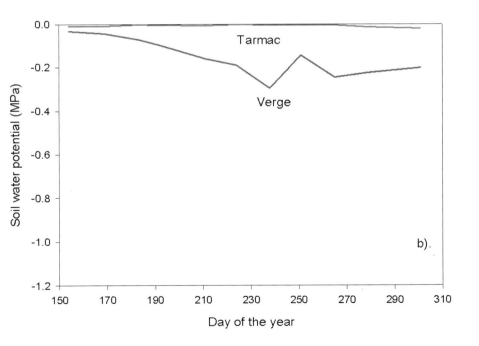

Figure 11.6 Soil water potential measurements recorded at the surface **(a)** and 70 cm below the surface **(b)** of a tarmac covered area of soil and an adjacent grass verge. (After Kopinga, 1994.)

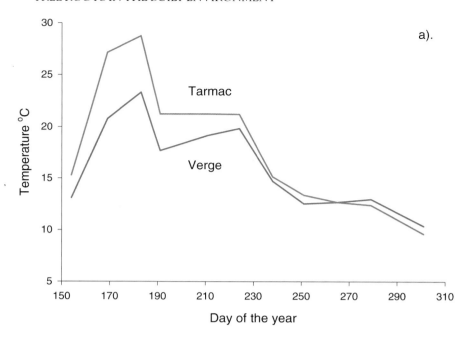

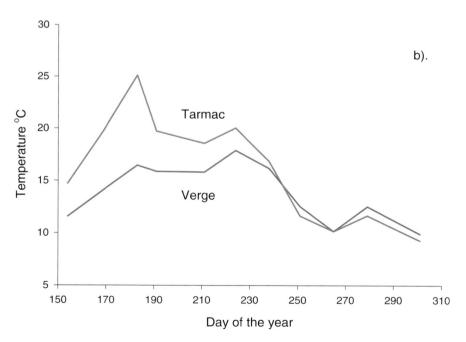

Figure 11.7 A comparison of the temperatures recorded at the surface **(a)** and 70 cm below the surface **(b)** of a tarmac covered area of soil and an adjacent grass verge. (After Kopinga, 1994.)

1995). Wagar and Barker (1983) ranked San Francisco street tree species from most (*Liquidambar*, ash) to least damaging (*Platanus sp.*, privet and *Prunus sp.*). Wong et al (1988) surveyed more than 2000 out of 17000 trees in the city of Manchester and ranked the species in terms of both damage to kerbs and to pavements. The results are reproduced in Table 11.1.

Table 11.1 Trees of the eight major species from the Manchester survey, ranked according to the damage caused to both pavements and kerbs (after Wong *et al*, 1988). The numbers refer to the numbers of trees of the particular species associated with the individual damage categories, ranging from no damage to severe damage. The percentage values represent the percentage of all the trees of that species that were monitored that fall in the particular damage category.

PAVEMENT DAMAGE

Tree species	No damage		Minor damage		Moderate damage		Severe damage	
Ash	171	(51%)	86	(26%)	47	(14%)	30	(9%)
Lime	218	(58%)	93	(25%)	43	(11%)	24	(6%)
Horse chestnut	66	(63%)	23	(23%)	12	(2%)	3	(3%)
Oak	119	(77%)	27	(17%)	7	(5%)	2	(1%)
Platanus sp.	192	(77%)	43	(17%)	9	(4%)	4	(2%)
Birch	94	(78%)	19	(16%)	7	(6%)		
Whitebeam/ rowan	261	(83%)	37	(12%)	13	(4%)	2	(1%)
Cherry	177	(84%)	22	(10%)	7	(3%)	5	(2%)
Total	1298	(69%)	350	(19%)	145	(8%)	70	(4%)

KERB DAMAGE

Tree species	No damage		Minor damage		Moderate damage		Severe damage	
Ash	227	(68%)	77	(23%)	25	(7%)	5	(1%)
Lime	289	(76%)	57	(15%)	20	(5%)	12	(3%)
Horse chestnut	94	(90%)	7	(7%)	3	(3%)		
Platanus sp.	233	(94%)	12	(5%)	3	(1%)		
Whitebeam/	300	(96%)	9	(3%)	2	(1%)	2	(1%)
Birch	115	(96%)	5	(4%)				
Cherry	204	(97%)	5	(2%)	1	(1%)	1	(1%)
Oak	153	(99%)	2	(1%)				
Total	1615	(87%)	174	(9%)	54	(3%)	29	(1%)

Figure 11.8 Trees planted between pavement and adjacent land. (Redwood City, USA).

11.5 Planning ahead – how long before street trees present a problem?

In trying to avoid problems in the future, thought should be given to both the geometry and design of paved areas. Improved materials for use in street tree planting beneath paved areas, such as the Cornell and Amsterdam tree soils are discussed in Chapter 4, and factors influencing street tree establishment are dealt with in Chapter 5.

11.5.1 Planting geometry

How long will it normally take before trees in the newly planted residential street cause kerb/pavement problems, assuming that they ever do? In a 1975 survey, 15 Californian cities reported an average time taken of 15 years, with a range of 7 to 20 years (Hamilton, 1984a). The *Trees in Towns* survey (LUC, 1993) recognised the fact that newly planted trees are unlikely to cause damage until many years in the future. It stated '*A primary concern arising from the present study is that most decisions on tree planting and management appear to address short term needs only and take little or no account of the combined long term effects on townscape. In consequence, the standards and performance of urban environmental enhancement schemes are often measured by the numbers of trees planted rather than the quality of the design, appropriate choice of species, and careful assessment of maintenance costs.*'

However, every situation in which street trees are planted is unique, and pavement plantings are the most difficult problem in the urban situation (Urban, 1999). One must design each planting detail to fit each separate

Figure 11.9 Trees planted between pavement and adjacent kerb. (Redwood City, USA).
Source: Gordon Mann.

application, and it should be based on the surrounding soil conditions. Barker (1976) and Barker and Durrant (1978) studied the geometry of tree planting strips, and the determining relationships between trees, planting geometry and soils were examined by Wagar and Barker (1983). The severity of pavement and kerb damage increased as tree stem diameter increased and decreased with wider planting strips. Damage to pavements exceeded damage to kerbs perhaps due to thicker and deeper concrete used in kerb construction. Wong *et al* (1988) found similar correlations with tree diameter for pavement damage in Manchester. This study showed that the most severe pavement damage occurred within a 2 m radius from the tree, and recommended planting trees in strips (> 3m) where possible, or leaving adequate (at least 2 m × 2 m) areas of unpaved ground if the trees had to be planted into pavement.

Four options for planting trees along pavements have been identified by Urban (1999):

- Best design option: Planting the tree between the pavement and the adjacent land, and constructing the pavement closer to the kerb (Fig 11.8). The soil in the planting space should be improved. This method assumes that the rooting medium on adjacent land is often significantly better than the soils beneath the pavement and the public highway, and seeks to reduce the conflict of the tree roots growing under the pavement to reach the better soil.

- Acceptable design option: Plant the trees in a continuously improved soil band between the kerb and the pavement (Fig 11.9). However, this can lead to damage as the tree roots try to access the better soil on the other side of the pavement.

- Less acceptable option: Trees planted in individual planting holes within the pavement. In this case the openings in the pavement are made as long and wide as possible. The paved space between the trees is made as small as possible, ensuring less compaction, and a greater root access to both water and air. The tree is also moved slightly back from the kerb, soil is improved and interconnected from tree to tree under the pavement. Root/paving conflicts are still possible with this method.

- Least acceptable design option: Trees are planted in narrow pavements with insufficient room for long term development. The pavement is made as narrow as possible at the tree and the tree opening made as long and wide as possible. Soil is improved and interconnected from tree to tree under the pavement. Root/paving conflicts are likely.

11.5.2 Synchronising tree and pavement life spans

The amount of time taken for problems to develop is something that has often been overlooked (McPherson and Peper 1995). One cannot expect a pavement, however well built, to last for hundreds of years (Sydnor et al, 2000). The Public Works Department estimates that the pavement design used in Cincinnati has an average life span of just 20 to 25 years. At the same time, it is not unreasonable to expect street trees to have a similar life span, although obviously examples exist of street trees that are much older than this, particularly in the UK. A number of suggestions were made at a recent arboricultural conference at University of California Davis (on street tree damage to infrastructure) that it would be logical to aim to replace both trees and pavements at similar, regular intervals. Matching the life expectancy of both trees and pavement, and synchronising replacement, would get the maximum service life from each (Costello and Dodge, 2001), and would lower both costs and disruption to the public, allowing more care to be taken in the planning and execution of street tree planting.

11.5.3 Tree selection for minimising potential problems

Tree selection must also be a major consideration when planning to avoid infrastructural conflicts. In one of the only surveys of its kind, the California Department of Forestry noted that urban foresters accept that appropriate species selection can be 90% effective at reducing damage to pavements (Gilman, 2001). Santamour (1972) started the first large-scale attempt to screen genetically superior amenity trees for urban situations, with the aim of selecting improved trees from a wide range of genera whose different characteristics 'fit' different urban environments. As described in Chapter 3, the phenology of rooting habit is said to be 'plastic' in that it adapts to fit the environment in which a tree is growing. Nevertheless, certain species (eg cherry, some ash, mulberry, and elm) are more prone to surface rooting than are other species such as oak (Harris et al, 1999). Similarly, surface roots in some trees (eg elm, poplar and *Robinia*) are given to producing suckers, particularly when injured, and this can lead to pavement damage.

Although there may be apparently valid reasons why 'problem species' are selected, such as maintaining continuity within a monoculture, or historic/local factors, one must realise that there are situations where specific plants are inappropriate and should be avoided. Trees suspected of being predominantly surface-rooted, those with a tendency to produce suckers, or with a potential to outgrow the area in which they are planted and either obstruct the pavement or cause direct action in pushing out kerbs etc should be avoided.

One approach that has not been much researched is the identification and subsequent selection and propagation of species or individuals on the basis of rooting habit. The sort of trees that one would prefer would be those with either naturally deep, vertically oriented root systems, or else those that might respond early on in their development to interventions to encourage vertical (or at least less horizontal) root growth (Burger, 2001). Variability in the growth and distribution of tree roots is common (Barker, 1988; Barker and Wagar, 1987; Coutts, 1989), especially in terms of different rootstocks used. The long-term solution to root damage should therefore include the selection of better species (Harris *et al*, 1999). Many amenity street trees are grafted onto rootstocks of seedling origin with a consequently broad genetic variation (Nicoll and Coutts, 1997). Nicoll and Coutts (1997) suggest that pavement damage could be reduced by selecting tree species for street planting which have less capability for upward lateral root growth, and which would also spread their root biomass evenly between a large number of structural roots. One option for most tree species is genetic improvement to enhance their usefulness in urban areas (Day, 1991).

At present the most frequently planted trees are often the species likely to do the most damage to pavements and kerbs and, consequently the most expensive to maintain during their lifetime. The main reason for this seems to be the widespread availability of these species and, conversely, a general lack of trees that are of conservative size (Barker, 1988). In countries where the provision of shade from the sun is a major role for street trees, species may be selected to produce the necessary canopy size. In cooler climates like the UK, the need to continue planting large-growing species along narrow streets should be reconsidered or justified, especially where smaller species may be more appropriate.

11.6 Remedial action for damaged pavement

Action that can be taken following root-related damage to pavements can be divided into two areas. The first group involves reducing the disruptive tendency of the tree, and the second addresses repairing and possibly improving the design of the pavement. The most radical approach is removing damaging street trees completely. However, concern about recurring problems sometimes makes highway engineers reluctant to allow replanting (Patch, 1994).

11.6.1 Reducing direct damage

A common solution, but usually not the best, is to prune the offending roots, and then reinstate the pavement. Often, a root-pavement conflict can be remedied through pruning a single root or several smaller surface roots. This can usually be achieved without a noticeable effect to the above-ground part of the tree. However, if more extensive pruning of the root system is required, the tree canopy should also be pruned to reduce the wind sail and to reduce the likelihood of the tree blowing over (Phillips, 1999). Wessolly (1996) conducted numerous tip-over experiments and attempted to model street tree stability in terms of a single load (wind force) and a single lever (anchoring load point). The results of that study suggested that major root pruning would threaten tree stability only when carried out close to the base of the tree. The question of how much root pruning causes the tree to become structurally unsafe will depend on the depth and extent of the rooting systems and may necessitate further investigation.

Ideally, all trees with pruned roots should be indicated on the inventory list so that annual inspections can be made to check the tree stability and recovery. In practice, this would depend on the resources available to carry out inspections and a flexible approach to tree inspection is suggested. Ideally, where it is planned to root prune a tree, the canopy should be pruned or thinned a year beforehand. This will reduce the wind sail and lessen the chance of a windthrow. However, pruned roots will often rapidly regrow, and the problem may return with even greater severity. Root pruning of mature ash trees in the San Francisco area required repeat pruning every 4–5 years at a cost of $400–500 per tree (Hamilton, 1984b). In addition, pruning often results in damage to the trees themselves (Nicoll and Coutts 1997). Roots that have caused damage are either removed or ground down, creating wounds that can lead to infection with disease and threatening the stability of the tree. For these reasons, root pruning is rarely considered a good solution to the problem of pavement damage.

In areas where either the climate or the paving situation dictates that street trees must be provided with supplementary irrigation, improved watering practices and the reduction of the total amount of water applied is probably the most effective and cost-efficient means of minimising pavement distortion caused by tree roots (Hamilton, 1984b). However, it must be remembered that irrigation is sometimes essential around trees that have a root barrier installed, or are planted in containers, concrete sewer rings etc. In many cases irrigation may only be required during the establishment phase, but restricted rainfall input, high urban evaporation rates and other factors may dictate that this is continued, possibly throughout the lifetime of the tree.

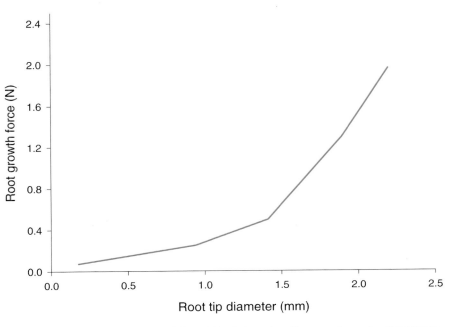

Figure 11.10 Maximum root growth force in Newtons produced by pea, cotton and sunflower roots of various diameters as they grow. (After Misra *et al.*, 1986.)

11.6.2 Root barrier methods

In addition to the variety of obstructions in the soil that roots can encounter, such as rocks, kerbs, pavements and pipes, there may also be barriers deliberately installed in an attempt to deflect tree roots from damaging pavements and low-rise structures (Nicoll and Coutts, 1997). Root barrier methods have been described in some detail in Chapter 10 and therefore any discussion here will focus on their applicability to root damage to paved areas.

As has been mentioned earlier in this chapter, axial root pressures may often be enough to distort and damage paved surfaces, but the force a root can exert depends on its diameter, and hence on the ability of the root to expand radially as it grows (Fig 11.10). Kopinga (1998) reported results of tests of different thicknesses of horizontally installed geotextile root barrier material laid below an asphalt sub-base. The study showed that the number of large roots likely to cause significant damage to the asphalt was greatly reduced by the root barrier (Fig 11.11). Other studies have shown that roots are unlikely to increase in diameter again after having passed through a root barrier material. Thus their individual capacity for damage is reduced, although if enough fine roots coincide, they may be sufficient to cause damage (Wagar and Barker, 1993). Although continuous horizontally installed root barriers may, in some cases, prevent root damage to pavement, vertically installed root screens are the more commonly thought of root barriers. In these cases it is obviously important to ensure that the depth of the barrier is sufficient to deflect root

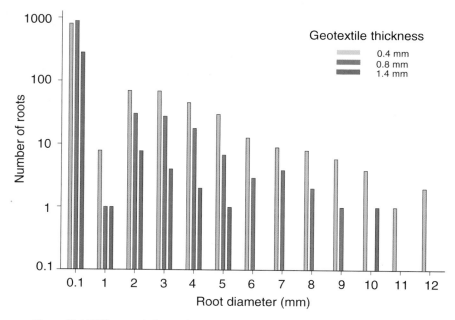

Figure 11.11 Differences in the numbers and size distributions of roots penetrating various thicknesses of a geotextile root barrier material laid horizontally below an asphalt roadbed in the Netherlands. (After Kopinga, 1994.)

growth to such an extent that they will not simply grow under the barrier and resurface, or even grow over the barrier.

One trial of vertical root barriers at 16 locations in The Netherlands (Kopinga, 1998) showed that in every case the roots had circumvented the barriers. Indeed the less compacted soil resulting from the installation of the barrier makes the roots more likely to resurface than would normally be the case (Gilman, 2001). For this reason, in cases where roots quickly resurface, it may be necessary to deploy barriers that retard or inhibit root growth chemically, (as mentioned in Chapter 10) as well as deflecting them (USDA Forest Service, 1999). Critics of root barriers have pointed out that the stability of the tree may be threatened if horizontal roots are not established within 2 to 3 m of the trunk of large trees. Additionally, any buttress roots produced will become contorted, causing premature decline in the tree's health and vigour (Phillips, 1999). Supporters of the technique point out that while this may happen, it is likely to take 20–30 years for the problem to become severe, and that this is likely to be near the end of the average life of an urban tree in the USA. However, in the UK, the life span of a street tree may be much longer than this. Until proven strategies for root control have been developed, it is prudent to simply plan for and allow ample space for root growth, and where that is not feasible, to plant smaller trees.

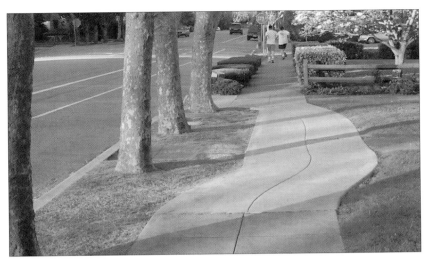

Figure 11.12 Curved pavement designed to afford as much unobstructed rooting volume to the trees as possible. (Redwood City, USA).

11.6.3 Improving pavement design

Several strategies exist for improving the design and build of pavement following root-related damage. Pavements can be removed and then reinstated at a raised level (Phillips, 1999), or long concrete spans can be replaced with flexible materials such as asphalt or compacted gravel. If long concrete spans are essential, expansion joints can be installed so that if any uplift occurs, it is limited to a single section that can be easily replaced after the root problem is corrected. Pavements can be altered and curved to go around existing trees (Fig 11.12). Recent research has made other options available for alleviating post-construction problems in pavement and low-rise situations (Seegebrecht, 2001). These include:

- ramping pavement across/over existing roots (eg Fig 11.13);

- re-laying pavement (and rebuilding low walls) using bridging over roots or elevating an entire section to allow roots to grow below;

- re-laying pavement over roots but leaving a void, or backfilling with gravel and/or foam or sand to provide expansion space (NKAPC, 2000).

Wong *et al* (1988) found that significantly more damage occurred to pavements in Manchester that were sealed with tarmacadam (asphalt), than to those paved with concrete slabs. However, they noted that displaced slabs more commonly pose a safety hazard to pedestrians. This 'trip and slip' risk is a major determining factor in pavement design and construction in the USA. It is becoming more so in the UK where the local Highway Authority is responsible for the repair and maintenance of pavements, so that they are free from hazards, where the highway is maintained at public expense (Round and Lawson, 1999; Highways Act, 1980).

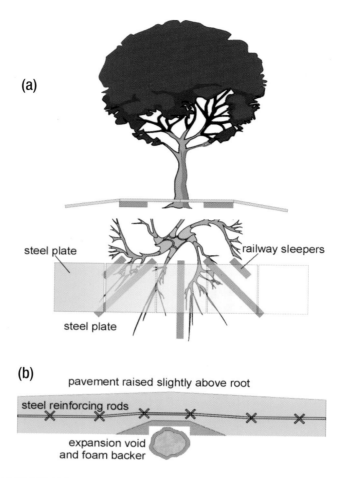

(a)

steel plate

railway sleepers

steel plate

(b)

pavement raised slightly above root

steel reinforcing rods

expansion void
and foam backer

Figure 11.13 (a) bridging section of pavement spanning 'problem roots, (after Shrock, 1994) (b) relaying a section of pavement with an expansion void, backer/buffer and reinforcement to 'bridge' a large problem root. (After Seegebrecht, 2001.)

Future research and field testing of alternative pavement materials will be important, including stronger or flexible (rubberised) concrete and asphalt, the addition of reinforcing rods or wire mesh and inclusion of allelopathic chemicals or root toxins (Costello and Dodge, 2001). There is increasing interest in so-called 'permeable pavement' in the USA to reduce stormwater runoff in cities (Carleton, 1990). It is interesting to speculate what the effects of the adoption of this technology would mean for root damage to paved surfaces in the UK. It may be that the increased rates of rainwater infiltration reported under permeable pavement (Thelen et al, 1972; Andersen et al, 1999) would lead to increased surface root growth. On the other hand, increased soil evaporation and light levels might encourage downward root growth, away from surface infrastructure, assuming O_2 levels in the deeper soil layers are sufficient.

11.6.4 Directed root growth

One idea involves the idea of break-out zones for roots which will encourage root growth into preferred areas. It is possible to improve soil conditions in specific areas to direct tree roots to grow away from the kerbs and pavements. Roots growing in a resource-poor situation will seek out adequate resources, and proliferate where those resources are present in large quantities. Knowledge of root extension processes can be used to direct roots away from kerbs and pavements. This strategy is discussed fully in Section 6.4.1.2.

11.7 Summary

• Roots are unlikely to cause damage to pavements and low-rise structures when trees are young because the majority of root growth is longitudinal as the root system establishes. Damage is likely to begin to occur when trees become older and secondary thickening of the roots occurs to support the increasing weight of the tree and to provide stability against wind loading.

• The environment below pavements may be particularly suitable for roots if there is adequate soil moisture, temperatures are high and soils may not be too compacted.

• Pavement damage is likely to be greatest in association with shallow-rooted tree species. Various surveys have identified such species but because of the intrinsic variability of root growth in response to the environment it is difficult to provide hard and fast rules on which species will always cause damage.

• Nevertheless there is scope to identify and genetically select tree types with rooting patterns compatible with pavements and low-rise structures.

• There is substantial evidence that root barriers may not prove to be a long-lasting solution in preventing root invasion. One study showed that in all cases tree roots bypassed the barriers. It is possible that the looser soil remaining after barrier installation proves to be a pathway for the roots.

• An important consideration in design of new pavement types should be the problem of root damage. It is not clear whether more permeable paving materials will lead to deeper or shallower rooting of tree roots.

REFERENCES

Andersen, C.T., Foster, I.D.L. & Pratt, C.J. 1999. The role of urban surfaces (permeable pavements) in regulating drainage and evaporation: development of a laboratory simulation experiment. *Hydrological Processes*, 13, 597–609.

Atwell, B.J. 1993. Response of roots to mechanical impedance. *Environmental and Experimental Botany*, 33, 27–40.

Barker, P.A. 1976. Planting strips in street rights of way; a key public land resource. In: *Trees and Forests for Human Settlements* (Ed. by J.W. Andresen), pp. 263–274. University of Toronto Press, Toronto, Ontario, Canada.

Barker, P.A. 1988. Proactive strategies to mediate tree-root damage to sidewalk. *Combined Proceedings International Plant Propagators Society*, 37, 56–61.

Barker, P.A. & Durrant, M.G. 1978. Space for trees in street rights of way. In: *North America's Forest; Gateway to Opportunity. Proceedings of the Society of American Foresters and the Canadian Society of Foresters*, pp. 463–467. Society of American Foresters, Bethesda, Maryland, USA.

Barker, P.A. & Peper, P.J. 1995. Strategies to prevent damage to sidewalks by tree roots. *Arboricultural Journal*, 19, 295–309.

Barker, P.A. & Wagar, J.A. 1987. Tree roots and sidewalks. *Proceedings of the 3rd Urban Forestry Conference*, pp. 136–139.

Bernhardt, E. & Swiecki, T.J. 1988. *The State of Urban Forestry in California: Results of the 1988 California Urban Forestry Survey*. California Department of Forestry and Fire Protection, Sacramento, California, USA.

Burger, D.W. 2001. Selection and propagation of deep-rooted ornamental trees for urban environments. In: *Strategies to reduce infrastructure damage by tree roots: Proceedings of a symposium for researchers and practitioners* (Ed. by L.R. Costello, E.G. McPherson, D.W. Burger and L.L. Dodge), pp. 23–25. Western Chapter, International Society of Arboriculture, Cohasset, CA., USA.

Carleton, M.G. 1990. Infiltration, on-site detention and other methods used to reduce local stormflows. In: *Proceedings of the 5th International Conference on Urban storm drainage*. Volume 2. Drainage systems and runoff reduction (Ed. by Y. Iwasa and T. Sueishi), pp. 859–869. Osaka, Japan.

Coder, K.D. 1994. *Flood damage to trees*. University of Georgia extension forest resources.
www.forestry.uga.edu/warnell/service/library/index.php3?docID=104&docHistory%5B%5D=2

Costello, L.R. & Dodge, L.L. 2001. Symposium objective, goals and overview. In: *Strategies to reduce infrastructure damage by tree roots: Proceedings of a symposium for researchers and practitioners* (Ed. by L.R. Costello, E.G. McPherson, D.W. Burger and L.L. Dodge), pp. 5–11. Western Chapter, International Society of Arboriculture, Cohasset, CA., USA.

Coutts, M.P. 1989. Factors affecting the direction of growth of tree roots. *Annales des Sciences Forestières*, 46 suppl, 277–287.

Day, R.W. 1991. Damage of structures due to tree roots. *Journal of Performance of Constructed Facilities*, 5(3), 200–207.

DETR. 1999. *Roots and Routes: Guidelines on Highways Works and Trees.* Chapter 3 – Highway Construction and Maintenance. Department of the Environment, Transport and the Regions, London, UK, consultation document.

DETR. 2001. *Your garden walls. Better to be safe.* Construction series leaflet 91HCN0227. Department of the Environment, Transport and the Regions, London, UK. www.safety.odpm.gov.uk/bregs/br20.htm

Duryea, M.L.& Malavasi, M.M. 1993. *How trees grow in the urban environment.* University of Florida cooperative extension service circular 1093. http://edis.ifas.ufl.edu/FR002

Gilman, E.F. 2001. Root barrier usage in urban landscapes. In: *Strategies to reduce infrastructure damage by tree roots: Proceedings of a symposium for researchers and practitioners* (Ed. by L.R. Costello, E.G. McPherson, D.W. Burger and L.L. Dodge), p. 29. Western Chapter, International Society of Arboriculture, Cohasset, CA., USA.

Gilstrap, C. 2001. The city of Modesto's strategies to reduce infrastructure damage by tree roots. In: *Strategies to reduce infrastructure damage by tree roots: Proceedings of a symposium for researchers and practitioners* (Ed. by L.R. Costello, E.G. McPherson, D.W. Burger and L.L. Dodge), pp. 46–48. Western Chapter, International Society of Arboriculture, Cohasset, CA., USA.

Halverson, H.G. & Heisler, G.M. 1981. *Soil temperatures under urban trees and asphalt.* USDA Forest Service research paper NE-481.

Hamilton, W.D. 1984a. Sidewalk/curb-breaking tree roots. 1. Why tree roots cause pavement problems. *Arboricultural Journal*, 8, 37–44.

Hamilton, W.D. 1984b. Sidewalk/curb-breaking tree roots. 2. Management to minimise existing pavement problems by tree roots. *Arboricultural Journal*, 8, 223–234.

Hamilton, W. D., Owen, W. & Davis, W. 1975. *Street tree root problem survey.* University of California Cooperative Extension, Alameda County, USA.

Harris, R.W., Clark, J.R. & Matheny, N.P. 1999. *Arboriculture, Integrated Management of Landscape Trees, Shrubs, and Vines*, 3rd Edition. Prentice Hall, New Jersey, USA. 687 pp.

Kays, S.J., Nicklow, C.W. & Simons, D.H. 1974. Ethylene in relation to the response of roots to physical impedance. *Plant and Soil*, 40, 565–571.

Kopinga, J. 1994. Aspects of the damage to asphalt road pavings caused by tree roots. In: *The landscape below ground: Proceedings of an International Workshop on Tree Root Development in Urban Soils* (Ed. by G.W. Watson and D. Neely), pp. 165–178. International Society of Arboriculture, Savoy, IL.,USA.

Kozlowski, T.T. 1999. Soil compaction and growth of woody plants. *Scandinavian Journal of Forest Research*, 14, 596–619.

LUC. 1993. *Trees in towns: A survey of trees in 66 towns and villages around England*. Land Use Consultants. Department of the Environment: Research for Amenity Trees, No. 1. 51 pp.

MacLeod, R.D. & Cram, W.J. 1996. *Forces exerted by tree roots*. Arboriculture Research and Information Note 134. Arboricultural Advisory and Information Service, Farnham, UK. 5 pp.

McPherson, E.G. 2000. Expenditures associated with conflicts between street tree root growth and hardscape in California. *Journal of Arboriculture*, 26, 15–18.

McPherson, E.G. & Peper, P. 1995. Infrastructure repair costs associated with street trees in 15 cities. In: *Trees and Building Sites: Proceedings of an International Workshop on Trees and Buildings* (Ed. by G.W. Watson and D. Neely), pp. 49–63. International Society of Arboriculture, Champaign, IL., USA.

McPherson, E.G. & Peper, P.J. 1996. Costs of street tree damage to infrastructure. *Arboricultural Journal*, 20, 143–160.

McPherson, E.G. & Peper, P.J. 2001. Costs due to conflicts between street tree root growth and hardscape. In: *Strategies to reduce infrastructure damage by tree roots: Proceedings of a symposium for researchers and practitioners* (Ed. by L.R. Costello, E.G. McPherson, D.W. Burger and L.L. Dodge), pp. 15–18. Western Chapter, International Society of Arboriculture, Cohasset, CA., USA.

Misra, R.K., Dexter, A.R. & Alston, A.M. 1986. Maximum axial and radial growth pressures of plant roots. *Plant and Soil*, 95, 315–326.

Moss, G.I., Hall, K.C. & Jackson, M.B. 1988. Ethylene and the response of roots of maize (*Zea mays* L.) to physical impedance. *New Phytologist*, 109, 303–311.

Nicoll, B.C. & Armstrong, A. 1997. *Street tree root architecture and pavement damage*. Arboriculture Research and Information Note 138. Arboricultural Advisory and Information Service, Farnham, UK. 6 pp.

Nicoll, B.C. & Coutts, M.P. 1997. Direct damage by urban tree roots: Paving the way for less damaging street trees. In: *Arboriculture Practice – Present and Future* (Ed. by J. Claridge), pp. 77–84. DETR. HMSO, London.

NKAPC. 2000. Northern Kentucky Area Planning Commission: Cold Spring zoning ordinance. *Planting Manual and Landscape Regulation Guidelines*. 47 pp. www.nkapc.cog.ky.us/AppDocs/ZoneOrds/ColdSpri/csplant.pdf

Patch, D. 1994. Management of trees and the environs in which they grow. *Scottish Forestry*, 48, 96–101.

Patch, D. & Dobson, M. 1996. *Driveways close to trees*. Arboricultural Practice Note APN1. Arboricultural Advisory and Information Service, Farnham, UK. 5 pp.

Perry, T.O. 1982. The ecology of tree roots and the practical significance thereof. *Journal of Arboriculture*, 8, 197–211.

Phillips, L.E. 1999. Tips for the Municipal Arborist: Tree Roots versus Sidewalks. *City Trees*, 35(5).
www.urban-forestry.com/citytrees/v35n5a05.html

Rindels, S. 1995. Sidewalks and trees. *Horticulture and Home Pest News*, March 31 1995, p. 36.
www.ipm.iastate.edu/ipm/hortnews/1995/3-31-1995/sidetree.html

Round, L. & Lawson, M. 1999. *Amenity trees and insurance issues – the local authority perspective*. ISA Sustainability of Resources Programme (SORP). ISBN 0953702502. pp119.

Santamour, F.S. Jr. 1972. Shade-tree improvement research at the US National Arboretum. *Proceedings of the International Shade Tree Conference*, 48, 132–133.

Sealana and Associates. 1994. *City of San Jose Sidewalk Survey and Analysis Study*. City of San Jose, Department of Streets and Parks, San Jose, California, USA.

Seegebrecht, G. 2001. Strategies to reduce infrastructure damage by tree roots. In: *Strategies to reduce infrastructure damage by tree roots: Proceedings of a symposium for researchers and practitioners* (Ed. by L.R. Costello, E.G. McPherson, D.W. Burger and L.L. Dodge), pp. 67–69. Western Chapter, International Society of Arboriculture, Cohasset, CA., USA.

Stankovich, M. 1990. Sidewalks and Trees. Village of Oak Park, Oak Park, Illinois, USA.

Sydnor, T.D., Gamstetter, D., Nichols, J., Bishop, B., Favorite, J., Blazer, C. & Turpin, L. 2000. Trees are not the root of sidewalk problems. *Journal of Arboriculture*, 26, 20–29.

Thelen, E., Grover, W.C., Holberg, A.J. & Haigh, T.I. 1972. *Investigation of porous pavements for urban runoff control*, 11034 DUY. Washington, D.C.: U.S. Environmental Protection Agency, 1972, pp. 104–105.

Urban, J. 1999. New approaches to planting trees in urban areas. In: *L'arbre: de la rue à l'autoroute*. Proceedings of conference. Societe de l'arbre du Quebec, Canada. 1999.
www.sodaq.qc.ca/realisations/colloque_99/urban-an.html#urban

USDA Forest Service. 1999. *The Technical Guide to Urban Forestry*, 2nd Edition. World Forestry Center, Portland, USA.
www.na.fs.fed.us/spfo/pubs/uf/techguide/toc.htm

van der Werken, H. 1982. Effects of physical and chemical root barriers on growth of *Koelreuteria bipinnata*. *27th Annual Report and Proceedings of the Southern Nurserymen's Association Research Conference*, Nashville, TN, p. 74.

Wagar, J.A. & Barker, P.A. 1983. Tree root damage to sidewalks and curbs. *Journal of Arboriculture*, 9, 177–181.

Wagar, J.A. & Barker, P.A. 1993. Effectiveness of three barrier materials for stopping regenerating roots of established trees. *Journal of Arboriculture*, 19, 332–338.

Wagar, J.A. & Franklin, A.L. 1994. Sidewalk effects on soil moisture and temperature. *Journal of Arboriculture*, 20, 237–238.

Wessolly, L. 1996. Stability of trees: explanation of the tipping process. *Stadt und Grün*, 1996 No. 4, 268–272.

Wilson, B.F. 1967. Root growth around barriers. *Botanical Gazette*, 128, 79–82.

Wong, T.W., Good, J.E.G. & Denne, M.P. 1988. Tree root damage to pavements and kerbs in the City of Manchester. *Arboricultural Journal*, 12, 17–34.

CHAPTER 12

Tree Root Damage to Sewers, Drains and Pipes

12.1 Introduction

Sewer systems drain sanitary water or 'foul sewage' (Bartlett, 1976), surface stormwater or runoff, and ground drainage either in separated systems, or occasionally in the same pipe. Combined systems are now unusual, and the general approach is to separate foul water from surface water.

The problem of tree roots proliferating within sewer systems has been reported by several authors for a number of years and in various locations (Randrup *et al*, 2001). These include the United States (Baxter, 1958; Geyer and Lentz, 1966; McPherson and Peper, 1996) and Scandinavia (Rolf and Stål, 1994; Randrup, 2000). In the UK, root intrusion may be the cause of up to 5% of all blocked sewers and is responsible for a large proportion of recurring drainage problems (Davidson, 1999), but cases where pipes have broken as a result of root growth are reported to be rare (Brennan *et al*, 1997).

12.2 Nature of the problem

12.2.1 Pipework construction and state of repair

Mains water pipes have at various times been constructed from different materials: cast iron pipes installed since the middle of the 19th century, asbestos cement laid since the 1960s, both ductile iron and PVC used since the early 1970s, and MDPE (medium density polythene) laid since the 1980s. Intrusion of tree roots into water mains is thought unlikely, given the positive water pressures inside the pipes (Brennan *et al*, 1997). However, the current state of some of this pipework in the UK is poor. As of March 1998 7% of mains water pipes were classified as grade 4 ('considerable corrosion affecting service performance; nearing end of useful life; frequent bursts') and 5% as condition 5 ('substantially derelict and source of service problems. No residual life.'), ie 12% were in very poor condition (Binnie, 1999). Even if internal pressures prevented root intrusion, any leakage will encourage root growth in the locality of the leak and may, at some future date, contribute to further damage to infrastructure.

Figure 12.1 Photograph taken inside a main sewer showing a root mass almost completely blocking the pipeline.

Some sewer pipe materials are more resistant to root intrusion than others. In the UK, from the second half of the nineteenth century onwards, brickwork was the most common form of construction for large sewers (DOE, 1977), whereas the most frequently used materials for drains and small diameter sewers were salt-glazed ware pipes and vitreous-enamelled fireclay pipes (Escritt, 1978). Both these types of construction have been reported to be relatively easily penetrated and damaged by tree roots (Anon, 2000). More recently, materials such as asbestos cement and reinforced concrete have been used, as well as glass-reinforced plastics (GRP) and PVC plastics. Concrete pipe and no-corrode pipe may also permit root intrusions, but to a lesser extent than the earlier clay tile pipes. PVC pipe is more resistant to root intrusion because longer runs are possible and hence there are fewer joints, and these are usually tightly fitting and are less likely to leak as a result of settlement of backfill around the pipe. Different building techniques over a period of time have lead to a situation where pipe runs often show abrupt changes of construction, with converters required to join lengths of pipe of dissimilar material. It has been suggested that these may pose a risk in terms of root intrusions into sewers, as mistakes sometimes occur when different pipe materials are joined (Randrup and Faldager, 1997).

It is the joints between pipe sections that tend to be the point of entry for tree roots. Jointing techniques have changed over the years, and a typical pipeline may consist of many short sections of different pipe materials, each joined in different ways. Joints may be made from hemp and bitumen, which tend to harden and may crack if any soil settling occurs. Similarly, concrete joints between sections are rigid and are vulnerable to subsidence and soil

Figure 12.2 20 m of fibrous sycamore roots removed from a drain.

movement. More recently rubber joints were introduced. These joints are usually tight but flexible, and pipes can also flex somewhat without cracking.

In 1982, the UK had a total of 234,278 km of both surface and foul water sewers (Reed, 1982), rising to over 300,000 km by 1993 (WRc, 1993). Even today, much of these are known to be in a generally poor condition. Similarly, the water distribution system in the UK has substantial leaks, with total leakage estimated at 21% of the water put into supply between 1999 and 2000 (NAO, 2000), although this was a reduction of previous years' values. Unlike water mains, flows inside sewers and drains generally rely on gravity and are insufficient to prevent root intrusion. In 1992/93, the proportion of sewers in England and Wales that were either nearing the end of their useful life or had no residual life was 10% (OFWAT, 1997), and was still 10% at the end of 1998 (Binnie, 1999). These figures include appreciable regional variations, eg an increase from 2% to 23% in sewers covered by Southern Water.

12.2.2 What 'attracts' roots to sewers?

Contrary to opinion, trees do not go on 'search and destroy' missions against sewers or stormwater pipes (Moore, 1995), but they follow water gradients in the soil. If these lead to a leaking pipe then roots will tend to grow along lines of least resistance such as are likely to be found around cracked, poorly installed or leaking pipework. It is not uncommon for tree roots to completely block pipes and sewers (Fig 12.1) and impressive lengths of roots have been recovered from pipes (Fig 12.2). Gasson and Cutler (1998) assert that since there is no way in which roots can 'sense' the presence of water in intact pipes, sewers and drains almost always have to be leaking *before* roots are 'attracted' to them. In the absence of any cracks along the pipe, roots clearly must enter at joints between pipe sections. Stål (1998) reported that tree roots are most likely to intrude into sewerage systems at joints between pipes constructed of different materials (eg concrete and PVC), or at the junction of pipes and manholes or inspection covers. Lateral sewers that connect the household to the main sewer generally show a greater likelihood of root intrusion than main pipes (Randrup, 2000), probably reflecting the proximity of the trees in question, often in the garden. In one survey in the United Sates, Sullivan *et al* (1977) found that most cities surveyed cited root intrusion problems in pipes connecting households to main sewer lines. Wall (1983) reported that in Albuquerque, serious root intrusion occurred from many of the city's amenity trees as the sewers provided the only perpetual source of water.

While cracked or leaking pipework may often be to blame, other factors affect how roots are 'attracted' to sewers. When intact drains and other service pipes are cooler than the surrounding soil, water may condense on the outer surface and root growth may develop along the moisture gradient developed in the soil (Cutler, 1995; Coder, 1998). This can give a false impression that roots are 'attacking' the drain (Brennan *et al*, 1997), but equally it can 'attract' roots towards potentially vulnerable joints in the pipework. In contrast, water flowing through sanitary drains in particular can be substantially warmer than the surrounding soil. Root activity, including cell division and nutrient uptake is likely to be significantly greater than in other parts of the colder soil, leading to a mass of fine roots forming around the pipe.

Most authors concur that roots do not break pipes or force their way into pipes (eg Brennan *et al* 1997), but a few studies disagree, citing examples where this has occurred (Jeffries, 1987; Harris *et al*, 1999). It is possible that in very confined spaces, such as those likely to be found in built up areas, root growth may displace pipes or may exert new direct pressures on the pipes (Coder, 1998), sufficient to cause them to break. Indirect damage to pipes can occur due to soil movement, either heave or settlement, that may sometimes be caused by water abstraction by tree roots as explained in detail in Chapter 10. This may occur in areas where expansive clay soil is common (Gasson and Cutler, 1998), but can also occur in situations where the structure of the pipe bed leads to settling faults. Direct and indirect damage are not necessarily linked.

In some cases, sulphide attack on concrete causes pipe failure (Wall, 1983), permitting roots and debris to enter the system. Similarly several authors have mentioned concrete failure due to corrosion from de-icing materials used on roads, including sodium chloride (Craul, 1992), calcium chloride (Ramachandran, 1974) and sulphates (Hutcheon, 1961; Dobson, 1991). It is possible that high concentrations of these compounds, present in slow flowing surface drains, might cause corrosive failure of the concrete and/or the reinforcing metal making up the pipe.

Rolf *et al* (1995) have suggested that in the case of street trees, if the soil surrounding the tree-planting pit is extremely compacted, tree roots might escape into nearby pipe or other trenches, where both the underlay and backfill would be less compacted and more easily explored. Brennan *et al* (1997) suggest that some sewer and pipe displacement may also occur as a result of root movement caused by the wind-rock of the trunk and canopy. This should not occur with more deeply buried pipes, but can affect lateral infrastructure servicing households. A detailed analysis of stresses imposed on underground pipes by tree roots is provided by Mattheck and Breloer (1994). If there is a distinct prevailing wind direction, then pipelines only on the windward side of the tree are normally affected by root growth (Fig 12.3a). In addition, this effect is localised in the area of the root plate (see Chapter 3), through which wind-imposed stresses on the trunk and canopy are transferred to the ground.

Roots on the windward side of the tree will be under tension, while those on the leeward side of the root plate will be compressed. Figs 12.3(a) and (b) show the various effects of roots growing over or under pipelines close to the root plate. In the case where a root grows underneath a pipeline on the windward side of the tree, a 'tensioning sling' may form (Fig 12.3(a)). As the above-ground portion of the tree flexes in the wind, a considerable amount of the strain is transferred to the pipeline. This load transfer occurs in a jolting fashion, and can cause cracks to appear on the pipe's upper side. As the tree grows larger and the wind load increases, it makes sense that the size of the root, and the likelihood of pipeline damage, increases. In comparison with 'tensioning slings', roots pressing down on pipes on the leeward side of the tree transfer loads less effectively, with a smaller chance of damage to the pipeline. Biddle (1998) has commented that if a pipeline passes directly underneath the tree, at right angles to the prevailing wind, it will be very near the neutral pivot point, and therefore will be less prone to root damage. In fact, if it is impractical to install pipes at the recommended safe distance from trees according to the NJUG 10 guidelines (NJUG, 1995), BS 5837 (BSI, 2005) suggests routing them directly beneath the tree as an acceptable alternative (see Section 8.4.2).

Given the demands on space under pavements and roads in the UK, it is not unusual to find several pipelines lying one over another, particularly in the case of sewer laterals and mains pipelines running from the street to the household perimeter. Where this occurs, the formation of 'knots' or root wedges between pipes is possible (Fig 12.4). Both tensional forces and levering transverse forces develop and can distort and break one or both of the pipelines.

12.3 Root growth in pipes and drains

Roots require oxygen to survive and will therefore not grow in pipes that are full of stagnant water or where high ground water conditions prevail. However, some species such as willow (*Salix*) and swamp cypress (*Taxodium*) are able to tolerate waterlogged conditions by 'piping' oxygen to the roots through layers of aerenchyma tissue (see Chapter 3).

All drains are run as shallow as local contours will permit, but built to include a fall (slope) steep enough to ensure that they are self-cleaning. The larger the pipe diameter the smaller the fall ratio will be (ie 1:40 for 100 mm pipes to 1:100 or more for main sewers). Where sewers are deep the only roots present, if any, are anchor roots, and these can coexist with *intact* sewer pipes

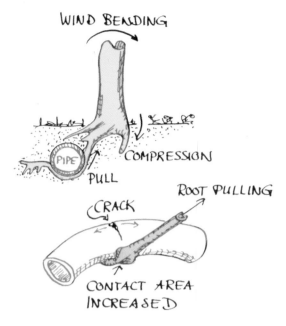

Figure 12.3 (a) Tree roots forming a 'tensioning sling' below a pipeline on the windward side of the tree root plate. (After Mattheck and Breloer, 1994.)

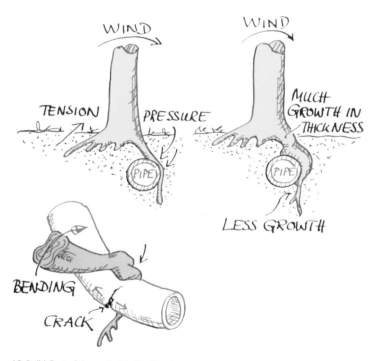

Figure 12.3 (b) Part of the root plate forcing down on a pipeline on the leeward side of the tree. (After Mattheck and Breloer, 1994.)

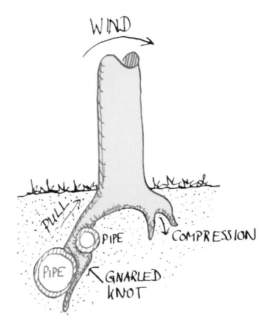

Figure 12.4 Tree roots forming knots between overlying pipelines. (After Mattheck and Breloer, 1994.)

indefinitely without causing problems (Anon, 1999a). However, if one of these deep sewer lines cracks, moisture and air (containing methane and carbon dioxide as well as oxygen) escape into the surrounding area. The anchor roots can then produce opportunistic feeder roots at the site of the leak, if the ratio of air, water and nutrients at that depth becomes similar to the ratio found near the surface. These newly formed feeder roots can then enter the sewer through the defect. However, if large quantities of methane or carbon dioxide are present, these are likely to inhibit the production of new roots.

In a survey of Danish sewer systems, Randrup (2000) found that tree roots were more likely to intrude into pipes that always carry water, such as sanitary drains where wastewater is produced almost 24 hours a day. In contrast, fewer roots were found in surface water drains where water is present only after rainfall events. It is hardly surprising to find more roots in wet pipes than in dry pipes. Once a tree root manages to gain access to a sewer, the warm, moist, nutrient-rich atmosphere above the water surface (especially inside sanitary sewers) provides ideal conditions for it to thrive and proliferate until it clogs the sewer (Harris *et al*, 1999). Sometimes roots enter the pipe from one end, usually at the lateral connecting the house, and grow along the length of the pipe. There appears to be no data available on the rate of root growth inside pipes, as opposed to growing in the soil nearby; such data would be a useful addition to our understanding of root-infrastructure interactions.

Even in cases where a root mass is blocking a drain, careful examinations usually reveal that the root remains constricted to a thin, flattened section at the point where it has entered the pipe through a crack or leaking joint. If the edges of the crack are sufficiently weak, the growth of the root may enlarge the original defect (Biddle, 1998). If roots enter through a crack or leaking joint, they will often grow in a ring around the inside of the pipe, occasionally developing into a complete blockage. In either case, the presence of the roots in the pipe can become a point at which sewage solids may begin to accumulate. The combination of roots and solid wastes can develop into a partial or complete blockage of the pipe. If not disturbed, roots may completely fill the pipe with multiple hairlike root masses at each point of entry. The root mass inside the pipe becomes matted with grease, tissue paper and other debris passing along it.

Factors adversely affecting the growth of roots once inside the sewers and drains include chemicals from both domestic and industrial sources. Pretreated industrial wastewater released into publicly owned systems for further treatment, is often phytotoxic to some degree (Wang, 1990). Some sewer systems may vary substantially from having well aerated to **anoxic** conditions, and waterlogging is common, especially after roots have clogged a sewer. Following waterlogging, all the oxygen available is used up by the respiring roots in 1–3 hours (Coder, 1994) and prolonged anoxic conditions lead to the formation and accumulation of carbon dioxide, methane, hydrogen and nitrogen gas, all unsuitable for root survival. Persistent waterlogging can lead to root death and decay (Colinbelgrand *et al*, 1991).

Concentrations of plant growth regulators (PGRs) such as auxin, ethylene and abscisic acid are known to increase in flooded roots, and when these are translocated throughout the tree, can lead to leaf senescence and abscission over a period of a few weeks. It is unclear as to how much of the root system must be flooded in order to lead to significant leaf drop, and it is certain to vary from species to species. Increased levels of these PGRs can, however, stimulate adventitious root production if oxygen levels recover. Once the situation is reversed and drainage occurs, roots can regenerate or new lateral (secondary) roots will be produced (Nicoll and Coutts, 1998). For trees to adapt to waterlogged conditions inundation must be gradual, an infrequent occurrence in sewers. If **hypoxic** (low oxygen conditions) occur before anoxic (oxygen free conditions) set in, then it is possible that some species may adapt. Ethylene production requires oxygen, and once produced stimulates production of adventitious roots, lateral roots, and aerenchyma which are air channels that form within roots that increase the supply of air by diffusion.

12.4 Tree species involved

Many tree species are reported as causing damage to sewers and drains. Species that had been reported to have caused damage to drains was one of the categories of data collected in the Kew tree root survey (Cutler and Richardson,

1989). Species common to the UK are listed in Table 12.1, although this does not take account of the frequency of each species in the overall population. Biddle (1998) discusses the propensity of different species to cause indirect damage (refer back to Chapter 10).

Table 12.1 Identification of root samples from drains as a percentage of all recorded cases of root intrusion into drains. (After Cutler and Richardson, 1989.)

Species	Percentage
Populus spp.	24.0
Willow	18.5
Horse chestnut	11.0
Acer spp.	9.6
Plane	7.5
Birch	5.5
Prunus spp.	4.5
Ash	4.5
Oak	3.5
Cypresses	2.5
Apple/pear	2.0
Hawthorn	1.6
Lime	1.0
Beech, elm, *Sorbus*, *Robinia*	each <1

Most eucalyptus species are unsuitable for planting close to sewer lines (DNR, 1996). Stewart (1983) listed maple (*Acer* spp) and sweet chestnut (*Castanea*) or horse chestnut (*Aesculus* spp), and especially willow (*Salix*), as problem species in sewers in Washington DC. Harris *et al* (1999) mention willow, poplar (*Populus* spp) and *Acer* spp as having particularly invasive root systems. Randrup (2000) also cites *Salix*, along with poplar and birch as causing the majority of sewer root problems in Danish cities, and both poplar and willow were the most likely genera to cause damage in sewers in Sweden (Stål, 1998). As these are riparian species, they are more likely to have adapted to waterlogged conditions found in sewers and pipes. Similarly, one might expect root systems from other riparian species to cause similar infestation problems (DNR, 1996), such as ash (*Fraxinus*) and alder (*Alnus*), although alder is not extensively planted in the urban environment, except on reclamation sites (Cutler and Richardson, 1989). In addition, many of the species towards the top of Table 12.1 are those that favour expansive clay soils (I. Hopcraft, pers. comm.) and it is possible that a link to subsidence-related damage to drains exists.

12.5 Prevention and repair of damage to pipes and drains

Root intrusion can often be avoided by careful planning and construction in the first place, making sure that all the joints are watertight and fitted correctly. Flexible telescopic joints in 'new build' sewers can help to minimise root problems (Morling, 1963). Wrapping sewer joints with copper wire screen, can delay root intrusion, due to copper's toxicity to small roots. However, Harris *et al* (1999) point out this cannot prevent cracks due to enlarging roots. Root barriers and root-deflecting materials mentioned elsewhere in this book (Chapter 10), such as geotextiles, and herbicide-impregnated material can be used to wrap sewer joints. While these materials will not prevent pipe joints from loosening, they should delay and even prevent roots from entering cracks. Brennan *et al* (1997) have queried the use of sealing rings containing phytotoxic or growth-regulating compounds, as they would have to release the chemical in sufficient quantity to control roots throughout the expected lifetime of the pipe (eg 50+ years for PVC pipes).

Table 12.2 BS 5837 recommended minimum distances between new trees and drains in order to avoid direct damage. (After BSI, 2005).

Diameter of stem at 1.5 m above ground level at maturity	Drain installed < 1 m deep	Drain installed > 1 m deep
< 30 cm	0.5 m	n/a
30 –60 cm	1.5 m	1.0 m
> 60 cm	3.0 m	2.0 m

To avoid direct damage to drains, BS 5837 recommends certain minimum distances at which newly planted trees and drains should be separated. These vary for different mature size trees (Table 12.2) and for shallow drains (eg sewer laterals) or deeper pipes (eg sewer mains). Biddle (1998) notes that as the likelihood of damage is often unpredictable, trees that are closer to pipes and drains than these recommendations should not automatically be suspected of causing damage.

Regardless of whether damage to a drain is root-related or not, it is usually necessary to repair the damage/defect in the pipe. If it is possible to repair the damage to such a standard as to prevent future incursion by tree roots, then tree removal will not be necessary. If access to the damaged pipe is available, excavation and re-laying with modern, more robust materials is often the best option. However, techniques exist for repairing damaged pipes and drains in situ using trenchless technology. One such involves installing a resin impregnated fabric in the old pipe and then expanding and curing the liner in place, where it fits snugly against the damaged pipeline's interior surfaces,

Figure 12.5 A Victorian sewer with crumbling brickwork and eroding joints.

providing a watertight seal to both the main line and to branching laterals (Figs 12.5 and 12.6). The resin liner can be used to fit pipes of 100 mm to >2.4 m diameter (ITL, 2000). Many installations using this technique can be found around the world. Utz (1983) describes one such installation where the use of a resin liner enabled five large elm trees (80–90 cm diameter) growing close to the sewer to be maintained, rather than felled which full sewer replacement would have necessitated.

As well as offering large savings compared with digging and replacement, relining actually increases the flow because the lining offers less friction resistance (Edwards, 1999). It appears that using liners such as these prevent reinvasion of pipes and drains by tree roots (Biddle, 1998).

Another similar technique involves the use of a deformed high density polyethylene (HDPE) pipe which is inserted into damaged pipes or drains, and reformed to fit tightly against the walls (Fig12.7). It is flexible and chemically inert and has been used widely for sanitary sewer lines, storm sewer lines and mains water lines. The material has a minimum life of 50 years. One such HDPE pipeline installed in 1943 between Baltimore and Washington was dug up and tested after 25 years. It had retained virtually the same physical and molecular characteristics as it had when it was first put into the ground (Sureline, 1999). The deformed liner process can line pipes from 100 to 600 mm diameter, including vitrified clay, reinforced concrete, cast iron, ductile iron, asbestos cement and steel. As with resin liners, the coefficient of friction is decreased. These techniques should ensure that a watertight and root-resistant liner is formed. Where these techniques have been applied in the

Figure 12.6 The same sewer as in Fig. 12.5 after lining with joint-less liner to prevent root intrusion through cracks.

Figure 12.7 High-density polyethylene (HDPE) pipe insert used to reline existing sewer pipes.

USA, root intrusion is considered unlikely to recur during the lifetime of the pipe or drain, or at least of the tree whose roots pose a threat, and there is therefore no need to remove the tree or trees in question. However, the design life of pipelines vary significantly, and in the UK the design life of a street tree is often thought to be significantly greater than in the USA. Nevertheless, tree removal should be a measure of last resort for three reasons (SLC, 1999):

1. Tree roots can grow considerable distances from the base of the tree, and therefore determining which tree is the exact and only source of roots in a pipe used to be inexact at best. DNA sampling may now offer some assistance (see Section 10.7.1).

2. Tree removal will not correct the structural fault in the pipe that provided roots access into the line.

3. Unless the fault in the pipe is rectified or the line is replaced, access will remain open for roots from neighbouring trees and/or newly planted trees. In addition, continuing water escape can lead to out-wash and collapse of nearby soil.

12.6 Methods of controlling root intrusion in pipes and sewers

12.6.1 Mechanical removal of roots

Tree roots that have invaded pipes or drains can be removed in a number of ways. Some blockages can be cleared by simple rodding, using sets of connectable rods and a cutter head, but this procedure will leave the broken ends of the roots still in the sewer or drain. It has been demonstrated that root removal or pruning often leads to roots growing back in a denser formation than originally encountered (see Chapter 10; Watson, 1994). Drains that are so badly blocked, that they cannot be cleared by rodding can be cleared using cutters. In the US, the standard procedure for unblocking drain and sewer lines is to use a mechanical router (a powered rotary blade) attached to a flexible steel cable) to physically cut and remove the roots (Harris *et al*, 1999). Roots can also be cut using precision high-pressure water cutters eg Fig 12.8 (Wall, 1983), operating at pressures up to 800 bar (Telespec, 1999). Water cutters such as these have been used to cut through roots up to 150 mm diameter, as well as through fibrous material that completely blocks pipelines. A closed-circuit television camera (CCTV) attached to the device allows precise cuts to be made, as care must be taken not to damage the defective pipe itself.

12.6.2 Chemical removal of roots

An alternative to mechanical removal of roots would be to use chemicals to kill roots in the sewer, and several authors have reported on the efficacy of these techniques, (Leonard and Townley, 1971; Groninger *et al*, 1997; Harris *et al*,

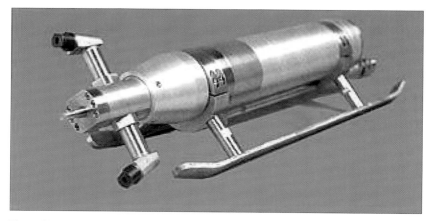

Figure 12.8 High-pressure water cutter used to clear roots and other obstructions from sewers and drains.

1999). Some compounds normally used to sterilise soil have been used to control root growth in sewers in the USA (Rayner, 1965), but these products are not approved under the Control of Pesticide Regulations, 1986 for use in Britain (Brennan *et al*, 1997).

Copper sulphate has been shown to control root growth in sewers in the USA (Tuwiner, 1977) and Australia (Jeffries, 1987) as long as the roots are exposed to the solution for a sufficient time, usually several days to several weeks to work, which is usually impractical. Tree roots in contact with or immersed in copper sulphate solution only absorb copper a short way into the root system, as the absorptive function of the roots seems to be destroyed before the copper can travel too far. The result is localised root killing, and the use of this treatment has yet to cause the loss of a tree or shrub (Mitchell and Schnelle, 1999). Even if copper sulphate only reduces rather than eliminates root growth, it often increases the time needed between mechanical root removal operations (Anon, 1999b). The efficacy of inorganic metal salts, including copper sulphate, as chemical root control methods has not been tested in Britain. Where copper sulphate is used in the USA, it should be applied sparingly as the toxicity has sometimes been reported as interfering with sewage treatment (WPCF, 1980). There is some confusion in this regard, as the United States Environmental Protection Agency (EPA, 1977) found that copper sulphate was able to reduce root growth for up to 3 years with no apparent detrimental effects reported at sewage plants.

Various herbicides have been shown to control root growth in sewers and drains. In laboratory studies the effectiveness of various herbicides has been shown to be lower at reduced tree transpiration rates (Ahrens *et al*, 1970). Over the last 30 years a mixture of metam-sodium (Vapam©) and dichlobenil (Carsoron©) has had particular success (Leonard and Townley, 1971), and has gained widespread uptake in the United States under the trade name of Vaporooter Plus© (Stewart, 1983). Metam-sodium (sodium methyldithiocarbamate) decomposes to release methyl isothiocyanate that has been reported to be effective against growing rhizomes and root systems of some perennial weed species (Nazer and Clark, 1982), and has been shown to kill tree roots a short distance beyond the area treated (Sutton, 1984). Dichlobenil (2,6-dicholorbenzonitrile) acts primarily on apical growing points and root tips, inhibiting roots from growing back (Nazer and Clark, 1982). The chemicals do not appear to injure other parts of exposed plants (Harris *et al*, 1999).

Roots are exposed to the herbicide mixture in a variety of ways. The first involves sealing off a length of the sewer usually between 75 and 125 m in length and filling it with the solution. Any roots protruding into the sewer are 'soaked' in the solution for up to an hour. The dead roots lose their structural strength, become brittle and break off with the flow of liquid once the sewer is unblocked. It is recommended that any dislodged root masses are removed after they have been killed to prevent stoppages. Instead of soaking roots in large volumes of the herbicide solution, roots can also be exposed to the active compounds in foam form, and this technique was found to be more than 20 times as effective as the root-soak technique (Leonard *et al*, 1974). Some studies suggest that foam treatments may be effective for 3 to 5 years (Monck, 1980, in Harris *et al*, 1999), possibly due to the fact that the dead ends of the roots block the points of ingress into the sewer until they gradually biodegrade and allow new roots to gain access. Jeffries (1987) reports that the city of Brisbane uses the foam-based version of *Vaporooter* but after the dead roots have been removed, the sewer is then regrouted to prevent regrowth through any cracks. Similarly, Wass and Bush (1977) describe regrouting following root removal as being particularly effective, especially as the grout used contained a root-growth inhibitor to prevent future problems.

Metam-sodium is known to have toxic effects on nitrifiers used in sewage treatment plants (Ake, 1995), and therefore other authors have investigated alternative compounds (eg Groninger *et al*, 1997). They found that another herbicide, glufosinate, effected the greatest root control, but at the expense of damage to other parts of the test plants. They point out that in comparison with the test plants, the proportion of a tree's root system present in a sewer, and thus compromised by the treatment, is likely to be far smaller than in the experiment and therefore the technique may be of value.

However, in much of Europe there are stringent controls on what few chemicals may be disposed of through wastewater systems. Consequently chemical control of roots is not allowed in many areas eg Scandinavia (Rolf and Stål, 1994). It is even likely these methods may be banned in parts of the United States in the near future for ecological reasons (Randrup, 2000). Brennan *et al* (1997) note that the water authorities in Britain are reluctant to allow sudden or prolonged increases in chemicals present in effluent that might adversely affect the sewage treatment process. Under the Water Resources Act 1991, it is an offence to 'cause or knowingly permit' a discharge of poisonous, noxious or polluting matter to enter any controlled waters without the proper authority. To release such compounds into a sewer you need a Trade Effluent

Consent from the local Water Service Company (EA, 1999). Specifically concerning substances prescribed by the Water Resources Act, the approval of the Environment Agency is needed before consent is obtained from the local Water Services Company (MAFF, 1998).

12.7 Summary

- Direct damage to underground services such as sewers and drains appears to be uncommon. However, frequent blockages of these systems occur as a result of root intrusion into already damaged pipework. The sewer and water supply system in the UK is gradually being renovated, and it is to be expected that the problem of root intrusion will lessen as the more dilapidated systems are repaired or replaced.

- Measures can be taken to eliminate or at least reduce the incidence of root intrusion. The simplest of these is to consider avoiding planting species known to be more likely to invade cracked and leaking pipework, such as willow and poplar close to existing sewers and drains. Where damaged pipework is accessible and trees will not be compromised, the pipes can be removed and replaced. Where this is impossible or inadvisable, other techniques exist for *in situ* remediation.

- Identification and repair of damaged sections of pipework will become easier as the use of CCTV inspection becomes more common. Rapid surveying and repair can prevent small defects becoming larger and more problematic.

- Mechanical and chemical techniques for root removal exist, but both have their drawbacks. Cutting roots has been shown to promote root regrowth in a dense form ideal for reblocking pipes. Chemical methods are controversial or already illegal in many parts of Europe, and this may soon be the case in other parts of the world.

- Removal of the tree should not generally be considered as an effective solution to root intrusion, particularly where one cannot be certain where the problem roots have originated. In addition, the defect in the pipe that allowed them entry in the first place still exists, leading to outwash and collapse of the immediate area. However, there may be occasional circumstances where there is no other option but to remove the problem tree.

REFERENCES

Ahrens, J.F., Leonard, O.A. & Townley, N.R. 1970. Chemical control of tree roots in sewer lines. *Journal of the Water Pollution Control Federation*, 42, 1643–1655.

Ake, T.N. 1995. *The evaluation of metham sodium and dichlobenil impacts on activated sludge nitrification.* Unpublished M.Sc. thesis, Virginia Polytechnic Institute and State University, Blacksburg, VA., USA. 115 pp.

Anon. 1999a. *Tree roots and sewer blockages.* City of Winnipeg, Canada. Public Works Department: Parks and Open Space Division, Canada.
www.city.winnipeg.mb.ca/PWDForestry/rootdoc.html

Anon. 1999b. *Basement flooding control.* Palatine, Illinois, Public Works Dept., USA. www.palatine.il.us/publicwrks/home.htm

Anon. 2000. *Root growth in sewers: Getting to the root of the problem.* City of Edmonton, Public Works Dept., Canada.
www.gov.edmonton.ab.ca/ampw/drainageservices/whatwedo/opsgettingrootproblem.html

Bartlett, R.E. 1976. *Surface water sewerage.* Applied Science Publishers, London, UK. p. 3–4.

Baxter, S.S. 1958. Subsurface problems of trees and utility structures. *Trees Magazine*, Ohio, USA. 19, 7–8.

Biddle, P.G. 1998. *Tree root damage to buildings. Volume 1: causes, diagnosis and remedy.* Willowmead Publ., Wantage, UK. 376 pp.

Binnie, C. 1999. *Future Water and Sewerage Charges 2000–2005: The implications for capital maintenance expenditure.* A report commissioned by Water UK Ltd.
www.water.org.uk/magazine/bulletins/waterinfo/34.html

Brennan, G., Patch, D. & Stevens, F.R.W. 1997. *Tree roots and underground pipes.* Arboriculture Research Note No. 36. Arboricultural Advisory and Information Service. Farnham, UK. 3 pp.

BSI. 2005. BS 5837: *Trees in relation to construction – Recommendations.* British Standards Institution, London, UK. 32 pp.

Coder, K.D. 1994. *Flood Damage to Trees.* Extension Forest Resources, University of Georgia, USA. 7 pp.
www.forestry.uga.edu/warnell/service/library/index.php3?docID=104&docHistory%5B%5D=12

Coder, K.D. 1998. Root growth control: managing perceptions and realities. In: *The Landscape Below Ground II. Proceedings of a Second International Workshop on Tree Root Development in Urban Soils* (Ed by D. Neely, D. and G.W. Watson), pp. 51–81. International Society of Arboriculture, Champaign, IL., USA.

Colinbelgrand, M., Dreyer, E. & Biron, P. 1991. Sensitivity of seedlings from different oak species to waterlogging – effects on root growth and mineral nutrition. *Annales des Sciences Forestières*, 48, 193–204.

Craul, P.J. 1992. *Urban soil in landscape design*. John Wiley, New York, USA. 396 pp.

Cutler, D.F. 1995. Interactions between roots and buildings. In: *Trees and Building Sites. Proceedings of an International Workshop on Trees and Buildings* (Ed. by G.W. Watson and D. Neely), pp. 88–98. International Society of Arboriculture, Champaign, IL., USA.

Cutler, D.F. & Richardson, I.B.K. 1989. *Tree roots and buildings*, 2nd Edition. Longman, London, UK. 71 pp.

Davidson, P. 1999. *WRc getting to the root of the problem*. WRc plc, Swindon, UK.

DNR. 1996. *Tree Root Problems*. Department of Natural Resources, Queensland, Australia. 4 pp. www.nrm.qld.gov.au/factsheets/pdfvegetation/v83.pdf

Dobson, M.C. 1991. *De-icing salt damage to trees and shrubs*. Forestry Commission Bulletin 101. HMSO, London, UK. 63 pp.

DOE. 1977. *Sewers and water mains – a national assessment*. National Water Council, Standing Technical Committee, Report 4. Department of the Environment, London, UK. 34 pp.

EA. 1999. *Works in, near or liable to affect watercourses*. Environment Agency Pollution Prevention Guidelines 5. 4 pp. www.environment-agency.gov.uk/commondata/105385/ppg05.pdf

Edwards, H.R. 1999. *The resistance of isopolyester resins to sewer environments*. Insituform Technolgies Ltd www.insituform.com/resourceroom/rr207.pdf

EPA. 1977. *Economic analysis, root control and backwater flow as related to infiltration/inflow control*. Cincinnati, OH., USA: Environmental Protection Technology Series EPA 600/2-77-017a.

Escritt, L.B. 1978. *Public health engineering practice volume II*. Sewerage and sewage disposal. Macdonald & Evans, London, UK. 494 pp.

Gasson, P.E. and Cutler, D.F. 1998. Can we live without trees in our towns and cities? *Arboricultural Journal*, 22, 1–9.

Geyer, J.C. & Lentz, J.J. 1966. An evaluation of the problems of sanitary sewer system design. *Journal of Water Pollution Control Federation*, 38, 1138–1147.

Groninger, J.W., Zedaker, S.M. & Seiler, J.R. 1997. Herbicides to control tree roots in sewer lines. *Journal of Arboriculture*, 23, 169–172.

Harris, R.W., Clark, J.R. & Matheny, N.P. 1999. *Arboriculture, Integrated Management of Landscape Trees, Shrubs, and Vines*, 3rd Edition. Prentice Hall, New Jersey, USA. 687 pp.

Hutcheon, N.B. 1961. Concrete. Canadian Building Digest CBD 15. http://irc.nrc-cnrc.gc.ca/cbd/cbd015e.html

ITL. 2000. Insituform Technologies Ltd, UK. *Design guide and specification: rehabilitation of pipelines and conduits with cured-in-place pipe (CIPP)*. www.insituform.com/designguide/designindex.cfm

Jeffries, C. 1987. Australian sewerage problems and their solutions. *Municipal Engineer*, 4(2), 87–94.

Leonard, O.A., Bayer, D.E. & Glenn, R.K. 1974. Control of tree roots. *Journal of Arboriculture*, 22, 520–522.

Leonard, O.A. & Townley, N.R. 1971. Control of tree roots in sewers and drains. *Californian Agriculture*, 25, 13–15.

McPherson, E.G. & Peper, P.J. 1996. Costs of street tree damage to infrastructure. *Arboricultural Journal*, 20, 143–160.

MAFF. 1998. Code of Good Agricultural Practice for the Protection of Water. Ministry of Agriculture, Fisheries and Food, London, UK. 109 pp. www.defra.gov.uk/environ/cogap/watercod.pdf

Mattheck, C. & Breloer, H. 1994. *The body language of trees – a handbook for failure analysis*. Department of the Environment. Research for Amenity Trees, No. 4. TSO, London. 240 pp.

Mitchell, P.J. & Schnelle, M.A. 1999. *Controlling tree roots in sewer lines with copper sulfate*. Oklahoma Cooperative Extension Service: OSU Extension Facts CR-6428. www.okstate.edu/OSUAg/agedcm4hpearl/hort/ornament/cr-6428.pdf

Monck, J.W. 1980. *Root growth in sewers*. Speech at American Public Works Association convention in Kansas City, USA.

Moore, G.M. 1995. *Trees and the hard landscape*. Horticulture in New Zealand, 6, 57–60.

Morling, R.J. 1963. Trees: Including preservation, planting, law, highways. *London: Estates Gazette*.

NAO. 2000. *Leakage and water efficiency*. Report by the comptroller and auditor general, National Audit Office. Office of Water Services (OFWAT). TSO, London, UK. 51 pp.

Nazer, C.J. & Clark, J.D. 1982. Prevention of tree root invasion. *Australian Parks and Recreation*. Feb 1982, 58–61.

Nicoll, B.C. & Coutts, M.P. 1998. Timing of root dormancy and tolerance to waterlogging in clonal Sitka spruce. *Trees, Structure and Function*, 12, 241–245.

NJUG. 1995. *NJUG 10: Guidelines for the planning, installation and maintenance of utility services in proximity to trees*. National Joint Utilities Group, London. 23 pp.

OFWAT. 1997. *Serviceability of the water and sewerage networks in England and Wales, Information Note 35*. Office of Water Services. January 1997.

Ramachandran, V.S. 1974. *Calcium chloride in concrete.* Canadian Building Digest CBD 165. http://irc.nrc-cnrc.gc.ca/cbd/cbd165e.html

Randrup, T.B. 2000. Occurrence of tree roots in Danish municipal sewer systems. *Arboricultural Journal*, 24, 283–306.

Randrup, T.B. & Faldager, I. 1997. Tree roots in sewer systems – a survey of the extent of the problem with roots from trees and shrubs in Danish sewer systems. *Park-og Landskabsserien nr.* 14-1997. Danish Forest and Landscape Research Institute, Hoersholm, Denmark. 86 pp.

Randrup, T.B., McPherson, E.G. & Costello, L.R. 2001. Tree root intrusion in sewer systems: Review of extent and costs. *Journal of Infrastructure Systems*, March 2001, 26–31.

Rayner, G.Z. 1965. Soil fumigants control roots in sewers. *American City*, 80(6), 135.

Reed, E.C. 1982. The Assessment of the problem in the UK. In: *Restoration of sewerage systems* (Ed. by J.E.V. Holmes, D.F. Rees, J.N. Rushbrooke and W.B. Varley), pp. 3–8. The Institution of Civil Engineers, Thomas Telford Ltd, London, UK.

Rolf, K. & Stål, Ö. 1994. Tree roots in sewer systems in Malmo, Sweden. *Journal of Arboriculture*, 20, 329–335.

Rolf, K., Stål, Ö. & Schroeder, H. 1995. Tree roots and sewer systems. In: *Trees and Building Sites. Proceedings of an International Workshop on Trees and Buildings* (Ed. by G.W. Watson and D. Neely), pp. 68–77. International Society of Arboriculture, Champaign, IL., USA.

SLC. 1999. *Sewer lateral/tree root policy.* Urban Forestry Program, Salt Lake City, USA.

Stål, Ö. 1998. The interaction of tree roots and sewers: the Swedish experience. *Arboricultural Journal*, 22, 359–367.

Stewart, S. 1983. Root out those sewer clogs. *American City and County*, 98(8), 27–28.

Sullivan, R.H., Gemmell, R.S., Schafer, L.A. and Hurst, W.D. 1977. *Economic analysis, root control, and backwater flow control as related to infiltration/inflow control.* Municipal Environmental Research Laboratory, Office of Research and Development. U.S. Environmental Protection Agency, Cincinnati, Ohio. 103 pp.

Sureline. 1999. *An environmentally safe & cost effective solution for today & through the 21st century.*

Sutton, M.K. 1984. Chemical root control program reduces sewer stoppages. *Public Works*, July 1984, 68–69.

Telespec. 1999. *The precision root and intrusion high pressure water cutter.* Product description. www.telespec.co.uk

Tuwiner, S.B. 1977. Copper sulfate fights root growth in sewer systems. *Water and Sewage Works*, 124, 40–41

Utz, J.H. 1983. Solving a difficult sewer rehabilitation problem. *Public Works*, 114, 59–60.

Wall, W.D. 1983. City improves control over sewer line intrusion. *Public Works*, 114, 72–73.

Wang, W.C. 1990. Toxicity assessment of pre-treated industrial wastewaters using higher plants. *Research Journal of the Water Pollution Control Federation*, 62, 853–859

Wass, V.C. & Bush, C.M. 1977. Benefits from grouting an entire sewer system. *Public Works*, 108, 55–57.

Watson, G.W. 1994. Root development after transplanting. In: *The landscape below ground: Proceedings of an international workshop on tree root development in urban soils* (Ed. by G.W. Watson and D. Neely), pp. 54–68. International Society of Arboriculture, Savoy, IL., USA.

WPCF. 1980. *Operation and maintenance of wastewater collection systems*. Manual of Practice No. 7. Water Pollution Control Federation, USA.

WRc. 1993. *Manual of sewer condition and classification*, 3rd Edition. WRc plc, UK. 77 pp.

CHAPTER 13

Research Needs and Sustainability

13.1 Introduction

In this, the final chapter, we review the information contained in previous chapters and consider where, in the case of the understanding between the interaction of trees and built structures, there is a need for further research. It may be that although some information is available the research supplying the understanding was rather narrow in focus, based on one or just a few tree and/or shrub species, carried out on a limited age range of trees or in otherwise rather specific circumstances.

Alternatively there may be situations where the understanding may be sufficiently good and broad-based but that this knowledge has not yet been converted into good practical advice for the care and management of trees in the built environment.

Research information will have little applied value unless conclusions of a practical nature are disseminated effectively and used widely. Often the information needs to be distributed outside of the tree care industry, for example to operatives who will excavate close to trees. It is important that relevant information is available in a simple, concise manner and in a durable format for operatives to have at hand during work.

In a world in which resources are becoming more and more limited sustainability and long-term care of the environment have become important considerations for all our activities. Growing trees in the built environment should be sustainable and not a drain on resources. It is also important to consider the possible impact of sustainability initiatives on urban trees.

13.2 Research requirements

In Chapter 1 some questions were raised about the form and function of roots. These questions are repeated in Box 13.1. The first two of these questions could in fact be answered without further research. In fact much of the understanding to answer these questions, at least in general terms, is available

---

Box 13.1 Questions and Issues about Root Form and Function

1. What is the role of roots in sustaining water relations?

2. In what ways is water, lost from foliage by transpiration, replenished by water entering roots?

3. Can the relation between root impairment (for example that inflicted by trenching), stability and dieback be quantified? How will roots and root systems respond to damage?

4. Remembering that the balance of fine and structural roots in mature trees differs from that in saplings, can the responses of one be used to predict those of the other?

5. Much more needs to be known about the likely responses of roots to impenetrable barriers.

6. What are the responses of roots affected indirectly as well as directly by environmental and habitat variables including soil type and atmospheric pollutants?

7. What are the mechanisms that roots invoke on sites of dereliction that are compacted and/or contaminated with toxic concentrations of obnoxious chemicals?

8. Bearing in mind the notoriety that instances of damage attract it is not inappropriate to be reminded that these instances implicate a very small minority of trees. But exactly how is this damage brought about? What are the relative contributions of direct and indirect damage?

---

in texts about the availability of water in soils and how plants acquire that water. The posing of these questions illustrates perhaps, a need for much better dissemination of basic information to any professionals who interface with trees in the built environment. To a certain extent this basic information is repeated here in Chapters 2, 3 and 6, but could be issued in a convenient way as suggested in Section 13.4.

The other questions posed in Chapter 1 (Questions 3 to 6) reflect the need for more practical information. In cases such as these queries, it is reasonable to say that the literature reviews that were necessary to prepare Chapters 8, 9, 10 and 11 showed that there are still many gaps in our knowledge about tree root form and function in the built environment.

Even a casual reader of the earlier chapters, relating to the interaction of tree roots and the built environment, will have noticed that a great deal of information came from studies in North America. The studies often involve tree species that occur uncommonly or not at all in the streets of the UK and

Europe. Furthermore, many of the studies will have tended to be done on fairly young trees.

At the Warwick conference of 1997 (see Chapter 1) the need for increased information about roots and their form and function was identified. Having completed this review we have identified questions of and omissions in our current knowledge. Although certainly not exclusive, the identified priorities can be grouped in generic terms as:

- The form and growth of root systems
- The environment below ground in the built environment
- Tree soils
- The water requirements of trees
- The mortality spiral
- Species tolerances.

Key areas for which fundamental research needs to be carried out will be discussed more fully below.

13.2.1 The form and growth of root systems

In the literature about forest ecosystems there is a lot of information about the depth distribution of roots and a key piece of information is that much of the root density occurs close to the soil surface. This type of information is particularly relevant for tree roots in the built environment and the impact on trees of activities such as excavation which disturb the upper soil horizons either by digging or through compaction.

Unfortunately there is no equivalent large body of information about the horizontal extent of roots. What information we have often comes indirectly by investigations of the possible implication in the damage to building foundations by tree roots (Cutler and Richardson, 1989). There is a major shortcoming with this type of information, however. The physical presence of roots close to the foundations of damaged structures does not indicate the furthest extent of the root system. In fact, the lateral extent could be even more.

There is a great deal we do not know about the lateral growth of tree roots that would help us manage trees and activities close to them more readily. It would be valuable to have the answers to a number of questions.

If we had a better understanding of the reasons why tree roots extend significant distances beyond the crown radius and are sometimes involved in structural damage to buildings we might be able to better manage trees to avoid problems.

- Is the extent of a tree's roots a consequence of its search for water or are other factors involved?

We have some information (eg see Chapter 3) that shows that the lateral extent of roots of some species is far greater than others, and that the relationship of the radial spread of roots does not have a unique relationship with crown diameter. We need far more of this information for UK conditions and the samples should not be biased ie only trees which are associated with damage being sampled.

- Are there species differences in the degree of root extension?
- What are the relationships between root extent and simple measures eg crown radius or trunk diameter?
- What are the dynamics of the rate of lateral growth of tree roots as a tree grows and matures?
- What determines which direction lateral roots grow in?
- Can damaged lateral roots extend as far as undamaged ones?

There is considerable damage done to pavements and boundary walls linked to the increase in diameter of tree roots. However, we have very little quantitative information about the rates of diameter growth of tree roots that can be used in the planning of infrastructure in relation to tree development.

- What are the rates of diameter growth of roots?

13.2.2 The environment below ground in the built environment

At a number of points in this text we have declared a lack of knowledge about the environment and root and soil processes below ground and especially where the soil surface is partially or completely sealed by built surfaces. Without this knowledge we are unable to determine many of the limits to tree growth and therefore to offer a remedy. We need answers to a number of questions about the constraints for trees growing in hard landscapes.

- What is the water and nutrient supply for these trees?
- With no new inputs of organic matter via canopy litter, what has been the fate of the original soil organic matter?
- Has there been mineralisation and has there been a concomitant rise in soil bulk density?
- Is the turnover of fine roots a major source of nutrients?
- What component of the soil diversity contributes to the welfare of the tree?
- What mycorrhizal populations occur below street trees?

Figure 13.1 Mature lime trees surrounded by an asphalt surface, Witney, Oxfordshire.

Some urban soil surfaces have been largely sealed with hard surfaces for up to many decades. Many street trees have grown, developed and matured in these conditions (Fig 13.1).

- Does the development of soil conditions mean that the replacement of old, moribund or dead street trees with young trees face serious soil constraints such as low organic matter, high soil bulk density, inadequate soil nutrients and an inappropriate population of soil mycorrhizae?

These are only a few of the questions but answers to some of them would probably help us to manage and protect our trees better. Furthermore, a better knowledge of conditions below-ground, where the soil surface has been largely covered with a hard surface for extended periods, might better enable the establishment of thriving young trees as replacement of old trees becomes necessary.

13.2.3 Tree soils

A major issue in the growth of trees in the built environment is the conflicting need to provide trees growing in pavements with sufficient soil resources for

Figure 13.2 The market place at Ripley, Derbyshire showing London plane (*Platanus* x *hispanica*) trees growing in Amsterdam tree soil. Photograph taken July 2001.

good growth but at the same time providing sufficient engineering strength in the soil to support the pavement or road. Research is being pursued at a number of centres to develop soil mixtures that have sufficient engineered strength to support sufficient loads but to still allow adequate tree root growth. Details of some of the specific approaches have been referred to in Sections 4.2.3 and 4.5.3. An important issue in this research area is the need to continue the studies beyond the age of the trees already used in the previous trials. For example Fig 13.2 shows London plane trees growing in pits filled with Amsterdam tree soil at Ripley, Derbyshire. The trees were planted in 1994 (cf Couenberg, 1998). The trees appear healthy but are small for their age and have less dense crowns than might be expected had they been growing in a lawn situation. There has been some recent research on various types of tree soils in the UK carried out by Richards, Moorehead and Laing. This study which was referred to in Section 4.23 concentrated on the below-ground requirements of young trees (Fig 13.3). It is important to know the answers to some key questions for which so far there is very little research evidence.

- Can structural soils provide the requirements of semi-mature trees?

- Does the matrix of stones retain soil over long time periods?

- What is the fate of the organic matter introduced as part of the tree soil? Does the proportion of mineral soil increase when the organic matter decays and is there an associated increase in soil bulk density?

- Is there any tree stability problem associated with these soils?

Figure 13.3 Growing young plane and poplar trees in various media, TRL, Crowthorne, UK.

13.2.4 The water requirements of trees

At several places in previous chapters the issue of the water requirements of trees has been raised. The need for information in relation to the irrigation needs of young trees was discussed in Section 5.5.1. In Section 6.3.3 the water needs of trees and the capacity of the volume of soil in tree pits to supply this water adequately was evaluated. Finally in Section 10.3.5 the relative water uptake of different tree species is discussed in relation to the drying of shrinkable clay soils and the attendant threats to the foundations of buildings.

In terms of all of these types of requirements there is still a considerable shortage of information about tree transpiration: how it varies with species, tree age, how transpiration fluctuates with environmental conditions and soil water content. Some of this information might be regarded as an above-ground issue but in fact there is an obvious, close link to the requirements of the soil water supply needed to sustain the water demand of the tree.

The technology to accurately measure the transpiration of individual trees over a range of sizes is readily available. The vast majority of tree water use studies have been conducted in closed forests. Because of the very different canopy structure of forest trees compared to isolated, amenity trees the results from forests are not easy to extrapolate to the built environment. Only rarely have comprehensive studies been implemented on individual trees such as those occurring in amenity situations. A study carried out by a consortium led by Dr Neil Hipps (Horticulture Research International, East Malling, Kent, UK) investigated the water use of a limited number of species and the impact of crown reduction on transpiration (BRE, 2004). It is a priority to extend this type of study considerably to include a wider range of species and a wider span of ages. Ideally such studies would span a number of years to cover a broad range of weather and soil water conditions. Studies would also need to be carried out on trees growing on a range of soil types.

An important consideration in such studies is to extend their generality as far as is possible. To do this it is important that key ancillary measurements of leaf area, weather variables and soil water conditions are also measured. These additional measurements would be used to separate the influences of weather, soil moisture and canopy size on transpiration. Ideally, the output from such studies would not simply be a listing of transpiration on a day to day basis but robust predictive models of tree transpiration for a number of species covering a range of ages that can be extrapolated to other situations of climate and soil water availability.

The water use of trees and other tree characteristics, such as crown size, are basic inputs to assessments of the likelihood that trees are likely to be a causal risk to building subsidence. Considerable effort has been spent in attempts to develop reliable, robust assessment methods. Such a method, TreeRAT, was launched by Royal & Sun Alliance and is referred to in Section 10.6. The research possibilities to improve subsidence risk assessment are, however, far from exhausted. Assessment methods used so far rely heavily on empirical functions to determine a risk factor for the trees involved. These factors are largely pragmatic and have little physiological meaning. Large old trees are not distinguished from large young trees for example. Not only does this lumping ignore known physiological differences but it will mean that remedial measures applied to reduce the risk of subsidence eg pruning, may be applied unnecessarily to trees less able to withstand them. There is by now a very large amount of data present in the claims archive about trees involved with subsidence. There will also be information about soils and in many cases historical rainfall and climate data for the area can be obtained. Combining these data it should be possible to develop a physiological model of tree water use. This would be available to predict more realistically the tree (species, age, etc), soil and climate combinations most likely to be associated with subsidence.

A major problem with developing an understanding about the risks to buildings from subsidence associated with trees is the very biased sample that serves as a source of information. An example is the body of tree root data associated with building damage presented in Cutler and Richardson (1989). As a source of information about the extent of tree roots it is limited only to those trees involved in damage to buildings, there is no information about the roots systems of trees not associated with damage. There must be many cases where damage to buildings is associated with a particular tree but nearby is an identical situation (tree species, age, soil and climate) where there is no damage. In terms of robust science and research opportunity it does seem to be a major omission that there has not been a detailed study of individuals associated with damage in direct comparison with those growing nearby with which no damage is associated.

Box 13.2 Measurements of stress and physiological performance in trees

Stomatal conductance. Uses a porometer to measure the capacity of the leaf to lose water. Leaf conductance responds to environmental variables and is the control of transpiration at the leaf level. Reduction of stomatal conductance occurs when trees are short of water or otherwise stressed. Requires canopy access and because of variability significant sampling. Equipment expensive ~ £4,000.

Leaf gas exchange (photosynthesis). Uses an infrared gas analyser (IRGA) to measure photosynthesis and transpiration of a leaf (or leaves) enclosed in a small, transparent chamber. Climate-controlled chambers can be used to construct response curves of foliage to eg light, air humidity conditions or even CO_2 concentrations. Leaf conductance (see above) can be calculated from the transpiration information. Requires canopy access and because of variability significant sampling. Equipment expensive ~ £13,000. With an additional chamber the equipment can be used to measure soil respiration.

Leaf chlorophyll fluorescence. Stress is indicated by reductions in the rate of photosynthesis. This can be monitored with a chlorophyll fluorescence meter. Requires access to canopy foliage. Equipment is portable and relatively cheap (~£1,500). Recently discussed by Percival (2001).

Xylem water potential. Uses a high-pressure chamber to measure the pressure needed to bring water back from inside a detached twig or leaf to the cut surface. Indicates directly the stress in the plant. Values can be directly linked to water potential measurements made for the soil. A key parameter controlling the level of stomatal conductance and leaf gas exchange.

13.2.5 The mortality spiral

There are only a few documented examples of the tree mortality spiral cf Section 8.3.3.4. However, it is a useful concept with which to consider the various threats to a tree through its life and how the risk increases as the tree descends the mortality spiral. However, what is not yet clear is how to monitor the position of the tree on the mortality spiral and how this might be done in an easy, repeatable and in, at least, a semi-quantitative way.

There are some well-documented procedures eg visual tree assessment – VTA – (Harris *et al*, 1999; Mattheck and Breloer, 1994) to evaluate trees for the likelihood that they present a hazard to persons or property because of detachment of parts. The VTA does not necessarily offer an indication that a tree is suffering from stress from a variety of impacts, it evaluates the structural integrity of the tree.

Leaf to air temperature. When leaves are actively transpiring, especially in sunny conditions and high temperatures, their temperatures are significant lower than air temperature ~ transpirational cooling. Closure of the stomata because of stress causes the leaf – air temperature difference to reduce or even reverse. Can be measured directly with thermistors (needs canopy access) or indirectly with an infrared thermometer (infrared gun needs to focus on the actively transpiring canopy).

Transpiration from sap flow. Uses low-level heat pulses as tracers of the rate of transpiration. Requires additional information on the sap wood area of the tree. Needs implanting of small probes at the base of the tree and will require calibration. Will require associated weather data to interpret the results. Equipment (including batteries and solar panels) left in place for days to weeks therefore risk of vandalism. Commercial equipment to measure 5 large trees would be ~ £9,000.

Girth increment. Foresters have long used girth bands to monitor long-term girth increment of trees. They can be used over shorter time intervals to monitor tree diurnal shrinkage and recovery in response to evaporative demand. Failure to recover on the daily basis suggests the development of stress. Inexpensive but used at ground level therefore there is a risk of vandalism.

Fluctuating leaf asymmetry. An emerging approach (eg Rettig *et al*, 1997). Compared to individuals that are unstressed trees that are stressed may have leaves which are asymmetrical from one side of the leaf blade to another. Likely to indicate long-term stress development in a tree. Simple and could be evaluated on leaf litter. Needs validation for urban tree species.

There are a number of methods that can be used to measure stress in trees (see Box 13.2). Most of these techniques are used routinely in research programmes to study water stress and its impact on tree physiology but unfortunately are less suited to simple surveying of many trees because each method has one or two drawbacks. The methods are mostly technically not easy to achieve and most require expensive equipment. A further drawback is that most of the approaches need some degree of access to the canopy that will be a constraint in the mature trees for which there is most concern in terms of the mortality spiral.

The measures in Box 13.2 are to do with water stress which of course must be present before it can be detected. Evaluating the position of a tree in the mortality spiral demands something else. It means that we need to measure predisposition to stress. So far we do not have the techniques to do this but there would be considerable value if this could be developed.

The lack of information about many aspects of the form and function of tree roots in the built environment points to a lack of investment in substantial research. Information such as that coming from foundation damage about tree root extent (Cutler and Richardson, 1989) is opportunistic. It has not come from the following of a well-supported research strategy. There are other cases where there is considerable common ground between the research needs of commercial forestry and arboriculture eg the growth and establishment of young trees. In cases such as this where there is convergence of research needs a lot of information is available to the amenity tree community. What is clear, however, is that there are many cases where the needs for research and new knowledge are unique to the situation of trees growing alone in the built environment. Here the investment in research has been very poor and the state of our knowledge reflects this.

13.2.6 Species tolerances

There is a need to accumulate information about tolerances of species to various stresses. These stresses might be damage to their roots by excavation, soil compaction influences or salt applications. There are many cases where we have detailed knowledge of the impact of a specific stress on a particular species. The earlier chapters have many examples. What is now needed is a more comprehensive spread of combinations of species and stresses. This information will enable professionals to judge a far wider number of cases of tree damage based on more than a few limited examples.

13.3 Accumulating new knowledge

There are a number of ways that new knowledge and understanding will be obtained. Recognising these ways might help focus on how best to improve the knowledge base. Information that will help us to grow and manage our trees better is likely to come from three main sources. These are 1) directed research, 2) accumulation of observations and 3) external sources.

13.3.1 Directed research

Many of our research needs can only be obtained from a research programme involving new measurements. Such studies are likely to be somewhat specific and intensive in terms of equipment and resources and therefore expensive. The research is likely to answer questions that are very specific to growing trees in the built environment. Examples of this type of research are those studies on tree requirements and urban soils by Richards, Moorehead and Laing and the tree water use studies carried out by Dr Neil Hipps and his colleagues at East Malling. This type of research is largely limited by the amounts of funding money. The availability of manpower and technical resources is usually not a constraint.

13.3.2 Accumulation of observations

A lot of what we need to know about tree roots and their interactions with the built environment might be developed from recorded observations. In the course of their work most professionals associated with trees encounter incidences of damage and stresses and the species involved and what age they were. It might also be quite common to observe features of root systems, such as distances from trees, diameters of roots, their depths etc. The scope is very large indeed. The value of these observations is immense both in terms of knowledge it represents and also in terms of research costs if this information was obtained by a more direct route. There are major constraints, however, to the exploitation of such a rich observational source of data. Professionals associated with trees are very busy people. It would be another significant burden to record all that they come across. The other major issue is the lack of a repository and collation centre for such information. An appropriate institution might be the Tree Advice Trust but again the workload of the staff there could not accommodate a further major role. It is important that serious consideration is given to how we might capture valuable observational data.

13.3.3 External sources

Chapter 5 contains information about the growth and establishment of young trees. Much of this information comes from very large tree growing enterprises associated with commercial forestry. The strong message here is there is a great deal that is common to forestry and amenity plantings when it relates to growing young trees. Expensive research need not be duplicated but it is important to recognise the existence of relevant research in other fields and seek the appropriate reports accordingly.

13.4 Implementation requirements

Particularly on building sites compaction of soils has an extremely deleterious effect on tree health. Largely, there is good understanding of the influence of soil compaction on the soil processes that have such a serious influence on the ability of roots to grow and function. It is appreciated that soil compaction increases soil bulk density which increases the resistance to root penetration. There is also reduction in the diffusion of oxygen leading to poor aeration conditions in the soil. There is, however, a need for more information about the tolerance of different species to soil compaction. In practical terms the strategy for protecting trees on building sites largely consists of defining protection zones around trees. There is no question that every effort should be made to implement these recommendations for protection zones.

At present there seems no strong scientific basis to substantially modify the zones of protection around trees given as recommendations for the UK (BSI, 2005). However, these recommendations should emphasise the important role that soil compaction plays in disrupting soil processes and thereby seriously compromising root function. The need to avoid soil compaction cannot be overstated. It is very important that any parties involved in projects at any stage, from planning to completion, recognise how important it is to eliminate the likelihood of soil compaction close to trees and where it is planned to plant trees. This increase in information should address three main topics. Firstly, recommendations should spell out the very serious consequences of soil compaction for root growth and function. Secondly, particular emphasis should be put on the very early need to protect trees before any site access is pursued. This is now a strong message that comes through from BS 5837 (BSI, 2005). The literature on compaction during logging in forestry has consistently shown that it is the first few passes of vehicles that cause the largest fraction of the total compaction. Thirdly, there needs to be better planning for the protection of soil in anticipation that trees will be planted there as part of the development. It is therefore satisfying to see that current recommendations (BSI, 2005) for construction near trees have adopted the suggestion made by Nicholson (2001) that zones to be occupied by trees in the future should be demarcated and protected. Furthermore, outside of construction sites, the need to protect trees from the consequences of soil compaction must be recognised. There can be damage from parking around the bases of trees but also intensive pedestrian traffic near trees can also have deleterious influences.

The worst cases of compaction are most likely to occur in construction projects. Nevertheless there are significant risks of soil compaction from routine activities near trees such as grass cutting with heavy machinery or even from foot traffic. The development of compaction in soils around trees from such agencies as these are likely to be more insidious than the passage nearby of heavy construction vehicles but the impact can be just as devastating for trees.

There is also a need for tree care professionals and any others involved with activity near trees to be able to identify compacted soils more readily. Often the first indication that a soil is too compact for the effective functioning of the root system of a tree is indicated by symptoms of the tree itself eg leaf yellowing or crown thinning. Unfortunately, when symptoms such as these are apparent it may be too late. There are technical devices (penetrometers) available to measure soil strength, and bulk density can also be determined with basic laboratory equipment but whether there is time available for a busy local authority tree officer to use such methods is questionable. There still seems to be a place for ways to be developed by which compacted soils can be identified quickly and simply in the field.

A number of means have been developed for decompacting soils. While it may be a reasonable option to use soil ripping equipment to decompact soils in areas away from trees, options for decompaction within the vicinity of tree roots are less convincing. The results of using the injection of air under high pressure below the soil surface has yielded less than convincing evidence that it is a universal panacea for compacted soils. The method seems to be reasonably effective in sandy soils but less effective in heavy wet soils, where fracturing of the soil often seems to be localised. Using high-pressure air or water to remove soil from around roots may be a useful approach for root investigations or for removing contaminated soils. However, the approach is unlikely to be practicable over the rooting area of a large tree and would in any case be inadvisable on the basis that tree stability might be seriously compromised. Without question, there still seems considerable scope for the research and development of effective measures to treat compacted soils around trees.

13.5 Engaging with technology

There are a number of approaches available that may be used as alternatives to conventional trenching and can contribute to reducing damage to root systems. These approaches use high air or water pressures to expose services and or roots and may be used with vacuuming to remove soil or other backfill. Also becoming far more common are various trenchless installation methods which offer considerable promise of reducing damage to tree root systems. Some of these approaches are relatively new and do not seem to be used as widely as might be expected, given their potential advantage over conventional trenching with hydraulic excavator. Although there is some experience in the USA and limited take up in the UK the alternatives are still not widely and routinely used. The use of air or water at high pressures with soil vacuuming and trenchless technologies have already been referred to in previous sections. It is important that professionals involved with trees recognise more widely the potential there is with these methods. It would be valuable for case studies to be implemented and reported widely. A dramatic example of the use of high-pressure air (the 'Soil Pick') was in the recent relocation of a large sugar maple at Myerscough College, UK (Fig 13.4). The approaches can be used for a wide variety of purposes, such as exposing roots and utilities, decompacting soil and loosening contaminated soil prior to its removal.

There are a number of misconceptions commonly held by persons not directly involved with trenchless technology. The view exists that trenchless technology involves very large machinery and is a technique dedicated to projects where there are particular difficulties in using conventional trenching eg installing pipelines under rivers, harbours and railways. Mistakenly, it is also thought that only one or two companies are specialists. Neither of these two perceptions is correct. Importantly to persons involved in any way with excavation close to trees, there are small machines available for directed boring if necessary and there are numerous companies who operate all types of machinery. For example there is very compact machinery available capable of trenching a few tens of metres eg Fig 13.5. With trenchless technology as with other methodologies it would be most valuable for tree care professionals to have case studies to refer to when they come to drawing up specifications. For instance, they should be aware that the depth that the drilling rods pass through the ground can be varied to some degree and specify accordingly. This

Figure 13.4 Exposing tree roots during transplanting of sugar maple (*Acer saccharum*) at Myerscough College, UK.

Figure 13.5 Small horizontal directional drilling machine made in New Zealand by Terramacs (weight 210 kg, 2.45 m (h) x 1.5 m (l) x 0.4 m (w)).

will be important with narrow bore drilling. In the field of trenchless technology, because of soil compression upwards and 'bulging' at the soil surface, there is a rule of thumb that the minimum depth should be at least three times the diameter of the drill rods. With small bore drilling it will be necessary to specify a depth to avoid boring in the surface 30–50 cm where most large tree roots occur. It would be particularly unfortunate to cut through tree roots with a technique chosen especially to avoid damaging them!

13.6 Dissemination requirements

There are several cases where sufficient understanding of the requirements to protect tree roots are available but there is a need for this information to be made available in a simple, convenient and compact form. As well as the need for text books and manuals on tree care and management there is a need for other material to disseminate advice and good practice on the various activities which have a potential to conflict with trees, especially their roots, eg construction and excavation near trees.

Presently, there are various ways in which information about the interactions of tree roots and built structures is being disseminated. Widely distributed are products from the Arboricultural Advisory and Information Service (AAIS) (www.treeadviceservice.org.uk) based in the UK. Arboricultural Research and Information Notes (ARIN) summarise the results of research carried out in Britain and overseas, Arboricultural Practice Notes (APN) set out the best current practise on a wide range of important issues. They are produced in consultation with industry and the APNs are meant to provide answers to questions arising in a number of arboricultural issues. The Tree Damage Alert (TDA) is an informal information sheet about various issues related to trees, largely to do with current threats from pests and diseases. A large number of ARINs have been produced (earlier ones were known as Arboricultural Research Notes) with eleven APNs being available at the present time. A significant proportion of ARINs and APNs relate to issues to do with tree roots and have been referred to in relevant sections of this book. A large amount of similar material is available from various arboricultural and urban forestry extension units in the USA. Much of this material can be downloaded from the world wide web.

Much of the material referred to above is directed at the tree care professional. There is an important need for information about specific tree issues to be produced in a condensed and readable form directed at operatives, not from the tree care industry, who work near trees. There are examples of these types of leaflets. The National Urban Forestry Unit produced a leaflet advising how to proceed to install trenches for cable communication (see Fig 8.21). Lambeth Council also produced a leaflet in a similar format advising good practice for construction near trees.

There are numerous situations where a simple, concise and durable leaflet would produce a benefit for trees, for example, a simple guide to excavating a tree pit. This would emphasise important features such as those given in Section 6.4. In Section 7.3.3.1 we discussed the risks to trees from de-icing salts applied to pavements and footways in shopping areas and pedestrian precincts. The application of these salts might well be carried out by local retail traders. Are they aware of the risks to trees from injudicious applications? A leaflet or poster could pay dividends.

Disseminated information that gives important advice about various tree root issues will only be truly effective if it reaches the groups or individuals who carry out work near trees. Important targets for disseminated material should be machinery operatives whose work is frequently near tree roots but who receive no training for such work. In the Cheltenham Case Study (Section 8.5.2 and Box 8.2) there was a benefit obtained from direct training of operatives of how to proceed when excavating near trees. A development of this approach that was suggested by Eden (2002) was to instigate a formal qualification (eg National Vocational Qualification, NVQ or Scottish Vocational Qualification, SVQ) for work close to trees. Formal training such as this could include an established protocol for excavating near trees, eg NJUG

10, added to which could be other sound procedures related to tree-related work eg building site practice and excavating tree pits. The existence of a formal qualification linked especially to tree roots and associated soil ought to emphasise the importance of the care needed when working near trees and promote the idea that working near to trees is an important skill.

13.7 Sustainability issues

13.7.1 What is sustainable development?

The definition of sustainable development prepared by the World Commission on Environment and Development (WCED, 1987) reads: *Sustainable development is that development that meets the needs of the present without compromising the ability of future generations to meet their own needs.*

All UK administrations agree that the goal should be to enable all people throughout the world to satisfy their basic needs and enjoy a better quality of life, without compromising the quality of life of future generations (HM Government *et al*, 2005 and HM Government, 2005). The UK Government follows a set of guiding principles to achieve this goal (Fig 13.6) and measures its progress against a set of 68 indicators which are regularly assessed and reported on (HM Government, 2005 and Defra, 2005).

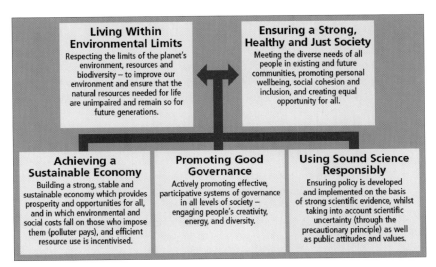

Figure 13.6 The principles forming the basis for sustainable development policy in the UK. (After HM Government *et al*, 2005.)

It is not open to question, of course, that trees enhance the quality of life by their visual presence and by offering shade and shelter. However, the growing of trees in the built environment, of which the form and function of their root systems is a fundamental part, has links into a subset of the indicators given in the UK strategy for sustainable development (HM Government, 2005). In the following sections we will examine aspects related to climate change; air quality; water quality; wildlife; land use – housing and waste.

So in the sections below, procedures related to establishment and growth of trees in the built environment, particularly in the context of the form and function of tree root systems, are examined from the viewpoint of sustainable development. A number of issues related to sustainable development are examined with the following questions in mind:

Are there unsustainable practices in the context of growing trees in the urban environment?

Are there activities aimed at sustainable development which have an impact on the below-ground environment and the function of tree root systems?

How are we to gauge if our trees are growing sustainably?

13.8 The carbon balance of planting trees in the built environment

There is considerable evidence that the level of greenhouse gases, predominantly carbon dioxide, are responsible for increase in global temperature. The United Nations Framework Convention on Climate Change Kyoto Protocol of 1997 is a major international initiative attempting to combat rising atmospheric CO_2 concentrations. Following the protocol, a number of countries have agreed to reduce greenhouse gas emissions by about 5% of 1990 levels by the commitment period (2008–2012). In the UK the commitment is 12.5%. The most effective way to achieve these reductions will be by a reduction of fossil fuel use by encouraging better energy use efficiency and using alternative energy sources. Additional related projects are being carried out in the UK (http://www2.defra.gov.uk/research/project_data/projects.asp?M=KWS&V= soil+and+carbon&SCOPE=0). The Kyoto Protocol also encourages the sequestration of carbon through changes in land use/management as a means to offset national CO_2 emissions).

Soils, their humus content and accumulation of surface litter constitute a major carbon pool and because of the relatively slow rate of carbon turnover within the principal soil organic pools even small increases in total carbon stored in the soil will have a long-term effect on net carbon emissions. Increasingly, therefore it is recognised that an important contribution to the global carbon budget of different vegetation types is the amount that is stored below ground, in the root systems, in soil-dwelling organisms and especially in soil organic matter. The interest in below-ground storage of carbon is not only because a large fraction of the total storage is below ground but also what environmental and management factors influence that level of storage.

The strategy to reduce CO_2 levels in the atmosphere is by reduction of emissions of green house gases, especially CO_2. While it is recognised that planting of forests and trees to sequester carbon will be beneficial the influence will only be secondary. Therefore the planting of trees is going to make only a small contribution to the carbon budget but it will serve as an acceptable if limited contribution. Although likely to be a small part overall, various activities related to trees in the built environment can influence carbon storage in trees and soil. Nevertheless, it is important to ensure that tree planting in the built environment is a net benefit to the global carbon balance and is not an added burden. Nowak *et al* (2002) calculated the carbon costs and benefits of urban trees based on a number of scenarios. The scenarios include (a) the carbon costs, eg fuel, of establishment and removal of trees and various levels of maintenance (b) the influence of different species over different life spans, (c) the benefits of trees to energy conservation and (d) the fate of the carbon in the tree on removal and disposal eg by burning, composting or in a sealed landfill.

Nowak *et al* (2002) came to the conclusion that trees planted in urban areas need to live a minimum amount of time to compensate for the base carbon emissions used in planting, establishment, maintenance and tree removal. In a scenario involving *Acer rubrum*, a medium size species of medium growth rate, a tree would need to reach a minimum age of 5–10 years to cover the carbon costs. To maximise the net benefits of urban forestry on atmospheric carbon dioxide, managers should focus on:

- planting long-lived, low maintenance, moderate to fast growing species that are large at maturity and matched to site conditions;

- using maintenance activities that increase tree survival and longevity;

- minimising fossil fuel use related to management and maintenance activities;

- using wood from removed trees to delay decomposition or decrease the need for energy from fossil fuel-based plants (eg, develop long-term wood products; burn wood to heat residences); and

- planting trees in energy-conserving locations.

The latter of these points reflects situations in the USA and is regarded as not so relevant to Northern European situations (cf. Section 9.1).

Cultivation of soils reduces soil organic matter and therefore carbon content drastically. These changes are a consequence of higher temperatures and aeration that increase decomposition rates. Therefore, even under individual trees if they have occupied the site for long enough, there will be a high carbon content in the soil. In the circumstances of a tree growing and maturing on land previously used for arable agriculture or other uses eg industry we would expect carbon content to slowly increase. Post and Kwon (2000) have documented a number of studies in which the increase in soil carbon content has been determined after agricultural lands have been converted to forest use. A very long-term study at Rothamsted, Hertfordshire showed that the soil of abandoned arable land that developed a cover of oak woodland accumulated approximately 60 g carbon m^{-2} $year^{-1}$ (Jenkinson, 1971). A study in Southern Carolina examined the differences in soil carbon under different land uses (Richter and Markewitz, 2001) related to the abandonment of land intensively cultivated for cotton in previous times. Fig 13.7 shows the percentage of soil carbon in different soil layers under a range of land uses. The data come from a very long-term study carried out in the USA to evaluate changes in soil properties following abandonment of agricultural land in the cotton belt. The hardwood forest is the original vegetation, pines were planted or invaded abandoned land, hay fields represent permanent grassland and soil beneath row crops were also studied. The highest level of carbon storage is below hardwood forest with permanent grassland more or less equal. Lower levels of carbon storage were found below the pine plantation and the row crop. The largest differences were observed in the upper 30cm of soil.

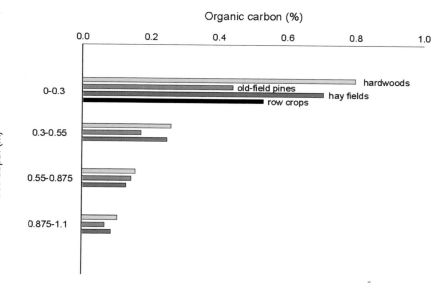

Figure 13.7 The concentration of soil organic carbon in the upper soil profile of uncultivated hardwoods, old field pines, hay fields and a row crop. (After Richter & Markewitz, 2001.)

There seems no question, therefore, that agricultural land planted to trees will accumulate carbon. So, in terms of some of the tree planting in the built environment, eg in the field margins alongside roads, there should be an increase in soil carbon content. Unfortunately we have less certainty that this will occur below trees around which the soil is decoupled from the atmosphere by hard surfaces such as asphalt or concrete. A substantial contribution to the soil carbon flux in natural ecosystems and man-made plantations comes from the return of various forms of litter to the soil. This litter will be comprised of various sizes of woody stems, leaves and also roots. This return to the soil balances the losses from respiration. When trees are largely surrounded by asphalt or concrete, the return of leaf and woody matter is precluded. Also in parks and formal gardens woody or leaf litter is normally removed. When this is burnt the carbon contained will be returned promptly back into the atmosphere. We are far less certain about the fate of carbon contained in the fine roots which turn over rapidly and we have very little knowledge of the rates of turn over of fine roots in urban situations in comparison to more natural systems.

It has long been recognised that routine removal of litter from forest ecosystems can eventually lead to decline in productivity. It is unfortunate that leaf and small branch litter surrounding trees is routinely removed completely from the site. Consideration should be given to leaving litter in shrubberies or anywhere else where it will not pose a health and safety problem. Left to decompose where it falls, leaf and woody litter will contribute to the return of organic matter and carbon storage at the site but there are other benefits. Organic matter in the soil contributes to the soil pore space essential for good soil properties and root functioning. It is not known to what extent components of the soil fauna, especially earthworms, require regular inputs of tree canopy litter and if populations decline when the litter is routinely removed. The burrowing of these soil animals is, of course, a major contributor to maintaining the large pore space in soil.

Net accumulation of soil carbon occurs through practices that increase the amount of plant-fixed carbon that is returned to soils in the forms of residues (ie leaves, stems, and branches and especially roots (Balesdent and Balabane, 1996)) and/or reduce the specific rate of decomposition. In addition, reducing the removal or burning of biomass increases the portion of total productivity that is returned to soil. IPCC (2000) suggests that specific rates of decomposition (ie, CO_2 emissions per unit soil carbon per unit time) can be reduced by creating a less favourable environment for soil organisms that decompose organic matter. Decomposition proceeds at its highest rate when soil temperatures are high and soil is moist. Attempts to reduce soil temperature could use mulching for example. Any reduction in soil disturbance is also likely to reduce soil organic decomposition.

There is of course very little input of wood and leaf litter to the soil of trees surrounded by hard surfacings and buildings. This will reduce the input of a source of nutrients as well as organic carbon. It is also possible that if rainfall infiltration is limited the input of nutrients will be further limited. We might speculate that to release sufficient nutrients to sustain new growth there needs to be a rapid turnover of fine roots. The prospect then is that very little below-ground sequestration of carbon occurs in such circumstances. As has been emphasised elsewhere an important research need is to study the below-ground environment, root and carbon dynamics especially where trees are decoupled from above-ground inputs.

13.9 Air quality

It is the UK Government target to improve air quality in our towns and cities. One indicator used is the number of days per year when air quality is poor. This means that the levels exceed values thought to affect human health. Recent figures show that there are still over 20 days per year on average at each urban monitoring site when this occurs. The UK Government is currently reviewing their Air Quality Strategy with the aim to identify additional measures that will further improve air quality. This review is due to be completed in 2006. In any case reduction in pollution from road vehicle exhausts is likely to figure prominently in any mitigating measures.

Nevertheless there is limited evidence that urban trees and woodland can make an improvement to reducing particulate and gaseous pollution (eg Broadmeadow and Freer-Smith, 1996). Trees can, however, in some circumstances, contribute to ground level ozone formation and so be detrimental to air quality. The degree that trees in urban areas affect air quality needs further research.

The role of tree roots is obviously indirect in achieving improvements in air quality. Nevertheless it is important to acknowledge that for trees to function effectively in filtering pollutants and taking up gases through their stomata their root systems must be functioning fully and not be compromised by space restriction or damage. A tree requires a healthy root system to develop a full vigorous canopy and for the stomata to remain open.

13.10 Water quality

There is a Headline Indicator in the UK Strategy referring to river water quality. There are two aspects of water quality, the chemical content of streams and rivers and the flow regime of the river. Both have very important influences on animal and plant life in and close to these running waters.

The natural, pristine state of rivers and the wildlife that is supported has been seriously affected by pollution with chemicals coming from a variety of sources. The sources of the pollutants are many and various, including inputs of sediments, fertilisers and chemicals from agriculture, industrial discharges and leaks and contributions from urban runoff containing a variety of chemicals that are deleterious to the quality of receiving waters. There are various ways that the presence of trees on the land can ameliorate some water quality problems but it is also necessary that we avoid situations where the establishment and growth of trees in the built environment can add to water quality problems. For example, in Section 13.8.2 below the use of pesticides and fertilisers is discussed. Water quality issues are relevant at all stages in growth cycle of trees. A recent document (ADAS, 2002) covers good irrigation practice at the stage when young plants are being cultivated. Some recent specific advice about pesticide use will be found in a publication produced by the Crop Protection Association as part of the Voluntary Initiative (CPA, 2002).

Already in Section 7.4.1 the value of trees acting in the phyto-remediation or phyto-containment of contaminants in soils has been recognised. These functions can contribute greatly to the quality of surface and ground water draining from the specific areas. The ability of the root systems of trees to tolerate the conditions and to contribute in remedying of contamination is substantial.

13.10.1 Sustainable drainage

Both the timing of runoff from urban areas and its quality has important implications to streams and rivers draining urban catchments. Urbanisation increases both the volume and speed with which water from rainfall reaches streams. This increase in stream response means that the sharpness of the flood peaks are magnified. This is particularly the case if the catchment is small and urbanisation is a dominant land-use in the catchment. Because so much rainfall reaching the ground surface in urban areas is shed so rapidly into drains there is a reduction in the opportunities for recharge of soil moisture deficits. It is drainage from the soil profile into groundwater that often maintains the low flow status of streams and rivers draining catchments. Therefore, urbanisation also means that low flows from the catchment will be reduced. Low flows are the residual flows of streams that persist even after long periods without rain. They are fed from groundwater or water draining from deep layers in the soil. Some minimum level of low flow is necessary to sustain stream life. The other problem with traditional impermeable surfaces in urban areas is that pollutants from a variety of sources are washed off directly from hard surfaces and can find their way readily into watercourses. Piped watercourses have no light. Oxygen may be limited and therefore there is minimal biological activity to act on the water quality.

Any built-up area will require drainage to manage surface water. Conventionally this has been achieved by using underground pipe systems designed mainly with the quantity of water in mind, to prevent flooding locally by conveying the water away as quickly as possible. More recently, water quality issues have grown in importance, due to pollutants from urban areas being washed into rivers or the groundwater. Conventional drainage systems cannot readily control poor runoff quality. Spillages for example, are washed from the urban surfaces and reach the streams by a fairly direct route. There are few opportunities for pollutants to enter the soil and be stored or decomposed by soil organisms. There are many amenity values offered by water in the built environment. These include water resources, community facilities, landscaping potential and the provision of various wildlife habitats. Conventional drainage systems are not designed with these wider considerations in mind. Continuing to drain built up areas with limited objectives is not a sustainable long-term option (CIRIA, 2004; DTLR, 2001).

Drainage systems can be developed with aspects of sustainable development included. Sustainable drainage systems (SUDS) offers an approach to surface water drainage which takes account of quality, quantity and amenity issues. The SUDS approach uses a wide range of techniques to control surface water runoff as close to its origin as possible, before it enters a watercourse. This involves moving away from traditional piped drainage systems to engineering solutions that mimic natural drainage processes. SUDS are more sustainable than conventional drainage methods because:

- Runoff rates are managed, reducing the risk of flooding through urban development

- Water quality is protected or enhanced

- They are sympathetic to the environmental setting and local community needs

- Wildlife habitats can be created in urban watercourses

- Groundwater recharge is encouraged where appropriate.

SUDS work by:

- Dealing with runoff close to where the rain falls (source control)

- Managing pollution at its source

- Protect water resources from point source pollution e.g accidental spills and diffuse sources.

In terms of the second characteristic sought of SUDS, the management of pollution at source, there is still a need for more research to evaluate how each SUDS technique attenuates the wide range of pollutants that are likely to be present. In the case of the treatment of runoff from highways, but not necessarily for all urban surfaces, the Highways Agency has issued advice (HA, 2001) about the use of vegetative treatment systems to treat runoff.

The design of a SUDS solution for drainage of a site will need to take into account the likely sources of pollution and the suitability of each of the techniques used to retain and treat the pollutants. The likely impact of any discharge of pollutant from the system to surface and groundwater should also be taken into account.

SUDS are comprised of one or more structures built to manage surface water runoff. The five general methods are:

- Green roofs and rainwater harvesting

- Filter strips and swales

- Filter drains and permeable surfaces

- Infiltration devices
- Basins and ponds.

A universal feature of the built environment is a substantial covering of the areas around tree roots with a partially – or completely impermeable surface. Almost always this will mean that the delivery of water from rainfall to the root zones of trees will be restricted to some degree. There may be many situations where the recharge of soil water required/used by a tree is insufficiently provided for because of this limited infiltration. This will be a serious problem if no other sources of water are available. In some cases, though, this will not be a problem – water can sometimes move laterally, especially downslope on inclined sites and at some low-lying sites the water table may be very shallow. At many of these shallow water table sites the rise of water in winter may fully replenish the soil water store. Crucially, a further supply of soil nutrients may also be delivered as the water table rises.

A number of the approaches likely to be adopted within SUDS have potentially important benefits for trees growing in built areas. However, there may also be threats.

13.10.1.1 Pervious surfaces

A potentially pervious surface uses unit paviours (paviours set as individual pieces, rather than continuous sheet like poured concrete). This type of surface has been referred in terms of driveway construction in Section 9.4.3. The paviours themselves are usually of two main types. One form of paviour is not porous and drainage of water through a surface comprised of such blocks is in the gaps between the units. Another, not so common, type of paviour is made of low-fines concrete or other material, which means that the blocks have many small, interlinked internal voids throughout. In addition to water infiltrating through gaps between the paviours, the paviours themselves can retain and transmit water. Overall, however, the infiltration has been shown to be predominantly through the gaps (eg Abbott *et al*, 2000).

An important message coming from a recent review of source control using constructed pervious surfaces (CIRIA, 2004) is the need for regular maintenance in the form of brushing and vacuuming to remove fine debris on the surface of and between the paviours (see Section 6.2.3 and Fig 6.6). The key to providing infiltration through the paved area is that the paviours must be laid on sand, crushed stone or some other permeable material. The choice of underlying material is important, as if the paviours are set in or over concrete – as may be the case where vehicle loading is intended – then the resulting surface is defined by the concrete. Where **percolation** takes place solely in the joints between the paviours, the width and the material in the joints is critical (Thompson and Sorvig, 2000). A report by Evans *et al* (1990) produced some guidance in the design of pavements, pedestrian areas, parking zones and even streets constructed with unit paviours. The Cornell study recommends:

- Use wide joints (6 mm is probably the maximum without reducing stability) or smaller paviours, either of which maximises total joint area.

- Use thicker paviours to compensate for loss of rigidity if necessary.

- Use permeable joint-filler materials. Coarse, sharp sand bound with bitumen was found to be the most permeable.

- After initial installation, settling of the paving occurs; brush in more coarse joint-filler material, rather than allow finer debris to accumulate and block the pore space.

- Where possible, leave joints lower than the walking surface; this increases the infiltration rate by creating tiny 'reservoirs' between paviours.

- Make the base course beneath the paviours as coarse as possible to prevent water being retained in the surface layer.

- Do not compact the base course excessively, or vibrate the whole pavement after construction.

The issue of providing adequate support for paviours or indeed any other hard surface without causing compaction is a particular challenge and will remain a research and development priority. The research into structural soils that can solve the compromise of supporting hard surfaces but will also allow tree root growth is referred to in Section 4.5.3.

There are some constraints to the provision of permeable surfaces (CIRIA, 2004; DTLR, 2001). These are when:

- The soil is not very permeable.

- The water table is shallow.

- The ground water at the site may be put at risk from pollutants, e.g. where there is contamination in the soil.

- Infiltration of water into the ground, particularly if concentrated over a limited area could adversely affect ground stability.

The issue of soil permeability (first bullet above) has particular relevance in consideration of permeable surfaces close to trees planted in pits. Elsewhere (eg Section 4.2.5.4) the risk to trees if the tree pit acts as a sump for water drained from surrounding areas, the 'teacup effect', has been discussed. If the drainage from the tree pit is impeded or poor then providing permeable surfaces round the tree may increase the periods when waterlogging may occur. This type of circumstance, where excess water may drain into the tree pit, emphasises the need for good drainage out of the pit and that sound information should be available about the conditions prevailing where trees are planted in such situations. In other words, site investigations and site-specific prescriptions formulated.

There is also a need to provide contingency measures for extreme rainfall events (duration or intensity) when the quantity of runoff exceeds that for which the permeable surface was designed.

13.10.1.2 Filter strips and swales

These are vegetated surface features that receive water from impermeable areas. Filter strips are gently sloping areas of ground, whereas swales are long shallow channels. They allow rainwater to run through the vegetation, slowing and filtering the flow. Trees can be planted in swales and filter strips, which are effectively wide channels, provided this is taken account of in the design. Trees may disrupt flow patterns in a way detrimental to their ability to retain sediment and increase difficulties of maintenance. Swales are normally planted with grass so trees are likely to limit its growth.

13.10.1.3 Basins and ponds

Basins are normally dry areas that can temporarily store surface water. Ponds contain water in dry weather but can contain more when it rains. Both of these features offer many opportunities for tree-planting and if the water supply can be guaranteed tree species considered to have higher water usage eg poplar and willow can be accommodated. The impact of planting of trees needs to be carefully considered however. Water movement might be slowed and silting up and reduction of the water holding capacity of the basin or pond might occur. Leaf drop will provide organic detritus that could lead to high and unwanted oxygen demand in the autumn and winter months.

13.10.1.4 Rain water harvesting

Most of the research on water harvesting is directed at the objective of providing drinking water quality. However, for landscape applications, purity need not be as high as for drinking water, although some caution needs to be exercised if significant amounts of heavy metals are thought to be present. In Sections 7.4 and 7.4.1 the tolerance of trees to different heavy metals is discussed. There is considerable scope for using harvested rainwater to irrigate trees in adjacent landscapes. This water may be collected off roofs or surfaces at the ground. Schemes are available that contain roof rainwater from small domestic properties up to large commercial premises. An important issue for irrigation of trees relates to the same point above dealing with impermeable soils in the zone surrounding and underneath the trees. Excess irrigation may cause the tree waterlogging problems which might lead to poor aeration in the root zone and death. It will be necessary to be able to store the harvested rain water so that it may be applied as irrigation in judicious quantities, when needed, thus avoiding waterlogging problems.

13.10.1.5 Use of grey water

Grey water is prime quality mains-supplied water that has already been used. Except for water coming from toilet facilities much further use can be made of water that has already been used for some domestic or industrial purposes.

There is considerable scope for grey water uses that do not demand high quality such as flushing toilets, vehicle washing and landscape irrigation. The point made above in connection with using harvested rainwater for irrigation applies here. It is important that grey water can be stored and used when needed rather than applied at the time of production.

It is relevant to note that SUDS are not yet welcomed universally by environmental managers in the UK. One of the areas of disagreement is the capacity of soils beneath porous surfaces to accept rainfall especially when the soil is saturated and rainfall is extended in duration. Because the soils beneath hard surfaces in urban areas are usually highly compacted their capacity to infiltrate water is limited. We have already mentioned how the tree pit can very easily become a sump, 'the teacup effect', when compacted soil surrounding it channels water into the pit. There are those who counsel caution about wholesale acceptance of SUDS as the singular way to deal with urban storm water. It is suggested that for both SUDS and conventional drainage systems there remains a need for a traditional, engineering approach to deal with excess rainfall, which is direct and rapid discharge to storm sewers. The very severe flooding in parts of the UK in the autumn and winter of 2000/2001 provided many examples of situations where soils were completely saturated for long periods and any urban drainage scheme that relied solely on natural drainage into the soil would have failed. Any soil has only a finite capacity for water. It seems clear that a considered approach should be taken in which the real benefits of porous surfaces are recognised but the rare but realistic occurrence of conditions like the rainfall of 2000/2001 on top of saturated land should be remembered and appropriate traditional schemes considered as a backup. The very important implications and risks to urban trees if their tree pits become sumps for urban runoff have already been referred to. Plans for implementing SUDS schemes, especially those related to porous paving, should reflect the views of tree care specialists.

13.10.2 Pesticides and fertilisers

There are also water quality issues that should be borne in mind and these relate to pesticide and fertiliser use. The problem of weeds for the establishment of young trees was discussed in Section 5.5.2. Although herbicide application is one way over the problem, care needs to be taken to avoid excessive use and application near water bodies. In the UK there are regulations about the use of chemicals near water bodies. The Water Resources Act of 1991 (eg MAFF, 1998) allows for individuals responsible for causing pollution to be prosecuted. The use of mulches to control weeds seems a far more sustainable option offering less of a risk to soil organisms and water resources. There is also a problem of weeds in pavements and here mulches can have no role. Chemical are usually applied to clear the pavements and this is one of the commonest situations where chemicals damage trees and presumably where there is a significant risk that the chemicals running off hard surfaces might influence water quality.

The need for fertilisers has been discussed at various points. Particularly in the case of young trees, there seemed little merit in providing copious fertiliser in a very soluble form to a tree that could not exploit it quickly. There are risks that excess fertiliser will be leached away and will add to the nutrient load of nearby waters. There is the option to use slow (controlled) release fertilisers instead of conventional types. These have the advantages that excessive leaching is much less likely to occur and maintenance is less because repeated applications are not required. Controlled release fertilisers are more expensive however.

13.11 Wildlife

13.11.1 Urban trees and wildlife

In general terms the wildlife associated with the above-ground parts of trees in the built environment will be limited in comparison with individuals growing in forests. Nevertheless the wildlife that is there will benefit from the canopies being healthy and complete and this will largely depend on the correct functioning of the tree below ground. Observers (eg Gilbert, 1989) concede that in most cases the diversity of species associated with urban trees is small. Nevertheless, there is scope for urban tree planting to serve as links between otherwise fragmented woodlands of a more substantial nature. It is recognised that fragmentation of habitats has a large part to play in reducing species numbers in individual parts.

There are numerous examples eg from European cities such as Helsinki, Stockholm and several in The Netherlands where 'Green wedges' have been retained or established between woodlands at the edge of the city and its centre (Beatley, 2000). These wedges provide habitats for wildlife and a means of dispersal between larger woods. Clearly the majority of trees in these wedges should be vigorous and healthy which will depend to a large extent on the size and adequate functioning of their root systems. However, the presence of some deadwood also increases the range of habitats available for wildlife, especially invertebrates and fungi.

It is a major indictment that our knowledge with respect to the diversity of life below ground close to trees in the built environment is so poor. This is not surprising given there is a common difficulty to obtain such information in any natural terrestrial ecosystem but this becomes particularly troublesome in the context of the situation below urban covers. Nevertheless we cannot understand what we do not know and we cannot know what has yet to be observed. Already in the context of research needs the importance of a far better knowledge of both the physical environment and the biology below ground in the built environment has been mentioned.

13.11.2 Peat and peat alternatives

Supporting sustainable practices would mean that the establishment and growth of trees in the built environment should not have negative impacts on natural ecosystems. In the past there was considerable use of natural peat in the propagation and planting out of young trees. Many would consider that it is no longer environmentally acceptable to remove peat from remaining peatlands that have a significant wildlife and archaeological value. The environmental cases against the use of natural peats are well established. There can be considerable loss of habitat. In addition the excavation of peat, its transport and its decomposition in use will lead to a substantial release of CO_2. The various issues to do with peat and alternatives to it are comprehensively reviewed by Holmes et al (2000).

The consumption of peat in the UK in 2001 was over 3.4 million m^3. Over half of that was imported. Peat from the Irish Republic accounted for 80% of the imports, the remaining 20% coming from the Baltic region. The UK Government's aspirational target is that alternatives to peat should constitute 90% of the total market by 2010. Persuading the amateur gardener to use peat alternatives will make an important impact because 60% of all the peat used is purchased by non-commercial growers (ODPM, 2001).

Alternatives to peat are being sought but there are challenges to find a material of the consistency and quality of natural peat. A major issue is that peat has been used for many years and there are developed practices of management in relation to irrigation, fertilisation, pests and diseases. For the alternatives to peat new approaches to the management will have to be developed. Until these protocols emerge and are reliable there might be problems for the regular supply of healthy young trees.

The alternatives to peat that are likely to be realistic in the short to medium term for commercial horticulture products are timber industry by products, coir and certain grades of high quality green compost.

As well as the evaluation of peat alternatives reported by Holmes et al (2000) tests have also been reported by 'Gardening Which?' magazine, in the last instance in 2006 (CA, 2006). These tests used peat, reduced-peat brands and peat-free brands for seed germination and growing on of hanging basket or patio type herbaceous plants (Impatiens, Petunia and Verbena). Obviously the relevance to young trees may not be direct. The studies found that peat-free products were less satisfactory for seed germination but that peat free composts can be as good as peat-based ones for older plants. Information from the Royal Horticultural Society indicated that differences between plant species in performance seem much more evident with peat alternatives than with peat (RHS, 2002). It is also stated that in certain circumstances eg for sustaining containerised woody plants over more than one season peat alternatives are not yet completely satisfactory. In these cases peat based mixes are being diluted with other materials.

13.12 Land use

13.12.1 Housing

Planning Policy Guidance Note 3: Housing (PPG3[1]) (DETR, 2000) sets out a national Government target that by 2008 60% of additional housing should be provided on previously developed land and through conversion of existing buildings. This target is being achieved. The percentage in 2000 was 60% rising to 72% in 2004. The challenge is to maintain the rate by continuing to promote brownfield development. PPG3 emphasises the reuse of land in urban areas in order to promote sustainable patterns of development and promote urban renaissance. The lands included in this definition of previously developed land include sites that were previously contaminated or have been used for mineral extraction and waste disposal.

In Section 7.4.1 the ability of certain trees to tolerate contaminated sites was discussed as was the prospect that trees could be used in the remediation of sites. Nevertheless, unless the contamination level is very low it is unlikely that the end use will go beyond woodland, at least for the foreseeable future. If the brownfield site is non-contaminated then residential development is an option. The needs for housing on land that has previously been developed offers a number of opportunities and challenges for the growth of trees and their functioning below-ground.

In PPG3 (paragraph 46) the desire for a 'greener residential development' is expressed. Nicholson (2001) reconciles the divergent requirements of this with 'the most efficient use of land' by quoting paras. 52 and 53.

Para. 52. 'The Government attaches particular importance to the 'greening' of residential environments. Greening initiatives can enhance quality, assist permeability of land for storm drainage and contribute to biodiversity. Well-designed layouts can also contribute to the energy efficiency of new housing. Landscaping should be an integral part of new development and opportunity should be taken for the retention of existing trees and shrubs, and for new planting.

Para. 53. Local planning authorities should have clear policies for the protection and creation of open spaces and playing fields, and new housing development should incorporate sufficient provision where such spaces are not already adequately provided within easy access of new housing...'

The retention of existing trees and shrubs requires the same type of guidance as regards protection below ground during development as provided in BS 5837 (cf. Section 8.4.2.1). In the case of new plantings it is important to recognise that the previous history of a brownfield site will almost certainly have left many areas of the soil compacted. This situation will need to be remedied if new tree plantings are to establish effectively. This remedy will also be desired

---

[1] This is under review.

to achieve the fullest 'permeability for storm drainage' referred to in para. 52 of PPG3. Nicholson (2001) rightly stresses the need for detailed planning of the development to take into account the daylight requirements of dwellers and users of the development. It is also important that sufficient space below ground is planned for the future root growth of existing and new plantings to avoid conflict with buildings.

13.12.2 Woodland cover

Although there may be difficulties in establishing new trees and sustaining the existing populations in towns and cities, overall the woodland cover in England is at its highest for many centuries (FC, 2001). One of the types of woodland that would have contributed to this increase comprises narrow belts of woodland and hedgerows adjacent to roads. In the broad sense this woodland can be included under the category of trees in the built environment. Hedgerows have also been shown to have increased in the last 10 years (CS, 2000). There are many amenity and wildlife benefits to be gained from these plantings. Nevertheless, there are some negative influences of these roadside plantings and these relate to their likely impact on water resources, both in terms of quantity and quality.

The reason for the likely high water use and enhanced atmospheric deposition of chemicals to narrow or isolated woodland fragments, rows of trees, hedgerows and isolated trees is a function of the highly exposed, well ventilated nature of the canopies in contrast with extensive woodland. Compared to adjacent grassland there is substantial evidence of enhanced water use (both transpiration and interception losses) by small patches of woodland or woodland edges (eg Finch, 2000; Kinniburgh and Trafford, 1996). It is also known that capture and deposition of chemicals from the atmosphere is high in small blocks of forest or at the woodland edge (Ineson, 1994; Neal, 2002). Therefore, compared to the adjacent agricultural land, we would expect drier soils and increased soil nitrogen contents in narrow patches of woodland planted nearby. There may, however, be some benefits to highway drainage from the drier soils where woodland plantings border the road.

13.13 Waste

Activities associated with trees have a number of implications related to waste, its management and its disposal to landfills. Not only is there considerable pressure on landfill space, but costs of disposing of waste in landfill are rising year on year. Therefore all efforts should be made to reduce material deposited in them, especially biodegradable waste, which breaks down in landfills to form methane, a powerful greenhouse gas. Fig 13.8 is a simple schematic illustrating that there are various points along the waste stream where a reduction in the amount of materials deposited to the landfill can be reduced.

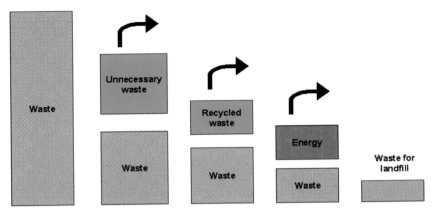

Figure 13.8 Means of reducing the amounts of waste going to landfill. (After Ashman and Puri, 2002.)

Unnecessary waste is packaging and wrapping. The horticultural and tree supply industry contributes to this unnecessary waste particularly through the use of disposable containers. These could easily be made from recyclable material or reused. It is also clear that any marked improvement in the successful establishment of young trees might reduce the needs to produce further young trees to replace the failures.

In Section 13.6 it has already been noted that an attempt should be made to maintain the fertility and carbon balance of a particular site through efforts to utilise dead material and live prunings from trees and felled trees for compost. These materials are also likely to constitute an important resource needed to produce an alternative to natural peat. It would be an increased bonus if the material could be well composted and eventually incorporated back into the soil locally.

The incineration of urban tree waste to generate energy at a community scale is not yet a viable option in the UK. The issue is largely one of scale with not enough material being produced locally to make it efficient.

Of course, some material cannot be recycled and will become landfill waste. When the landfill is full it is sealed with a compact clay cap and clean inert material placed on top. Landscaping with trees is an important option as an after use for the closed landfill. In the past gases emitted from the decomposing material in the landfill could prove toxic to tree roots but in more modern schemes the gases are usually vented effectively (Section 7.6.3).

There have been concerns about trees planted on closed landfill sites because of fears that tree roots may penetrate the clay cap seal of the landfill and compromise its role as a seal. There are also worries that trees might be unstable in exposed windy conditions. Studies into growing trees on landfills (Dobson and Moffat, 1993; Bending and Moffat, 1997) indicate that there is little risk to the landfill cap closure from tree roots. The threat of wind being a big risk to tree stability on landfills was also discounted, provided a minimum 0.75m depth of rootable material is available to the trees. In the UK, the planting of trees on closed landfill sites underlain by non-toxic materials have been used in a number of the community forests to enhance the landscape and provide amenity and recreational benefits.

13.14 Measuring sustainability

Sustainability can be evaluated by one or a number of indicators about a particular criterion. There is now a considerable literature about the development of criteria and indicators to determine if development is sustainable. There are a number of features that indicators should possess to be useful in practice. They should be capable of being measured easily and quickly and reported quantitatively. It should be possible to reliably repeat the evaluation of the indicators at intervals. Indicators need not be direct measures of an important feature of a tree or population of trees. The issue of concern may be expensive and time-consuming to measure directly. Instead indicators are often proxy measures that indirectly give insight into the area of interest. An example might be the indication of tree health or successful growth from an estimate of the percentage of trees that are replaced in their first three years of life in a local authority area.

So far what is missing from any readily available official indicators is a list of verifiable indicators that relate to the numbers and health of trees in the built environment. In this respect it seems that with trees in the built environment we lag far behind other areas where sustainability indicators are already well developed eg forest management. We need to know a number of things. What is the size of our population of amenity trees? What is the state of its health?

Without quantitative information we are not able to say we are managing our trees well and that our knowledge of below-ground processes is contributing sufficiently to this management.

13.15 Summary

- There are many areas where new and directed research is required to improve our knowledge and capacity to manage trees better.

- We need to know more about the form and distribution of roots and the environment and functioning of trees in hard landscapes.

- There needs to be an evaluation of tree soils and their suitability over long durations and their value for semi-mature trees.

- We need to know much more about the water requirements of trees and how to determine the predisposition of trees to stress.

- Guidance needs to be better implemented but also there is a need in some cases for additional guidance. Often this needs to be in a very concise and durable form.

- Trees in the built environment can make a small but positive contribution to limiting the rise of atmospheric carbon dioxide concentrations by storing carbon. However, there will be releases of carbon in a range of activities associated with establishing and maintaining the trees. A tree has to survive for a minimum of 5–10 years to balance the carbon dioxide emitted during production, establishment and maintenance. The most effective means of storing carbon in amenity trees is that they should be long-lived, medium growth trees requiring a modest amount of maintenance. The below ground storage of carbon is a major contribution to total stored carbon associated with trees. We have no knowledge of the effectiveness of this function in the soil beneath trees in the built environment.

- Root systems of urban trees do not make a direct contribution to the improvement of air quality, this is a function of the crowns that filter the air and absorb toxic gases. Nevertheless, the effectiveness of the crowns in improving air quality will depend on their size and the openness of the stomata in the leaves. Therefore, the effective functioning of the root system is an essential prerequisite.

- The greater use of the sustainable drainage systems (SUDS) approach might extend the opportunities for landscapes in which to plant trees requiring more permanent high water levels. Permeable surfaces are promoted as a major part of SUDS. The overall effectiveness of permeable surfaces depends on the soil conditions below the permeable surfaces. They should not be too compact and should drain readily. There is a risk that tree pits surrounded by compacted soils over which a permeable surface is laid will become sumps into which drainage is channelled.

- There is considerable scope to use collected rainwater or grey water to irrigate landscape trees. Excessive irrigation can cause harm through waterlogging and poor aeration around roots. Therefore storage of collected water and application to trees in a regulated way will be important.

- There can be a substantial contribution to the conservation of water resources and maintenance of water quality in nurseries that produce young trees. There is a large potential for savings in water and for the careful application of fertilisers and pesticides to reduce the risk of pollution.

- Trees in towns offer a limited potential for habitat for other wildlife but this will be enhanced if the trees are healthy. Urban trees can acts as a link between more substantial area of woodland habitat. In natural forest ecosystems, below-ground biodiversity can be very rich. This diversity would comprise entirely of small organisms including plants and animals. This diversity is changed in urban forests but we have very little knowledge of what lives below trees in the built environment.

- Alternatives to natural peat used as a growth medium for the propagation and establishment of young trees are being developed. Aspects that need refinement are the consistency of quality of peat alternatives and the evolution of management protocols for irrigation, fertilisation and pest control.

- It is the objective of the UK Government that 60% of additional new housing shall be built on previously developed land. It is considered important that these developments will have significant 'green' landscaping and they will contribute to good local infiltration of water. Providing a significant tree population in these developments will require the careful protection of existing trees, following guidelines such as BS 5837, for example. Soil compaction is likely to be a problem in previously developed land. This needs to be recognised and remedied to achieve best permeability for drainage and good tree growth.

- We need to know the size of our population of trees and its state of health. Without this information we cannot know if we are managing our trees well and if we have sufficient knowledge to do so. Indicators can help us know how well we are managing our trees and if we are doing this sustainably.

REFERENCES

Abbott, C.L., Comingo, L. & Angood, C. 2000. *Monitoring performance of infiltration drainage systems.* Report SR 569, HR Wallingford, Wallingford, UK. 22 pp.

ADAS. 2002. *Irrigation best practice: A guide for container-grown ornamentals.* ADAS Consulting Ltd., Aylesford, Kent, UK. 19 pp.

Ashman, M.R. & Puri, G. 2002. *Essential Soil Science.* Blackwell Publishing, Oxford, UK. 198 pp.

Balesdent, J. & Balabane, M. 1996. Major contribution of roots to soil carbon storage inferred from maize cultivated soils. *Soil Biology and Biochemistry, 28,* 1261–1263.

Beatley, T. 2000. *Green Urbanism: Learning from European cities.* Island Press, Washington, DC. 491 pp.

Bending, N.A.D. & Moffat, A.J. 1997. *Tree establishment on landfill sites: research and updated guidance.* DETR, Forestry Commission, Edinburgh, UK. 53 pp.

BRE (on behalf of the Consortium for Horticulture LINK Project No. 212). 2004. *Controlling water use of trees to alleviate subsidence risk.* Building Research Establishment, Watford, UK. 114pp.

Broadmeadow, M.S.L. & Freer-Smith, P. 1996. *Urban woodland and the benefits for local air quality.* Research for Amenity Trees, No. 5. TSO, London. 89 pp.

BSI. 2005. BS 5837: *Trees in relation to construction – Recommendations.* British Standards Institution, London, UK. 32 pp.

CA. 2006. Compost on trial. *Gardening Which?*, January 2006, pp. 16–21. Consumers' Association, London, UK.

CIRIA. 2002. *Source control using constructed pervious surfaces: Hydraulic, structural and water quality issues.* Construction Industry Research and Information Association, Publication C582. London, UK. 156 pp.

CIRIA. 2004. *Sustainable drainage systems – hydraulic, structural and water quality advice.* Construction Industry Research and Information Association, Publication C609. London, UK. 324 pp.

Couenberg, E. 1998. Urban tree soil and tree-pit design. In: *The Landscape Below Ground II: Proceedings of an International Workshop on Tree Root Development in Urban Soils* (Ed. by D. Neely and G.W. Watson), pp. 189–202. International Society of Arboriculture, Champaign, IL., USA.

CPA. 2002. *Every drop counts, keeping water clean: Practical advice for pesticide users.* Crop Protection Association, Peterborough, UK. 15 pp.

CS. 2000. *Accounting for Nature: Assessing Habitats in the UK.* Countryside Survey 2000. DETR, London, UK. 134 pp.

Cullingworth, B. & Nadin, V. 2002. *Town & Country Planning in the UK, 13th Edition*. Routledge, London, UK. 481 pp.

Cutler, D.F. & Richardson, I.B.K. 1989. *Tree Roots and Buildings*, 2nd Edition. Longman, London. 71 pp.

DEFRA. 2005. *Sustainable development indicators in your pocket 2005 (SDIYP)*. Department for Environment, Food and Rural Affairs, London, UK. 97 pp.

DETR. 2000. *Planning Policy Guidance Note No. 3. Housing*. Department of the Environment, Transport and the Regions, London, UK.
www.planning.odpm.gov.uk/ppg3/1.htm

Dobson, M.C. & Moffat, A.J. 1993. *The potential for woodland establishment on landfill sites*. Department of the Environment. HMSO, London, UK. 88 pp.

DTLR. 2001. *Planning Policy Guidance Note 25: Development and Flood Risk*. Department for Transport, Local Government and the Regions, London, UK.

Eden, N. 2002. *Cable trenching and trees - the Cheltenham experience*. Presentation at the Annual Arboricultural Association conference, Cambridge, September 2002.

Evans, M., Bassuk, N.L. & Trowbridge, P. 1990. Sidewalk design. *Landscape Architecture* (March 1990), 102–103.

FC. 2001. *National Inventory of Woodland and Trees, England*. Forestry Commission, Edinburgh, UK. 68 pp.

Finch, J.W. 2000. Modelling the soil moisture deficits developed under grass and deciduous woodland: the implications for water resources. *Journal of the Chartered Institution for Water Engineers and Managers*, 14, 371–376.

Gilbert, O.L. 1989. *The Ecology of Urban Habitats*. Chapman and Hall, London, UK. 369 pp.

HA. 2001. *Vegetative treatment systems for highway runoff*. Design Manual for Roads and Bridges, Volume 4, Section 2, Part 1, HA103/01. The Highways Agency. TSO, London, UK.

Harris, R.W., Clark, J.R. & Matheny, N.P. 1999. *Arboriculture: Integrated Management of Landscape Trees, Shrubs and Vines*. Prentice Hall, Upper Saddle River, NJ. 687 pp.

HM Government et al. 2005. *One Future – Different Paths*. HM Government, Scottish Executive, Welsh Assembly Government and Northern Ireland Office. London, UK, 15pp.

HM Government. 2005. Securing the Future – UK Government sustainable development strategy. HM Government, London, UK, 186pp.

Holmes, S., Lightfoot-Brown, S. & Bragg, N. 2000. *Peat alternatives: A review of performance, future availability and sustainability for commercial plant production in the UK*. ADAS, UK. www.adas.co.uk/horticulture/govreports/ptaltrev.htm

Ineson, P. 1994. Aerial transport of ammonia from agriculture to forest. *NERC News*, April 1994, pp. 4–6. Natural Environment Research Council, Swindon, UK.

IPCC. 2000. *Land use, Land Use Change, and Forestry*. Intergovernmental Panel on Climate Change. Cambridge University Press, Cambridge, UK. 377 pp.

Jenkinson, D.S. 1971. The accumulation of organic matter in soil left uncultivated. *Report of the Rothamsted Experimental Station for 1970*, Part 2, 113–137.

Kinniburgh, D.G and Trafford, J.M. 1996. Unsaturated zone pore water chemistry and the edge effect in beech forest in southern England. *Water, Air and Soil Pollution*, 92, 421 – 450.

MAFF. 1998. *Code of Good Agricultural Practice for the Protection of Water (the water code)*. Ministry of Agriculture, Fisheries and Food, London, UK.

Mattheck, C. & Breloer, H. 1994. *The body language of trees: a handbook for failure analysis*. Research for Amenity Trees. TSO, London, UK. 240 pp.

Neal, C. 2002. Interception and attenuation of atmospheric pollution in a lowland ash forested site, Old Pond Close, Northamptonshire, UK. *The Science of the Total Environment*, 282–3, 99–119.

Nicholson, R. 2001. APN1, BS 5837 & PPG3 guidances for trees: Conflict or complement? *Arboricultural Journal*, 25, 361–376.

Nowak, D.J., Stevens, J.C., Sisinni, S.M. & Luley, C.J. 2002. Effects of urban tree management and species selection on atmospheric carbon dioxide. *Journal of Arboriculture*, 28, 113–122.

ODPM. 2001. *Monitoring peat & alternatives as growing media & soil improvers in the UK 2001*. Office of the Deputy Prime Minister, London, UK.

Percival, G. 2001. Super shrubs. *The Horticulturalist*, Winter 2001, 5–8.

Post, W.M. & Kwon, K.C. 2000. Soil carbon sequestration and land-use change: Processes and potential. *Global Change Biology*, 6, 317–328.

Rettig, J. E., Fuller, R.C., Corbett, A.L. & Getty, T. 1997. Fluctuating asymmetry as an indicator of ecological stress. *Oikos*, 80, 123–127.

RHS. 2002. *Peat and the gardener*. Conservation and Environment Guidelines. Royal Horticultural Society, Wisley, UK. 4 pp.

Richter, D.D. & Markewitz, D. 2001. *Understanding Soil Change*. Cambridge University Press, Cambridge, UK. 255 pp.

WCED. 1987. *Our Common Future*. The World Commission on Environment and Development. Oxford University Press, Oxford. 400 pp.

Glossary

Abscisic acid (ABA) A plant growth regulator which inhibits growth and transpiration of plants. An increase in abscisic acid occurs in the sap stream of plants experiencing soil drying. This increase in concentration can cause stomatal closure and reduction of transpiration.

Acid rain Rain with a pH less than about 5.5. The acidity is due to inorganic acids such as sulphuric and nitric acid formed by the solution of oxides on sulphur and nitrogen from the air by the rain.

Acidification A continuing loss of acid neutralising capacity indicated by increasing hydrogen ion concentration and/or declining alkalinity. The term can be used for soils, catchments or streams draining catchments. *See also* **pH**

Actinomycetes A group of soil microflora, intermediate between bacteria and fungi that form hyphal mycelia. Some species form symbiotic relationships with roots and can fix nitrogen.

Aerenchyma Parenchyma tissue in roots characterised by particularly large intercellular spaces which can allow transfer of air from the atmosphere to the lower parts of the root system. Develops in some tree species in response to waterlogging and poor aeration.

Aerobic respiration Respiration occurring only in the presence of air or molecular oxygen.

Agroforestry A land-use system based on the intentional integration of trees in crop and/or livestock production systems.

Allelopathy The inhibition of germination and growth of one species by a chemical or chemicals released, usually in the soil, by another species.

Amsterdam Tree Soil A structural soil consisting of medium coarse sand (~0.25 mm diameter) including 4–5% organic matter and 2–4% clay. Can be compacted to 85–90% Proctor density. *See also* **Structural soil**

Anaerobic In the absence of oxygen.

Anaerobic respiration Respiration occurring only in the absence of air or molecular oxygen.

Anion *see* **Ions**

Anoxic *see* **Anaerobic**

Antitranspirant (Antidesiccant) Chemical compounds that, when applied to plants, reduce the amount of water lost through stomata and the cuticle. This can be done by physically sealing the surface of the leaves and twigs or chemically by closing the stomata.

Arboriculture The science and practice of caring for trees, shrubs or other woody plants in an amenity landscape context.

Arbuscule In endomycorrhizae, the portions of the hyphae deepest in the root cortex may invade cortical cells and branch profusely. A branched portion of the hyphae is the arbuscule. *See also* **Vesicular-arbuscular** and **Vesicle**

Auxins (IAA, IBA, NAA) A group of plant growth regulators (hormones) involved in cell elongation, apical dominance and rooting.

Back-reaming A term used in the technology of trenchless tunnelling. Using a larger cutting head to enlarge an initially drilled hole. The back-reamer is attached to the end of the set of drilling rods as they are wound back into the drilling machine. Other terms used in trenchless technology can be found at www.digging-deep.demon.co.uk/gloss.html

Bare-root Describes a type of nursery stock in which the plant is delivered without soil around the roots.

Biomass The total dry mass of living material within a specified area at a given time.

Broadleaf A tree having broad, often laminar, leaves rather than needles. Produces seed in a fleshy fruit (eg rowan) or hard nut (eg oak). In the UK most are **deciduous**.

Bulk density The mass of dry soil per unit of bulk volume, including the air spaces. The bulk volume is determined before drying to constant weight at 105°C.

California Bearing Ratio The CBR is the ratio of the force required to achieve a given penetration of a prescribed piston into a soil to the force required to produce the same penetration into a standard sample of crushed rock.

Cambium The meristematic tissue located in a concentric cylinder between the xylem and phloem. The cells of the cambium can divide and produce xylem to the inside and phloem to the outside.

Casparian strip A band-like impregnation of the upper, lower and side walls of endodermal cells of roots. Prevents the passage of water within the endodermis cell walls forcing transport through the cell via the inner and outer cell walls.

Cation An ion having a positive electrical charge (eg potassium, K^+).

Cation exchange capacity (CEC) The total of exchangeable cations that a soil can adsorb. Also known as the base exchange capacity.

Chlorophyll Green pigment involved in capturing light energy that drives photosynthesis.

Chlorosis A condition in plants relating to the failure of chlorophyll to develop adequately. Chlorotic leaves range from light green, through yellow to almost white. Often represents an imbalance of nutrients or a failure in root function.

Compaction The loss of pore spaces in soil caused by surface traffic or excessive cultivation. Wet soils of heavy texture (clays) are particularly susceptible, and deterioration of structure results.

Conduction The movement of heat from a leaf through the air without movement of the air mass.

Conifer A type of tree usually with needle leaves and having seeds in cones. In the UK most conifers are evergreen, except for larches (*Larix* sp).

Consolidation The process by which a saturated body of soil is compressed and which results in the reduction of pore volume by expulsion of water. It is not a response to temporary pressure, eg from traffic. It is usually associated with long-term loading of the soil, eg by a heavy building.

Container-grown Describes a tree grown and distributed/marketed in a container.

Containerised Describes a plant that is placed in a container for storage and transport.

Contaminated land Land which represents an actual or potential hazard to health or the environment as a result of current or previous use.

Convection The movement of heat from a leaf by movement of the warm air away from the leaf, usually by wind.

Cortex The ground tissue region between the vascular system and the epidermis in young tissue including roots.

Cornell University Structural Soil (CU soil) A structural soil developed at the Department of Horticulture, Cornell University, USA. It uses stones (10–40 mm diameter) with soil mixed amongst them. A hydrogel is used to help bind the soil to the stones. Excess soil should not be used or when the soil is compacted there will be insufficient pore space left for roots to grow in. The CU soil can be compacted to a Proctor density of 95%.
See also **Structural soil**

Cytokinins Natural plant growth regulators that stimulate cell division and are also involved in cell enlargement and tissue differentiation. Growing root tips are a main source of cytokinins in plants. The decline in cytokinin production in roots during water stress may influence shoot development.

dbh (diameter at breast height) The diameter of a tree at 1.3 m above ground level. Because trees are rarely a true circle in cross-section, it is more usual to measure girth and divide by π (3.1416) to obtain an average diameter. *See also* **Caliper**

Deciduous Describes a tree that sheds its leaves every year at a certain season.

Deflocculation Separation of compound soil particles, usually clay, into individual components by chemical and/or physical means.

Derelict land Land so damaged by industrial or other development that it is incapable of beneficial use without treatment.

Desiccation Complete drying of parts or whole of a tree. Occurs when transpiration exceeds moisture absorption with the result that there is wilting and death. Can also be used for soils when they are in an advanced state of drying.

Dripline The perimeter of the crown as determined by the lateral extent of the foliage.

Drought A prolonged period of little or no rainfall.

Ectomycorrhiza (Ectotrophic mycorrhiza) Fungus whose mycelium has a symbiotic association with the roots of certain plants. The fungal hyphae form a compact sheath on the surface of the roots and extend into the

surrounding soil and inward between the cells of the root cortex but not into those cells. Associated primarily with certain trees.
See also **Endomycorrhiza**

Elongation zone In a growing root the zone where cells are elongating after being formed in the meristematic zone.

Endomycorrhiza (Endotrophic mycorrhiza) Fungus whose mycelium has a symbiotic association with roots of a variety of plants in which the fungal hyphae penetrate directly into root hairs, other epidermal cells, and occasionally into cortical cells. Individual hyphae also extend from the root surface outward into the surrounding soil. *See also* **Ectomycorrhiza**

Energy balance An energy budget for the soil, vegetation and atmosphere at the land surface. A small fraction of the net radiation (R_n) received above the vegetation is utilised as heat storage in the soil (G) or biomass (S). The remainder is partitioned into either sensible heat flux (H) or latent heat flux (λE) ie evaporation. Estimation of any one component as a residual can be made if all the others are measured. The energy balance equation is $R_n + G + H + \lambda E + S = 0$.

Evaporation (Evapotranspiration) (E or λE) The vaporisation of liquid water at the leaf, vegetation or land surface and its passage into the atmosphere. Comprises transpiration, evaporation of intercepted rainfall and/or soil/litter evaporation.

Evergreen Describes trees that retain their leaves for more than one growing season.

Field capacity The amount of water remaining in the soil after the downward movement of water due to drainage has largely ceased. This point can usually be found by making observations during the winter months, when transpiration from vegetation is negligible, using a neutron probe.

Field-grown Describes young trees grown in nursery fields. For use in landscaping, they are dug up with a ball of soil around the roots. This is wrapped in hessian or plastic or the root system is put in a container.

Geogrid A honeycomb-like structure made of semi-rigid rubber or plastic. Used, for example, as a framework in which to locate sub-base material for roads, pavements or driveways. The sub-base included in individual cells of the geogrid is prevented from spreading sideways and lowering the finished surface applied above.

Geotextile A strong, durable, synthetic fabric that is buried below ground. Used, for example, to limit the horizontal or vertical extension of tree roots.

Gibberellic acid One of the natural growth regulators of the gibberellin group.

Gibberellins A class of plant growth regulators (hormones) involved in stem elongation and seed germination.

Global change Climate warming on a global scale usually attributed to an enhanced greenhouse effect. The greenhouse effect occurs because of increased concentrations in the atmosphere of gases such as carbon dioxide, methane, nitrous oxide and chlorofluorocarbons (CFCs).

Homogeneous Composed of similar or identical parts, of a uniform nature.

Humus The natural organic product of decomposition of plant material in the soil. It is colloidal, composed largely of compounds of large molecular weight and is dark in colour. The compounds are resistant to attack and contribute substantially to carbon storage in soil. Humus also contains non-humic groups, eg polysaccharides that stick soil particles together and contribute to soil structure. Humus colloids are negatively charged and contribute a large part of the soil cation exchange capacity.

Hydraulic conductivity An indication of the readiness with which water flows through a soil (or plant tissue) in response to a given potential gradient.

Hydrogel *see* **Polyacrylamide hydrophilic gel**

Hydrophobic Tending to repel water, not readily wettable.

Hypha A single filament of a fungal mycelium.

Hypoxic Describes soil conditions in which there is little available oxygen. *See also* **Anaerobic**

Impermeable Not allowing the passage of a fluid through the spaces.

Impervious Resistant to penetration by fluids or by roots.

Infiltration The entry of rain or irrigation water into the soil. Infiltration rate gives the volume of water entering a specified cross-sectional area of soil per unit time, $m \ sec^{-1}$ or $m \ day^{-1}$.

Interception loss Water that is retained on a tree (leaves, branches and trunk), both during and immediately after rainfall, and then evaporated back into the atmosphere. The difference between gross and net rainfall.

Ions Atoms, groups of atoms or compounds that are electrically charged as a result of loss of electrons making them positively charged (cations), or the gain of electrons making them negatively charged (anions).

Leaching Removal of materials in solution from the soil by percolating water.

Leaf area index In a vegetation canopy, the area of foliage per unit of ground area. Values are presented using the projected area, that is, one side of the leaves. In a sparse canopy values can be less than $1 \ m^2 \ m^{-2}$ but the leaf area index of dense canopies can be as much as 10 or more.

Load-bearing soil A soil required to bear a load without further compaction and distortion, eg soil below a pavement.

Macropores Larger soil pores, generally having a diameter greater than 0.06 mm, from which water drains by gravity.

Maturation zone The zone in a root, behind the actively growing root tip. In this zone length growth has stopped and differentiation of tissue is taking place.

Meristem Embryonic or undifferentiated tissue, the cells of which are capable of active division.

Meristematic zone A zone in the plant where active cell division and growth is taking place, eg at the root or stem tips or in the cambium.

Metabolite Any final product of synthesis processes in the tree.

Micropores Relatively small soil pores, generally occurring within soil aggregates, and having a diameter less than 0.06 mm.

Mortality spiral A sequence of circumstances describing a change in tree health from vigorous to stressed and declining to death.

Mulch Any material eg chipped bark or wood, leaves, straw or plastic that is spread on the surface of the soil in the rooting area of a tree to reduce evaporation, suppress weeds, protect the roots from extremes of temperature and prevent soil erosion by raindrop impact.

Mycelial mantle A sheath of hyphae of ectotrophic mycorrhizae surrounding an infected root.

Mycelium A string-like mass of individual fungal hyphae.

Mycorrhiza The symbiotic association of fungi with the roots of plants. *See also* **Ectomycorrhiza**, **Endomycorrhiza** and **Vesicular-arbuscular mycorrhiza**

Necrosis Death

Nitrification The oxidation of ammonia to nitrite and nitrite to nitrate by micro-organisms.

Paclobutrazol (PBZ) A plant growth regulator that slows down vegetative growth by inhibiting gibberellin biosynthesis. It can be used to limit top growth of young trees prior to transplanting. It has also been used to reduce top growth or regrowth after pruning in trees near overhead utility lines. It can be applied as a drench to the soil and also injected directly into the stems of trees. Paclobutrazol is marketed under names such as Clipper 50, Profile and Bonzi.

Pan In soils, a layer or zone formed of deposited mineral materials that can become cemented and compact. The pan layer will be impervious to water, air and roots.

Particulate Small piece of solid material such as smoke particles in diesel exhaust gases, smoke particles from fires or ash from industrial plants dispersed into the atmosphere.

Pathogen A micro-organism that causes disease in another organism.

Peak bulk density The maximum bulk density that can be achieved for a soil at a given water content.

Penetration resistance The resistance offered by a soil to entry by roots. A gauge of this resistance can be acquired from penetrometer measurements.

Penetrometer (cone) A device for measuring the strength of soils and their resistance to penetration by roots. It consists of a rod with a cone-shaped tip linked to a means of measuring the force required to push the rod into a known depth of soil. A penetrometer cannot exactly replicate the ability of roots to penetrate soil because the rod is rigid whereas a root is able to follow a tortuous pathway to enter between soil particles.

Perched water table The surface of a local zone of saturated soil maintained above the main level of groundwater by an impermeable layer, eg clay. The perched water table will be separated from the main groundwater by an unsaturated zone.

Percolation Movement of free water through the soil profile.

Pericycle Part of the ground tissue of the stele located between the phloem and the epidermis.

Permanent wilting point *see* **Wilting point**

Permeable Allowing the passage of fluids through the spaces.

Persistent moisture deficit A soil moisture deficit which has developed because of removal of water by trees or other vegetation and which is not eliminated by rainfall.

Pervious Allowing the passage of water through.

pH (soil) The negative logarithm of the hydrogen ion concentration of a soil solution. The degree of acidity (or alkalinity) of a soil presented in terms of the pH scale between 2 (extremely acid) to 10 (extremely alkaline). Soils with a neutral pH would have values between 6.5 and 7.5.
See also **Acidification**

Phenolic Relating to a group of chemical compounds containing the phenol radical. Many phenols are toxic or inhibitory to a range of micro-organisms.

Phloem The portion of the vascular tissue involved in conducting sugars and other organic compounds. Occurs as a sheath outside the cambium and underneath the bark.

Photoassimilate A product of photosynthesis.

Photosynthesis The process in which light energy is used to create sugars from carbon dioxide (CO_2) and water; oxygen is released. It takes place in chloroplasts, structures in the leaves containing chlorophyll. The CO_2 required for photosynthesis diffuses into the leaves through the stomata, and during this process water vapour is lost from the leaves by transpiration.

Phytoremediation The use of plants (trees included) to manage polluted soils. There are three main ways by which this can be done – *see* **Phytostabilisation**, **Phytodegradation** and **Phytoextraction**

Phytostabilisation Involves the immobilisation of pollution by growing plant species that are tolerant of pollutants. Owing to the presence of these plants, the erosion and run-off processes of particles carrying pollutants and the movement of these pollutants deep down in the soil are all reduced.

Phytotoxic Usually used in the case of chemicals that at certain concentrations may cause injury or death to plants or their tissues. Often used in the case of contaminating chemicals in the soil, eg various herbicides or heavy metals and in the air eg gases such as sulphur dioxide or ozone.

Plant growth regulator Substances that in very small amounts control plant growth and development. They are usually produced in one organ and translocated to part of the plant where they produce an effect. There are five groups of plant growth regulators: auxins, gibberellins, cytokinins, abscisic acid and ethylene.

Plastic limit The water content of fine-grained soil (eg a clay soil) corresponding to an arbitrary limit between the plastic and semi-solid states of the soil consistency.

Plasticity A characteristic of a soil that is capable of being moulded or deformed continuously and permanently by moderate pressure.

Plasticity index The difference between the plastic and liquid limits of a soil. Soils with a high plasticity index have a high potential for shrinkage on drying.

Polyacrylamide hydrophilic gel (hydrogel) A polyacrylamide is a long-chain synthetic polymer that has the capacity to store up to 500 times its own weight of water. Adding hydrogels to soil has a potential for increasing the water available per unit soil volume for trees growing in containers and when planted out. These compounds are also used as tackifiers and have a possible role in reducing soil erosion.

Pore space The continuous and interconnected spaces in soils.

Porosity The fraction of the total soil volume occupied by pore space.

Potential gradient *see* **Water potential gradient**

Precautionary area A protection zone around a tree. This is an area surrounding a tree in which excavation and other construction activities should not take place.

Proctor density The maximum bulk density to which a soil can be compacted by a given force.

Radiation load The amount of solar radiation incident on an object eg the crown of a tree.

Redox potential The electrical potential (measured in V or mV) of a system (soil) due to the tendency of the substances in it to give up or gain electrons.

Root electrolyte leakage (REL) The electrical conductivity of distilled water in which fine roots have been rinsed. If the roots have been damaged there will be a high leakage and an increase in conductivity of the water compared to a standard determined using undamaged roots.

Reradiation The reflection of radiation away from a surface (foliage/trunks or built surfaces). The radiation might be reradiated at a different wavelength to that received.

Respiration Series of reactions by which sugars are broken down to provide energy for plant functions. Oxygen is normally required (aerobic respiration) and carbon dioxide is released.

Root growth potential (RGP) An indication of the capacity of the root system of young transplants to grow, and used to evaluate the likelihood of young transplants establishing successfully. Usually measured by growing a sample of the transplants in a box of soil or compost with a removable side. After 10–14 days the new root growth is assessed.

Rhizodeposition The release of materials from the root and its surface into the soil immediately surrounding the roots.

Rhizosphere The portion of the soil in the immediate vicinity of plant roots in which the abundance and composition of the microbial populations are influenced by the presence of roots.

Riparian Relating to the banks of a natural watercourse.

Root-ball The intact ball of earth or growing medium containing the roots of a tree.

Root cap A sheath-like mass of cells covering and shielding the apical meristem of a root.

Root dip Application of chemicals to the roots of bare-rooted trees by immersing the roots, eg application of antidesiccants prior to transporting to planting sites.

Root SA (specific area) The surface area of the roots divided by the root volume.

Root(ing) zone The volume of soil occupied by the entire root system of a plant.

Sail area The projected side area of a tree crown which when exposed to winds acts as a sail and imposes a force on the root system.

Sap flow The measurement of water flow (and hence transpiration) in tree stems from measurements of sap velocity (from rates of heat movement or heat dissipation) and the cross-sectional area of conducting wood. The high time resolution values can be scaled up to hourly, daily or seasonal values.

Settlement Movement within a building structure due to the distribution or redistribution of loading and stresses within various parts of the construction.

Shoot water potential (leaf or twig water potential) *see* **Xylem water potential**

Soil aeration Indicates the ease with which air can exchange with the soil atmosphere to supply needed oxygen and remove carbon dioxide produced as roots and microbes respire and humus decomposes. Sands are well aerated. Air exchange is reduced by poor structure and high clay content, and by excess water that fills the smaller soil pores and 'bottleneck' sections of pores. Oxygen does not move readily through even very thin films of water. The reduced aeration in water-blocked pores hinders the oxygen supply to roots, slows growth and can cause root death. Very few trees can bring oxygen down to their roots through their stems.

Soil moisture deficit The decrease in available water in a soil profile from a reference value – field capacity.

Soil profiles Vertical section of the soil through all the upper horizons which may influence the distribution and functioning of roots.

Soil structure The combination of primary soil particles into a group eg a soil crumb.

Soil suction *see* **Water potential**

Soil texture The relative proportions of the various soil particles (sand, silt and clay).

Stele The vascular system (xylem and phloem) and associated ground tissue.

Stomata (stomatal pore) Microscopic pores/valves in the surfaces of plant leaves. Usually on the underside of broadleaf tree leaves but on all surfaces in some conifers (eg pines). Closed during the night, the pores open in daylight to allow CO_2 to enter as a prerequisite for photosynthesis and the inevitable loss of water vapour (transpiration). If soil water becomes limiting, the stomata close progressively earlier each day as drought develops. Many species, including trees, close their stomata with increasing air humidity deficit.

Stomatal conductance A measure of the degree of opening of the stomata in the leaf surfaces. A healthy leaf in full sunlight and well supplied with water is likely to indicate its highest value of stomatal conductance. This will vary from species to species in the same conditions. Closure of the stomata – reduction in stomatal conductance – will occur because of a variety of factors acting alone or in combination. Water stress, low light, high air humidity deficit or low temperatures can all cause reductions in stomatal conductance. Conductance is measured on leaves placed in the chamber of a porometer. Alternatively, there are other types of equipment that measure all aspects of leaf gas exchange and can provide measurements of stomatal conductance, transpiration and photosynthesis at the same time.

Structural roots Long-lived roots of large diameter (> 25 mm) which form the structural framework of the tree root system.

Structural soil A highly compactable mixture designed to support pavements but also to enable the growth of tree roots. The structural soil retains a high level of porosity allowing for good infiltration and oxygen diffusion. The nature and proportions of the constituents of the mixture, eg stones, soil or sand, varies with individual structural soils.

See http://students.washington.edu/jadet/Structural%20Soils/index.html

See also **CU soil** and **Amsterdam tree soil**

Suberin A substance that is composed of fatty substances (lipids) and phenolics and is present in plants as an impregnation of cell walls. It makes the walls more or less impervious to water and resistant to degradation by microbes. Suberin is a main constituent of cork.

Subsidence The downward movement of a building and its foundations caused by loss of the support beneath the foundation. One of the causes of subsidence is the drying by water abstraction by roots and shrinkage of certain clay soils.

Tackifier In the context of structural soils a substance, eg a hydrogel that is employed to improve adhesion between different components such as the soil and the stone fractions.

Translocation The movement of organic compounds through the plant. A variety of organic compounds are translocated, including carbohydrates, nitrogen-containing compounds, growth regulators, vitamins and applied pesticides. Most of the organic compounds are translocated in the phloem.

Transpiration Uptake of water from the soil by plant roots and loss as water vapour from plant leaves through pores in their surfaces (stomata).

Tree shelter An entire or perforated tube (usually plastic) placed over a small tree (<1 m) after planting. Usually, the tube is also staked vertically. Tree shelters protect young trees from browsing by animals and overtopping by surrounding vegetation, and they alert operatives working close to trees of their presence.

Undercut Technique used in tree nurseries to cut seedling roots from below to promote a denser root system without transplanting. This is done by drawing a tensioned thin blade horizontally through the soil.

See also **Wrenching**

Vesicle In endomycorrhizae, a swollen part of the hyphae.

Vesicular-arbuscular (VA) **mycorrhiza**. The most common type of endomycorrhiza, in which the fungal hyphae are able to penetrate host cells and form **vesicles** or **arbuscules**.

Water balance (budget) The water balance or budget of a soil (or catchment) shows that evaporation (E) is equal to precipitation or rainfall (P) plus or minus the change in soil moisture (ΔS) and minus runoff (R) and drainage (D). The water balance equation is $E = P \pm \Delta S - R - D$.

Water potential Water potential is the chemical potential of water and is a measure of the energy available for reaction or movement. The concept of water potential applies equally to soils, plants and the atmosphere. Water moves along a water potential gradient from the relatively wet soil through the plant to the atmosphere, which has the lowest water potential.

Water potential gradient Either in the soil or in the tree water moves from a zone of high water potential (eg from soil well supplied with water) to zones of low water potential (eg drier soil around roots). The difference in water potential between the zones is the potential gradient.

Water stress A term to indicate that a deficit of water occurs within a tree. It can be quantified by measures of leaf water potential. Water stress can arise in a number of ways, eg low availability of soil moisture, inadequate or damaged roots or high evaporative demand.

Water table The upper surface of groundwater or that level below which the soil is saturated with water.

Waterlogging Describes soil saturated with water, a situation which is serious for roots as all the soil air will have been replaced by water. Normal root respiration will eventually cease and root function will be compromised.

Wilting point The moisture content of a soil (on an oven dry weight basis) at which leaves wilt and fail to recover at night.

Wrenching A technique used in tree nurseries to cut seedling roots in the ground to promote good root development without transplanting. Wrenching is achieved by drawing a thick, angled blade through the soil beneath the seedlings. This severs the roots and loosens and aerates the soil. *See also* **Undercut**

Xylem The water and mineral conducting portion of the vascular tissues. Occurs inside the phloem and cambium.

Index

Page references to figures are in *italics*, to tables and box text in **bold**.
The glossary has not been indexed, and readers are advised to refer to pages 456 to 466.

asphalt *continued*
  soil gas concentrations 85
atmosphere, composition 32
atmospheric deposition 32, 227–33
auxins 55, 138

backfilling 106–7, *107*
  soil organic matter 107
  soil settlement 107
back-reaming 274
bare-roots **126**, 126–7
  desiccation 145
  transplantability 129
  water stress 156, *157*
base layer 94
basins 443
biomass 8
'bleeding', from wounds 59
boring systems
  guided 274, *275*
  unguided 274
boron 222
branch roots *see* lateral roots
break out zones
  baiting 201
  channelling 201
  growth medium 201
  pavement damage 389
British Standard BS 3936: Nursery
  stock 129
British Standard BS 4043:
  Transplanting root balled trees
  135, 147
British Standard BS 5837: Trees
in relation to construction (2005)
  262–5
  building damage 346, **347**
  drains 404, **404**
  fencing 296–7, *298*
  protection radius 266
  protection zones 262, **263**, 295–6,
    298
  surveys 292, **296**
  tree selection 292–5, **293**
  trenching 262–3, *264*
Broadleaf P4 151, 152
brownfield sites 447

building damage (and subsidence) 5,
    319–68
  assessment 348–9
  climatic change 358–9
  determining factors *328*
  guidelines 343–6
  history 319–20
  indirect *48*, 49
  insurance claims *320*, *321*, 350–1
  investigation 350–58
  mitigation 350–58
  prevention 346–8
  research needs 423
  tree species variation 340–43, **342**
  tree water demand 333–7
  underpinning 358
  vegetation 327–33
  water balance *328*
  see also entries beginning
    construction
Building Research Establishment
    Digest: 298
  building near trees guidelines 343
  ground/formation movement 327
  tree water demand 335, **339**
buildings
  construction over tree roots
    311–12
  design and root health 300–11
  existing/newly planted trees 347
    building guidelines 346–8
    new structures 346–8
bulk density, soil 18–20
  air injection 114
  compaction effect 79, 82
  consolidation 19–20
  intentional compaction 79
  peak 94
  root growth 55, 83, *83*
  root penetration *51*, *52*, 55
  testing 79
burrowing animals
  soil pore size 78
  water infiltration 86
  see also earthworms
'butterflying' 137